MINERAL PROCESSING

Developments in Mineral Processing

Developments in Mineral Processing, 2: Part A

Thirteenth International
Mineral Processing Congress
Warsaw, June 4–9, 1979

MINERAL PROCESSING

Thirteenth International Mineral Processing Congress,
Warsaw, June 4–9, 1979

Proceedings
Part A

Edited by

J. Laskowski
*Institute of Inorganic Chemistry and
Metallurgy of Rare Elements,
Technical University of Wrocław, Wrocław, Poland*

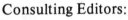

Consulting Editors:
R. Bortel
F. Łętowski
J. Szczypa

ELSEVIER SCIENTIFIC PUBLISHING COMPANY
Amsterdam – Oxford – New York
PWN – POLISH SCIENTIFIC PUBLISHERS
Warsaw
1981

Distribution of this book is being handled by the following publishers:

for the U.S.A. and Canada
ELSEVIER/NORTH-HOLLAND, INC.
52 Vanderbilt Avenue, New York, N.Y. 10017

for Albania, Bulgaria, Chinese People's Republic,
Cuba, Czechoslovakia, German Democratic Republic,
Hungary, Korean People's Democratic Republic, Mongolia,
Poland, Romania, Vietnam, the U.S.S.R.
and Yugoslavia
ARS POLONA
Krakowskie Przedmieście 7, 00-068 Warszawa 1, Poland

for all remaining areas
ELSEVIER SCIENTIFIC PUBLISHING COMPANY
335 Jan Van Galenstraat, P.O. Box 211
1000 AE Amsterdam, The Netherlands

Graphic design: Zygmunt Ziemka
Congress sign: Krystyna Filipowska

Library of Congress Cataloging in Publication Data

International Mineral Processing Congress, 13th, Warsaw,
  1979.
  Mineral processing.

  (Developments in mineral processing; 2)
  1.   Ore-dressing-Congresses.   I. Laskowski, Janusz,
1936-   II.   Title.   III.   Series.
TN497.I57   1979   622'.7   80-12411
ISBN 0-444-99775-X

Copyright © by PWN – Polish Scientific Publishers – Warszawa 1981

Printed in Poland

ORGANIZING COMMITTEE

General Committee

F. Kaim (Honorary Chairman), Minister of Metallurgy
J. Bojakowski (Chairman), Deputy Minister of Metallurgy
J. Laskowski (General Secretary), Wrocław Technical University,

T. Babisz, K. Franasik, H. Filcek, F. Grzesiek, J. Kucharczyk, J. Nawrocki,
R. Ney, T. Porębski, B. Seweryński, B. Stranz, Z. Śmieszek, W. Woźniczka

Program and Publications Committee	Arrangements and Post Congress Tours Committee
J. Laskowski (Chairman)	B. Seweryński (Chairman)
Z. Banach	W. Blaschke
R. Bortel	L. Bogusz
F. Łętowski	St. Gustkowicz
W. Pilch	St. Koziarski
A. Pomianowski	A. Nadolny
J. Szczypa	M. Oktawiec
M. Ślusarek	Z. Polesiński
S. Zieliński	M. Prażmowski
	Z. Szecówka
	E. Załęski
Secretary: Mrs. B. Romanowska	J. Warzybok

INTERNATIONAL SCIENTIFIC COMMITTEE

Mr. J. E. Astier   – France/President
Prof. J. Maia   – Brazil/Co-President
Mr. O. Burghardt   – FRG
Prof. M. Carta   – Italy
Prof. M. G. Fleming   – United Kingdom
Prof. D. W. Fuerstenau   – USA
Prof. P. G. Kihlstedt   – Sweden
Prof. J. Laskowski*   – Poland
Prof. V. I. Revnivtsev   – USSR
Prof. J. G. Sabariegos   – Spain
Prof. H. Schubert   – GDR
Prof. F. Špaldon   – Czechoslovakia

Corresponding members

Prof. V. A. Altekar	– India	Prof. D. Očepek	– Yugoslavia
Prof. M. H. Buckenham	– New Zeland	Prof. S. Pethö	– Hungary
Prof. J. de Cuyper	– Belgium	Prof. J. Q. Rogado	– Portugal
Prof. L. Dobrescu	– Romania	Prof. N. Semkov	– Bulgaria
Dr. H. Kettani	– Marocco	Dr. L. Sirois	– Canada
Prof. R. T. Hukki	– Finland	Prof. H. J. Steiner	– Austria
Prof. T. Imaizumi	– Japan	Prof. A. Sutulov	– Chile
Dr. D. F. Kelsall	– Australia	Mr. G. Zambrana	– Bolivia
		Dr. B. Yarar	– Turkey

* now Co-President of the Committee

V

FOREWORD

The Thirteenth International Mineral Processing Congress
which took place in Poland in 1979 was a continuation of the
debate of previous Congresses held in: London (1952), Paris
(1953), Goslar (1955), Stockholm (1957), London (1960), Cannes
(1963), New York (1964), Leningrad (1968), Prague (1970),
London (1973), Cagliari (1975) and Sao Paulo (1977).

The opening ceremony of the Thirteenth Congress took place
in Warsaw on the morning of Monday, 4th June, 1979. This was
followed by technical sessions which continued until Saturday,
9th June, 1979. A welcoming reception was given on the evening
of June 4th and a farewall banquet was held on June 8th.

The Organizing Committee received more than 200 abstracts
from 29 countries. Some 70 papers were preliminarily selected.
Priority was given to papers in which emphasis was placed on
the fundamentals of processes, fine particle technology, optimisation and automatisation and treatment of raw materials with
total utilization of all mineral constituents. The papers which
were finally accepted were published in two preprint volumes
in the Congress languages in which they were originally written
with abstracts translated into all the official Congress
languages. Eight of the initially accepted papers were published
in a special issue of the Polish professional journal "Rudy i
Metale Nieżelazne" (Ores and Non-Ferrous Metals) and were not
discussed at the technical sessions.

The Proceedings contain the 61 papers accepted for the technical sessions, 6 invited lectures, the inaugural lecture, as
well as the opening and closing addresses. The Proceedings also
contain discussion, contributions sent in later in written form
and the authors' replies.

Two Round-Table seminars were held concurrently with the Congress technical sessions. These seminars were on the subject of the Processing of Oxidized and Mixed Oxide-Sulphide Lead-Zinc Ores and the Treatment of Iron-Titanium Ores.

The first of these was held on the afternoon of Thursday, 7th June, under the chairmanship of Professor M. Carta, and the second took place on the afternoon of Friday, 8th June, under the chairmanship of Dr. S. Zieliński.

The third Round-Table on the "Beneficiation of Clay Raw Materials" was held in Bolesławiec on the 12th of June and was included in the programme of one of the Congress Tours.

The papers discussed at the seminars were published separately in three volumes; the first volume contains 8 papers dealing with the processing of oxidized lead-zinc ores, the second volume contains 10 papers on the treatment of iron-titanium ores and the third volume contains 13 papers on the beneficiation of clay raw materials. The papers in the seminar volumes were published in the Congress languages in which they were originally written with abstracts translated into all the other Congress languages. These volumes were available on registration.

The Congress was attended by over 700 participants from 39 countries. All sessions were conducted with simultaneous translation into the official Congress languages (English, Russian, French, German).

Much of the success of the Congress was due to the ladies' programme and the social programme arranged parallel to the technical sessions. They provided relaxation and an excellent forum for informal discussion.

The congress programme also included one pre-Congress and three post-Congress tours of mineral processing and smelting operations in various parts of Poland.

In the closing ceremony there were speeches from Professor J. Laskowski and Professor M. G. Fleming, who also spoke on behalf of the President of the International Scientific Committee, and announced that the XIV IMPC was to take place in Toronto, in Canada. Dr D. Everell then spoke on behalf of

the Organizing Committee of the 1982 Toronto Congress.
Dr B. Seweryński speaking on behalf of Minister of Metallurgy,
expressed his sincerest thanks to every-one and declared the
XIII IMPC closed.

The work of many people has gone into the preparation of
the Proceedings. The editor wishes to acknowledge the assist-
ance provided by R. Bortel, F. Łętowski and J. Szczypa.
Special thanks go to W. Tomaszewska, B. Romanowska, R. Hierzyk,
M. Watson, T. Ligus, N. Śmigielska, M. Spiżewski, J. Neczaj-
Hruzewicz and K. Wojtasik.

A special thank-you is extended to Professor Douglas W.
Fuerstenau of Berkeley University for valuable discussion.

We are indebted to Julitta Płoszaj of Polish Scientific
Publishers for accomplishing the great feat of producing these
volumes.

J. Laskowski

Editor

Wrocław, Poland
December 10, 1979

TABLE OF CONTENTS

PART A

XI

Session 3: COMMINUTION

Session 4: HYDROMETALLURGY

PART B

Session 5: NEW TRENDS IN TECHNOLOGY

Session 6: NEW MACHINES

Session 7: OPTIMIZATION AND AUTOMATION

Session 8: TREATMENT OF RAW MATERIALS WITH TOTAL UTILIZATION OF ALL CONSTITUENTS

Session 9: WASTE TREATMENT AND ECOLOGY

Closing Speeches

OPENING ADDRESS

by T. Zastawnik

Deputy Minister of Energetics and Atomic Energy

Mr Chairman, Ladies and Gentlemen,

It was a great pleasure for us that the International
Scientific Committee decided to charge Poland with the organization of the XIIIth Congress. And because of that decision
I am today able on behalf of the Polish Organizing Committee
to greet the participants of this Mineral Processing Congress
on welcoming Polish soil in our beloved capital - Warsaw. Our
country has a mining and metallurgy industry which goes back
many centuries and these occupations enjoy high standing and
respect in Polish society.

Mineral beneficiation processes and technologies have been
known as long as mining and metallurgy themselves.

Rich and long has been the history of mining and metallurgy
in Poland.

Chalk and Jurassic flint mines were in operation on Polish
soil - as early as the Neolithic period in the Opatowski
Silicate region near Kielce.

A large iron mining and smelting centre developed on the
northern slopes of the Świętokrzyskie Mountains about 700 B.C.
In the 11th Century during the reign of Bolesław Chrobry gold
was retreived from alluvial openings in the Złotorya region in
Lower Silesia. It was during this period that salt started to

be mined in the region of Wieliczka and Bochnia near Kraków.

In the 14th century there existed silver and lead mines in the Świętokrzyskie Mountains and the Tarnowski region.

In the 15th century sulphur ore was mined in Swoszowice near Kraków.

The 19th century saw the development of the geological sciences which became the foundation of the modern approach to mineral problems.

Between World Wars I and II there was a growth of interest in applied geology, and with it the identification of Poland's useful minerals.

After the 2nd World War there was an intensification of search activities and enormous investments in geological investigations which lead to the discovery of many deposits that have become the basis for the present development of mining, beneficiation and metallurgy in the Polish People's Republic.

The extent of the development of this branch of industry is indicated by the fact that in 1978 over 600 million tons of raw ores was mined. As far as area and population are concerned, Poland is the 7th largest country in Europe, but it is the biggest producer and exporter of bituminous-coal, the biggest producer of copper and sulphur, the 6th largest producer of lead and is the 8th largest producer of zinc.

In the 35-year post-war period we have developed the traditional mining and metallurgy of zinc and lead.

We have created a modern copper industry, from mining to beneficiation, and metallurgy to the production of items made of copper and its alloys. We have created an aluminium industry from its very foundations, and most importantly, we have developed our national industry of iron-ore smelting, admirably symbolized by Huta Katowice.

Our Government invests heavily in the development of these branches of industry and plans for the future guarantee the further appropriate development of Polish mining and smelting.

Ladies and Gentlemen, our achievements in this field are not only measured by the size of production and its rate of growth. We also have at our disposal the priceless capital which is the body of specialists and experts in this country. Due to enormous grants made by our authorities we have created a large scientific research and design potential and great numbers of highly-trained technologists. Five technical universities brain specialists to degree level in the fields of mining and the smelting of iron and non-ferrous metals. Research for these two industries, apart from being carried out in centres of higher education, is also performed in 5 industrial research institutes employing 2700 members of staff, of whom 477 are research staff. Eight design offices meet industrial needs.

Congress participants will have the chance to become acquainted with the achievements of our research and design back-up teams both in the form of the papers which will be delivered during the Congress and by visiting our plants. These by no means small achievements of which we are proud provide and should provide a plane for international cooperation based on partnership, and the development of such cooperation is one of the goals of this Congress.

Ladies and Gentlemen, by what I have said I have tried to express the great significance we attach to the development of mining and metallurgy. We realise that although we possess very significant resources, they are not unlimited. It is our duty to society and to future generations that we exploit this resources rationally. Rational exploitation we take to mean not only the maximum utilization of basic useful constituents, but the rational use of all mineral constituents. This line of action has become binding in Poland and is backed by an appropriate statute. We are sure that analogous steps have been, or will soon be taken in other countries.

Since we attach such a great importance to questions concerning the multi-purpose treatment of raw materials with total utilization of all mineral constituents, we have put this forward as the main theme of our Congress. We are convinced that the papers which have been prepared for the Congress, the discussion and the conclusions which will be formulated will go far towards solving this problem.

I wish all Congress participants fruitful debate and hereby declare the XIII International Mineral Processing Congress open.

MINERAL PROCESSING IN POLAND

Inaugural lecture by Prof. T. Laskowski

Formerly Rector of the Silesian University of Technology, Founder and Director of the Institute of Mineral Processing and Coal Preparation

Mineral reserves are limited in supply and are rapidly and irreversibly becoming exhausted. Fir this reason they must be rationally, and most of all economically, exploited.

Mineral processing has a multi-faceted role in this rational exploitation.

- In geology, results of mineral technology provides the basis for estimating the industrial feasibility of mining specific ores and submitting them to further technological processing;

- In mining, mineral processing determines the indices of workability involved in the excavation of a given ore or of specific deposits;

- For consumers, concentrates obtained during beneficiation are further submitted to processing techniques.

The need for raw minerals is continuously growing but rich ores are running out, and this has led to the mining of poorer and poorer deposits which are increasingly difficult as regards beneficiation. Today, the further development of mineral processing is determined by two factors. The first involves the closing of the water circuit in the new processing plants but the other involves the use of all mineral constituents, that is production without tailings, and this is a much more diffi-cult problem to solve.

In a paper read at the World Mining Congress 10 years ago (Madrid 1968) we presented the question of the complex utiliza-tion of ores (Fig. 1). Our mining legislation has introduced, in addition to the concept of the main ore, the concept of ac-companying ore, and with it the obligation to exploit it ratio-nally and economically.

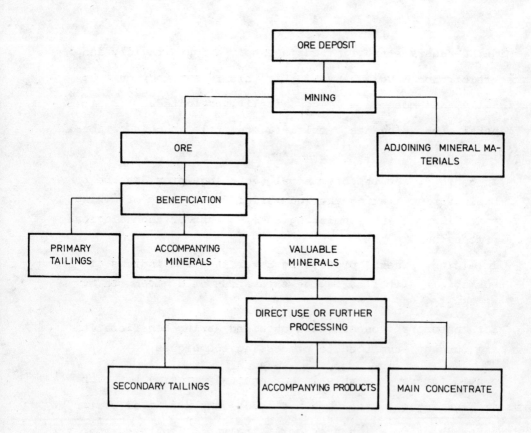

Fig. 1

Tailings and accompanying ores may occur during mining but mainly arise during beneficiation. They are used in various ways. Accompanying ores may either be regarded as material which is ready for use or which may be submitted to further beneficiation. In the same way, tailings may also be a useful raw material for further treatment.

Poland has played its part in the history and development of mineral processing. One of the first world experts in the field was the mining engineer, Professor Henryk Czeczott, whose publications date from 1908. On the basis of many years' research and teaching, he published a 4-volume work in the thirties entitled "Processing of Usable Ores". This is one of the first books of its type in the world literature.

The main subject of the XIII Congress is the treatment of raw materials with total utilization of all their mineral constituents. I will use the examples of several modern processing plants in this country to illustrate this theme.

Zinc and Lead

In the Triassic Dolomites a belt of lead-zinc deposits stretches from Tarnowski Mountains to Kraków. These deposits occur in several levels, the lower of which are encrusted with zinc sulphide - sphalerite, lead sulphide - galena and iron sulphide - marcasite together with oxidized secondary minerals. The upper levels comprise the ore containing mainly zinc and lead carbonates - smithsonite and cerusite as well as iron oxides - limonite. Silver occurs with the galena and cadmium with the sphalerite. The sulphide ores which are mined contain from 3 to 4.5% Zn and 0.5 to 2% Pb. These ores are mined in four mines with modern beneficiation plants.

The beneficiation of sulphide ore begins by crushing it to below 50 mm and classifying it into two size fractions: -50 +15 mm and -15 +5 mm, these fractions are then concentrated in a heavy media separators to obtain an intermediate product and tailings used in the building industry and in road construction. A galena concentrate with over 60% Pb content is obtained by gravity concentration from the -15 +5 mm and -5 +0.2 mm size fractions. The intermediate product from the -50 +15 mm fraction and the tailings after separation of the galena and the final slurries become feed for grinding and classification, after which it is beneficiated by flotation. Classification takes place in two steps; in spiral classifiers and in hydrocyclons. The overflow from the hydrocyclones becomes the feed for the selective flotation of galena and subsequently of sphalerite. In one of the plants sphalerite and marcasite are collectively flotated. Galena concentrates of 55-70% Pb content and sphalerite concentrates of 52-54% Zn content are obtained on flotation. Recovery depends on the degree of oxidation of the ore.

Beneficiation plants were designed by the design office "Bipromet" on the basis of technologies worked out at the Institute of Non-Ferrous Metals and are largely fitted out with Polish equipment; only the Drew-boy type separators for preconcentration were bought from PIC in France. In one of the plants a Polish Disa type separator is used in the preconcentration stage - with good results.

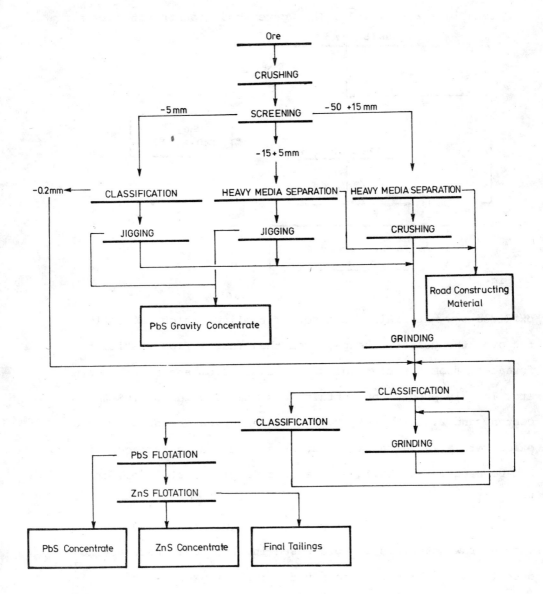

Fig. 2

9

Zn-Pb oxidized ore is hard to beneficiate in a flotation process and so a smelting process in rotary kilns was applied in Poland in 1928 (Fig. 3). This gave good results not only for

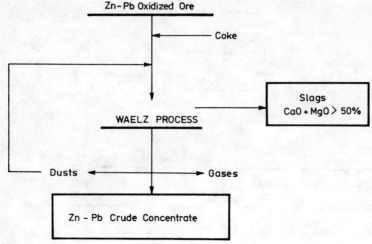

Fig. 3

oxidized raw materials but also for tailings which had collected over the years in heaps, from the cinders from distillation furnaces, from the electrolysis of zinc, from shaft furnaces, etc. In this process one obtains a sintered oxide of 70% Zn content and 2.5% Pb content. At the same time one obtains lead oxide with a large cadmium content and the basic furnace tailings can be used in agriculture as a deacidifying fertiliser for the soil.

Poland is the only country where low-grade oxidized zinc-bearing raw materials are processed in this way. There are now over 40 rotary kilns in the country for the processing of oxidized ores and industrial tailings. One should also note that we are not only a producer but also an exporter of this kind of equipment.

Copper

In 1957 the Lubin-Głogów deposit was discovered - the largest copper deposit in Europe and one of the largest in the world. The ore is not homogeneous; it is composed of three kinds of ore which are lithologically different:

(a) sandstone ore,
(b) shale ore,
(c) carbonate ore.

The main minerals in the copper ore are chalcocite, bornite and chalcopyrite. The accompanying metals are lead, zinc, silver, vanadium, cobalt, molybdenum, nickel and rhenium. Silver, rhenium and lead and small quantities of the remainder are now being recovered. The copper content of the ore varies between 0.7 and 3.5%.

The mineral technologies developed in Poland at the Institute of Non-Ferrous Metals in Gliwice in cooperation with the "Cuprum" Experimental Station in Lublin have tried to take into full account the specific characteristics of the deposit and mineralogical and petrographic features of the ore, as well as its flotation properties with the aim of maximum simplification of flowsheets through the elimination or combination of some operations. For this reason each of the processing plants and even various technological lines have different flowsheets characterized by, among other things, multi-stage beneficiation and developed systems for the grinding and cleaning of concentrates. The classification of ore after initial selective grinding to sand and carbonate fractions and initial flotation in the grinding circuit are among the achievements in this field. That is to say, a sand fraction below 0.3 mm is separated in a classifier after initial grindings (Fig. 4), this fraction contains copper sulphides totaly liberated. This relieves the ball mill of unnecessary over-grinding of sand grains.

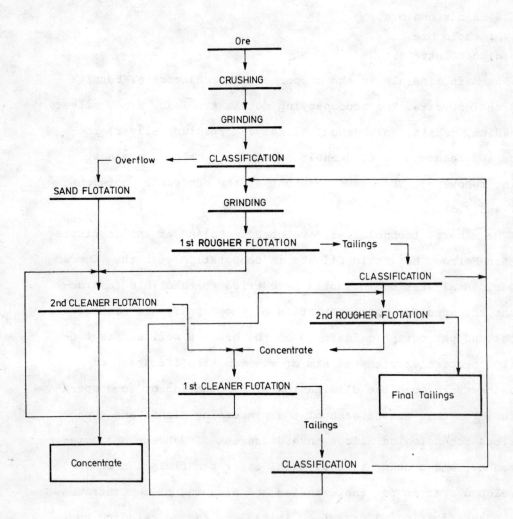

Fig. 4

This simplification has allowed the automation of the measurement and control and in consequence the reduction of the overall dimensions of the flotation and grinding sections; it has allowed the productivity of the plants to be increased, e.g., in Lublin from 4.5 to 7.5 mill. t/year and in Polkowice from 5 to 8 mill. t/year. Recovery of copper is about 90%. The metallurgical plants receive concentrates with 14-23% Cu content and from 300 to 760 g of silver.

The processing plants were designed by "Cuprum" Research and Design Establishment and built by Polish factories equipped with Polish-made machines. Imported equipment is only used in a few areas.

Sulphur

Large deposits of native sulphur occurring in calciferous layer of 10-13 m in thickness was discovered in the Tarnobrzeg region in 1953. The sulphur content of the deposit varies between 16-35% with an average of 24%. The shallower parts of the deposit are strip mined and beneficiated by a combination of flotation and refining; the deeper deposits are smelted underground.

The raw material obtained in the open-pit mine is first ground and then beneficiated by means of flotation. A concentrate of about 80% sulphur is dehydrated in centrifugal separators and subsequently melted and filtered to obtain a pure sulphur of 99.90-99.95% S. Italian and Russian experience was utilized in the construction of processing plant I and plant II designed by the Design Office "Biprokop" and constructed by

Polish factories with the Polish-made machines. The overall production of sulphur exceeded 4 mill. t in 1978.

In a period of 25 years the flotation of sulphur ore has become more efficient and the technical and economic indices have been improved by reducing the d_{50} particle size from 0.5 to 0.3 mm, prolonging flotation time from 8 to 12 min, introducing more effective reagents, by constructing the pneumatic KFP flotation machines, filters and centrifugal separators, by an increase in the efficiency of the pulp pumps etc. A technique for the recycling of water in the circuit has been developed and introduced. The research into the effective exploitation of the overlay and accompanying ores and by-products which has been carried out by the Research Centre for the Development of the Sulphur Industry, "Siarkpol" has produced considerable results. A technology for the production of sulphur for the rubber industry was developed and brought into production.

Coal

For the 65 coal mines in Upper and Lower Silesia which produced 192.6 mill. t in 1978 (the planned figure for 1979 is 200 mill. t), there are 99 preparation plants with an overall production figure of 60.000 t/h of which the coarse fraction (above 20 mm) of coking and the steam coal are beneficiated in heavy media separators, and fines -20 +0.5 mm in jigs and in heavy medium hydrocyclones. Coking coal slimes (below 0.5 mm) are beneficiated by means of flotation (Fig. 5). Steam coal fines are sent to the power generators in their untreated form. The intermediate cleaning product of coking coal after it has been ground is again beneficiated by means of flotation.

14

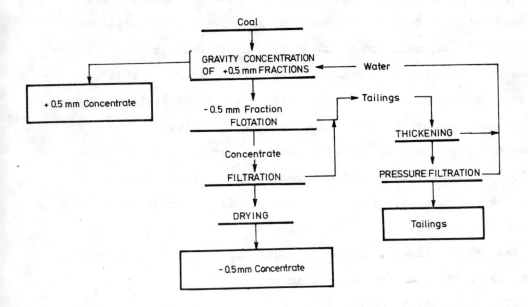

Fig. 5

The recycling of the flotation water in the circuit by the use of filter-presses for the dewatering of flotation tailings has facilitated their handling and storage. Most of all this clarifies the post-flotation slurries with water recycled to flotation and also prevents the pollution of ground-water.
Apart from two plants which were built by French factories, all the new plants and all those which have been extended or modernized were designed by the Polish Design Office "Separator" and built by Polish factories.

In 1959 "Haldex", a Polish-Hungarian Company was opened in Katowice with the task of recovering the remainder of the coal from old heaps with the utilization of processed tailings. The concentration of properly comminuted tailings takes place in

heavy medium hydroclones with the finest particles of the processed material forming the heavy media. Five such plants have
so far been in operation which in 1978 processed 4,868,000 t,
recovering 414,000 t of coal. In the third quarter of this year
a sixth plant will come into operation. The final tailings obtained in concentration are used by building industry, the
cement industry and by the coal mining industry as filling. In
1975 a light-weight aggregate plant producing light but very
hard porous materials for the building industry and road construction was built adjacent to plant I.

The present level of mineral processing in Poland is attributable to three groups of institutions:

(1) The technical universities,
(2) Industrial research institutes and centres and
(3) Design and construction offices.

The first group, the technical universities, train specialists to man the industrial processing plants, processing plant
designers, machine constructors, researches for the industrial
research centres and the research and teaching staff for university departments. The Academy of Mining and Metallurgy in
Kraków has the oldest Mineral Processing Institute in the
country which was founded in 1922 by Prof. Czeczott. The second
was founded in 1950 and is the Institute of Mineral Processing
and Coal Preparation at the Silesian University of Technology
in Gliwice. The Laboratory of Mineral Processing in the Institute of Inorganic Chemistry and Rare Element Metallurgy has
been in existence at the Technical University of Wrocław since
1973. Also involved in the basic research are the research

centres of the Polish Academy of Sciences: the Institute of
Rock Mechanics in Kraków, the Institute of Catalysis and Surface
Phenomena in Kraków and Institute of Chemistry of the Marie
Curie-Skłodowska University in Lublin.

The second group of institutions are industrial research
centers such as:

(1) The Institute of Non-Ferrous Metals in Gliwice - for
    non-ferrous ores,

(2) The Central Mining Institute in Katowice - for coal,

(3) The Institute of Ferrous Metallurgy in Gliwice - for
    ferrous ores,

(4) The Institute of Glass and Ceramics in Warsaw - for
    raw materials connected with ceramics and glass,

(5) The Institute of Refractory Materials in Gliwice - for
    refractory raw materials and metallurgical engineering,

(6) The Research Centre for the Development of the Sulphur
    Industry "Siarkpol" in Tarnobrzeg - for sulphur.

The third group of design and construction institutions are
developing mineral processing on the basis of research and
implementation studies and also technological ideas developed
by centres in groups I and II. Design offices play a large
part in Polish export to countries where whole processing
plants are being built with Polish-made machines and equipment.
These are:

(1) The Copper Research and Design Establishment "Cuprum"
    in Wrocław,

(2) The Central Design Office for Coal Preparation Plants
    "Separator" in Katowice,

(3) The Industrial Design Office for Nonferrous Metals "Bipromet" in Katowice

(4) The Design Office for the Mining of Ferrous Ores "Biporud" in Częstochowa,

(5) The Design Office for the Mining of Chemical Raw Materials "Biprokop" in Chorzów.

It has to be said that scientific meetings of every form play a large role in progress in mineral processing. However, international conferences where the latest research results are presented and where there is opportunity for an exchange of information, are most important of all. The XIII International Mineral Processing Congress which is currently taking place in Warsaw has this task to fulfill.

Session 1

Flotation

Chairmen: D. W. Fuerstenau
J. Laskowski

KINETIC THEORY OF THE FLOTATION OF FINE PARTICLES

Invited lecture by B. V. Derjaguin[1] and S. S. Dukhin[2]

[1] *Institute of Physical Chemistry of the USSR Academy of Sciences, Moscow, U.S.S.R.*
[2] *Institute of Colloid Chemistry and Chemistry of Water, Kiev, U.S.S.R.*

Until recently, flotation theory has been restricted to the thermodynamic study of the adhesion of particles to the surface of a bubble. This allowed the question of the selectivity of coarse particles (of size of the order of 100 μm and greater) to be analyzed, this question being of major importance for ore processing.

The flotation of fine particles represents an independent scientific problem, inasmuch as the transition from rough to fine grinding may be accompanied by qualitative changes in the mechanism of the elementary flotation act which is construed as the interaction of a particle with a bubble.

Generally speaking, two phases involved in elementary flotation act may be distinguished; (a) where the surface of the particle approaches that of the bubble, and (b) the fixing of the particle onto the bubble. A more detailed examination shows that more phases are involved, and that the subdivision of the process into phases is conventional.

21

In changing over from course to fine particles, the mechanism of the elementary flotation act changes qualitatively, both in the approach stage and in the fixing stage. Derjaguin and Dukhin were the first to have noted this almost two decades ago [1-10]. In recent years [11-22], these authors together with Rulev have amended, supplemented and partly revised the concepts developed in those earlier studies.

Peculiar Features of the Mechanism Involving the Fixing of Fine Particles on the Surface of a Bubble

The probability of the fixing of a particle is determined by the probabilities of the adhesion and the retention of the particle on the bubble, since in the general case the tearing off of an originally adhered particle is quite possible. The tearing off occurs either under the effect of gravity or under the effect of inertial forces. These forces grow in proportion to the volume of particles - that is, in proportion to the cube of the linear dimensions of a particle, hence they are very great for coarse particles and very small for fine particles. This trivial fact   has   radical consequences when analyzing the role played by the size of particles in the mechanism of the elementary act of flotation.

If the size of a particle is about 100 μm, the tearing-off forces are a million times greater than those arising when particle size is about 1 μm. Therefore in the case of coarse particles there is only one possible form of fixing, namely by forming a three-phase wetting perimeter that will be able to resist great tearing-off forces. This will be called contact flotation. In the case of fine particles, apart from contact flotation, contactless flotation is also possible, that is,

22

without formation of the three-phase wetting perimeter, for the tearing-off forces that are million times smaller may be balanced by the London-van der Waals universal forces of molecular attraction.

Sheludko points out the difficulty of fixing fine particles on the surface of a bubble due to the necessity of overcoming the energy barrier of the formation of the three-phase wetting perimeter [23].

Like the formation of an interface, the formation of the three-phase wetting perimeter involves the consumption of energy.

Sheludko's theory so far is of a qualitative character. Even if this factor proves to be by no means insignificant this does not imply the impossibility of the flotation of small particles. Because of Sheludko's effect, contact flotation of fine particles may prove to be impossible. But this effect does not prevent contactless flotation. In the case of the flotation of fine particles, the formation of the wetting perimeter is redundant. In this case, of primary importance are long-range surface forces, in particular London-van der Waals' attraction forces or, what is essentially the same thing, the molecular component of the disjoining pressure of the liquid interlayer separating them.

This is the first basic feature of the flotation of fine particles. But surface forces also include electrostatic interaction forces that are set up due to the overlapping of the double layers of a particle and a bubble which is usually negatively charged [24], that is, the electrostatic component of the disjoining pressure of the interlayer separating them [25].

In the case of coarse particles, the disjoining pressure of double layers is overcome by an inertial impact on the bubble surface. Fine particles do not undergo such an impact; approach occurs without inertia.

The disjoining pressure component set up owing to the overlapping of double layers is an important factor which can interfere with the adhesion of fine particles to the bubble surface. This is the second important feature of the flotation of fine particles which was noted by Derjaguin and Dukhin as early as 1960 [2].

The general laws governing the influence of both components of the disjoining pressure on the fixing of fine particles may be established on the basis of the known dependence of the interaction energy on the shortest distance between the surfaces of the particle and the bubble which are usually charged to different potentials [26].

This dependence was derived by Derjaguin in the theory of heterocoagulation; it has subsequently been applied many times to the interpretation of flotation processes. Where the bubble and the particle are charged to the same potential, and the molecular component of the disjoining pressure is negative, the general theory of the stability and coagulation of lyophobic colloids is applicable, this theory having been developed by Derjaguin [27, 28], Derjaguin and Landau [29] and Verwey and Overbeek [30].

In view of the differences between the bubble and the particle, the equality of their potentials is extremely rare and atypical. It is usually observed when the potentials of both are so big that the electrostatic component of disjoining pressure reaches its maximum. It is true that this occurs rarely and only in the presence of such ionactive surfactants that are able to strongly charge, not only the particle but also the bubble. Figure 1a represents the free energy of electrostatic interaction, G_{el}, of an equally charged spherical particle and bubble as a function of distance "y" between them.

In this case, G_{el} is equal to:

$$G_{el} = \int_y^\infty F(H)\, dH \qquad (1)$$

where F is the interaction force which is found by the familiar formula:

$$F(H) = 2\pi a \int_H^\infty \Pi_e\, dh \qquad (2)$$

where "a" is the radius of the particle, h is the thickness of the plane-parallel interlayer between a plate-like particle of the same substance and the air phase.

Formulas (1) and (2) have been derived on the assumption that the curvature of the bubble may be neglected as compared with that of the particle.

At great and small distances, molecular attraction forces are prevalent; at medium distances, electrostatic repulsion may prevail.

As a matter of fact, the bubble and the particle may differ from each other, not only in the potentials of their surfaces, but also in their respective behaviour; this may change the ensuing interaction drastically.

Thus, it is more usual that the surface potential of the particle and the charge (density of the charge) on the bubble surface remain constant as the interlayer thickness changes. In the particular case where this charge is equal to zero, as Frumkin [31] and Langmuir [32] have shown, there arises electrostatic repulsion which is exactly equal to the repulsion of two identical particles at the double thickness of the interlayer.

In the light of the theory of heterocoagulation it would be expected that inertialess flotation would be impracticable if the bubble and the particle were charged with charges of equal sign, where the absolute values of their surface potentials are not small (Fig. 1). In this case, the theory of heterocoagulation enables one to calculate at which values of the potential (or charge) of one of the interacting objects electrostatic repulsion decreases to such an extent that the barrier of electrostatic repulsion forces (Fig. 2) disappears.

This may be guaranted by effects of a double kind. As electrolytes are added, the thickness of the diffusion part of the double layer decreases, which results in the decreasing of the electrostatic repulsion forces. The negative potential of the surface can be decreased by the adsorption of surface-active cations; this may also lead to heterocoagulation.

Derjaguin and Shukakidze [33] were the first to have experimentally proved the intensification of the flotation of fine particles by reducing electrostatic repulsion. The interpretation of the adhesion process during the flotation of fine particles suggested by Derjaguin and Dukhin [2] on the basis of the theory of heterocoagulation has been reflected in a number of review articles on the theory of flotation [34-36]. The decreasing of the electrostatic repulsion forces facilitates flotation. This has been experimentally established in recent

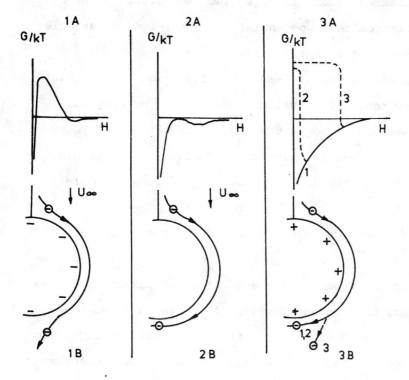

Fig. 1. Variation of the bubble-particle interaction energy, G, with distance between bubble and particle. The case of the negatively charged bubble and negatively charged particle.

Fig. 2. Variation of the bubble-particle interaction energy, G, with distance between bubble and particle. The case of the neutralized bubble and negatively charged particle.

Fig. 3. Variation of the bubble-particle interaction energy, G, with distance between bubble and particle. The case of the recharged bubble and negatively charged particle.

years in many research papers [37-40]. Ottewill and co-workers [37] detected maximum flotability at the isoelectric point by varying the electrokinetic potential of silver iodide particles through adsorption of a cation-active surfactant.

It has been established [37-39] that flotation rate is high within a narrow range of pH values and very low outside this range. The latter corresponds to very small values of ζ-potential of a particle near its isoelectric point. An addition of aluminium hydroxide extends the range of pH values that are favourable to flotation.

The authors of the works quoted interpret their data as proof of the decisive influence of the electric component of disjoining pressure on the process of the adhesion of particles to the bubble. However, Collins and Jameson [40] have admitted the possibility of a different interpretation of these results. The disappearance of the barrier of electrostatic repulsion forces can bring about an intense coagulation of particles at an isoelectric point. In such a case, aggregates arise which can deposit more intensely on the bubble surface than individual particles do.

In order to exclude this possibility, Collins and Jameson measured changes in the distribution of polystyrene spherical particles of about 4 to 20 μm in size during the course of flotation at different concentrations of electrolyte, and accordingly different electrophoretic mobilities, i.e., at different electrokinetic potential values. For each of eight fractions that were studied, the flotation rate increases monotonically as ζ decreases, reaching its maximum value at the isoelectric point. These experiments enable one to examine separately the influence of the size and the charge of particles on flotation. These researchers have thus proved unambiguously that the elimination of the disjoining pressure is an indispensable condition for flotation.

It is disadvantageous from the practical point of view to introduce electrolytes to ensure flotability. A more economical method for controlling the electrostatic component of disjoining pressure and, accordingly, flotability, consists in using ionic surfactants in certain concentrations; being adsorbed by a bubble, those ionogen surfactants recharge it. Very small concentrations of surfactants however, would not guarantee flotability if it were hampered, not only by an electrostatic barrier, but also by non-electrostatic factors interfering with the approaching of the surfaces of the particle and the bubble to each other. The presence of a polymolecular hydrate layer on the particle surface might be just such a factor. A number of research workers have demonstrated [41-43] the possible existence of polymolecular hydrate layers on lyophilic surfaces, which would interfere with the thinning out of wetting films owing to the structural component of disjoining pressure.

In Fig. 2, the barrier due to the structural component of disjoining pressure is schematically represented for the cases where its range of action is smaller or greater than the thickness of electric double layer. One of the ways of improving flotability in the presence of the structural component is to use surfactants. Adsorption of surfactants causes hydrophobization of the particle surface; it either destroys the structural component of disjoining pressure or changes its sign.

Another way of overcoming the difficulty of flotation of dispersions in the presence of a non-electrostatic stability factor was indicated by Derjaguin and Dukhin in 1960 [2]. This involves stimulation of electrostatic attraction. For this, it is necessary to charge a bubble strongly through considerable adsorption of surfactants, the bubble charge being opposite to the particle charge sign; as a result, the interaction of double layers causes attraction forces. If the thickness of the double electric layer exceeds that of the hydrate layer, the attraction forces between the particle and the bubble charges with opposite signs act beyond the effective radius of the repulsion forces. Thus, a bubble-particle aggregate may be formed; a gap with a thickness comparable to the radius of the action field of the non-electrostatic repulsion forces may be maintained between the surfaces of this bubble and particle.

If the effective radius of repulsion forces is increased and the thickness of the double electric layer held constant, the potential pit proves to be increasingly shallow. It is expedient to choose surfactants in such a manner as to not only enchance electrostatic attraction, but also to simultaneously decrease repulsion caused by structure.

Thus, if the effective radius of electrostatic attraction forces exceeds that of the non-electrostatic repulsion forces (as caused by structure), flotability is quite possible (Fig. 3, curve 2). If the effective radii of these forces are commensurable, flotation proves to be impracticable (Fig 3, curve 3).

Thus, the third characteristic of the flotation of fine particles is that it can be controlled by aid of ionic surfactants, and flotability is guaranteed even where non-electrostatic stability factors exist.

To corroborate this, let us consider research into the flotability of quartz. Kitchener and Laskowski [44] have shown that the surface, not only of pure quartz but even of methylated quartz, exhibits hydrophilic areas that contribute to the stability of slurries and hinder flotation. In [45], the flotability of quartz was guaranteed within the range of concentrations of dodecyl amine chloride in which the signs of the charges of the surfaces of bubble and particle are opposite.

Systematic research by Schulze [46-48] has shown the following to be true - the interphase water films separating the quartz and air phases become unstable under the influence of adsorption of three-valent cations or cationic surfactants, if their thickness is less than a certain thickness h_{cr}, which is called critical. On recharging the quartz surface with three-valent cations, the critical thickness is within the range of 300 to 450 Å. Recharging the bubble surface by the adsorption of cationic surfactants may rupture the film at thicknesses of about 150 Å if the electrolyte concentration is high, and at thicknesses of about 1500 Å if the electrolyte concentration is low. This is in agreement with the electric nature of the attraction. Schulze also suggests that flotability be guaranteed by the recharging of the bubble surface through adsorption of sur-

factants at as low an electrolyte concentration as possible.
This leads to an increase in the thickness of the double electric layer and accordingly to an increase in h_{cr}.

The suggestions of Schulze are in accordance with the experimental data of Goddard et al. [49] which guarantee the flotation
of quartz particles by the adsorption recharge of the bubble
surface by anions. An abrupt increase in flotability corresponds
to an abrupt growth of the adsorption of amines. The enhancing
of flotability is usually based on hydrophobization of the particle surface. Hence, we are dealing with quite a new trend in
flotation when the bubble surface charge is modified by adding
surfactants. That the quartz surface changes but insignificantly is
proved by the fact that in Goddard's experiments the ζ-poten-
tial of quartz was also altered to some degree by the addition
of surfactants.

In recharging the bubble surface, the depth of a potential
pit forming beyond the limits of the barrier of non-electrostatic repulsion forces is insufficient for the contactless flotation of coarse particles. Therefore, in the presence of the
non-electrostatic disjoining pressure component, the contactless
flotation of particles can only be guaranteed by recharging in
the case of sufficiently small particles.

Characteristic Features of the Mechanism of Transfer of Fine
Particles to the Bubble Surface

The process involving the approach of a particle to a bubble
surface undergoes qualitative changes when the distances between
their surfaces change from being large (as compared with the
particle size) to being small.

Where distances are great, this process is determined by the effect of one or both of two factors, inertia forces and the long-range hydrodynamic interaction.

A sufficiently large-size particle moves under the effect of inertial forces in an almost rectilinear way until it collides with the bubble surface, which takes place if $b < R + a$ (Fig. 4).

The liquid flow streamlines the bubble surface, the liquid flow lines bend, particles being entrained to some extent by that liquid flow. The smaller the particle size and the difference between its density and that of the medium, the smaller will be the inertia forces affecting it, and the more exactly does the particle trajectory coincide with the liquid flow line. Thus, at the same target distance, sufficiently large-sized particles move almost rectilinearly (Fig. 4, line 1), while sufficiently small-sized particles move in the corresponding liquid flow line (line 2). The trajectories of particles of an intermediate size are distributed within the area defined by lines 1 and 2; as the size of particles decreases, the trajectories shift from line 1 to line 2, and the probability of collisions thus decreases.

Actually, the deviation of the trajectory of fine particles from the rectilinear path at distances comparable to the bubble size is caused by a hydrodynamic interaction which could naturally be termed long-range. The bubble distorts the liquid flow lines and thus bends the trajectory of fine particles - that is, it affects them hydrodynamically through the liquid velocity field. Now, in the case of coarse particles, the inertia forces are consideranly greater than the long-range hydrodynamic inter-

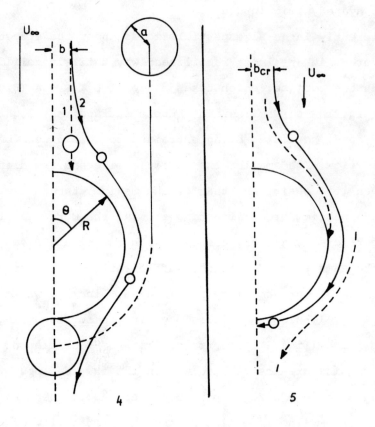

Fig. 4. The influence of the inertia of particles on their
trajectory in the vicinity of the floating bubble.
Trajectories of coarse (inertia) (line 1) and fine
(inertialess) (line 2) particles at the same target
distance "b".

Fig. 5. Schematic diagram showing the behaviour of particles
near the floating bubble. The limit trajectory is
indicated by the continuous line. The dotted lines
indicate the trajectories of the particle where
$b < b_{cr}$ and $b > b_{cr}$.

action forces which have, therefore, only a weak effect. Yet in the case of fine particles inertia forces are comparatively small [1].

Thus, the process involving the approach of coarse particles to the bubble is ensured by inertia forces, while in the case of fine particles this process occurs in an inertialess manner, being strongly disrupted by a further hydrodynamic interaction. This is the first characteristic feature of the transport of fine particles towards the bubble surface. Along with the long-range hydrodynamic interaction in which the motion trajectory of the inertialess particle coincides with the liquid flow line, hydrodynamic interaction at small distances will have to be taken into account; this causes the particle trajectory to deviate from the liquid flow line and should naturally be ter-med the close-range hydrodynamic interaction. Using Taylor's solution of a hydrodynamic problem involving extrusion of liquid from a gap as a spherical particle approaches a flat surface, Derjaguin and Dukhin [2] have shown that the close-range hydrodynamic interaction may prevent the particle from touching the bubble.

According to Taylor [50], when gap thickness, h, is much smaller than "a", the hydrodynamic resistance of the film to the thinning-out process is:

$$f = Va/h \qquad\qquad (3)$$

where V is the velocity at which the particles approach a cer-tain surface area of the bubble which may be considered as flat, because the bubble radius is much larger than the par-

ticle radius. If the constant pressing force F is applied to
the particle, then according to Eq. (3)

$$V \sim Fh/a \qquad (4)$$

Hence, it may be inferred that to remove the liquid completely
from the gap requires an indefinitely long period of time:

$$T = \int_{h_o}^{o} \frac{dh}{Fh} = \frac{1}{F} \ln h \Big|_{h_o}^{o} \qquad (5)$$

In connection with this paradox, a question arises as to
the nature of the forces pressing the particle to the bubble
surface. In the area above the equatorial line, the liquid
flow lines approach the bubble surface. This means that here
the radial component of the liquid velocity is directed to the
bubble surface. The motion of the particle towards the surface
being rendered difficult within the zone of close-range hydrodynamic interaction, the radial velocity of liquid is higher
than the radial velocity of the particle, while where there is
a small gap thickness and an accordingly high viscous resistance, the radial velocity of liquid will be even greater. Thus,
the radial flow of liquid streamlines the particle whose
approach to the bubble has been retarded, and presses the former to the latter.

In the first approximation, this pressing hydrodynamic force
may be estimated according to Stokes' formula by substituting
into it the radius of the particle and the difference in the
local values between the velocity of the liquid and that of the
particle. Thus, in the case of coarse particles, the thinning-

out of an interphase film is effected through an inertia shock, and in the case of fine particles through a pressing hydrodynamic force.

In the case of coarse particles, the interphase film thinning-out process is complicated by an indentation which is caused on the bubble surface by particle inertia impact. We have shown [21, 22] that in the inertialess deposition of fine particles on the surface of the bubble, the deformation of the latter under the influence of the pressing hydrodynamic force is insignificant.

This third important feature facilitates the development of a quantitative kinetic theory of flotation of fine particles.

Kinetic Theory of Flotation of Fine and Medium-Sized Spherical Particles

The process involving the approach of particles to the bubble surface may be described quantitatively by taking into account both long-range and short-range hydrodynamic interaction. For evaluating flotation efficiency, let us introduce the dimensionless parameter E, equal to

$$E = b_{cr}^2/R^2 \tag{6}$$

where R is the bubble radius, b_{cr} is the maximum radius of the stream pipe flowing over the bubble, all particles of which deposit on the bubble surface (Fig. 5).

The particles moving along the flow line at a target distance less than b_c deposit on the bubble surface (Fig. 5, as indicated by a broken line). In the opposite case, the particle is carried off by the flow. From Fig. 5, it is evident that the calculation essentially reduces to calculating the so-called "limit trajectory" (continuous curve) and accordingly the target distance[*]. The flow of liquid around the floating bubble is of a potential character if the motion of its surface is not hindered by surfactants, and if Reynolds' criterion is

$$Re = \frac{2 \, R U_\infty}{\nu} \gg 1 \tag{7}$$

where U_∞ is the rising velocity of the bubble and ν is the kinetic viscosity of water.

If the square of the dependence of the velocity of a bubble on its radius is taken into account, it will be easy to see that Reynolds' criterion changes very quickly with the radius. Reynolds' criterion is equal to unity at R ~ 80 μm. In order to understand the influence of the particle's inertia deposition mechanism on the floating bubble, it is important to introduce the concept of particle inertia path, l - that is, the distance which the particle is able to travel in the presence of the viscous resistance of liquid owing to the initial velocity,

$$\ell = \frac{2}{9} \frac{U_\infty a^2 \rho'}{\eta} \tag{8}$$

where ρ' is the difference between the densities of the particle and the medium and η is the viscosity of the medium.

The bubble surface being impermeable to liquid, the normal component of the liquid velocity on the surface is equal to zero. As the distance from the bubble surface increases, the

---

[*] A similar approach has long been used in the science of aerosols [52].

normal component of the liquid velocity also increases. However, the thickness of a liquid layer in which the normal component of the liquid velocity decreases due to the bubble effect is comparable to the bubble radius. The inertia run allows the particle to pass through that liquid layer. Thus, it becomes evident that the possibility of particle inertia deposition depends on the dimensionless parameter:

$$\lambda = L/R \tag{9}$$

Where $\lambda > 1$, deposition is obviously possible. Calculation, however, has shown that it will also be possible at $\lambda < 1$, although this value should not be too small. This becomes clear if the following is taken into account. In a layer of thickness R, the particle moves towards the surface not only due to inertia but also together with the liquid; the motion component of this liquid, which is normal to the bubble surface, turns to zero only at its very surface. The inertia deposition proves to be impracticable if λ is smaller than a certain critical value, λ_{cr}. In the case of the potential streamlining mode, and disregarding the particle dimensions, Levine obtained [52]

$$\lambda_{cr} = 1/24 \tag{10}$$

Equating λ with this numerical value in accordance with formulas (8) and (9), it is easy to derive a formula for the critical radius of the particle below which the inertia forces do not guarantee the approaching of the particle to the bubble.

$$a_{cr} = \frac{9}{\sqrt{48}} \sqrt{\frac{\partial \eta}{g \rho 'R}} \sim 4 \cdot 10^{-4} R^{-\frac{1}{2}} \tag{11}$$

where g is the gravitational acceleration. Where $a > a_{cr}$ the
inertia deposition of particles is effected on the bubble surface, but its intensity decreases as the value of "a" decreases. This is reflected in the formula for   collision effectiveness, first derived by Langmuir [53] , with respect to the
coagulation of aerosols. This formula was then adapted by
Dukhin and Derjaguin [2] for an elementary flotation act,

$$E = \frac{\lambda^2}{(\lambda + 0.2)^2} \qquad (12)$$

Recently, this formula has been corroborated by the experiments
of Samygin et al. [51] within the range of values 0.07-3.5. In
the course of these experiments, the effectiveness of entrapp-
ing particles by a single bubble of a strictly fixed size was
measured.

The measurements were carried out for several fractions of
particles, which allowed the dependence of E on the particle
radius and accordingly on criterion λ to be measured.

In the light of the research described above, it is expedient to subdivide particles into coarse, medium, and fine.
Coarse particles are those for which the value of E, calculated according to formula (12), is close to unity. It would be
natural to call those particles where $a < a_{cr}$ fine particles.
Those particles for which inertia deposition is possible, but
collision effectiveness is smaller than unity, are then medium-
size particles.

As will be shown below, in the process involving the inertialess approach of particles to the bubble surface, particle size
plays an important part.

It is in the equatorial plane (Fig. 6) that the flow line approaches the bubble surface most closely. In Fig. 6, a dotted line represents the liquid flow line (curve 1) whose distance from the bubble surface in the equatorial plane is equal to the particle radius. Certain authors erroneously consider this liquid flow line to be the limit for particles of that radius. The error lies in the fact that the short-range hydrodynamic interaction is not taken into account. Under the influence of the short-range hydrodynamic interaction, the particle is displaced from liquid flow line 1, so that its trajectory (curve 2) in the equatorial plane is removed from the surface at a distance which is greater than its radius. Therefore no contact with the surface occurs, and so "b" is not the critical target distance.

Since in short-range hydrodynamic interaction the distance from the particle to the surface in the equatorial plane is larger than the distance from the liquid flow line with which the trajectory of the particle coincided at large distances from the bubble, it may be concluded that $b_{cr} < b(a)$. The limit liquid flow line (curve 3) is characterized by the fact that the particle trajectory (curve 4) branching off from it under the influence of short-range hydrodynamic interaction passes through the equatorial plane at distance "a" from the bubble surface. Thus, the value of b_{cr} decreases, first of all, owing to the deviation of the liquid flow line under the influence of long-range hydrodynamic interaction, and secondly, due to the deviation of the particle trajectory relative to the liquid flow line under the influence of short-range hydrodynamic interaction.

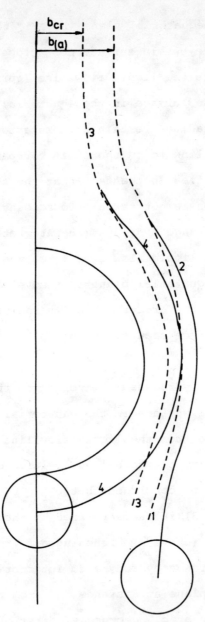

Fig. 6. The influence of the finite dimension of particles in inertialess flotation on their trajectory in the vicinity of the floating bubble. The liquid flow lines corresponding to target distances b(a) and b_{cr}, are indicated by the dotted lines. The continuous lines are characteristic of the deviation of the trajectory of particles from the liquid flow lines under the influence of the short-range hydrodynamic interaction.

In the case of the potential flow mode,

$$E_{op} = 3a/Rp \qquad . \qquad (13)$$

where Re < 1, liquid flow becomes viscous. In this case, the motion of the bubble surface is usually prevented by the adsorption layer of surfactants, so that here the distribution of velocities is described by Stokes' formula. Moreover, according to the data of Okazaki [54], the bubble surface is also immobile in the absence of surfactants.

The formula similar to (13) in Stokes' mode and to which index s corresponds, has the form*:

$$E_{os} = \frac{3}{2} (\frac{a}{R_s})^2 \qquad (14)$$

The problem involving the pressing hydrodynamic force contributing to the thinning-out of the interphase film during short-range hydrodynamic interaction was solved by Horen and O'Neil [47] for the Stokes mode, and by Dukhin and Rulev [18] for the potential mode. In this case, it has been established that the pressing force is over 2 times greater than the value calculated by Stokes formula. The pressing hydrodynamic force is not sufficient to guarantee contact between the particle and the

---

* Formulas (13) and (14) were derived in [1] on the basis of an analogy with the mechanics of aerosols. Unfortunately, these results were not mentioned by us in [2], and have remained little known. Formula (14), which has been rendered more accurate by taking into account the gravitational component, was derived for the second time by Reay and Ratkliff [55].

bubble for it is of a finite value, while the resistance increases indefinitely as the interphase film grows thinner.

We have shown [2] that inertialess flotation proves possible
owing to the effect of surface forces. Here, two cases present
themselves.

It is known [57, 58] that the interphase films may lose their
stability and disintegrate spontaneously as critical thickness
h_{cr} is attained in the course of thinning-out. Substituting h_{cr}
for zero in the upper integral limit (5), we obtain $\ln h_o/h_{cr}$
instead of infinity. Thus, inertialess flotation proves possible
in the presence of flotation reagents providing $h_{cr} \neq 0$.

The molecular force of interaction of the spherical particle
with the flat surface at a fairly small "h" is expressed [59] by
the formula

$$F = Aa/6h^2 \qquad (15)$$

where A is the Hamaker   constant.

As h decreases, the attraction force (15) grows more quickly than
the resistance of the viscous interlayer to thinning-out (3).
Hence, contact may be realized even at $h_{cr} = 0$. The influence of
short-range hydrodynamic interaction on particle entrapment efficiency was calculated [11-12], while neglecting the long-range
effect of molecular forces. The formulas derived by using the
Stokes and the potential distribution of velocities in the
liquid streamlining of the bubble have the form:

$$E_s = E_{os} f_s \qquad (16)$$

$$E_p = E_{op} f_p \qquad (17)$$

where f_s, f_p are functions expressing the influence of the short-range hydrodynamic interaction on the elementary act of flotation and which are correlated with the dimensionless para- meter $H_{cr} = h_{cr}/a$. For all values considered, these functions are smaller than unity; they decrease as H_{cr} decreases, and turn to zero where $H_{cr} = 0$. This tallies with the aforementioned con- cept of the mechanism of the influence of the short-range hydro- dynamic interaction on the particle deposition process.

As H_{cr} decreases from 10^{-1} to 10^{-3}, "f" decreases from 0.5 to 0.15, i.e., the dependence of E_s, and thus E_p, on the abso- lute value of h_{cr} is very weak. Thus, it is important to take the short-range hydrodynamic interaction into account not only in considering the question of the possibility of flotation; this effect significantly reduces the number of contact of par- ticles with the bubble. Rulev [13] has extended the short-range hydrodynamic interaction theory to the case where $h_{cr} = 0$, but the influence of the molecular long-range forces is most im- portant. The formulas derived have the form:

$$E_s = E_{os} \, f_s \, (W_s), \quad W_s = \frac{2A \, R_s^2}{27 \, U_s \, \pi \, \eta \, a^4} \tag{18}$$

$$E_p = E_{op} \, f_p \, (W_p), \quad W_p = \frac{4A \, R_p}{27 \, U_p \, \pi \, \eta \, a^4} \tag{19}$$

where U_s and U_p are the bubble rising velocities according to the Stokes and the potential mode. A numerical analysis of uni- versal functions f_s, f_p allowed formulas (18) and (19) to be approximated (SI units) in the following way:

$$E_s \simeq 0.11 \cdot \frac{a^{1.4}}{R_s^2} A^{1/6} \tag{20}$$

$$E_p \simeq 1.1 \frac{a^{0.8}}{R_p} A^{1/15} \tag{21}$$

Though the absolute value of E depends very slightly on Hamaker's constant which varies within the range of values of 10^{-21} J to 10^{-19} J, flotation is still impracticable at A $<$ 0, i.e., if the dispersion force is directed away from the bubble surface. Thus, the molecular forces act almost according to the principle "yes" - "no", depending on sign.

The pressing hydrodynamic force [19, 56] can exceed the force barrier of disjoining pressure and thus provide a possibility of flotation without the use of reagents below the coagulation threshold. This question may be examined by considering the motion of the particle along the symmetry axis of the bubble from the side of the oncoming liquid flow [60]. Under this condition, the pressing hydrodynamic force is at a maximum. Hence on this path one succeeds in obtaining the necessary and sufficient condition of deposition of the particle on the surface of the floating bubble.

The tangential liquid flow rate is equal to zero on the bubble axis, so that the duration of the deposition process may be indefinitely long. But this means that the viscous resistance of the interphase film is of little importance and may be neglected in the balance of acting forces [60]:

$$F (h, a) = F_v + F_E + F_H + F_G < 0 \tag{22}$$

where F_V is the pressing hydrodynamic force, F_H are the molecular attraction forces, F_E is the electrostatic component of the forces and F_G is the gravitational component of forces. Condition (22) means that for all values of h, the particle must be affected by the force directed to the surface (upper pole) of the bubble, otherwise deposition proves to be impracticable. Condition (22) imposes limitations on the value of the parameters entering into the formula indicating where the disjoining pressure can be overcome. This limitation is represented graphically in Figs. 6 and 7 by a curve which is characteristic of the dependence of the particle radius on the coordinates. This curve defines the area close to the origin of the coordinates in which flotation is impracticable. The flotability regions caused by a pressing hydrodynamic force were calculated for the Stokes (Fig. 6), and the potential (Fig. 7) mode, and for several values of the product of the surface potentials of the bubble, Ψ_R, and the particle, Ψ_a. As might be expected, flotation is practicable even considerably below the heterocoagulation threshold where particle size is not too small. In the potential mode, the pressing hydrodynamic force is much greater than that in the Stokes mode. Because of this, flotation proves to be practicable with greater electrostatic repulsion forces or with smaller particle size.

Flotation is difficult without overcoming the electrostatic barrier because of particles tearing off from the lower pole of the bubble. The liquid flow velocity component at the upper pole which is normal to the bubble surface induces a force pressing the particle onto the surface, whereas that at the lower pole induces a tearing-off force. Consequently, the tea-

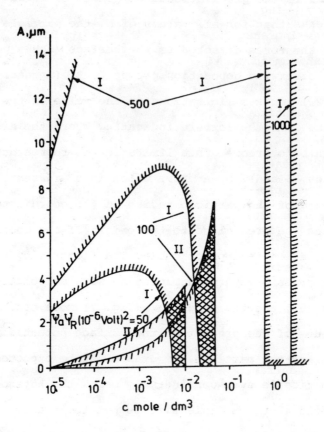

Fig. 7. Regions of flotability in the case of Stokes flow
(shaded). I - the lower boundary of flotation in
the primary minimum, II - the upper boundary of flotation in the secondary minimum. In terms of SI units,
$\varepsilon = 7.1 \cdot 10^{-10}$ F/m; g = 10 m/s^2, $\rho' = 0$.

ring-off force differs from the pressing force only in sign.
Therefore, the possibility of fixing particles in the secondary
energy minimum [30] may also be analyzed by means of condition
(22) [60]. Since the tearing-off force decreases as particle size
decreases, flotation due to fixation of particles in the secon-

dary minimum proves to be practicable for sufficiently fine particles. Therefore, curve II in Fig. 7 limits the dimensions of the particles being flotated from above. In the potential mode, because of an increase in the tearing-off force, fixation in the secondary minimum is possible only for   fine particles for which the effect is complicated by thermal motion. Thus, at present the quantitative description of   inertialess flotation is given only for limit cases, namely at sufficiently small and sufficiently great values of the product $\Psi_R \Psi_a$. In the first case, electrostatic interaction does not complicate flotation, so that formulas (20)-(21) can be used, but in the second case flotation proves to be impracticable.

It will in principle be possible to calculate E at arbitrary values of the parameter $\Psi_R \Psi_a$ by using the method which allowed formulas (20) and (21) to be derived, and at present this very program is being carried out.

As the concentration of the electrolyte increases, the double layer contracts and parameter $\Psi_R \Psi_a$ decreases. Hence, in the light of the data presented in Fig. 8, the possibility of the flotation of fine particles without the use of reagents may be expected below the heterocoagulation threshold, but at a sufficiently high electrolyte concentration if, of course, non-electrostatic stability factors are absent.

There are large differences between long-range hydrodynamic interaction and the process for overcoming the disjoining pressure considered in the Stokes and potential mode. This indicates the importance of adequately describing the hydrodynamic field of the bubble in the elementary flotation act. Therefore, Kitchener's indication [61] of the advisability of using the hydrodynamic

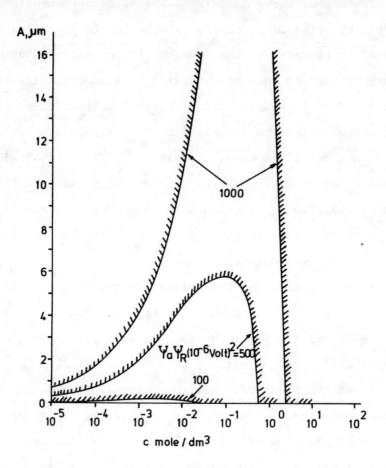

Fig. 8. Regions of flotability in the case of potential flow
(shaded). In terms of SI units, $A = 5 \cdot 10^{-21}$ J;
$\mathcal{E} = 7.1 \cdot 10^{-11}$ F/m; $R_p = 2.5 \cdot 10^{-4}$ m; $V_p = 0.15$ m/s;
$\eta = 10^{-3}$.

field calculated by Hamielec [62, 63] for intermediate values of
Re seems to be very valuable.

Kitchener [61] has derived a formula for E, which is similar
to (14) for conditions under which the Hamielec hydrodynamic
field is applicable and the bubble surface is immobile.

In the opinion of J. A. Kitchener and many other researchers, the bubble surface braking criterion occurs where the floating velocity of the bubble coincides with the value calculated for a solid sphere. In the light of theoretical studies on the braking of the surface motion of the bubble [64, 15] by a dynamic adsorption layer, this condition would be considered necessary though insufficient. Even if a considerable portion of the bubble is braked, a certain portion of it close to the upper pole may remain mobile [65]. A uniform, strong, but incomplete braking of the bubble surface may also be possible [66, 67]. In both cases, the bubble floating rate within the limits of the measurement error may be the same as in the case of a solid sphere. However, long- and short-range hydrodynamic interaction, collision effectiveness, and the possibility of overcoming the electrostatic component of disjoining pressure owing to the pressing hydrodynamic force, W and consequently E, may change essentially even at small surface rates equal to several hundredths of U_∞ [12].

Quantitative Experimental Research into the Flotation of Fine Particles

In recent years, great successes have been achieved in experimental research into the influence of the size of bubbles and spherical particles on collision effectiveness in the Stokes mode [40, 68]. The flotation of an oil emulsion by bubbles [15] was also examined; the size of the bubbles guaranteed proximity to the potential mode. In this case, it has been established with satisfactory agreement with formula (21) that $E_p \sim a$.

The strong influence of long-range hydrodynamic interaction in   inertialess flotation was amply corroborated by this experimental research. This is manifested most importantly in a rapid decrease in E as the particle size decreases, and an increase in   bubble size as well as an abrupt change in the character of E on R and "a" in passing over from the viscous flow to the potential mode.

It must be emphasized that formula (20) was found to be in quantitative agreement with the data of thorough experiments [40, 68] in respect to dependence, whether on the particle radius or the bubble radius. The fact that in accordance with the experimental data the dependence of E on "a" is characteri- zed by exponent 1.5, means a better agreement with formula (20) than with formula (14). But this should be considered as an experimental substantiation of the influence of the short-range hydrodynamic interaction on the elementary flotation act.

It should, however, be acknowledged that at present no syste- matic experimental research into the short-range hydrodynamic interaction has been carried out.

Anfruns and Kitchener [61] examined the effectiveness of the entrapment of several size fractions of hydrophobized (methyla- ted) quartz by individual bubbles 0.5 to 1.1 mm in diameter.

These experiments corroborated the formula which takes into account only long-range hydrodynamic interaction, the formula being derived on the basis of Hamielec's hydrodynamic field. The authors therefore arrive at the conclusion that the dis- joining pressure of double electric layers does not complicate the flotation act, at least not under their experimental condi- tions. A similar conclusion might also be formulated with regard to short-range hydrodynamic interaction. These conclusions, however, cannot be considered to be firmly substantiated, for at least one other possible interpretation of these interesting experimental data may be suggested.

This possible interpretation of study [61] is connected with the fact that short-range hydrodynamic interaction theory and the influence of the double electric layer have been developed for spherical particles; yet the object of the research in [61] were non-spherical particles - crushed Brasilian quartz.

The existence of ribs separating faces on the surface of such particles must therefore be admitted. The overcoming of resistance may be greatly facilitated as the interphase film grows thinner if the angles between the faces (or between the ribs) are sufficiently acute, so that the "cutting through" of the interphase film by a sharpened section of the particle surface may take place. Such geometrical conditions of the elementary flotation act also tremendously facilitate the overcoming of the disjoining pressure of the double electric layer.

The microrelief of the surface cannot strongly affect long-range hydrodynamic interaction, for formulas (13) and (14) and Kitchener's formula [61] which have been derived for spherical particles, also retain their significance as approximative formulas for non-spherical, but isometric particles.

When this, together with the results of study [61] are taken into account, the problem of the theory of fine particle flotation is rendered essentially more accurate; the laws governing the influence of short-range hydrodynamic interaction and surface forces on the elementary flotation act may markedly differ from one another in their applicability to spherical and non-spherical particles; they must therefore be investigated separately in both cases.

The part played in flotation by short-range hydrodynamic interaction and by the double electric layer may not only be decreased, but greatly increased by the deviation of the shape of particles from the spherical. The plane-parallel interphase film between the bubble and plate particle undergoes thinning-out still more slowly than in the case of a spherical particle, so that in this case the role of short-range hydrodynamic interaction is markedly enhanced. This should be expected for a thin plate particle. If the plate is not thin, it may be expected that its shifting along the bubble surface is accompanied by rotation (rolling). In rolling, such orientations of the particle relative to the bubble surface are realized at which the viscous resistance of the interphase film and the disjoining pressure of the interphase film of the double electric layer are so quickly overcome due to the influence of ribs that it affects the value of E only slightly.

Influence of Different Factors on the Tearing-off of Particles in Contactless Flotation

If flotation is not complicated by the presence of energy barriers and $h_{cr} \neq 0$, the approach of particles to one another is terminated by the break-through of the film, and the formation of a contact angle; thus, the possibility of tearing-off is here excluded.

If the double layer does not complicate flotation, but there is a barrier of a non-electrostatic nature with thickness h_o, one may attempt to evaluate the possibility of tearing-off [60], where the possibility of heterocoagulation is considered in the secondary minimum in flotation (Fig. 7). For this purpose, it is sufficient to consider the condition where the sum of hydrodynamic and gravitational tearing-off forces and the molecular attraction force at $h = h_o$ at the lower pole of the bubble are equal. This gives the particle radius a_{max} in the Stokes mode, below which contactless flotation is possible.

If we assume that A varies within the range of 10^{-14} (10^{-21} J) to 10^{-13} (10^{-20} J) erg and h_o within the range of 10 to 100 Å, then a_{max} varies within the range of 3 to 100 μm. Thus, complications for contactless flotation arise only in the case where Hamaker's constant is small and at the same time barrier extension is great. In this case, to guarantee contactless flotation it is useful to ensure opposite charges of the particle and the bubble while introducing an ionic surfactant (Fig. 3). This possibility may be realized at a greater thickness of the barrier and a lower electrolyte concentration, that is, at a greater thickness of the double layer.

Instead of evaluating (23) at Re $\gg$ 1, a similar evaluation may be obtained by using Hamielec's hydrodynamic field. In this case, a_{max} will decrease as the tearing-off force increases. Such a decrease will be insignificant even in the case of stall if the bubble surface is braked above the stall line. At still greater Reynolds numbers, the bubble surface is free or braked but not too strongly above the stall line.

In such a case, the normal velocity component at the surface and accordingly the tearing-off force of the particles greatly increase and a_{max} decreases markedly.

REFERENCES

1. Derjaguin B. V. and Dukhin S. S. Izv. AN SSSR, OTN, Metallurgiya i topl., 1, 82-89 (1959).

2. Derjaguin B. V. and Dukhin S. S. Trans. IMM, 70, 221-224 (1960).

3. Derjaguin B. V. and Dukhin S. S. Zh. fisich. khimii., 33, 2280-2287 (1959).

4. Derjaguin B. V. and Dukhin S. S. Zh. fisich. khimii, 34, 524-529 (1960).

5. Dukhin S. S. Zh. fisich. khimii, 34, 1053-1959 (1960).

6. Derjaguin B. V. and Dukhin S. S. Zh. fisich. khimii, 35, 1247-1257 (1961).

7. Derjaguin B. V. and Dukhin S. S. Zh. fisich. khimii, 35, 1453-1457 (1961).

8. Dukhin S. S. Doklady AN SSSR, 130, 1298-1301 (1960).

9. Derjaguin B. V. and Samygin V. D. Collection of papers of Gintsvetmet, No. 9, Metallurgizdat, 1962, pp. 240-254.

10. Derjaguin B. V. and Dukhin S. S. III Intern. Congr. für grenzfeachenaktiv Stoffe im Koln V. 2, sec. B, p. 324, Mainz, 1960.

11. Derjaguin B. V., Dukhin S. S. and Rulev N. N. Koll. zr., 38, 251-257 (1976).

12. Derjaguin B. V., Dukhin S. S., Rulev N. N. and Semenov V. P. Koll. zr., 38, 258-264 (1976).

13. Rulev N. N. Koll. zr., 40, 989-907 (1978).

14. Rulev N. N. Koll. zr., 40, 1202-1204 (1978).

15. Rulev N. N., Ososkov V. K. and Skrilev L. D. Koll. zr., 40, 590-594 (1978).

16. Rulev N. N., Ososkov V. K., Purich A. V. and Skrilev L. D. Koll. zr., 40, 1132-1138 (1977).

17. Rulev N. N. Koll. zr., 39, 80-85 (1977).

18. Rulev N. N., Derjaguin B. V. and Dukhin S. S. Koll. zr., 39, 314-323 (1977).

19. Dukhin S. S. and Rulev N. N. Koll. zr., 39, 270-275 (1977).

20. Dukhin S. S., Rulev N. N. and Semenov V. P. Koll. zr., 41 (1977) (in press).

21. Dukhin S. S. Abh. Akad. Wiss. DDR, No. 1, 561-567 (1976).

22. Derjaguin B. V., Dukhin S. S. and Rulev N. N. Koll. zr., 39, 1051-1059 (1977).

23. Scheludko A., Toshev B. V. and Bojadjev D. T. J. Chem. Soc. Faraday Trans. I., 72, 2845-2849 (1976).

24. Huddleston R. W. and Smith A. L. Intern. Conference Organized by the Soc. of Chem. Industry-10, Brunel University, 1975.

25. Derjaguin B. V. Koll. zr., 69, 155-164 (1934).

26. Derjaguin B. V. Koll. zr., 16, 425-438 (1954).

27. Derjaguin B. V. Izv. AN SSSR, ser. khim., No 5, 1153-1164 (1937).

28. Derjaguin B. V., Kusakov N. I. Izv. AN SSSR, OMEN, ser. khim., No 5, 1119-1152 (1937).

29. Derjaguin B. V. and Landau L. D. Zhurn. eksper. teoret. fisiki, 15, 663-682 (1945).

30. Verwey E. I. and Overbeek J. Th. G. Theory of the Stability of Lyophobic Colloids, Amsterdam, 1948.

31. Frumkin A. N. and Gorodetskaja A. V. Acta Phys. Chim., URSS 9, 327-340 (1938).

32. Langmuir I. Science, 88, 430-432 (1938).

33. Derjaguin B. V. and Shukakidse N. D. Dokl. AN SSSR, 134, 376-379 (1960); Trans. Inst. Mining and Metal, 70, 569-574 (1961).

34. Jay A. S. and Robinson A. I. Recent Progress in Surface Sci., Acad. Press, N.Y., 2, 1964, 169-260.

35. Usui S. In: Progress in Surface and Membrane Sci., Acad. Press, N.Y., 5, 1972, pp. 233-266.

36. Rao S. R. Miner. Sci. Engng., 6, 45-53 (1974).

37. Jaycock M. J. and Ottewil R. N. Trans. Inst. Mining and Metal, 72, 497-506 (1963).

38. Rubin A. J. and Lackay S. C. J. Amer. Water Works Assoc., 10, 1156-1166 (1968).

39. DeVivo D. G. and Karger B. L. Sep. Sci., 5, 145-167 (1970).

40. Collins C. L. and Jameson G. L. Chem. Eng. Sci., 32, 239-246 (1977).

41. Derjaguin B. V. and Churaev N. V. Croat. Chem. Act., 50, 187-195 (1977).

42. Derjaguin B. V. and Churaev N. V. J. Colloid Interface Sci., 49 (1974).

43. Derjaguin B. V. Chemica Scripta, 9, 97 (1976).

44. Laskowski J. and Kitchener J. J. Colloid Interface Sci., 29, 670-679 (1969).

45. Dibbe N. F., Sirois L. L. and Bredin R. Ottawa, Department of Energy, Mine and Resources, Research Rep., 1972, R. 248.

46. Shulze H. J. and Cichos Chr. Z. Phys. Chem., 251, 145-151 (1972).

47. Schulze H. J. and Cichos C. Z. Phys. Chem., 251, 252-268 (1972).

48. Schulze H. J. und Cichos C. Mitteilung aus der Forschunginstitut fur Aufbereitung, Freiberg, 7-27 (1972).

49. Bleier A., Goddard E. D. and Kulkarni R. D. J. Colloid Interface Sci., 59, 490-504 (1977).

50. Hardy W. Collected Scientific Papers (Cambridge, Cambridge University Press, 1936). p. 659, Proc. Roy. Soc., A 108, 1928, 1-27.

51. Samygin V. D., Chertilin B. S. and Nebera V. P. Koll. zr., 39, 1101-1107 (1977).

52. Levin L. I. Research into the physics of coarsely dispersed aerosols. Published in Russian by AN SSSR, Moscow, 1961, p. 267.

53. Langmuir J. and Blodgett K., Gen. El. Comp. Rep., July, 1945.

54. Okazaki S. Bull. Chem. Soc., 37, 144-150 (1964).

55. Reay D. and Ratcliff G. A. J. Chem. Eng., 51, 178-185 (1973).

56. Goren S. L. and O'Neill M. E. Chem. Eng. Sci., 25, 325-338 (1971).

57. Derjaguin B. V. and Zorin Z. M. Zh. fis. khimii, 29, 1755-1770 (1955).

58. Churaev N. V. In: Surface Forces in Thin Films and Stability of Colloids (Ed. Derjaguin B. V.), Moscow, published in Russian by "Nauka", 1974, pp. 81-83.

59. Mahanty J. and Ninham B. V. Dispersion Forces, Acad. Press, London, N.Y., San-Francisco, 1976, p. 236.

60. Derjaguin B. V., Rulev N. I. and Dukhin S. S. Koll. zr., 39, 680 (1977).

61. Anfruns J. P. and Kitchener J. A., Flotation, A. M. Gaudin Memorial Volume 2, (Ed. M. S. Furstenau), N.Y. Amer. Inst. Chem., Engng., 1976.

62. Hamielec A. E. and Johnson A. I. Canad. J. Chem. Eng., 40, 41 (1962).

63. Hamielec A. E. and Johnson A. I. Canad. J. Chem. Eng., 41, 216 (1963).

64. Savic P. Mech. Eng. Rep., MT-22, National Research Council of Canada.

65. Griffith R. M. Chem. Eng. Sci., 17, 1057 (1962).

66. Dukhin S. S. Doctoral thesis, Institute of Physical Chemistry of AN SSSR, Moscow, 1965.

67. Dukhin S. S. and Buykov M. V. Zh. fis. khimii, 39, 913 (1965).

68. Reay D. and Ratcliff G. A. Canad. J. Chem. Engng., 53, 481 (1975).

ABSTRACT

The following qualitative peculiarities of fine particle
fixation on a bubble during flotation have been investigated:
(1) the possibility of the fixation of the particles on a
bubble surface due to the long-range London-Van-der-Waals attraction forces without the three-phase perimeter of wetting;
(2) the disjoining pressure of electric double layers of the
particle and bubble as the main factor which prevents fixation;
(3) the possibility of fixation due to the recharge of the
bubble by the adsorption of a cationic surface-active agent.

The peculiar characteristics of the approaching stage are:
(1) the long-range hydrodynamic interaction which deflects the
stream lines of a liquid and hampers the inertialess deposition
of particles on a bubble surface; (2) the short-range hydrodynamic interaction which appears during the thinning of the interfacial film between a particle and a bubble.

The quantitative theory of the flotation of fine spherical
particles developed accords with the experiments on the effect
of the size and charge of the particles and bubbles upon the
elementary act of flotation. The authors have discussed the
possibility of the flotation of the lyophile particles due to
bubble recharge if the solvate layers are thinner than the
electric double layer.

RÉSUMÉ

On a démontré des particularités qualitatives de la fixation
de grains fins sur des bulles de la flottation:

1. La possibilité de fixation de grains sur la surface d'une
   bulle grâce aux forces attractives de longue portée de
   London-Van-der-Waals sans formation de contact triphasé
2. La pression de disjonction des couches doubles électriques
   du grain et de la bulle comme principal facteur empêchant la
   fixation
3. La possibilité de fixation due à la recharge de la bulle par
   adsorption d'un tensio-actif cationique.

Les particularité de l'étape d'approche sont les suivantes:

1. interaction hydrodynamique de longue rayon qui dévie les
   lignes d'écoulement du liquide et rend difficile le dépôt
   inerte de grains sur la surface de la bulle

2. interaction hydrodynamique de courte rayon apparaissant lors
   de la diminution de l'épaisseur du film entre le grain et la
   bulle.

On a élaboré une théorie qualitative de flottation des grains
fins sphériques en accord avec les expériences qui ont démontré
l'influence de la taille et de la charge des grains et des
bulles sur l'acte de flottation élémentaire. Les auteurs ont
discuté la possibilité de flottation des grains lyophyles due
à la recharge de la bulle au cas où les couches de solvate sont
plus fines que la couche double électrique.

ZUSAMMENFASSUNG

In der Arbeit werden die besonderen Merkmale des Flotations-
mechanismus von Feinstkörnern in der Etappe des Anhaftens der
Teilchen an die Blasenoberfläche qualitativmäßig nachgewiesen:
die Möglichkeit des Anhaftens des Teilchens, ohne daß eine
Dreiphasen-Berührung durch die London-Van der Waals-Kräfte
großer Reichweite hervorgerufen wird; der Spreizdruck der
elektrischen Doppelschichten des Teilchens und der Blase als
grundsätzlicher Faktor, der den Anhaftvorgang erschwert; die
Möglichkeit der Fixierung durch Überladung der Blase infolge
der Adsorption der oberflächenaktiven Kationenverbindung.

Die besonderen Merkmale der Etappe des Näherkommens sind:
die hydrodynamischen Einwirkungen großer Reichweite, wodurch
die Strömungslinien der Flüssigkeit abgelenkt werden und das
nichtinertiale Anhaften des Teilchens an der Blasenoberfläche
erschwert wird; die hydrodynamischen Einwirkungen geringer
Reichweite, die bei der abnehmenden Dicke des Films, welcher
das Teilchen von der Blase trennt, in Erscheinung treten.

Entwickelt wird die quantitative Theorie der Flotation der
feinen sphärischen Teilchen, in Übereinstimmung mit den durch-
geführten Untersuchungen, die den Einfluß der Größe und der

elektrischen Ladung der sphärischen Teilchen und der Blasen auf den elementaren Flotationsakt nachgewiesen haben. Diskutiert wird die Möglichkeit der Flotation von lyophilen Teilchen durch Überladung der Teilchen für den Fall, wenn die Dicke der Solvatationsschichten von der Dicke der elektrischen Doppelschicht geringer ist.

РЕЗЮМЕ

Выявлены качественные особенности механизма флотации малых частиц на стадии закрепления: возможность закрепления без формирования трехфазного периметра смачивания за счет дальнодействующих сил притяжения Лондона-Ван-дер-Ваальса; расклинивающее давление двойных электрических слоев частицы и пузырька, как основной фактор, препятствующий закреплению; возможность обеспечения закрепления посредством перезарядки пузырька адсорбцией катионоактивного ПАВ.

Особенностями стадии сближения являются: дальнее гидродинамическое взаимодействие, искривляющее линии тока жидкости и затрудняющее безинерцинное осаждение частиц на поверхность пузырька; ближнее гидродинамическое взаимодействие, проявляющееся при утоньшении межфазной пленки, отделяющей частицу от пузырька.

Развитая количественная теория флотации малых сферических частиц находится в хорошем согласии с экспериментами, выявляющими влияние размеров и зарядов сферических частиц и пузырьков на элементарный акт флотации. Обсуждена возможность флотации пиофильных частиц посредством перезарядки пузырька, если толщина сольватных слоев меньше толщины двойного электрического слоя.

INVESTIGATIONS OF THE HYDRODYNAMIC INTERACTION BETWEEN A GAS BUBBLE AND MINERAL PARTICLES IN FLOTATION

H. J. Schulze and G. Gottschalk

Akademie der Wissenschaften der DDR, Forschungsinstitut für Aufbereitung, Freiberg, DDR

In our previous experiments we dealt mainly with the film stability of liquid and the stability of suspensions under the influence of external forces.

In the present paper we would like to present the results of experiments on the hydrodynamic interaction between a single immobile air-bubble streamlined by a flow of liquid and solid particles. This is a model experiment performed within the framework of the investigations into the first stage of the attachment process. The advantage of experiments of this kind is that the trajectories of individual particles are recorded stroboscopically on only one photograph [6]. Brown et al. [3] have already performed this kind of experiment but because of the cinematographic method used, application of their results would have been very expensive.

The experimental device employed consisted of a vertical
flow-pipe 4.0 cm in diameter [1], a stroboscopic-photographic
device [2], and electronic equipment measuring the time interval.
An air-bubble is formed and maintained by a capillary tube. For
results, consult our other paper [4] (Fig. 1).

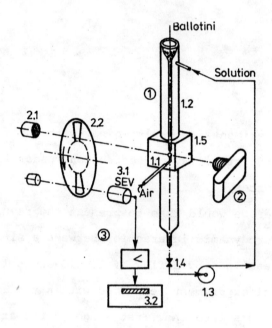

Fig. 1. Schematic diagram of experimental set-up.

The air-bubble radius was 1.53 mm on average; mean radius of
spherical solid-particle R_p = 80 µm. The particles were hydrophobized by dodecylamine hydrochloride 10^{-5} mol/l at pH = 10.
The flow rate of the particles V_∞ was 10 cm/s on average.

The following parameters were determined from the experiments
Ψ – axisymmetric stream function expressing the motion of the
   fluid round a spherical body (Fig. 2),

V_B, V_r, V_ϕ - radial components of particle velocity,

E_{st} - kinetic energy on collision of particles and the bubble,

τ_{st} - time of contact on collision,

ϕ_{Gr} - polar angle representing a transition from collision to sliding,

τ_{Gl} - sliding time,

ϕ_B - polar angle at which the limiting particle trajectory is intercepted by the bubble

E - hydrodynamic efficiency of collision.

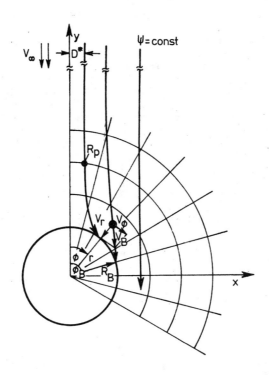

Fig. 2. Coordinate system of particle bubble interaction.

Particle Trajectories

Figure 3 gives three possible interactions that may occurs:

(1) **elastic repulsion of the particles (I)**

(2) **sliding of the particles (II)** and

(3) **attachment of the particles (III)**

The experimental particle trajectories (Fig. 4) follow the streamline given by the potential flow round the bubble. For preliminary theoretical calculations a complete theory does not yet exist because particles of the dimensions used in the flotation (such as those in our experiment) have inertia forces which affect the motion of the fluid. Earlier theories, e.g., that of Sutherland [7] consider the motion of particles to be the same as the motion on the trajectory in a pure medium. Later theories, e.g., those of Flint and Howarth [6] take into account the specific settling velocity of particles but refer strictly to very fine particles only. We calculated the flow function first without considering the particles' specific velocity and subsequently obtained the equation of the stream function for a potential flow according to [6]:

$$\phi = \arg \sin \left(\sqrt{\frac{D^2 \, r \, (1 + g' \, R_p^2)}{r^3 \, (1 + g' R_p^2) - R_B^3}} \, \right) \tag{1}$$

The trajectories of particles are plotted in Fig. 4 where

Fig. 3a. Strobo-
scopic pic-
ture of
trajectory.

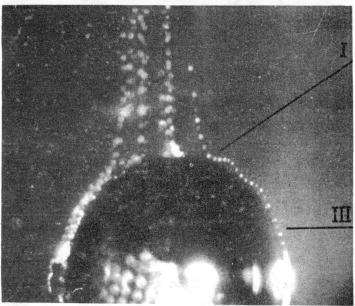

Fig. 3b. Strobo-
scopic pic-
ture of
trajectory.

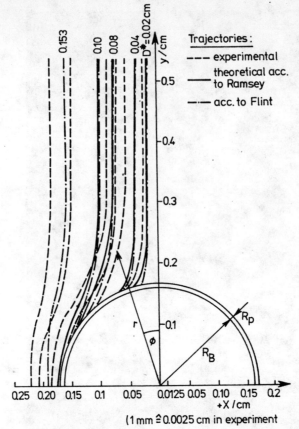

Fig. 4. Theoretical and experimental stream functions.

$$g' = \frac{2\,(\varrho_p - \varrho_{F1})}{9\,\eta\quad V_\infty}\,g \qquad (2)$$

(η = viscosity, ϱ_{F1} = medium density, ϱ_p = particle density, V_∞ = particles flow rate at $r_{\to \infty}$ and $\phi = 0^\circ$, r, R_B and D^* result from Fig. 2).

For g' $\ll$ 1 the relationship for potential flow according to Ramsey [5] is valid. It is evident that real flow trajectories have a more potential character than was calculated theoretical-ly but the approximation takes place only when the vertical dis-tance from the bubble surface $r_N > 2$ to 4 D_p (dp = 2 Rp). Thus

in the first approximation trajectories may be thought of as if
a potential flow is circulating around the bubble with velocity
V_∞ . For further calculations a simplified relationship from
Eq. (1) at $g' \ll 1$ was applied. This relationship was used for
the first time by Sutherlund [7] in preliminary theoretical
calculations for the process of flotation.

Particle Velocity Relative to Bubble

Velocity at point V_B as a function of ϕ (analogical curves
can be obtained as a function of r at ϕ = const.) is shown in
Fig. 5. Theoretical curves are obtained for each value of the
stream function, Ψ = const. (i.e., for a given D^*), by means
of Eq. (1) and the following relationships for a potential flow:

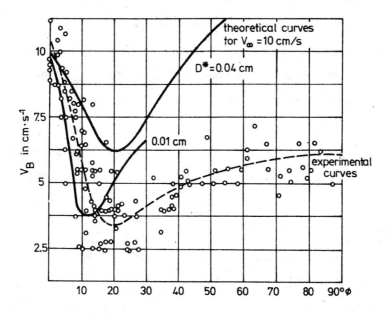

Fig. 5. Theoretical and experimental particle velocities
as functions of ϕ.

$$V_\phi = V_\infty \sin \phi \left(1 + \frac{R_B^2}{2r^3}\right) \qquad (3a)$$

$$V_r = V_\infty \cos \phi \left(1 - \frac{R_B^3}{r^3}\right) \qquad (3b)$$

$$V_B = \sqrt{V_r^2 + V_\phi^2} \qquad (3c)$$

Calculation were carried out for each polar angle ϕ and adequate radius r and then V. V_B is at a minimum at angles of about $\phi = 10$-$20°$, depending on the distance D^* of the trajectories from the symmetry axis, whereafter it should increase sharply. In fact, the increase of V_B at high values of ϕ is considerably smaller than was anticipated on the basis of theoretical assumptions. As it also follows from arcial velocity it is due to the fact that most observed particles attached themselves to the surface of the bubble and did not move freely over it. Figure 6 shows that the experimental arcial velocity V' is less than was calculated theoretically by substituting $r = R_B + R_p$ in Eq. (3a).

Theoretically, the radius component of the particle velocity on the surface of the bubble at $r = R_B + R_p$ equals zero. However, this does not hold true in reality because on one hand the bubble is subject to deformation and kinetic energy is expended for the elastic deformation of the bubble surface (thus $V_r = 0$ appears only at $r < R_B$), and on the other, energy dissipation occurs in a thin film of liquid. The deformation of the bubble surface results in the particle being repelled as well as in loss of energy. We would like to discuss this process.

70

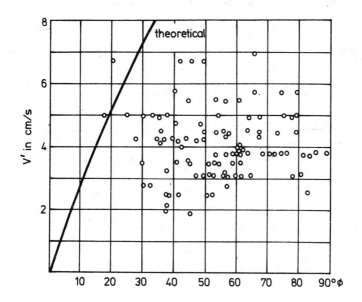

Fig. 6. Theoretical and experimental arcial velocities v'
as a function of ϕ, V_∞ = 10 cm/s.

Kinetic Energy and Time of Contact on Collision

Theoretical considerations show that at small values of ϕ,
$V_r \approx V_B$. Therefore, the experimentally determined velocity at
the point both before and after collision can be used for the
calculation of kinetic energy. Thus we can calculate the loss
of energy on the first collision. It is about 73%. Table 1
gives the results.

The time available for contact τ_{st} is given in Fig. 7 - the
smaller the angle ϕ, the shorter the time is. After extrapola-
tion to ϕ = 0° it amounts to 0.5 ms. Figure 8 shows that this
depends on the particle velocity. This is not in accordance

TABLE 1

Energy Balance on Collision (E in ergs)

$R_p = 80 \; \mu m, \; V_\infty = 10 \; cm/s$

E_{kin} at $r \to \infty$ $= E_1$	E_{kin} at $r \approx R_B + 3R_p$ $= E_2$	E_{kin} of repel	$\Delta E_1 =$ $E_1 - E_{rep}$	$\Delta E_2 =$ $E_2 - E_{rep}$	E_{ab}
$2.7 \cdot 10^{-4}$	$1 \cdot 10^{-4}$	$2.8 \cdot 10^{-5}$	$2.4 \cdot 10^{-4}$	$7.2 \cdot 10^{-5}$	$3 \cdot 10^{-3}$

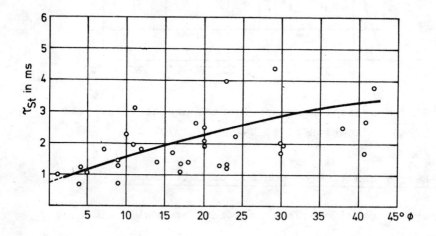

Fig. 7. Time of collision τ_{st} as a function of ϕ.

with the latest assumptions of Evans [8] and Philippoff [9.]
that:

$$\tau_{st} = \pi \sqrt{\frac{2 \; R_p^3 \; \rho p}{3 \; \sigma}} \qquad (4)$$

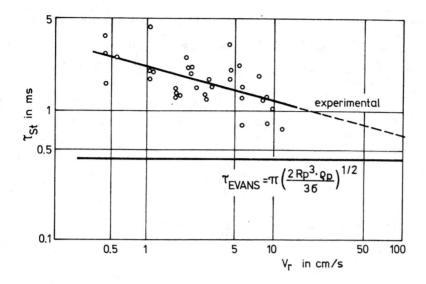

Fig. 8. Time of collision τ_{st} as a function of velocity V.

A slowing down of the process resulting from additional energy dissipation in a thin film of liquid (friction) may be the reason for the longer contact time   and its dependence on the energy of collision (according to Radoev). Experiments show that on collision at small angles of ϕ attachment of particles, generally speaking, does not take place. The reason may be twofold:

(1) The time of contact on collision is so short that the thin film between the bubble and the particle is not ruptured,

(2) Film rupture takes place but the attachment forces
between the bubble and the particle are smaller than the
repelling forces resulting from the elastic rebound of a
particle falling onto a bubble. This mechanism has
already been discussed by Scheludko [11].

It has been demonstrated previously [2] that the energy
needed for particle detachment from the liquid/gas interface
can be calculated by a numerical integration of Laplace's
equation which is necessary to balance the forces acting on a
particle at the gas/liquid interface. In accordance with the
above considerations the energy of detachment for a sphere
(Fig. 9) is

$$E_{ab} = \int_{h_{gl}}^{h_{krit}} \left\{ \frac{2\rho_p}{\rho_{Fl}} - 1 + \cos^3 \omega - \frac{3h}{2R_p} \sin^2\omega + \frac{3}{a^2 R_p^2} \sin \omega \sin (\omega + \theta) \right\} dh \quad (5)$$

$$a = \sqrt{\frac{\rho_w \cdot g}{\sigma}} \quad (6a)$$

$$h = -\frac{y_o}{a} - R_p \cos \omega \quad (6b)$$

For the system under investigation surface tension σ is
about 60 dyn/cm, ρ_p = 2.5 g/cm^3 and $\theta_{Adv} \approx 40^o$. Hence, E_{ab}
equals 3 x 10^{-3} erg as is given in Table 1. The energy of attachment
is therefore considerably greater than the energy of detachment
corresponding to the energy loss ΔE on collision. Thus, it is
not deficient attachment energy that is the reason for the
particle being repelled but probably too short a contact time

74

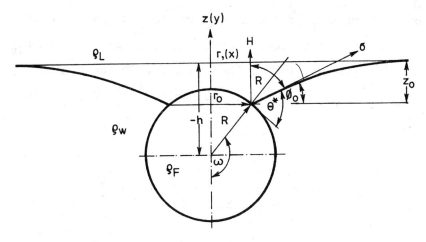

Attachment force: $H = f(R, 6, \theta^*, \omega)$
Buoyancy: $FA = f(R, \omega, \varrho_F, \varrho_W, \varrho_L)$
Hydrostatic pressure: $FHY = f(r_0, z_0, \varrho_L, \omega)$
Weight: $G = f(R, \varrho_F)$
Capillary pressure of a gas bubble: $F_6 = f(6, \varrho_L, r_0, \omega, z_0, R_B)$

Fig. 9. Forces acting on a sphere at a fluid interface.

for film thinning although the energy of collision itself would probably be great enough to lessen the thickness of the film. We may conclude that with the increase of angle ϕ the probability of attachment grows to the same extent as the time of contact. At the same time the energy of collision decreases until it is insufficient for film rupture although the time of contact is long enough. The period from colliding to sliding is characterized by boundary angle ϕ_{Gr}. From the histograms of the observed angles of collision $\phi_{st} = 19° \pm 10°$ and angles of sliding $\phi_{Gl} = 43° \pm 10°$ we obtain $\phi_{Gr} = 30°$. All interactions at $\phi < \phi_{Gr}$ are processes of collision and at $\phi < \phi_{Gr}$ - processes of sliding.

Sliding Time

Time of sliding τ_{Gl} is the time taken for the particle to move along the trajectory round the bubble starting from $\phi > \phi_{Gr}$ to $\phi = 90°$ the radius vector of the bubble, r, being slightly greater than $R_B + R_p$. According to Sutherland [7] τ_{Gl} results from Eq. (3a)

$$\tau_{Gl} = \frac{4 \; (R_B + R_p)}{V_\infty \left[2 + (\frac{R_B}{R_B + R_p})^3\right]} \; \ln \; \cot \frac{\phi}{2} \qquad (7)$$

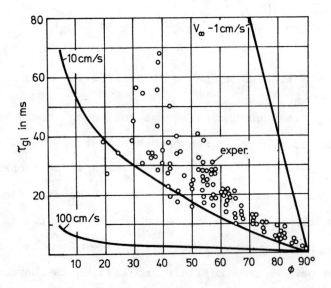

Fig. 10. Time of sliding τ_{Gl} as a function of ϕ and V_∞.

As follows from Fig. 10, the observed time of sliding is (as has already been stated) longer than that calculated theoretically because most of the observed particles have already attached themselves, to the bubble at $\phi > \phi_{Gr}$.

Angle of Contact

The angle of contact is the angle $\phi = \phi_B$ at which the trajectory curve is tangent to the bubble. It depends on the distance D^* of the particle trajectory from the symmetry axis and also determines the character of flow and collection efficiency. The particles moving along trajectories D^* at $\phi_B > 90°$ do not reach the bubble. Figure 11 compares the results with theoretical curves which would be obtained if $r = R_B + R_p$ were inserted into

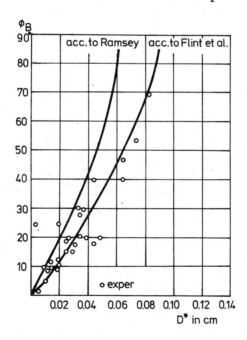

Fig. 11. Time of contact ϕ_B as a function of the distance D^* of the trajectory from symmetry axis.

77

the flow function. Thus, it is possible to calculate the value which D^* must attain to exceed $\phi = \phi_{Gr}$. In the investigated system D^* must be equal to $D^*_{Gr} \geqslant 0.04$ cm. Generally, $R' = (D^*_{Gr}/R_B) > 0.26$. All the particles that flow to the bubble in the flow-pipe of radius D^*_{Gr} are repelled.

Efficiency of Collision

The hydrodynamic collision efficiency can be calculated by the following formula

$$E = \frac{\pi D^{*2} N}{\pi R_B^2 N} = \left(\frac{D^*}{R_B}\right)^2 \tag{8}$$

where D^* is the distance from the limiting trajectory of the particles to the axis on which the bubble rises measured at an infinite distance from the bubble centre, and R_B is the radius of the bubble.

Many authors have calculated this value directly from flotation experiments [6, 13, 14, 15]. Our experiments make it possible to calculate D^* directly and to find the value of E. Figure 12 gives the results. For $R_p = 8 \times 10^{-3}$ cm and $R_B = 0.152$ cm, $E = 0.34 \pm 0.12$. There are many theoretical assumptions for E in the professional literature. For the sake of comparison, some of them are given in Fig. 12.

(1) According to Sutherland [7]

$$E_s = \left(\frac{\sqrt{3 R_p R_B'}}{R_B}\right)^2 = \frac{3R_p}{R_B} , \tag{9}$$

Theoretical and experimental efficiency:

1. acc. to Fonda and Herne
2. acc. to Sutherland
3. acc. to Fuks and Dukhin
4. acc. to Flint and Howarth

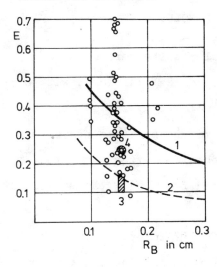

Fig. 12. Hydrodynamic efficiency of collision, E, as a function of R_B.

(2) According to Flint and Howarth [6]

$$E_{Fl} = \frac{G}{1 + G} \qquad (10)$$

$$G = \frac{2 (\rho_p - \rho_{Fl}) R_p^2 g}{9 \eta V_\infty}$$

(3) According to Fuks, Derjagin and Dukhin [13, 16]

$$E_F = \frac{3 R_p}{R_B} \qquad \phi < 90°, \qquad (11)$$

(4) According to Fonda and Herne [17]

79

It is evident that the experimentally obtained values are within the range of theoretical assumptions but because of the general character of these theories the evaluation of their qualities is not possible.

CONCLUSIONS

The following fundamental results were obtained:

(1) During the flow of spherical particles with a radius R_p = 80 µm and a mean flow velocity V_∞ = 10 cm/s against a bubble of radius R_B = 1.53 mm the particle trajectories follow a potential flow which is obtained after the first approximation in cases where the liquid flows with the same relative velocity round the bubble.

(2) The kinetic energy of particles flowing near the symmetry axis of the bubble is used for the elastic deformation of the bubble surface. These particles are repelled from the bubble once or several times. The time of contact on collision is less than 4 ms and the loss of energy on the first collision more than 70%. Before collision the kinetic energy is about 10^{-4} erg.

(3) At angles ϕ 30° there are no collisions at all - the particles slide over the bubble. The time of sliding is defined as the time taken from the moment of contact up to ϕ = 90°. This is ten to twenty times longer than the duration of collision.

(4) The attachment appears to occur mainly in the transition region between colliding and sliding.

(5) Hydrodynamic up-take efficiency values are highly scattered; however, they lie in the range predicted by several theories, that is between 0.2 and 0.5.

The following conclusions may be drawn:

(1) From hydrodynamic considerations of the flowing process
excluding the inertia forces of the particles, satisfactory
results are obtained after first approximation.

(2) In the investigated case attachment takes place within
a time interval longer than that of collision (1.....4 ms), but
much shorter than that of sliding (30...50 ms).

(3) Some points in the conclusions of Brown [3] must be
corrected:

- the time of contact does not generally decrease with increasing distance, but has a maximum at angles of about
  $\phi = 30°$. The longest time of contact does not occur during
  collision but during sliding.
- the possibility of attachment does not decrease in each
  case with increasing distance from the bubble trajectory
  but there is an optimum distance according to the considerations above.
- the relative velocity between particle and bubble does not
  increase with increasing distance from the bubble but has
  a minimum value at a certain angle ϕ.

The most important difference between the model experiments
presented in this paper and the processes taking place in an
impeller-flotation machine is the high relative velocity of up
to 200 cm/s in the latter and the fact that the bubble dimensions are 75% smaller. First of all, considerably shorter colli-

sion and sliding periods are thus obtained. Therefore, for the investigation of process efficiency the hydrodynamic efficiency is sufficient in itself, but energy dissipation in the film and the time of film rupture will have to be considered as has been shown by Dukhin [9 , 13] for small particles. For large particles this problem has remained unsolved until now.

The fact that high flow velocities always cause small bubble sizes is favourable from the point of view of hydrodynamic efficiency but unfavourable from the point of view of the time of contact. Therefore, it is necessary to use the smallest possible bubble sizes at low flow velocities in order to obtain sufficiently long contact periods between particle and bubble. On the basis of what has already been said, we feel that there are still some unexploited possibilities in the optimisation of technological parameters. However, very low buoyancy of the bubble-particle aggregates has to be maintained and this determines the lower limit for R_B.

The most important task in further experiments is a wide-range differentiating of the Reynold's flow number and the investigation into the influence of bubble radius on the process discussed.

REFERENCES

1. Schulze H. J. Moderne physikalisch-chemische Prinzipien der Flotationselementarvorgänge, Deutscher Verlag der Wissenschaften Berlin, Reihe: Moderne Trennmethoden, in Vorbereitung.

2. Schulze H. J. Int. J. Mineral Proc., 4, 141 (1977).

3. Brown D. I. Particle Trajectories, Collision and Attachment in Froth Flotation. In: Aerodynamic Capture of Particles (Ed. E.G. Richardson) London, 1960, p. 35.

4. Schulze H. J. and Gottschalk G. Experimentelle Untersuchung der Hydrodynamik der Wechselwirkung eines Partikelschwarmes mit einer Gasblase – ein Modell für den Flotationselementarprozeß, in Vorbereitung.

5. Ramsey A. S. A Treatise on Hydromechanics, Part II, Hydrodynamics, Bell and Sons, London, 1935, p. 160.

6. Flint L. R. and Howart W. I. Chem. Engng. Sci., 26, 1155 (1971).

7. Sutherland K. L. J. Phys. Chem., 52, 394 (1948).

8. Evans L. F. Ind. Engng. Chem., 46, 2420 (1954).

9. Philippoff W. Mining Engng., 4, 386 (1952).

10. Derjagin B. V. Doklad. Akad. Nauk SSSR, 51, No. 7, 517 (1946).

11. Scheludko A., Tosev B. and Bogadiev B. J. Chem. Soc. Trans. Farad. I, 72, 2815 (1976).

12. Schulze H. J. Coll. Polymer Sci., 253, 730 (1975).

13. Derjagin B. V., Dukhin S. S. and Rulev N. N. Koll. zh., 38, 251 (1976).

14. Dukhin S. S. Gesammelte Arbeiten des Instituts für Kolloid- und Wasserchemie bei der Ukrain. AdW, Kiev, personal communicate.

15. Ray D. and Ratcliff G. A. Canad. I. Chem. Engng., 51, 178 (1973).

16. Fuks N. A. Mechanics of aerosols. Izdat. Akad. Nauk SSSR, Moskau 1955. Russian text.

17. Herne H. The classical computations of the aerodynamic capture of particles by spheres. In: Aerodynamic Capture of Particles (Ed. E.G. Richardson), London, Pergamon Press, 1960, p. 26.

ABSTRACT

The paper deals with the flowing processes of the solid
particles relative to an air bubble in order to elucidate the
collision phenomena.

It is shown that during the flow of spherical particles with
the radius of 80 μm and the mean flowing velocity of 10 cm/s
against the bubble with the radius of 1.53 mm the particle
trajectories follow a potential flow. The kinetic energy of
particles flowing near the symmetry axis of the bubble is used
for the elastic deformation of the bubble surface. The time
of contact on collision is less than 4 ms and the loss of
energy on the first collision is more than 70%. The particles
approaching a bubble at a polar angle $\phi > 30°$ do not collide
with it but slide down the bubble. The attachment appears to
occur mainly in the transition region between the colliding
and sliding.

RÉSUMÉ

La conférence decrit le phénomene de la collision des
particules solides par rapport à la bulle de l'air dans le
processus de l'écoulement. On a montré, que pendant l'écoulement des particules sphériques à 80 μm de rayon et à la
vitesse moyenne d'écoulement de 10 cms^{-1} dans la direction de
la bulle à 1.53 mm de rayon, les trajectoires des particules
correspondent à l'écoulement potentiel.

L'énergie cinétique des particules écoulant près de l'axe
de la symétrie de la bulle est usée pour la deformation élas-
tique de la surface de la bulle. Le temps du contact pendant
la collision esr plus petit que 4 ms et la perte de l'énergie
de première collision est plus grande que 70%. Les particules
s'approchant à la bulle de l'air sous un angle $\phi > 30°$ ne
collisent pas avec une bulle mais elles glissent d'elle.
L'attachement semble avoir lieu, en principe, dans les zones
entre la collision et le glissement.

ZUSAMMENFASSUNG

Der Vortrag berichtet über den Strömungsvorgang der Fest-
stoffteilchen im Verhältnis zur Luftblase, mit dem Ziel die
Stoßerscheinungen zu beschreiben.

Es wird gezeigt, daß bei der Strömung der kugelförmigen
Teilchen, vom Radius 80 µm, mit einer durchschnittlichen
Strömungsgeschwindigkeit von 10 cm/s in Richtung einer Blase
vom Radius 1.53 mm, die Teilchentrajektorien der Potential-
strömung entsprechen. Die kinetische Energie der sich in der
Nähe der Blasensymmetrieachse bewegenden Teilchen wird für
die elastische Deformation der Blasenoberfläche verbraucht.
Die Kontaktzeit beim Anstoßen beträgt unter 4 ms und der Ener-
gieverlust beim ersten Stoß überschretet 70%. Teilchen, die
sich unter einem Winkel von $\phi > 30°$ einer Blase nähern,
stoßen nicht an, sondern gleiten über die Blase. Das Anhaften
scheint hauptsächlich im Übergangsbereich zwischen Stoßen und
Gleiten zu erfolgen.

РЕЗЮМЕ

В докладе рассмотрен процесс передвижения твердых зерен по
отношению к пузырьку воздуха с целью описания явления столкновения.

Показано, что во время передвижения шарообразных частиц
диаметром 80 µм, при их средней скорости 10см/с, по направле-
нию к пузырьку диаметром 1,53 мм траектория зерен соответствует потенциальному движению. Кинетическая энергия зерен, перед-
вигающихся вблизи оси симметрии пузырька, расходуется на элас-
тичную деформацию поверхности пузырька. Продолжительность соприкосновения в моменте столкновения составляет менее 4мс, а поте-
ря энергии в первом моменте столкновения превышает 70%.

Зерна приближающиеся к пузырьку под углом $\phi > 30°$, не сталки-
ваются с пузырьком, а соскальзывают по нему. Прикрепление, ве-
роятно происходит главным образом в момент между столкновени-
ем и соскальзыванием.

INFLUENCE OF NON-IONIC SURFACTANTS ON THE FLOTATION OF CASSITERITE

A. Doren, A. van Lierde and J. A. de Cuyper

Laboratoire de Traitement des Minerais, Université Catholique de Louvain, Louvain-la-Neuve, Belgique

Many papers dealing with the adsorption of non-ionic surfactants on solids and in particular, on silica [1 , 2 , 3]
have recently been published.

In fact, this mineral can adsorb these surfactants due to
hydrogen bonds existing between oxyethylene groups of the
reagent and silanol groups on its surface. The bond modifies
the mineral's wettability.

H. Kuno and R. Abe have determined adsorption isotherms for
polyoxyethylenenonyl-phenol on calcium carbonate [4] and on
carbon black [5]. K. G. Mathai and R. H. Ottewill have investigated the effect of non-ionic, compounds on the stability of
silver iodide. Many researchers have shown interest in the
interaction between the non-ionic surfactants and collectors
used in flotation as well as in their influence on flotation.
Fuerstenau and Yamada [7] demonstrated the favourable effect
of neutral molecules in the flotation of corundum using sodium

dodecyl sulphate. On the other hand, Leja and Schulman [8] suggest that a frothing reagent improves the process of flotation if it can interact with collector molecules at the solid liquid interface. Lekki and Laskowski [9] arrived at the same conclusions investigating the flotation of chalcocite using xanthate and α-terpineol, the latter having a beneficial effect on the zeta-potential of chalcocite and on the adsorption of xanthate. Bansal and Biswas [10] have clearly shown the existence of interactions between sodium oleate and polypropylene glycol monomethyl ether in flotation of rutile. These two reagents adsorb together at solid/liquid and liquid/gas interfaces. The present paper mainly investigates the collecting properties of the collector in relation to quartz and cassiterite for octyl-phenylpolyethoxyethanol (OPEG) applied separately or in combination with sodium sulfosuccinate. The observed phenomena may be discussed from the point of view of studies concerning adsorption, zeta-potential determination and measurements of surface tension in aqueous solutions of these reagents.

EXPERIMENTAL METHODS

Floatability of pure minerals was determined using -65 +100 mesh particles in a modified Hallimond cell. The flotation of natural and synthetic ores was carried out in a Denver cell. Zeta potentials were measured by a streaming potential method using the -48 +65 mesh size fraction for pure minerals. The apparatus used is similar to that invented by D. W. Fuerstenau [12], [13], but modified according to the suggestions of M. Robinson et al. [14]. OPEG adsorption on quartz and cassiterite was investigated by spectrophotometric measurement of reagent residual concentration after contact with pure minerals in the pulp at $25^{\circ}C$ for 18 h. The specific surface area of the samples used was 0.724 m^2/g for quartz and 1.806 m^2/g for cassiterite. These specific surfaces were determined by nitrogen adsorption measurement (the BET method). Surface tension in aqueous solutions of reagents was measured at $20^{\circ}C$ using Fisher's tensiometer.

MINERALS AND REAGENTS

Basic investigations were performed using a sand sample from Mol (Belgium) where the SiO_2 content was greater than 99.5% and a cassiterite sample of high purity 98.6% SnO_2, 0.92% Fe_2O_3, and 0.25% SiO_2. The sand fractions used for the flotability tests and for the determination of zeta-potential were washed many times with hydrochloric acid solution of 0.1 N and then with demineralized water until the silver nitrate test was negative. In the case of cassiterite these fractions were washed with demineralized water and dried at $105^{\circ}C$. Quartz and cassiterite fractions used in adsorption tests were obtained by careful grinding of preconditioned minerals in an agate mortar as described above.

The synthetic mineral flotated in a Denver cell was a mixture of unwashed cassiterite and sand. Grinding was performed in a steel ball mill. The OPEG used in the investigations is a commercial reagent manufactured by Rohm and Haas and labelled TRITON X-100. It contains from 9 to 10 units of "ethylene oxide" and its mean molecular weight is 624 [15].

The investigated sulfosuccinate is a tetrasodium salt of 1,2-
dicarboxyethyl-N-octadecylsulfosuccinate acid manufactured by
American Cyanamid (Aeropromoter 840). Its mean molecular weight
is 633. In some tests this reagent was replaced with a sulfosuccinate made by Allied Chemical Colloids i.e., Procol CA 540.

RESULTS OF THE EXPERIMENTS

Investigations on Pure Minerals

Flotation of Quartz and Cassiterite. Flotation curves for
cassiterite and for quartz   vs.   pH and at various OPEG concentrations are given in Fig. 1. It emerges that quartz flota-

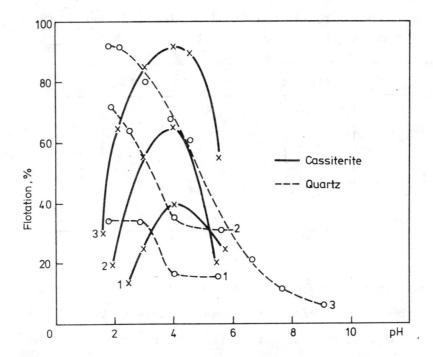

Fig. 1. Influence of pH on the flotation of quartz and
cassiterite at various OPEG concentrations
(1 - 20 mg/l; 2 - 40 mg/l; 3 - 100 mg/l).

tion is favourable at low pH values while cassiterite flotation
is maximum at pH = 4. Moreover, substantial improvements in tin
recovery are observed with an increase in reagent concentration.
For each concentration, maximum recovery obtained is of the
same order for quartz and cassiterite at pH 2 and pH 4, respectively. The selective separation of quartz and cassiterite at
pH = 4 could not be considered, while on the other hand it seems
that it is possible at pH = 2. These expectations were confirmed (Table 1) during the tests performed on a synthetic mixture
consisting of equal fractions of both minerals.

TABLE 1

Flotation of the Synthetic Mixture (1:1) Quartz-cassiterite
in the Presence of OPEG at Various pH

	OPEG Concentration: 100 mg/l				
pH	2.5	3.5	4.5	5.5	6.5
Concentrate					
Yield, %	43	55	69	46	25
Sn, %	1.8	23.0	50	49	53
Sn Recovery, %	2	33	90	59	35

At pH = 2.5 about 85% of quartz can already be flotated
selectively reducing tin entrainment to 2%. On the other hand,
at pH 4.5 about 90% of cassiterite can be flotated but with 50%
entrainment of quartz. Quartz flotation at pH 2 was not investigated. In fact, such a solution does not seem to be applicable on a large industrial scale because of the low tin content
in ores and the very complex character of their gangue. Further

investigations were therefore carried out in view of the direct flotation of cassiterite, simultaneously trying to improve selectivity and introducing some activators or additional collectors.

Flotation of the Minerals in the Presence of Lead Nitrate and Hydrosulphide

As follows from Fig. 2, pH exerts a considerable influence on cassiterite flotability in the presence of 1.5 mg/l $Pb(NO_3)_2$,

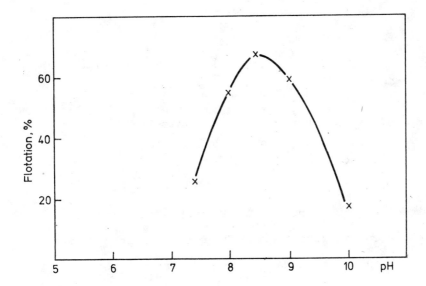

Fig. 2. Effect of pH on the flotation of cassiterite in the presence of 1.5 mg/l $Pb(NO_3)_2$, 10 mg/l NaSH and 62.5 mg/l OPEG.

10 mg/l NaSH and 62.5 mg/l OPEG. In fact, mineral recovery decreases considerably at the moment the optimum pH = 8.5 ceases to be maintained. Apart from pH there are other important process parameters such as concentrations of NaSH and $Pb(NO_3)_2$. In can be observed in Figs. 3 and 4 that at pH = 8.5 flotation

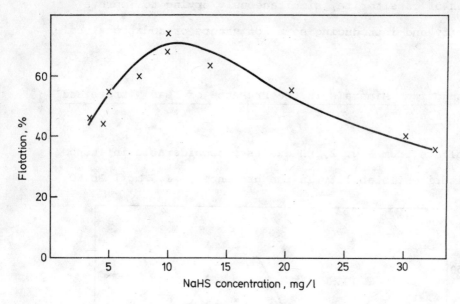

Fig. 3. Effect of NaSH concentration on cassiterite flotation at pH = 8.5 using 3.75 mg/l $Pb(NO_3)_2$ and
62.5 mg/l OPEG.

of cassiterite in the presence of OPEG reaches its maximum
depending on the concentration of each of these reagents. With
10 mg/l $Pb(NO_3)_2$ and 10 mg/l NaSH, tin recovery reaches 90%
and OPEG consumption is reduced to 62.5 mg/l.

These a priori very favourable operating conditions were
tested on synthetic quartz-cassiterite mixture (1:1). As can
be seen in Table 2, they permit a considerable increase in tin
recovery regardless of the amount of collector and they also
facilitate a significant improvement in selectivity (at least
for OPEG concentrations not exceeding 50 mg/l). Unfortunately,.
when compared with earlier results obtained with OPEG only and
at pH = 4.5 the new results do not allow the advantages of
reagents conditions discussed to be fully appreciated.

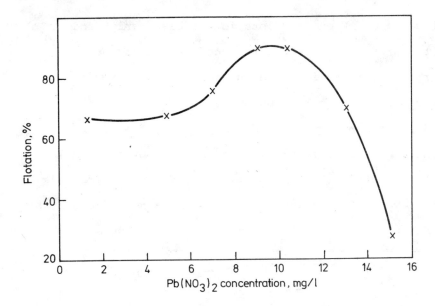

Fig. 4. Effect of Pb(NO$_3$)$_2$ concentration on cassiterite
flotation at pH = 8.5 using 10 mg/l NaSH and
62.5 mg/l OPEG.

TABLE 2

Flotation of a Synthetic Quartz-cassiterite Mixture (1:1) at
pH = 8.5 in the Presence of OPEG, Pb(NO$_3$)$_2$ and NaSH

Reagents (mg/l)						
OPEG	20	20	50	50	62.5	62.5
Pb(NO$_3$)$_2$	0	10	0	10	0	10
NaSH	0	10	0	10	0	10
Concentrate						
Yield, %	12.0	37	27	56	26	58
Sn %	30	60	35	53	51	51
Sn Recovery, %	10	60	25	80	35	80

The influence of pH on the flotation of cassiterite and quartz in the presence of OPEG introduced separately or together with Aeropromoter 840 is shown in Fig. 5. Figure 6 shows the influence of Aeropromoter 840 concentration on mineral flotation at pH = 5.5 for various amounts of OPEG ranging from 10 to 40 mg/1. While quartz flotation is not affected by the combined introduction of both collectors cassiterite flotation improves considerably. The observed improvements is most noticeable at pH values below 3 and above 5. Moreover, large amounts of

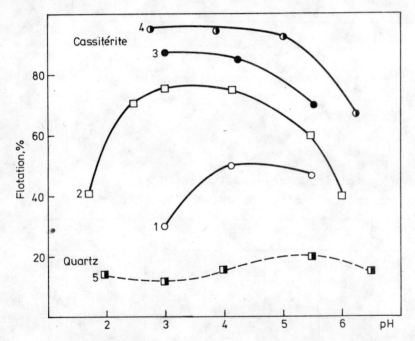

Fig. 5. Effect of pH on the flotation of quartz and cassiterite using Aeropromoter 840 only or a combination of OPEG and Aeropromoter (1 - 0.5 mg/1 Aero 840; 2 - 1 mg/1 Aero 840; 3 - 0.5 mg/1 Aero 840 + 10 mg/1 OPEG; 4 - 0.5 mg/1 Aero 840 + 20 mg/1 OPEG; 5 - 1 mg/1 Aero 840 + 20 mg/1 OPEG).

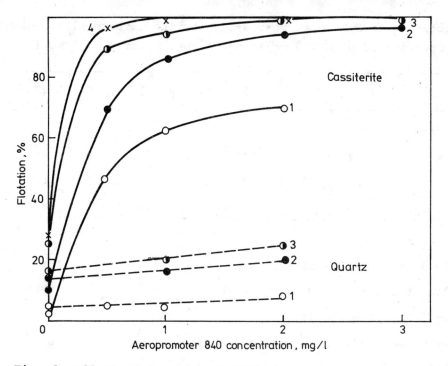

Fig. 6. Effect of Aeropromoter 840 concentration on the
flotation of quartz and cassiterite at pH 5.5 with
different amounts of OPEG added (1 - 0 mg/l;
2 - 10 mg/l; 3 - 20 mg/l; 4 - 40 mg/l).

Aeropromoter 840 are not required. Thus, at pH = 5.5 and with
20 mg/l OPEG the introduction of 0.5 mg/l Aeropromoter 840
improves tin recovery from 25 to 90%; at pH = 3 with 10 mg/l
OPEG the same concentration of Aeropromoter 840 leads to the
flotation of cassiterite as efficiently as in the case of pH = 4
with 100 mg/l OPEG.

These very promising results were controlled in the flotation of various synthetic mixtures of quartz and cassiterite in
Hallimond and Denver cells.

TABLE 3

Flotation of Synthetic Quartz-Cassiterite Mixture (1:1)
in the Presence of OPEG (20 mg/l) and Aeropromoter 840 (2 mg/l)

pH	2.5	3	3.5	4	5	5.5	6.5
Concentrate Yield, %	54	53	54	56	62	66	46
Sn, %	68	70	68	68	63	59	68
Sn Recovery, %	95	96	95	98	100	100	81

Table 3 gives the results obtained in a Hallimond cell for a mixture of two minerals (1:1) in the presence of 20 mg/l OPEG and 2 mg/l Aeropromoter 840.

At pH values between 2.5 and 4 tin recovery reaches 95% and selectivity in relation to quartz turns out to be very good (quartz entrainment does not exceed 15%).

Figure 7 gives the results obtained in a Denver cell at pH = 4 on synthetic ore (cassiterite-quartz) of 1% Sn. As it is evident from the change in yield of concentrate and from tin recovery against consumption of OPEG and Aeropromoter 840, the combined introduction of these two collectors considerably improves the flotation of cassiterite with respect to selectivity as well as recovery, providing that the concentration of Aeropromoter 840 is about 100 g/l and the ratio OPEG/Aeropromoter 840 is close to 1. In fact, the yield of concentrate obtained under these conditions equals 19% with tin recovery approaching 81%.

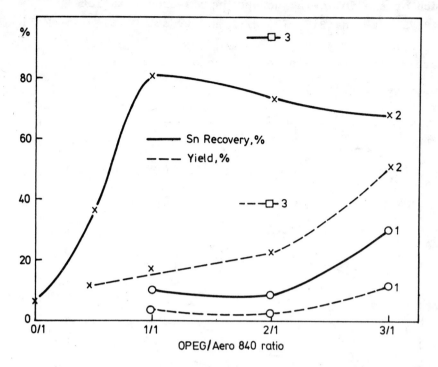

Fig. 7. Effect of OPEG and Aeropromoter consumptions on the flotation of the synthetic quartz-cassiterite mixture at pH = 4 (1 - 50 g/t Aero 840; 2 - 100 g/t Aero 840; 3 - 200 g/t Aero 840).

Tests on Natural Ore

The processed ore has 0.75% Sn and comes from Bolivia. The tin is in the form of cassiterite and the gangue consists mainly of quartz, fluorite and siderite. Flotation was performed adopting general conditions similar to those operating in the best comparative tests carried out using Procol CA 540 as the only collector. These are the conditions:

- ore grinding to 80% - 200 mesh;
- desliming at 10 μm by cyclone classification of the pulp;
- conditioning at pH = 2 after preconditioning in the pres-

97

ence of the following gangue depressors: Cataflot
P40 (75 g/t)- Na_2SiF_6 (75 g/t) and Procol DA 811 (75 g/t).

Figure 8 gives the main results obtained in a similar way to
that described in Fig. 7.

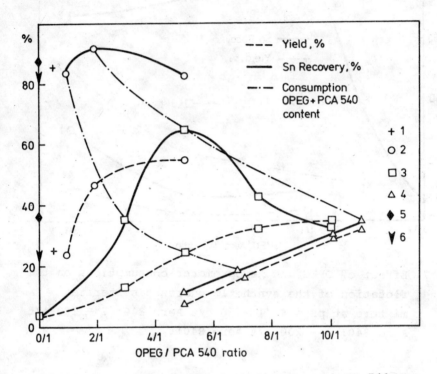

Fig. 8. Effect of the ratio of OPEG to Procol CA 540 consumption on the flotation of natural ore at pH = 2
for various consumptions of Procol 540 (1 - 800 g/t;
2 - 600 g/t; 3 - 300 g/t; 4 - 150 g/t; 5 - 1800 g/t;
6 - 1000 g/t).

It appears that the combination of two collectors (OPEG and
Procol 540) gives the best results where their total consump-
tion equals 1000 to 1200 g/t at least half of which is due to
OPEG consumption. The OPEG/Procol CA 540 ratio seems to be a

decisive parameter. Any increase of this relation exceeding 1:1 immediately results in a decrease of tin recovery even if the total consumption of the collector increases sharply. It should be noticed, however, that for processed ore the results of flotation in the presence of an OPEG and Procol CA 540 mixture are no better than that obtained during the best comparative tests using Procol CA 540 alone.

DISCUSSION OF THE RESULTS

The collecting function of OPEG in relation to cassiterite and quartz results both from the length of its hydrocarbon chain and the presence of some polar functional groups enabling the formation of bonds with OH groups on the surface of the minerals. Many tests prove that this reagent is the most effective collector for these minerals at pH values close to their iso-electric point (Fig. 9). OPEG adsorption is also highest at

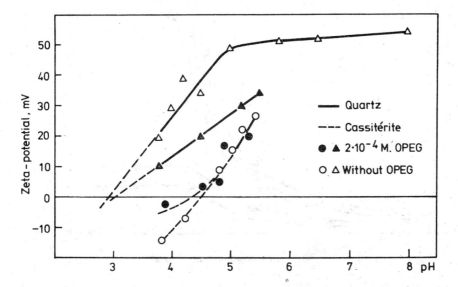

Fig. 9. Effect of pH on zeta-potentials of cassiterite and quartz with or without OPEG.

these values of pH, as can be seen in Fig. 10 which represents the change in the quantity of moles being adsorbed by m^2 of the quartz or cassiterite surface vs. an equilibrium concentration of this reagent.

At pH < i.e.p. adsorption and flotability decrease: protons are readily adsorbed in place of OH groups on the surface thereby reducing the number of disposable sites needed for the formation of hydrogen bonds with oxyethylene groups of the reagent. At pH > i.e.p., on the other hand, SnOH and SiOH sites

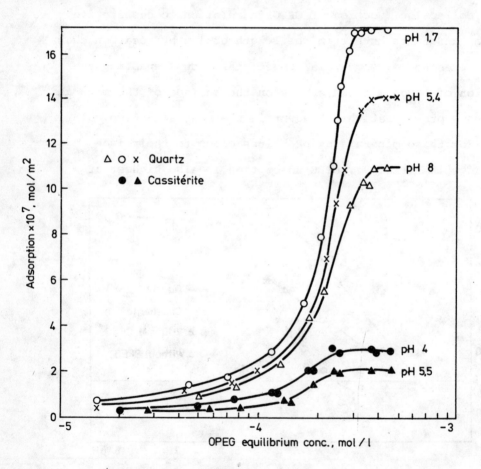

Fig. 10. Adsorption of OPEG on quartz and cassiterite at various pH values.

dissociate gradually yielding negative charges SnO⁻ and SiO⁻ together with an increase in pH which results in a decrease in surfactant adsorption and hence in mineral floatability.

This mechanism, which has been suggested by many researchers, seems to be valid only for concentrations of collector smaller than the critical micelle concentration. Hemimicelles are formed on the surface of the minerals when this concentration is reached due to the bonds between chains of the reagent in which polyoxyethylene groups in the double layer are directed to the solution, thus reducing the hydrophobic properties of the mineral [9].

This can clearly be seen in Fig. 11 for quartz. It follows from the Figure that for every concentration higher than the critical micelle concentration floatability drops while adsorption tends to stabilize at a constant value.

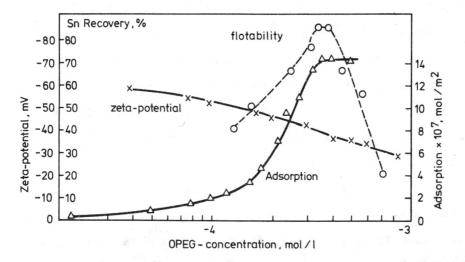

Fig. 11. Effect of OPEG concentration at pH = 5.4 on floatability and zeta-potential of cassiterite and on
reagent adsorption onto the surface of the mineral.

It should be noticed that OPEG adsorption on quartz is, regardless of pH, greater than that on cassiterite. This results in a clear zeta-potential decrease as can be seen in Figs. 9 and 11. This phenomenon was interpreted by Eremenko as the result of a dissociation drop of SiOH groups to SiO⁻ due to the fact that the bonds of OH surface groups with OPEG oxygen atoms are not so polar as the bonds existing between the same groups and water molecules [17]. The flotation of cassiterite using OPEG could be improved at pH = 8.5 by introducing (apart from the collector) specific amounts of lead nitrate, hydrosulphide and OPEG. This points to the fact that the improvement in the process results from the surface sulphidization and in our case the cassiterite surface has a tendency to act as the surface of heavy sulphide metals which is perfectly well collected by OPEG [22].

Sulphidization is directly caused by the interaction of HS⁻ and S⁻⁻ ions with the atoms of tin in cassiterite as well as by the interaction between those ions and the surface of the mineral via PbOH⁺ ions which are adsorbed on the surface. It is well known that at pH = 8.5 PbOH⁺ ions adsorb strongly on the surface of cassiterite making it positive [21]. It should be noticed that this modification of the surface charge is favorable for the adsorption of negative HS⁻ and S⁻⁻ ions and for their later combination with Sn⁺ and Pb⁺ groups. This interpretation is in perfect accordance with the results on the flotation of cassiterite and quartz mixtures. It is normal that quartz is less amenable to sulphidization than cassiterite because in the case of quartz only PbOH⁺ ions can act [20].

Under these conditions the collector will be adsorbed first by the more hydrophobic surface of cassiterite and will ensure the flotation of quartz only when it appears in higher concentration.

The simultaneous application of OPEG and sulfosuccinate improves the selectivity of cassiterite flotation regardless of pH value, due to a considerable increase in the hydrophobic properties of this mineral resulting from the simultaneous adsorption of both reagents. Due to polar carboxylic and sulphonate groups, sulfosuccinate can adsorb on the surface of cassiterite at adsorption centres, thus increasing the coverage of the surface. This layer can be maintained by van der Waals interaction between the molecules of both types of collectors at the solid/liquid interface. Such interactions really take

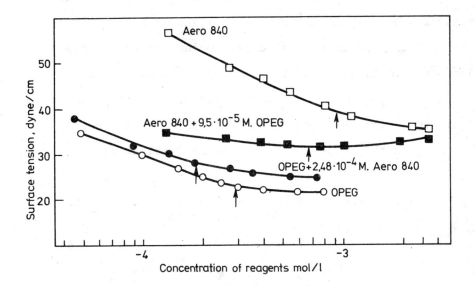

Fig. 12. Effect of OPEG and Aeropromoter 840 concentrations on the surface tension of aqueous solutions.

place because the critical micelle concentration of one of the reagents is modified by the introduction to a water solution of a small amount of the other. This can be seen from Fig. 12 which represents the change in the surface tension of a water solution for each collector depending on its concentration. It is seen that the inflection point of the straight line corresponding to the critical micelle concentration of each collector moves towards lower concentrations when small amounts of the other collector are added.

CONCLUSIONS

The application of non-ionic alkylpolyoxyethylene surfactants in the flotation of cassiterite was investigated in a Hallimond cell on pure minerals and on a mixture of pure minerals (cassiterite - quartz), and in a Denver cell on synthetic and natural minerals. The investigations showed a favourable influence of the combination of sulfosuccinate-alkylpolyoxyethylene on selectivity and tin recovery in flotation at pH = 4.5. Good results were also obtained using a non-ionic alkylpolyoxyethylene surfactant alone at pH = 8.5 after preconditioning in the presence of lead nitrate and hydrosulphide. Better selectivity and recovery were interpreted in terms of adsorption, zeta-potential and surface tension measurements.

REFERENCES

1. Griot O. and Kitchener J. A. Trans. Faraday Soc., 61, 1026 (1965).

2. Aronson M. P. and Princen H. M. J. Colloid Interface Sc., 52, 345-355 (1975).

3. Sun Hsiao, Dunning H. N. and Lorenz P. B. J. Phys. Chem., 60, 657-660 (1956).

4. Kuno H. and Abe R. Kolloid. Z., 177, 40-44 (1961).

5. Abe R. and Kuno H. Kolloid Z. u Z. Polymere, 181, 70-71 (1962).

6. Mathai K. G. and Ottewill R. H. Trans. Faraday Soc., 62, 750-758 (1966).

7. Fuerstenau D. W. and Yamada B. J. Trans. Am. Inst. Min. Engrs., 223, 50-52 (1962).

8. Leja J. and Schulman J. H. Min. Engng. N.Y., 6, 221-228 (1954).

9. Lekki J. and Laskowski J. Trans. Inst. Min. Metall. Sect. C., 80, C 174-180 (1971).

10. Bansal V. K. and Biswas A. K. Trans. Inst. Min. Metall. Sect. C, 85, C 131-135 (1976).

11. Fuerstenau D. W., Metzger P. H. and Seele G. D. Engineering and Mining Journal, 157, 93-95 (1957).

12. Fuerstenau D. W. Mining Engineering, 8, 834-835 (1956).

13. Fuerstenau D. W. Streaming Potential Studies on Quartz. Sc. D. Thesis, M.I.T., 1953.

14. Robinson M., Pask J. A. and Fuerstenau D. W. Journal of the American Ceramic Soc., No. 10, 516-520 (1964).

15. Shinoda K., et al. Colloidal Surfactants. Academic Press, New York, 1963, 97-178.

16. Doren A., Vargas D. and Goldfarb J. Trans. Inst. Min. Metall. Sect. C, 84, C 34-37 (1975).

17. Eremenko B. V., Platonov B. E., Uskov I. A. and Lyubchenko J. N. Kolloid zh., 36, 218-221 (1974).

18. Rubio J. and Kitchener J. A. J. Colloid. Interface Sc., 57, 132-142 (1976).

19. Gaudin A. M. and Fuerstenau D. W. Trans. Amer. Inst. Min. Metall.and Petrol. Eng., 202, 958-962 (1955).

20. Fuerstenau M. C., Miller J. D., Pray R. E. and Perinne B. F. Trans. Am. Inst. Min. Engrs., 232, 359-364 (1965).

21. Salas A. L'influence des ions Fe^{+++} et Al^{+++} sur la flottabilite de la cassitérite dans la flottation cationique et anıonique d'un minerai complexe d'étain. Thèse de doctorat en sc. appl., Univ. Cathol. Louvain, 1973.

22. Doren A. Thèse de doctorat en sc. natur. appl., Univ. Cathol. Louvain, en preparation.

23. Pryor E. J. and Wrobel S. A. Bulletin of the Institution of Mining and Metallurgy, 60, 201-237 (1950).

ABSTRACT

The paper deals with the use of non-ionic surfactants of the alkylpolyoxyethylene type in the flotation of cassiterite ores.

The first part of the investigation describes the flotation results obtained in a Hallimond cell with pure minerals or mixtures of pure quartz and cassiterite, at various pH values and for different concentrations of the non-ionic surfactant, with and without addition of sodium sulfosuccinate. By combining both collectors, at pH between 2 and 6, substantial improvements in selectivity and tin recovery are observed. Confirmation of these favourable results is obtained in batch flotation tests made on a synthetic ore containing quartz and cassiterite with a Sn content of 1%.

In the second part of the paper, the respective floatabilities of quartz and cassiterite are compared at alkaline pH, in the presence of the same collectors, after preconditioning with head nitrate and sodium hydrosulfide. Some further improvement of selectivity is observed under such conditions at pH 8.5.

The collecting effect of the alkylpolyoxyethylene on cassiterite is discussed in relation to the results of adsorption tests and of zeta-potential measurements.

RÉSUMÉ

Ce travail présente les résultats obtenus lors de l'étude de l'action collectrice sur le quartz et la cassitérite de surfactants non ioniques du type alkylpolyoxyéthylène.

La première partie de l'étude concerne les résultats de flottabilité, en cellule Hallimond, des minéraux purs et de mélanges de ces minéraux en fonction du pH, de la concentration du collecteur et de l'addition éventuelle, en quantité variable, de sulfosuccinate de soude. Ces essais ont permis de mettre en évidence à pH acide, compris entre 2 et 6, l'action nettement favorable sur le plan de la sélectivité et du rendement étain, de la combinaison sulfosuccinate de soude et d'alkylpolyoxy-éthylène. Ces résultats ont pu être confirmés lors d'essais de flottation en batch sur un minerai synthetique quartz-cassité-rite titrant 1& Sn.

La seconde partie de l'étude concerne la flottabilité comp-
drée, à pH alcalin, du quartz et de la cassitérite, avec de l'
alkylpolyoxyéthylène utilisé seul ou en mélange avec du sulfosuccinate de soude, après sulfuration des minéraux préalable-
ment conditionnés par du nitrate de plomb. Dans ces conditions
à pH 8.5, on assiste à une flottation sélective de la cassitérite légèrement meilleure que celle obtenue à pH 2.5 sans sulfuration ni activation au nitrate de plomb.

Enfin, l'action collectrice de l'alkylpolyoxyéthylène sur
la cassitérite a pu être mise en évidence à la lumière des
résultats d'essais d'adsorption et de détermination du potential Zêta. La mécanisme proposé fait appel à l'existence de
liaisons hydrogène et de forces de van der Waals entre la
chaîne non ionique du réactif et la surface du minéral.

ZUSAMMENFASSUNG

Der vorliegende Beitrag befasst sich mit der Verwendung
nicht-ionogener alkylpolyoxyäthylen-artiger kapillaraktiver
Reagenzien zur Flotation von Kassiteriterzen.

Im ersten Teil werden die in einer Hallimond-Zelle mit
reinen Mineralen bzw. Mischungen von reinem Quarz und Kassiterit bei verschiedenen pH-Werten und verschiedenen Konzentra-
tionen nicht-ionogener kapillaraktiver Reagenzien, mit bzw.
ohne Zusatz von Natriumsulfobernsteinsäuresalz erzielten Flo-
tationsergebnisse erörtert. Durch Vereinigung beider Sammler
bei einem pH-Wert von 2-6 lassen sich bedeutende Verbesserun-
gen der Selektivität und Zinnausbeute erzielen. Versuche
dosierter Flotation mit künstlichen Erzen, die Quarz und
Kassiterit mit 1% Zinngehalt enthielten, haben diese günstigen
Untersuchungsergebnisse vollauf bestätigt.

Im zweiten Teil wird die Flotationsfähigkeit von Quarz mit
der Flotationsfähgkeit des Kassiterits bei alkalischem pH -
Wert und in Gegenwart gleichen Sammler, nach vorangegangener
Regelung mit heissem Nitrat und Natrimhydrosulfid, verglichen.
Eine weitere Verbesserung der Selektivität konnte beobachtet

werden, wenn bei den gleichen Bedingungen der pH-Wert 8.5 betrug. Der Sammeleffekt des Alkylpolyoxyäthylens auf Kassiterit wird im Zusammenhang mit den Ergebnissen von Adsorptionsversuchen und Zeta-Potential-Messungen erörtert.

РЕЗЮМЕ

В докладе рассмотрено применение неионных поверхностно-активных веществ типа алкилполиоксиэтилена при флотации касситеритовой руды.

В первой части исследований получены результаты по флотации в камере Галлимонода чистых минералов или смесей чистого кварца и касситерита при разных значениях pH и при разных концентрациях неионного поверхностно-активного вещества, без добавки и с добавкой сульфоянтарнокислого натрия. При одновременном введении обоих собирателей, при pH 2 – 6, достигается значительное улучшение селективности и извлечения олова. Эти положительные результаты подтвердились при исследованиях периодической флотации, проведённых на синтетической руде, состоящей из кварца и касситерита, с содержанием I% олова.

Во второй части доклада проведено сопоставление соответствующих флотационных способностей кварца и касситерита в щелочном pH, в присутствии тех же собирателей, после предварительной обработки нитратом свинца и кислым сульфидом натрия.

В таких условиях наблюдалось некоторое улучшение селективности при pH 8,5.

Влияние алкилполиоксиэтилена на флотацию касситерита рассмотрено в связи с результатами абсорбции и измерений дзета-потенциала.

INVESTIGATIONS OF THE PRODUCTS OF ETHYL XANTHATE SORPTION ON SULPHIDES BY IR-ATR SPECTROSCOPY

J. Mielczarski[1], P. Nowak[1], J. W. Strojek[1] and A. Pomianowski[2]

Institute of Inorganic Chemistry and Technology, Silesian University of Technology, Gliwice, Poland
[2] Research Laboratories of Surface Chemistry and Catalysis Polish Academy of Sciences, Kraków, Poland

The fundamental problem in determining the mechanism of xanthate sorption on sulphide minerals is the qualitative determination of the sorption products being formed on their surfaces. In spite of many years' investigations concerning the mechanism of xanthate sorption on sulphide minerals there are still doubts as to what surface products are formed during xanthate sorption on the surfaces of sulphide minerals. Poling has mentioned in his recent review concerning galena[1] as many as eight possible sorption products.

Infra-red spectrophotometry is a useful method of determining the surface compounds. This method has already been applied to examine the surface compounds formed on sulphide minerals during the sorption process, but due to the techniques of sample preparation that are applied before the measurements, such as drying, extraction with solvents etc., the obtained results have been controversial. To examine the

sorption of xanthates on sulphides in our laboratory, infra-
red spectrophotometry has been applied for a number of
years [2-9]. In these experiments the total internal reflection technique has been used. This technique makes it possible
to obtain the infra-red spectrum of a sample when it is
contacted with an aqueous collector solution. The experiments have been carried out on samples of natural galena,
chalcocite and sphalerite and their corresponding synthetic
compounds. Powdered samples were subjected, if necessary, to
the following treatment: rinsing with water and sodium
sulphide solution, activation with copper salt solution
(sphalerite) etc. The sample (in most cases about 0.5 g) was
then mixed for some time with 200 cm^3 of xanthate solution
at a chosen pH value. After the decantation of the solution,
the sample with the remaining slution was contacted with the
surface of a germanium reflection element, and spectrophotometrically examined. The sensitivity of the system permits
the determination of even one monolayer of sorption products.
Changes in the concentration of the reagents during the
sorption process have also been examined. More attention has
been paid to the lead (II)-sulphide-xanthate system. For this
system combined electrochemical and spectrophotomeric
measurements have been carried out. A thin lead (II)-sulphide
layer was deposited on the surface of the germanium reflection element after which the reflection element was placed
in a special flow-cell (Fig. 1).

The system had made it possible to obtain spectra of
a sample after its polarization to a given potential [5, 7].
The properties of the minerals and compounds used in our
experiments have been represented in Table 1.

The specific surface areas of the powdered samples were
determined by the BET method, using nitrogen as an adsorbate.
The BET method gives imprecise-values for the samples of
the low surface. In that case, the nitrogen heat desorption
method was used.

A detailed description of the apparatus and procedure
applied may be found in other publications [2-8].

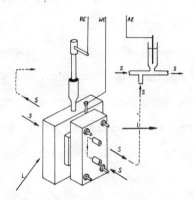

Fig. 1. Schematic view of a cell for combined electrochemical and spectrophotometric measurements:
RE-reference electrode (saturated calomel
electrode), WE-working electrode (reflection
element with a deposited lead sulphide layer),
AE-auxiliary electrode (platinum wire),
S-solution, L - radiation beam.

TABLE 1

Characteristics of the Samples

Sample		Analysis, Wt %			Specific surface area, m^2/g
	Pb	Cu	Zn	Fe	
galena	85.02	0.002	0.58	0.007	0.19*
chalcocite	0.05	75.8	0.034	0.66	0.55*
synthetic Cu_2S	0.03	79.5	0.008	0.002	0.28*
sphalerite	1.15	0.02	60.9	1.4	2.42**
synthetic ZnS	0.002	0.06	66.5	0.03	4.90**

*Determined by means of the nitrogen heat desorption method

**Determined by means of the BET method

The Sorption of Potassium Ethyl Xanthate on Samples of
Galena and Synthetic Lead (II)-Sulphide

The galena used in our experiments was from the "Bolesław"
Mine in Poland. Mineral specimens of ore were crushed into
particles of several milimetres in diameter and then ground
in an agate mortar. Samples which had been stored in the
open air for some time (for about one month) after their
grinding, and samples ground immediately before contacting
them with xanthate solution were used. The spectra of galena
samples analysed not later than several days after their
grinding did not show any absorption bands which would indicate the presence of galena oxidation products. An absorption band of low intensity (Fig. 2) was observed in the
spectra of the samples stored in the open air for about one
month. This band indicated the presence of some oxidation

product on the sample surface, being probably the mixture of compounds such as: PbO · $PbSO_4$, PbS_2O_3, $PbSO_3$, $PbSO_4$. The samples of lead (II)-sulphide were chemically deposited in the form of thin layers on the surface of the germanium reflection element [7]. These samples were subject to oxidation when contacted with air for several days. In the spectra of the oxidized samples absorption bands, which are characteristic of carbonate and hydroxyl groups, were to be observed. It has to be mentioned that the sensitivity of the measuring system was much higher in the case of lead (II)-sulphide samples used in the form of thin layers than in the case of galena. The measurements were performed on these samples directly after their deposition as well as after having been contacted with air for three days.

The xanthate sorption on galena samples was carried out with solutions of an initial concentration from $2.8 \cdot 10^{-5}$ to $1.1 \cdot 10^{-3}$ kmol/m^3. In all these cases the formation of lead (II)-xanthate on the sample surface was observed (Fig. 2). At the lowest xanthate concentration, almost all the xanthate was removed from the solution but above a certain concentration level the quantity of the sorption product formed increased only slightly with an increase of the xanthate concentration. The sorption products were mostly formed during the first few minutes of the sorption. The extension of the sorption up to several hours has led only to an inconsiderable increase of the quantity of sorption products. Experiments were performed with both basic (pH = 7.8-8.5) and acidic (pH = 5.4-5.8) xanthate solutions. No essential

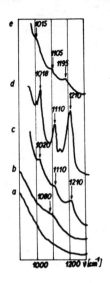

Fig. 2. Infra-red reflection spectra of galena samples:
a - immediately after grinding, b - after one
month's contact with air, c - freshly ground
sample after contacting with xanthate solution,
d - sample stored for one month in air before
contacting with xanthate solution, a - sample
washed with ammonium acetate solution before
contacting with xathate solution

differences were found in the course of either series of
experiments. In the case of galena samples that were contacted with air for several days the quantity of sorption
products on the surface was equal to its layer with a thickness of 5 nm and in the case of those contacted with air
for about one month it was approximately eight times larger.
The results of the experiments indicate that the sorption
process was a surface reaction occurring between the galena
oxidation products and the xanthate ion contained in the

solution. This was proved by experiments performed on lead
(II)-sulphide samples in the form of thin layers. Sorption
against the square root of time is shown in Fig. 3 where
R is the radation reflection coefficient for the 1200 cm^{-1}
band (lead (II)-xanthate, i.e., sorption product) and
1400 cm^{-1} band (carbonate. i.e., product of PbS oxidation).
It may be seen that the quantity of sorption product grows
when the quantity of the oxidation product decreases and
when the oxidation product disappears from the surface, the
quantity of the sorption product no longer increases. The
rate of the formation of sorption products depends on the
quantity of the oxidation product and xanthate concentration.
It does not seem that it is not possible to find a single
factor which wolud determine the rate of the sorption
process [6].

In another series of experiments the contact time of the
sample with air was shortened to a minimum. In the case of
galena, the time which elapsed from the moment when the grinding of the sample began to the recording of the spectrum
after the sorption amounted to 70 ÷ 220 min. In the case of
the thin layer samples the sorption process was commenced
immediately after the deposition of a layer. It was found
that a multi-layer coating of the sorption product (2-3
monolayers of $Pb(EtX)_2$) was formed during the sorption on
the surfaces of galena and lead sulphide which that were contacted with air for only a few minutes and the sorption is
similar to that occurring on highly oxidized surfaces [6].
In order to determine the nature of the sorption process on

surfaces which are free of oxidation products, samples of lead (II)-sulphide and galena were rinsed with ammonium acetate or sodium sulphide solutions. It was found that in the case of highly oxidized surfaces the sodium sulphide solution did not remove the oxidation products from the surface completely. If there was little oxidation product on the surface was low, the sodium sulphide removed it completely. The quanitiy of sorption products formed on such a surface was less than one monolayer.

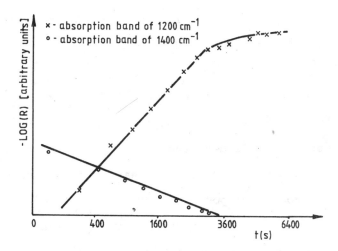

Fig. 3. Dependence of the quantity of the oxidation product (absorption band at 1400 cm^{-1}) and sorption product (absorption band at 1200 cm^{-1}) on the square root of time. Sorption on a thin film of a lead sulphide sample oxidized in air within three days - xanthate concentration $1 \cdot 10^{-3}$ kmol/m^3.

The results of experiments suggest that if the sample surface is rinsed with sodium sulphide solution and other

electrolyte solutions, the surface stoichiometry changes so
that the surface layer is enriched by sulphur. Xanthate
sorption either did not occur on such a surface, or it
occurred only to a small degree (below 1 monolayer). This
was proved by electrochemical experiments. A lead (II)-
sulphide sample of a thin layer previously rinsed with sodium
sulphide solution was polarized in xanthate solution (containing 0.1 kmol/m^3 $Na_2B_4O_7$ as the base electrolyte) to a potential which was negative in relation to the rest potential,
e.g., - 700 mV vs. SCE. Its potential was then changed stepwise to a value at which chemisorption of xanthate ions on
the lead (II)-sulphide surface would be expected e.g., -
200 mV vs. SCE [7].

In these experiments we have observed only the formation
of a low quantity of lead xanthate (below one monolayer)
and the more xanthate was formed, the more negative initial
potential was previously applied to the sample. If the sample
was then polarized to a more positive potential (above 0 mV
vs. SCE), the formation of a multilayer lead (II)-xanthate
coating was observed on the electrode surface. The formation
of dixanthogen was observed at potentials which were much
more positive than the redox potential of the dixanthogen -
EtX$^-$ ion system. When the lead (II)-sulphide surface was
rinsed with deoxidized ammonium acetate solution, the sorption from an aerated xanthate solution led to the formation
of sorption products on this surface in small quantity,
similarly as in the case of samples rinsed with sodium
sulphide solution. If, however, the sample of galena or lead

(II)-sulphide was rinsed with ammonium acetate solution contacting dissolved oxygen (due to its contacting with air) and
this surface was subjected to sorption from xanthate, the
quantity of the sorption product was equal to 1-2 monolayers.

Some part of the sorption product (approximately equal to
one monolayer of radicals) was strongly bound to the surface
and it was not possible to remove it from the surface by
repeated rinsing with acetone. The sorption product layer was
formed during the initial period of sorption (several minutes)
A further extension of the sorption to several hours did not
result in any further product formation. Perhaps the first
layer of the surface product is chemisorbed to the lead
sulphide surface. The results of experiments suggest that the
chemisorbed product might be formed on the surface during the
exchange between the surface oxiadtion product (no more than
one monolayer) and a xanthate ion from the solution [6, 7].
It was found that the sorption product considered to be chemisorbed did not form on highly oxidized surfaces. This was
illustrated by the following experiment. The lead sulphide
sample covered with oxidation products, was subjected to
sorption in a $1 \cdot 10^{-3}$ kmol/m^3 xanthate solution for 15 min,
after which it was rinsed with acetone, followed by sorption
and rinsing with acetone again; this operation was repeated
several times. Figure 4 shows the results of this experiment,
i.e., the height of the absorption band corresponding to the
oxidation products before their sorption, the absorption
band height of the sorption product after its sorption as
well as after a single rinsing of the surface with acetone.

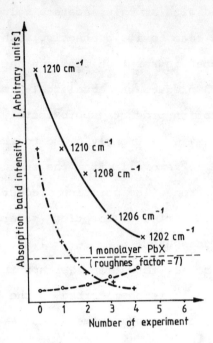

Fig. 4. Quantity of the oxidation product before the
sorption (dotted line), quantity of sorption
product after sorption (solid line) and quantity
of sorption product after acetone washing
(broken line) in successive experiments with
a lead sulphide sample.

From this diagram it may be seen that when the oxidation
product is removed from the surface the quantity of the
formed sorption product decreased, whereas the quantity of
the product remaining on the surface after rinsing with
acetone increased.

In our experiments we have not found any spontaneous formation of dixanthogen on galena or lead sulphide surfaces. The
only product observed was lead xanthate in different forms
and quantities. Differences have been observed in the position

of the absorption bands of lead (II)-xanthate occurring on
the sample surfaces (within the range of 1.190 cm^{-1}; 1.115 cm^{-1};
1.020 cm^{-1} to 1.212 cm^{-1}; 1.115 cm^{-1}; 1.010 cm^{-1}). These
differences may result from various physico-chemical properties of the formed sorption product. This should explain the
differences in the flotability of galena covered with xanthate
sorption products observed by various authors.

The Sorption of Potassium Ethyl Xanthate on Natural

Chalcocite and Synthetic Copper (I)-Sulphide

Natural chalcocite samples were separated from the ore
from the Lubin mines in Poland. Synthetic copper sulphide
was prepared by melting metallic copper with sulphur. The
properties of the samples are shown in Table 1. A detailed
description of the experiments performed previously and of
the apparatus used may be elsewhere found [2, 8].

After grinding, the chalcocite was contacted with air for
about one month. The oxidized chalcocite samples were subjected to sorption from both acidic (pH = 5.2-6.5) and basic
(pH = 8.4-9.8) solutions of an initial xanthate concentra-
tion from $2.2 \cdot 10^{-5}$ to $1.4 \cdot 10^{-3}$ kmol/m^3. When xanthate solutions with concentrations of less than $2 \cdot 10^{-4}$ kmol/m^3 were
used, the only observed sorption product was copper (I)-ethyl
xanthate, forming several monomolecular layers on the sample
surface (Fig. 5 c, d). The quantity of the formed sorption
product depended on the initial concentration of xanthate in
the solution, as almost all the xanthate was abstracted from
its solution. If the initial xanthate concentration was

higher than $2 \cdot 10^{-4}$kmol/m^3, a certain quantity of xanthate ions was left in solution and the quantity of the formed sorption products did not change so abruptly when some xanthate was introduced into the solution. The sorption products were: copper (I)-ethyl xanthate, and ethyl dixanthogen (Fig. 5 e, f). The course of the sorption process from both acidic and basic solutions was similar. During the sorption from acidic solutions the quantity of the formed sorption

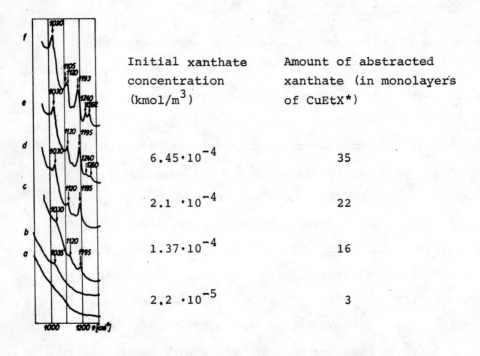

Initial xanthate concentration (kmol/m^3)	Amount of abstracted xanthate (in monolayers of CuEtX*)
$6.45 \cdot 10^{-4}$	35
$2.1 \cdot 10^{-4}$	22
$1.37 \cdot 10^{-4}$	16
$2.2 \cdot 10^{-5}$	3

Fig. 5. Reflection spectra of chalcocite samples: a - immediately after grinding, b - one month after grinding, c, d, e, f - after contacting with xanthate solutions of various initial concentrations.

*It was assumed that the monolayer coverage amounted to $5.72 \cdot 10^{-9}$kmol/m^2.

products (and the loss of xanthate ions from the solution) was larger than in the case of sorption from basic solutions. The pH of the solutions increased during the sorption from both acidic and basic solutions. The results obtained for synthetic copper (I)-sulphide samples were very similar to those for natural chalcocite.

The formation of dixanthogen was observed during the sorption of xanthate on highly oxidized samples and therefore its sorption was also examined. A saturated dixanthogen solution of about $2 \cdot 10^{-5}$ kmol/m^3 concentration and its emulsion with a concentration of $5.4 \cdot 10^{-5}$ kmol/m^3 were used. After the sorption from a solution of lower dixanthogen concentration (contact time - 60 min) only copper (I)-ethyl xanthate was observed (bands of 1.195; 1.118; 1.030 cm^{-1}) whereas after sorption from the dixanthogen emulsion, besides copper (I)-ethyl xanthate, ethyl dixanthogen (bands of 1.262; 1.240; 1.110 cm^{-1}) was also found. During sorption, the pH-value of the solution decreased. Similar results were obtained for cholcocite and synthetic copper sulphide.

Experiments of xanthate sorption were also conducted on the following samples: freshly ground, oxidized rinsed with water or 0.03 kmol/m^3 sodium sulphide solution. In all the experiments there was an excess of xanthate ions in solution. The rinsing of the samples with water (three times) decreased the quantity of the sorption product by about 20% in comparison with that found on unwashed samples. If the sample was contacted with the xanthate solution immediately after its grinding (about 2 h after its grinding had begun) the copper

(I)-ethyl xanthate was the only sorption product observed and its quantity was equal to 10 ÷ 20 monolayers. A lower quantity (about three monolayers) of copper (I)-ethyl xanthate was found on the samples rinsed with sodium sulphide solution. The obtained results indicated a strong relationship between the course of sorption and the degree of oxidation of sample surface before contact with xanthate solution.

Basing on experiments carried out on chalcocite and synthetic copper (I)-sulphide samples it may be concluded that the sorption of xanthate is a surface reaction between xanthate ions and the oxidation products of sulphide. The abstraction of xanthate from its solution may also occur, partly due to its reaction with dissolved chalcocite oxidation products. The sorption products are copper (I)-ethyl xanthate and ethyl dixanthogen, the latter reacting further to copper (I)-ethyl xanthate.

The sorption of ethyl dixanthogen probably undergoes via decomposition to xanthate ions. The composition of dixanthogen under the influence of such ions as OH^-, $S_2O_3^{-2}$ and other ions, which may be present in the solution has been shown by many authors. It is a rather quick reaction, therefore the presence of ethyl dixanthogen was confirmed only in the case of highly oxidized samples and ethyl xanthate solutions of high concentrations.

The Sorption of Ethyl Xanthate on Unactivated Synthetic Zinc Sulphide and Sphalerite

The synthetic zinc sulphide used in our experiments was manufactured by Riedel. Natural sphalerite was separated from ore mined in the Bytom basin in Poland. The compositions of the samples which were used are presented in Table 1. A detailed description of the experiments performed may be found in Mielczarski's thesis [8].

No sorption products were found when synthetic zinc sulphide was contacted with ethyl xanthate solutions with concentrations of $1 \cdot 10^{-4} \div 1.4 \cdot 10^{-3}$ kmol/m^3. The sensitivity of the measuring system has made it possible to observe that the quantity of the sorption product was equal to about 1/3 monolayer. In the case of the sorption from xanthate solutions on natural sphalerite grains, however, it was found that the sorption product was lead (II)-ethyl xanthate (the bands of 1.200; 1.115; 1.025 cm^{-1}). The quantity of sorption product observed was equal to approximately one monolayer coverage if the sorption was performed from acidic solutions (ph = 5.0-5.8). In the case of basic solutions (pH = 8.0-9.5) it was found that the maximum quantity of lead (II)-ethyl xanthate (a surface complex of xanthate ion and lead ion) amounted to about 50% of that obtained during the sorption from acidic solutions. The results obtained prove that it is possible to absorb short - chain xanthates on unactivated sphalerite samples. In this case the activation of the surface depended on the origin of the sample, to be precise, on the occurrence of other accompanying minerals.

The fact that a very small quantity of lead (1.2% by weight) activated the sample surface suggests that there is a strong tendency, for the collecting lead ions at the sphalerite surface contacted with xanthate solution.

The Sorption of Ethyl Xanthate on Synthetic Zinc Sulphide and Sphalerite Samples, Both Activated With Copper (II) Ions

Activation of Samples in Acidic and Basic Solutions. During tne activation of zinc sulphide and sphalerite in acidic solutions (pH = 5.0-6.3) the quantity of copper (II) ions removed from these solutions was equivalent to the exchange zinc ions in a 1.5 surface layer. The extension of the time of contact of the samples with copper sulphate solution from 10 min to several hours resulted in an increased amount of copper equivalent to 2-3 monolayers removed from the solution. During the activation in basic solutions (pH = 8.0-10.3), the copper (II) ions were almost completely removed in every case. The loss of copper was caused by the exchange of copper ions with zinc ions and their precipitation from the solution as hydroxides. The activated samples were then rinsed with water of an appropriate pH.

Sorption of Ethyl Xanthate on Activated Samples. During the sorption of ethyl xanthate from acidic solutions (pH = 5.0-6.3) on synthetic zinc sulphide the presence of surface complexes of xanthate ions and copper (II) ions was detected. An example of the spectrum of the sample after its sorption is presented in Fig. 6 b. The maximum quantity of the formed

sorption product was equal to one monolayer. A great extension
(up to several hours) of the time elapsing between activation and xanthate sorption resulted in the diffusion of copper
ions from the surface into the crystal lattice of zinc
sulphide, and in consequence the activated sample exihibited
the properties of an unactivated sample (there was no
xanthate sorption product).

When such a sample was contacted for long time with
xanthate solution, at first formation of surface complexes
of xanthate ions and copper (II) ions was observed, followed
by the formation of copper (I) xanthate (Fig. 6 e). When the
sorption process was carried out by means of basic solutions
(pH = 8.0-10.3) of the lowest copper concentrations during
their activation (below $2 \cdot 10^{-4} kmol/m^3$), the sorption took
course identical to that in the case of acidic solutions.
At higher concentrations of the activating solution the
samples contained both copper (I)-ethyl xanthate and ethyl
dixanthogen after their sorption (see the spectra in Fig. 6 d).
The quantities of both compounds mentioned above depended
on the quantity of copper precipitated from solutions as
hydroxides. The maximum quantity of the surface complexes of
xanthate ions and copper (II) ions was equal to one monolayer
coating. The higher coverage with a sorption product was due
to the formation of copper (I)-ethyl xanthate. Similar results
were obtained when the sorption of ethyl xanthate on natural
sphalerite was examined. However, in the case of activating
the samples with solutions of the lowest concentrations it
was also found that lead (II)-ethyl xanthate was present.

CONCLUSION

Considerable differences in the type and quantity of the products formed in the course of xanthate sorption on examined sulphide minerals have been found.

The sorption on chalcocite and galena tends to the formation of copper (I) and lead (II)-xanthates in the reactions of xanthate ions with sulphide oxidation products. The amount of oxidation determines the course of sorption and influence on both the quantity and quality of the formed sorption products.

The sorption of ethyl xanthate on sphalerite occurs only if the sample has been previously activated. This activation may be caused by copper (II) salts added to the solution and ions of various metals present in a sphalerite ore. The xanthate sorption products on sphalerite are surface complexes of xanthate ion with a metal ion activating the sample.

The only sorption product of xanthate on galena was lead (II) -ethyl xanthate. It was found that various forms of this compound may affect the different properties of the sample surface. The removal of the oxidation products from the galena surface by rinsing them with electrolyte solutions was accompanied by simultaneous changes in the stoichiometry of the sample surface that considerably influenced the course of sorption. In the case of galena, sorption of xanthate accompanied with the formation of product that may be chemisorbed to the surface can occur, but only on the surfaces from which the oxidation products were removed (except for the monomolecular layer of surface oxidation product).

128

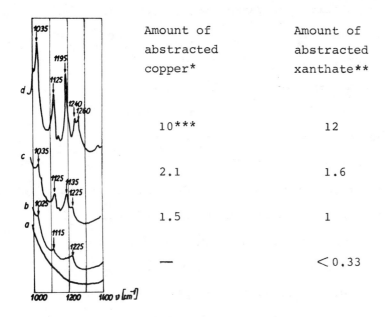

	Amount of abstracted copper*	Amount of abstracted xanthate**
	10***	12
	2.1	1.6
	1.5	1
	—	<0.33

Fig. 6. Reflection spectra of synthetic ZnS samples:
a - unactivated sample after sorption,
b - sample activated with acidic solutions,
c - sample activated for a long time with acidic
solutions, d - sample activated with a basic
solution of the high concentrations.

*In monolayers of exchanged zinc ions.

**In monolayers of CuEtX (see footnote to Fig. 5).

***Part of the copper precipitated as hydroxide.

The sorption of potassium ethyl xanthate on chalcocite
was accompanied by the formation of copper (I)-ethyl xanthate.
The presence of ethyl dixanthogen was also confirmed but
only in case of sorption on the highly oxidized samples.
The obtained dixanthogen was an intermediate product which
underwent further reactions that led to successive

quantities of copper (I)-ethyl xanthate. It has been also
found that on the sphalerite activated with copper (II) ions,
ethyl xanthate was sorbed by forming surface complexes of
xanthate ions and copper (II)ions. If during the activation
the added copper was not exchanged completely with zinc
ions in sphalerite, then the copper left in solution underwent a further reaction with an added xanthate resulting
a copper (I)-ethyl xanthate and an ethyl dixanthogen.

The course of sorption, as may be concluded from experimental results, depends to a great extent on the preparation of
the samples. The mineral surface can be subjected to different
changes such as oxidation by oxygen in the air, stoichometric
changes brought about by its contact with electrolyte solutions and activation with ions of other metals within the
period of time between its grinding and its contanct with
xanthate. These changes influence significantly the course
of sorption as well as the kind and quantity of the formed
sorption product. It may be finally stated that it is not
possible to suggest a uniform mechanism of sorption for all
sulphide minerals.

REFERENCES

1. Poling G.W. Reactions Between Thiol Reagents and Sulphide
   Minerals. In: Flotation. A. M. Gaudin Memorial Volume
   (ed. M. C. Fuerstenau), AIME, vol. 1, 1976, p. 334.

2. Strojek J., Mielczarski J. Roczniki Chemii, 48, 1747
   (1974).

3. Strojek J., Mielczarski J. Spectroscopic Investigations of Sorption of Ethyl Xanthate on Chalcocite. Paper presented at the Congress of The Polish Chemical Society, Toruń, 1974.

4. Mielczarski J., Nowak P., Strojek J. Roczniki Chemii, 50, 917 (1976).

5. Nowak P., Strojek J. Spectrophotometric Study of Surface Compounds on Sulphide Flectrodes in Xanthate Solutions. Paper presented at the Symposium of Electrochemical Section of The Polish Chemical Society, Jabłonna, 1977

6. Mielczarski J., Nowak P., Strojek J. Spectrophotometric investigations of products of potassium ethyl xanthate sorption on lead (II) sulphide and galena surface, Polish Journal of Chemistry, (in press)

7. Nowak P. Electrochemical and Spectrophotometric Study of Sorption in Selected Flotational Systems. Ph.D. Thesis, Silesian University of Technology, Gliwice, 1978.

8. Mielczarski J. Spectrophotometric Study of the Sorption of Some Flotational Collectors on Sulphide Minerals. Ph.D. Thesis, Silesian University of Technology, Gliwice, 1978.

ABSTRACT

The sorption of potassium ethyl xanthate from an aqueous solution on galena, chalcocite and sphalerite as well as on corresponding synthetic compounds was investigated. Internal reflection spectrophotometry in the infra-red range was used. Spectrophotometric observations of the sorption were carried out when the sulphide was in contact with an aqueous solution. Additional data were obtained from simultaneous electrochemical measurements of the xanthate concentration in the bulk of solution. The influence of such factors as: xanthate concentration, pH of the solution, the presence of oxygen, the polarization of the sulphide surface, the history of the specimen (freshly prepared, oxidized in air, washed with sodium sulphide solution etc.) on the process of sorption was investigated. On the basis of these results the relation between the kind and quantity of observed sorption products and the factors mentioned were determined.

RÉSUME

On a étudié la sorption de l'éthyl-xanthate de potassium d'une solution aqueuse sur de la galène, de la chalcosine, de la sphalérite, ainsi que sur les composés synthétiques correspondants en utilisant la spectrophotométrie à réflexion interne en infrarouge. Les observations spectrophotométriques de la sorption ont été effectuées lorsque le sulfure était en contact avec une solution aqueuse. Des données additionelles ont été obtenues par des mesures simultanées électrochimiques et des mesures de concentration du xanthate dans la pulpe de la solution. On a également étudié l'influence de facteurs tels que la concentration du xanthate, le pH de la solution, la présence d'oxygène, la polarisation de la surface du sulfure, l'origine de l'échantillon (récemment préparé, oxydé à l'air, lavé avec une solution de sulfure de sodium etc.) sur le procédé de la sorption. Sur la base des résultats obtenus, des relations ont été déterminées entre la qualité et la quantité de produits observés de la sorption par rapport aux facteurs mentionnés.

ZUSAMMENFASSUNG

Untersucht wurde die Sorption von Kaliumäthylxanthogenat aus
wässeriger Lösung an Galenit (Bleiglanz), Chalkozin und Sphalerit
(Zinkblende), sowie an entsprechenden synthetischen Verbindungen.
Dazu bediente man sich der Innerreflex-Spektralphotometrie im
infraroten Bereich. Spektrophotometrische Beobachtungen wurden
im Augenblick des Kontaktierens des Sulphids mit einer wässerigen Lösung durchgeführt. Zusätzliche Daten wurden mittels
gleichzeitig durchgeführter elektrochemischer Messungen sowie
durch Messungen der Konzentration des Xanthogenats in der gesamten Lösung erhalten. Untersucht wurde auch der Einfluss solcher
Faktoren wie Konzentration des Xanthogenats, pH-Wert der Lösung,
Anwesenheit von Sauerstoff, Polarisation der Sulphidoberfläche,
Zustand der Probe (frisch präpariert, an der Luft oxydiert, in
Natriumsulphidlösung gewaschen usw.) auf den Sorptionsprozess.
Anhand der Ergebnisse konnten die Beziehungen zwischen den
untersuchten Sorptionsprodukten und ihrer Quantität einerseits
und den erwähnten Faktoren andererseits ermittelt werden.

РЕЗЮМЕ

Исследована сорбция этилксантогената калия из водного раствора на галените, халькозине и сфалерите, а также на соответствующих синтетических соединениях.

В исследованиях применен метод нарушенного полного внут-
реннего отражения в инфракрасной области спектра. Спектрофо-
тометрические наблюдения сорбции проведены во время контак-
та сульфида с водным раствором. Дополнительные данные получены при одновременных электрохимических измерениях концентрации ксантогената в растворе. Исследовано влияние таких
факторов, как концентрация ксантогената, pH раствора, при-
сутствие кислорода, поляризация поверхности сульфида, характер пробы (свежеприготовленная, окисленная на воздухе, про-
мытая раствором сульфида натрия и т.д.) на процесс сорбции.
На основе этих результатов определены зависимости между ти-
пом и количеством наблюдаемых продуктов сорбции и упомянуты-
ми факторами.

CHARACTERIZATION BY ESCA SPECTROSCOPY OF SURFACE COMPOUNDS ON THE FINE SULPHIDE MINERALS IN THE FLOTATION

J. J. Predali[1], D. Brion[2], J. Hayer[1] and B. Pelletier[1]

[1] *Minemet Recherche, Trappes, France*
[2] *Institut National de Recherche Chimique Appliquée, Vert-le-Petit, France*

INTRODUCTION

Pyritic igneous-sedimentary ores represent an important part of the world reserves of Zn, Cu and Pb. Small amounts of Zn, Cu and Pb sulphides occur in these ores in the form of disseminated interlayers or the filling of microfissures in more or less crystallized pyritic gangue.

Very fine grinding (d_{80} equals 10 to 20 μm) is necessary to liberate valuable phases but unlike other ores of the same mineral composition and coarser grain-size distribution, the classical flotation methods present many difficulties resulting in various low-grade concentrates.

The object of the present paper is to clarify the mechanism of pyrite depression, particularly in relation to sphalerite, in order to improve the conditions of differential flotation. Of the many possible techniques that can be used to investigate the mechanism of flotation we decided to choose the direct chemical analysis of one surface monolayer using photoelectron spectroscopy (XPS or E.S.C.A.) which has not been used for such ores as yet.

This method consists of the analysis of the kinetic energy of the photoelectrons emitted by the solid exposed to soft, monochromatic X-rays and then the determination of inner-electron and valency electron bond energy of various atoms [1]. ESCA spectroscopy, a non-destructive method, permits the functional analysis of shifts in various bands as well as quantitative analysis of band intensity.

This method has not been used very often for mineralogy and mineral processing problems. There are only a few publications dealing with sulphide minerals and ores [2-5]. Clifford et al. attempted to characterize the surface of sulphide minerals investigated individually after having been subjected to various treatment (such as grinding, depression, activation and flotation) as they did with Pb-Cu-Zn ores with low pyrite content investigated at various stages of industrial flotation. They have shown that Cu (I) is present on the surface of sphalerite activated by copper sulphate and that $PbCrO_4$ is formed on the surface of galena conditioned with $Na_2Cr_2O_7$. The authors point out the difficulties connected with an analysis of xanthate sorption due to the presence in the minerals or sulphur atoms which can not be distinguished from sulphur atoms of the xanthate. Difficulties are also caused by the considerable contamination by carbon components. Three publications concerning the ageing of pure sulphide minerals (FeS_2, PbS, $CuFeS_2$) have recently appeared but they are only indirectly connected with flotation [3, 4, 10].

On the basis of numerous studies carried out with the ESCA method, Manocha and Park [4] concluded that lead sulphate is the main product of air oxidation of galena and oxidation in the aqueous phase but the induction period of oxidation is longer than time taken for conditioning and flotation. The chalcopyrite surface was analysed by Auger's spectroscopy [10] after oxidation in oxygen, air or water. From the onset of grinding to the onset of flotation, the chalcopyrite surface may be covered with oxidation products; the cover may be many atoms thick. ESCA investigations of many copper bearing minerals, and in particular sulphide minerals, provided interesting analytic data [5].

Preliminary studies [7] allowed the characterization of the state of the surface of four sulphide minerals ($CuFeS_2$, FeS_2, PbS, ZnS) during ageing on aeration and after conditioning with distilled H_2O. They also permitted the description for each group of minerals of various surface forms occurring at different flotation stages. Particular attention was paid to the differentiation of goethite (FeOOH) and hematite (Fe_2O_3) from pyrite oxidation compounds on the one hand, and to the analysis of chalcopyrite, covellite and chalcocite on the other.

Raw ore surface alterations were also studied after ageing in air, conditioning with distilled H_2O and grinding and were then compared with the changes observed for pure minerals. The most interesting results concerned the rapid oxidation of galena and sphalerite after exposure to air and the oxidation of galena after treatment with water. This water treatment results in an increase in the amount of lead and copper but

136

a reduction in the amount of zinc in the surface layer. For this complex ore no grinding effect (comparison of the size-fraction < 25 µm with the -100 +50 µm size fraction) could be traced in the surface changes after water treatment and ageing in air.

The present study describes the evolution of the surface state of fine-ground, complex, rich in pyrite raw ore of high pyrite content in different conditioning and flotation stages. The analysis is supplemented by experiments using pure minerals and investigations into the mineral-solution equilibria. The paper attempts to discover and explain the flotation principles and to specify the role of several classical flotation agents (CaO, NaCN, $ZnSO_4$, $CuSO_4$) and that of surface alterations.

Experimental Methods

Electron Spectroscopy (ESCA). Spectra were obtained using a Varian IEE-15 spectrometer (equipped with a magnesium anode) in vacuum 4 x 10^{-6} Torr. The bond energies cited in this paper were calibrated with reference to the Cl5 spectral line of energy 284 eV of carbon from hydrocarbons coming from con-taminations.

Semi-quantitative estimations of surface concentrations were carried out on the basis of the ratio of spectral line inten-sity (height and width) and intensity coefficients determined on freshly ground pure component powders. Possible changes in the composition of the layer investigated by the ESCA method (30 Å) are not taken into consideration in these quantitative data since the relative significance of data is of more importance.

137

Powders are spread on a double faced, adhesive belt after
ensuring that the size distribution of particles caught on the
belt is identical with that in the sample.

Flotation. The products are wet-ground in a steel rod mill
for 1 h. This gives a particle-size fraction of about 20 μm (d_{80}).

Flotation was performed on   a pulp of 18% solid concentration in a Minemet cell of 2.5 1 in volume for the ore and 0.4 1
for pure minerals or rough concentrates. Samples for the ESCA
analysis were taken directly from the cell and then washed in
a sintered glass crucible with demineralized water. Afterwards,
they are immediately dried in a vacuum at 40°C and stored for
ESCA analysis.

Materials

Cu-Zn-Pb ore from South-Iberian Province was used. Its chemical composition was as follows:

Cu: 1.20%; Zn: 2.80%; Pb: 1.2%; S: 48%; Fe: 41%

SiO_2: 3.5%; Ag: 30 ppm; Hg: 80 ppm; As: 0.8%; Sb: 0.1%

Bi: 180 ppm; Cd: 60 ppm

Mineral composition was as follows:

Pyrite: 84.3%
Mispickel: 1.6%
Sphalerite: 4.5%
Chalcopyrite: 3.4%
Galena: 1.2%
Bournonite: 0.3%
other: 4.7% quartz, sericite, chlorite, carbonates and rare
       minerals: tetraedrite, twinnite, native bismuth and
       covellite.

138

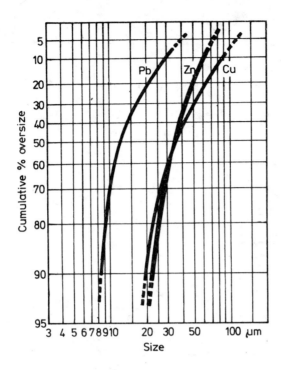

Fig. 1. Grain-size distribution "in situ" of chalcopyrite
(Cu), sphalerite (Zn) and galena (Pb) in the ore
(a fraction coarser than 500 μm of raw ore ground
to - 2.5 mm). Corrected linear size-fraction analysis with a microanalyser and electronic probe to
defect phases.

Figure 1 gives the grain-size distribution of the main
valuable mineral components.

Pure Minerals. The pyrite came from Rio Marino (Tuscany,
Italy) and contains trace impurities of iron silicate, hematite
and galena.

The galena came from Morocco and contained the following
impurities: 0.5% goethite, 0.5% quartz, 1% cerusite and traces
of chalcopyrite, proustite and covellite.

Surface Alterations in Fine Sulphide Ore during Flotation.

The raw ore surface was analysed after dry-grinding and for each stage of flotation as illustrated in Fig. 2, according to the classical flotation flowsheet of this kind of ore.

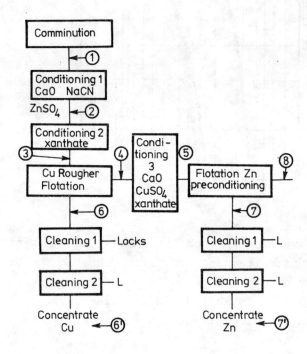

Fig. 2. Pyrite ore flotation flowsheet.

Figure 3 gives a part of the spectrum of raw ore sampled at the rod crusher outlet. The spectral lines of each main ore component can be easily seen despite the relatively low content of some of them.

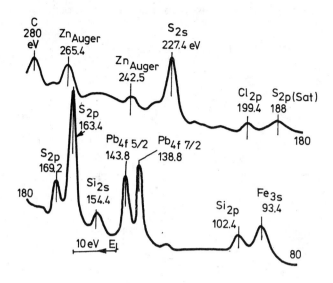

Fig. 3. ESCA spectrum of ground ore: sample 1.

Quantitative Results. Semi-quantitative estimations of the
atom content on the surface on the basis of the height of
spectrals of S2p, Pb4f, Fe3p, ZnL_3, $M_{4,5}$, and CuL_3, $M_{4,5}$, $M_{4,5}$
are given in Table 1 for each flotation stage (sample 0 is for
freshly dry-ground raw ore). The freshly dry-ground sample differs from the sample obtained by wet-grinding in that it has
a lower surface concentration of sulphur and higher concentration of iron. The sulphur surface concentration remains low
throughout the whole flotation process. After wet-grinding the
relative concentration of copper is reduced (in comparison to
dry-grinding) while the lead concentration increases. An increase in copper and zinc concentrations is observed for copper
(sample 6 and 6') and zinc concentrates (sample 7 and 7'). For
samples 2, 3, 4, 5, and 6 the copper concentration changes

TABLE 1

Atomic Surface Composition of the Ore Flotation Products (%)

Sample	Pb	Zn	Cu	Fe	S
0	1.0	1.2	3.5	30.6	63.7
1	2.6	1.9	1.6	61.5	32.2
1bis	2.2	2.2	1.8	61.0	32.8
2	2.5	2.4	1.8	51.5	41.6
3	3.2	2.5	1.3	52.9	40.0
4	3.4	3.1	1.3	51.4	40.7
5	3.6	3.2	1.7	51	40.7
6	4.5	2.3	5.8	37.7	49.4
6'	6.6	2.3	18.2	21.9	51.0
7	4.4	7.6	3.2	41.7	43.1
7'	6.0	17.7	4.6	27.0	44.1
8	3.3	3.0	1.9	48.2	43.5

according to expectations, the changes are small each time. The fixation of the collector does not at any point involve an increase in the surface sulphur content (nor the carbon content).

Table 2 gives a comparison of surface concentrations with total concentrations measured by chemical analysis.

After dry-grinding and at each flotation stage the surface concentration of lead is very high - between 5 and 17 times higher than in the total volume when the concentration was measured. We then observed the coating of the surface with galena for a second time. (Galena is the most fragile mineral in the whole powdered raw ore). These findings have already been reported by Clifford et al. for a different type of sulphide ore [6].

142

TABLE 2

Atom Content in the Bulk (M) and on the Surface (S) of the

Raw Ore

Sample		Pb	Zn	Cu	Fe
feed	S	3.8	2.9	2.4	91.0
	M	0.53	3.4	2.1	94.0
rough copper concentrate	S	9.0	4.6	11.6	74.8
	M	0.82	2.9	12.9	83.5
twice cleaned copper concentrate	S	13.4	4.7	37.1	44.8
	M	0.89	2.4	31.8	64.9
rough zinc concentrate	S	7.7	13.4	5.6	73.3
	M	1.3	18.4	2.2	78.1
twice cleaned zinc concentrate	S	10.7	32.6	8.2	48.4
	M	2.3	48.9	4.7	44.1
tailings	S	5.9	5.3	3.4	85.4
	M	0.34	0.73	0.31	98.6

The surface of the final tailings (sample 8) seems to be richer in lead, zinc and copper than the total volume. This enrichement results from various exchanges and induced surface fixations tending to make the surface less diversified. Copper fixation on the surface of sphalerite activated by $CuSO_4$, is confirmed by the strong copper concentration discovered on the surface of zinc concentrates and more exactly, by comparison of the Cu/Zn atom ratio determined by ESCA (spectral bands Zn2p and Cu2p) and by the Cu/Zn ratio in the bulk of particles (Table 3). As for depressants, a considerable fixation of lime on all samples except for twice washed copper concentrate has

TABLE 3

Cu/Zn Atom Ratio on the Raw Ore Surface
(measured on the basis of 2p bands)

Samples	1	2	3	4	5	6	6'	7	7'	8
Surface	0.56	0.61	0.66	0.53	0.67	1.7	5.6	0.70	0.59	0.71
Bulk	0.61	0.61	0.61			4.5	13.4	0.12	0.09	0.42

been observed. These high lime concentrations (2.5%-4% as compared with the amount of lime introduced during flotation) point to the strong fixation of these ions on the surface of the particles. The surface content of this element varies insignificantly from sample to sample.

Neither nitrogen nor sodium can be found on the surface of the investigated samples; sodium cyanide has no direct effect and does not result in the formation of stable cyanide complexes on basic minerals.

Chemical Nature of the Discovered Elements. Iron seems to be strongly oxidized throughout the whole flotation process. Figure 4 presents spectral bands Fe2p for different samples. The spectral band at 706.2 eV is characteristic for sulphidic iron and at 710.5 eV for iron, probably in the form of hydroxide. The surface oxidation of iron is particularly important on the surface of particles just leaving the crusher. Because the pyrite concentration plays an important role in the process, the iron is undoubtedly particularly representative of pyrite undergoing decomposition from the moment of grinding.

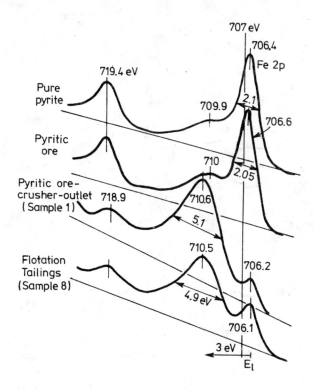

Fig. 4. ESCA spectra.

Sulphur shows a low degree of oxidation to sulphates (S2p peak at 168 eV) between 5 and 13% the spectral band S2p at about 162 eV expands insignificantly and does not shift to higher bond energies. Thus, the powder does not become completely coated with large amount of elementary sulphur or iron sulphate (jarosite type) (Fig. 5).

Copper spectral bands (Cu2p and Cu AUG) occurring throughout the flotation process characterize sulphide copper; their position is closer to the position of the $CuFeS_2$ spectral line,

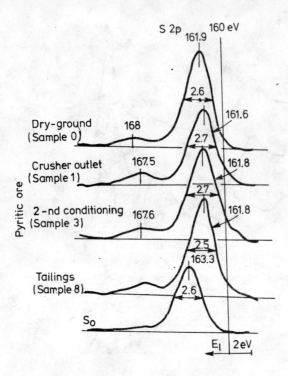

Fig. 5. ESCA spectra.

always different from the spectral lines of oxides, hydroxides and sulphates. On the surface of the zinc concentrate $CuL_3 M_{4,5} M_{4,5}$ the spectral band has a slightly higher energy but overlap with Auger's spectral band makes description of the band difficult.

Most of the zinc seems to remain in the form of sulphide and the position of the $ZnL_3 M_{4,5} M_{4,5}$ spectral band does not indicate the possibility of the "simple" forming of ZnO, $Zn(OH)_2$ or $ZnSO_4$.

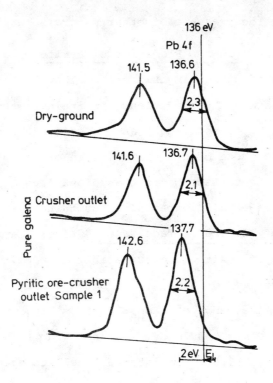

Fig. 6. ESCA spectra.

Pb4f electrons have 137.8 eV bond energy which is higher
for sulphide (PbS: 136.55 eV) but lower for sulphate (138.7 eV).
The same value has been observed for the group of samples and
it is higher when galena alone is flotated (136.7 eV) (Fig. 6).
Similar deviations have also been observed with galena and raw
ore when treating with water. These results can be compared
with those obtained by Clifford et al. [2] who confirmed that
the bond energy of Pb4f electrons is higher the greater the Pb
concentration. The spectral line Pb4f becomes wider from the

very beginning of grinding which indicates the rapid oxidation
of lead festered by the presence of other minerals in the pulp.

The State of Surface in the Flotation of Pyrite. Because of
the high percentage of pyrite in this ore we thought it useful
to investigate in detail the conditions for its depression.
This mineral was flotated separately and under conditions as
close as possible to those of ore flotation in order to determine the effect on the surface properties of various depressants,
copper sulphate and ageing in water after grinding.

The Properties of Altered Surface Layer. After leaving the
crusher the surface of pyrite is considerably damaged. The
oxidized form of iron (70 to 80%) is characterized by the
following spectral line band positions: Fe2p = 710.5 eV,
Fe3p = 55.2 eV and O1s = 530.35 eV, a rather wide spectral band
of oxygen O1s, and at 718.6 eV an intense satellite spectral
band (Fig. 7). These characteristics are close to those of
oxyhydroxides (FeO·OH)   and probably also to hydroxides
$Fe(OH)_2$, $Fe(OH)_3$ [8, 9].

	Fe2p	Fe3p	O^{--}	OH^-
FeO·OH	710.5	55.6	529.1	530.4
Fe_2O_3	710	54.7	529.1	-

Because of the formation of this hydroxide the amount of
surface sulphur is evidently reduced, a reduction which is the
more important since the percentage of iron sulphide is also

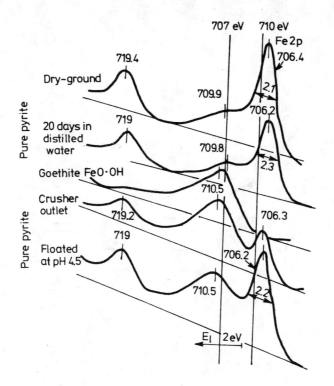

Fig. 7. ESCA spectra.

reduced as can be seen in Fig. 8 where experimental points correspond to samples of pyrite subjected to different conditions. The S2p band retains the same form and position as for freshly-ground pyrite. No significant formation of sulphur or oxidized sulphur occurs.

This alteration of the pyrite surface in the process of wet-grinding differs from that during ageing in air where it leads to the formation of basic sulphate preserving the ratio of sulphur to iron atoms. Ageing in distilled water does not result in any modification of the pyrite surface.

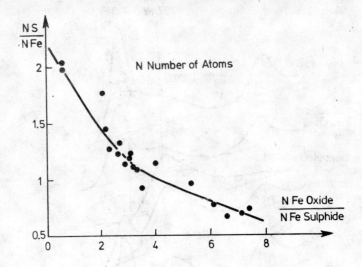

Fig. 8. Reduction of the surface sulphur amount.

ESCA SPECTRA

Ageing and Aeration. Several hours of wet-grinding does not cause surface alterations in this ore. A long period of aeration (60 min) results in only insignificant alterations of the same nature. On the other hand, several minutes' aeration in the presence of lime leads to the extensive formation of iron hydroxide (Table 4).

TABLE 4

The Influence of Ageing and Aeration

(Pyrite)

Sample	N Fe oxyd/N Fe sulf	N S/N Fe	% SO_4
Freshly ground	0.58	2.0	2 - 3
30 days in air	3.08	2.6	38
20 hours in distilled H_2O	0.66	1.80	5
at the crusher outlet	2.64	1.32	12
6 hours of wet grinding	2.20	1.45	14
1 hour of aeration in the cell	3.44	0.91	16.2
5 min of aeration in the cell at pH 12	6.15	0.77	17.8

Redox Potential Effect. After various treatments with lime either positive or negative redox potentials can be obtained. In the first case the ratio of the number of oxidic iron atoms to the number of sulphidic iron atoms is more than 6.2. In the latter case it is lower than 3.5. It seems that after ageing or conditioning with CaO there exists an effective relation between the redox potential and the number of sulphidic iron atoms that remain on the surface.

TABLE 5

Effect of CaO, $Ba(OH)_2$ and KOH
(Pyrite conditioning at pH 11.2)

Sample	$\dfrac{N \text{ of oxidic Fe}}{N \text{ of sulphidic Fe}}$	$\dfrac{N \text{ of S}}{N \text{ of Fe}}$	$\dfrac{N \text{ of react.}}{100 \text{ Fe}}$	$\% \ SO_4$
with CaO	4.03	1.14	4	14
with $Ba(OH)_2$	2.9	1.14	12	14.2
with KOH	2.1	1.71	2	13

N – number of atoms

The Effect of Depressants (Table 5). The pyrite was conditioned with CaO, $CuSO_4$ and NaCN introduced successively to the cell. Each introduction was followed by sampling and ESCA measurements. In the second experiment this mineral was conditioned with CaO, $ZnSO_4$ and NaCN introduced together and then flotated under conditions identical with those for the standard flotation of copper and zinc ores.

CaO. The results confirm the considerable fixation of lime on the pyrite surface but its form is difficult to specify due to the small degree of chemical variability of this element. We find that the number of atoms measured during the flotation process by the ESCA method (i.e., on the surface) ranges from 4 to 32 calcium atoms per 100 iron atoms while this ratio calculated for the whole material is 0.75 Ca per 100 Fe, which indicates a significant coating of the pyrite surface. However, it is not certain whether such a coating is due to the adsorption of calcium ions, calcium sulphate or $Ca(OH)_2$ precipitation on the surface of the pyrite.

Ba(OH)$_2$ and KOH. The same flotation experiments were carried out using Ba(OH)$_2$ and KOH replacing lime and achieving low iron recovery. Barium and potassium atoms were discovered on the surface of pyrite in proportions similar to lime for barium and in lower proportions for potassium. The surface oxidation of pyrite is not so clearly seen with KOH and Ba(OH)$_2$ as with CaO but is strong because there are twice as many iron atoms in the form of hydroxide than in the form of sulphide.

NaCN. In all experiments on conditioning and flotation with NaCN, neither nitrogen nor sodium could be detected on the surface of various powders. Thus, contrary to expectations, at high values of pH (between 10 and 12) no stable iron complexes were formed. In this situation the role of NaCN seems to be limited to the complexing of ions in solution.

CuSO$_4$ and ZnSO$_4$ Effect. ESCA investigations show that the fixation of copper and zinc atoms on the surface of pyrite also takes place. Despite the presence of this surface copper, pyrite is not activated under our experimental conditions as it was shown by the lack of recovery in flotation. CuSO$_4$ was added to the pyrite pulp either directly after wet-grinding (a condition corresponding to the activation in flotation of raw ore) or as in sphalerite activation. An estimation gave 5 atoms of copper per 100 atoms of iron. This copper has the characteristics of copper sulphide, similar to the characteristics of CuFeS$_2$ (Fig. 9). The amount of zinc on the pyrite surface is given by the ratio 2.2 atoms of zinc per 100 atoms of iron (a ratio which is 30 times higher than that for bulk phases). This amount of surface zinc does not seem to affect flotation process.

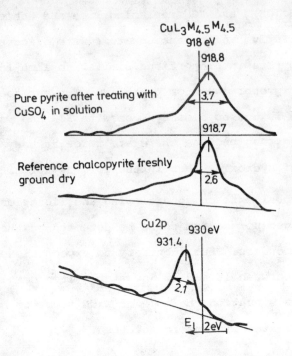

Fig. 9. ESCA spectra.

pH Effect. Flotation experiments with pyrite were carried out for different pH values. Table 6 gives the oxidation of sulphide to sulphate and the number ratios of iron atoms in the form of oxide to iron atoms in the form of sulphide. The pH was regulated by CaO or H_2SO_4. Pyrite was flotated with ethylxanthate without NaCN at three different pH ranges: acid, slightly basic and strong basic range. A good concentrate was obtained with an acid pH. Pyrite did not flotate under slightly alkaline and strongly alkaline conditions. The oxidation of iron seems to be independent of pH. After each conditioning

TABLE 6

Effect of pH on the Surface State of Pyrite

Sample	pH	N of oxidic Fe / N of sulphidic Fe	N of S / N of Fe	% SO_4	I C1s / I Fe 3p
Conditioning	5	3.1	1.23	15	3.3
Concentrate	4.5	1.2	2.38	6.7	4.9
Conditioning	7.5	5.25	0.96	16	3.8
Conditioning	8.5-8.7	3.2	1.11	12	3.2
Conditioning	9-10	3.04	1.20	14	3.3

N - number of atoms

I - intensity

the number of oxidic iron atoms was three times greater than the number of sulphidic iron atoms. As in previous experiments, the surface layer of oxidized iron approaches hydroxide rather than iron oxide forms. With an acid pH, the ratio Fe oxidic/Fe sulphidic which was very high before the introduction of ethyl-xanthate (3.1) is particularly low on the surface of the obtained concentrate; pyrite can flotate only with a sufficient number of iron sulphide atoms - the introduction of ethylxanthate could cause this modification. A very high surface content of sulphur, higher than might be expected for this degree of oxidation, was observed. This high sulphur content is a result of xanthate fixation as is confirmed by the I C1S/I Fe3p ratio.

ACKNOWLEDGMENTS

The authors wish to thank the D.G.R.S.T. for providing the contract which allowed the present paper to be completed.

REFERENCES

1. Siegbahn K. et al. ESCA. Atomic, Molecular and Solid State Structure Studied by Means of Electron Spectroscopy. Almquist et Wilsells book. Uppsala 1967.

2. Clifford R. K., Purdy K. L. and Miller J. D. AIChE Symp. Ser. 71 (150), 138-147 (1975).

3. Frost D. C., Leeder W. R., Tapping R. L. and Wallbank R. Fuel, 56, 277-280 (1977).

4. Manocha A. S. and Park R. L. Applic. Surf. Sci., 1, 129-141 (1977).

5. Nakai I., Sugitani Y., Nagashima K. and Niwa Y. J. Inorg. Nucl. Chem., 40, 789-791 (1978).

6. Purdy K. L. and Clifford R. K., ESCA Characterization of Flotation Products from a Lead-Zinc-Copper Concentrator on the New Lead Belt of Southeast Missouri. Ann. Meeting of Am. Inst. of Mining and Petroleum Engineers. New York, February 1975.

7. Brion D. Results to be published.

8. Asami K. and Hashimoto K. Corrosion Sci., 17, 559-570 (1977).

9. McIntyre N. S. and Zetaruk D. G. Anal. Chem., 49, 1521-1529 (1977).

10.Eadington P. Trans. Inst. Min. Metall., Sect. C, 86, 186-189 (1977).

ABSTRACT

Pyritic Zn, Cu and Pb ores, which represent an important part of the world reserves, are difficult to beneficiate using selective flotation, due to the very fine grinding needed to liberate phases (20 µm).   In such conditions depression of the pyritic gangue is particularly complex. A study of the mechanism of gangue depression has been carried out by E.S.C.A. which allows the direct chemical analysis of the few surface monolayers. These experiments, carried out with an ore and pure minerals, have shown the efficiency of the classical depressants, NaCN, CaO, $ZnSO_4$, and pyrite depression through the formation of iron oxi-hydroxide or hydroxide on its surface. Compounds more complex than jarosites, for example, have not been seen under our experimental conditions.

RÉSUMÉ

Les minerais Zn, Cu et Pb, à gangue pyriteuse, des amas volcanosédimentaires, importants sur le plan mondial, posent des problèmes de valorisation par flottation différentielle dus, en particulier, à la nécessité de broyer finement (20 µm) pour obtenir la libération des phases. Dans ces conditions la dépression de la gangue pyriteuse est particulièrement difficile. L'étude des mécanismes de cette dépression a été menée au moyen de la spectroscopie de photoélectrons (E.S.C.A.) qui permet l'analyse chimique directe des monocouches superficielles. Ces travaux effectués sur un minerai et sur des minéraux purs montrent l'action des déprimants classiques: NaCN, CaO, $ZnSO_4$, et la dépression de la pyrite en fonction d'un oxy-hydroxyde ou d'un hydroxyde de fer et non d'un composé plus complexe de type jarosite par exemple.

ZUSAMMENFASSUNG

Die einen wichtigen Teil der Weltvorräte bildenen blei- kupfer- und zinkhaltigen Pyriterze können sehr schwer mittels selektiver Flotation angereichert werden, da für das Heraus-

lösen der Erzkörner eine sehr feine Zermahlung des Erzes
(20 μm) notwendig ist. Unter solchen Bedingungen ist die
Depression des tauben Pyrit-Gesteins besonders kompliziert.
Die Untersuchungen des Depressionsmechanismus des tauben
Gesteins, wurden nach der ESCA-Methode durchgeführt die eine
unmittelbare Bestimmung der chemischen Zusammensetzung einiger
monomolekulärer Oberflächenschichten erlaubt. Die Untersuchungen des Erzes und der reinen Minerale zeigten die Effektivität
der klassischen Depressionsmittel wie: NaCN, CaO, $ZnSO_4$ und
der Pyritdepression durch Entstechen basischer Eisenoxide bzw.
der Eisenhydroxide an der Pyritoberfläche. Die Anwesenheit
kompliziertere Verbindungen wie z.B. Jarosit (basisches
Eisensulfat) wurde in unseren Versuchen nicht nachgewiesen.

РЕЗЮМЕ

Цинково-медно-свинцовые руды, содержащие пиритную пустую
породу вульканично-осадочного типа, являются важной частью
мировых резерв и вызывают проблемы в процессе селективной
флотации, вызыванные, в частности необходимостью проведения
тонкого размола (20 микронов) для получения раскрытия фаз.
В таких условиях депрессия пирита пустой породы особенно
сложна. Исследования механизма депресии были проведены с использованием метода ЭСКА, который дает возможность проведения непосредственного химического анализа нескольких поверхностных монослоев. Эксперименты, проведенные с рудой и чис-
тыми минералами, показали влияние классических депрессиру-
ющих реагентов: NaCN, CaO, $ZnSO_4$ и депрессии пирита в зависимости от образования на его поверхности окисно-гидрокис-
ных или гидрокисных соединений железа, а не более сложных
соединений, как например ярозита.

THE EFFECT OF AMINO ACID ADDITION ON THE FLOTATION OF SULPHIDE ORE

T. Wakamatsu[1], Y. Numata[2] and Y. Sugimoto[3]

[1] Department of Mineral Science and Technology
Kyoto University, Japan
[2] Akita University, Japan
[3] Sumitomo Metal Industries Ltd., Japan

INTRODUCTION

In order to obtain a successful flotation for slimy sulphide ore or partly oxidized sulphide ore, the effective reaction of collector ions onto the surface of a target sulphide mineral and the dispersion of harmful slime are indispensable.

Xanthates are superior collectors for the flotation of sulphide minerals. The authors have shown that xanthate ions can adsorb even on the surface of oxidized minerals in an aqueous solution if there is a suitable organic reagent present together with xanthate ions in the solution [1]. The fact that an xanthate can react onto the surface of an oxidized mineral indicates the importance of coadsorption phenomena as well as the action of the organic reagent in flotation.

Amino acids which contain both acidic and basic groups in a molecule exist in the form of cation acid, anion acid, and dipole ion in water, depending on the pH of the solution. The dipole

159

ions of amino acid are thought to adsorb at the solid-water interface in a suitable adsorption configuration regardless of the electronic charge on the solid. Accordingly, it may be assumed that the adsorption of amino acid dipole ions on the surface of a sulphide mineral would render its surface more hydrophobic so that the xanthate reaction on it might be promoted. On the other hand, the surface of oxidized minerals such as gangue minerals is generally very hydrophilic and is electronically charged in water. Therefore, it is thought that if amino acids in the form of dipole ion adsorb on the surface of gangue mineral, the electronic charge of the gangue mineral may increase to some extent to improve its dispersion state in water.

In this study amino acids were used with the xanthate to examine how amino acids promote the reaction between the xanthate and the mineral and affect the dispersion of gangue mineral.

EXPERIMENTAL PROCEDURE

The mineral tested was galena from the Toyoha mine, Hokkaido, Japan. High grade coarse pieces of the material were selected, ground in an agate mortar, and then screened to obtain a -200 mesh fraction. After having been deslimed at 10 µm the -200 mesh fraction was dried and stored in a vacuum drier for the measurement of both xanthate adsorption and amino acid adsorption. The potassium ethyl xanthate and four kinds of amino acids which were all provided by Nakarai Chemicals Co. were of "extra pure" grade. The amino acids used in this study were glycine, ß-alanine, γ-amino butyric acid and δ-amino valeric acid. They have the molecular formulas:

160

glycine	NH_2-CH_2-COOH
ß-alanine	$NH_2-(CH_2)_2-COOH$
γ-amino butyric acid	$NH_2-(CH_2)_3-COOH$
δ-amino valeric acid	$NH_2-(CH_2)_4-COOH$

and the acid dissociation constants and other constants as shown in Table 1 [2].

TABLE 1

Various Constants of Amino Acids

Amino acid	pKa_1	pKa_2	IEP	Dipole moment μ (Debye)
Glycine	2.35	9.77	6.06	12
ß-Alanine	3.60	10.19	6.90	15
γ-Amino butyric acid	4.03	10.56	7.30	18
δ-Amino valeric acid	4.27	10.69	7.52	20

Each amino acid exists in the form of a dipole ion in a wide pH range, depending on its pKa_1 and pKa_2, just as in the case of glycine shown in Fig. 1. It has also a high dipole moment value

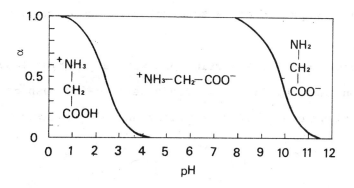

Fig. 1. Distribution diagram for glycine.

compared with that of water, 1.83 Debye. As listed in Table 1, the dipole moment value for amino acid increases with the increasing length of the $(CH_2)n$ chain in its molecular structure.

Adsorption experiments for xanthate and amino acids were carried out in a 400 ml flask in which 2 g of galena particles and 200 ml of the reagent solution were combined and gently stirred at a fixed temperature, 25 $\pm$ 0.1°C. After the desired interval, the reagent concentration of the bulk solution was measured. The amount adsorbed was determined from the difference in the concentration of the adsorbate before and after adding the galena particles. The same procedure was employed for quartz. The concentrations of xanthate in the solution were determined by ultraviolet spectrophotometry. The concentration of amino acid in the solution was analyzed by a Yanaco Amino Acid Analyzer.

The gangue mineral sample was quartz from the Otani mine, Kyoto, Japan. The quartz was ground, and then screened to obtain a -200 mesh fraction. The -200 mesh fraction deslimed at 10 μm was used for the adsorption test. A -10 μm slime fraction was prepared for the flotation tests of galena and quartz slime. A -1 μm fraction was also prepared for the electrophoretic mobility measurement of quartz particles. A Zeta Meter was used in this part of the study.

The flotation tests were carried out with an FW type laboratory flotation machine. Flotation feeds were a -200 mesh galena sample and a mixture of -200 mesh galena and -10 μm quartz.

Xanthate Adsorption on Galena in the Presence of Amino Acid and Xanthate in Water

Figure 2 shows the xanthate adsorption on galena as a function of time with a 1.0×10^{-4} mol/l addition of each amino acid. In these experiments, the addition of ethyl xanthate (KEX) was held at 6.24×10^{-5} mol/l and the pH of the solution was 5.90 ± 0.10. In each case, the adsorption amount of xanthate increases with increasing reaction time and attains an almost equilibrium value within about 90 min reaction time. When each amino acid is added to the xanthate, the xanthate adsorbs on the galena much more

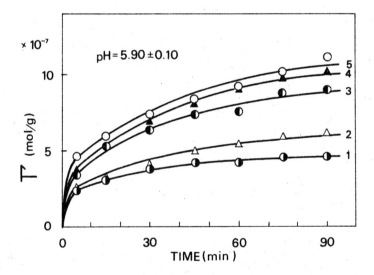

Fig. 2. Xanthate adsorption on galena as a function of time with a 1.0×10^{-4} mol/l addition of each amino acid, and a constant addition of KEX, 6.24×10^{-5} mol/l. (1 - KEX, 2 - KEX + glycine, 3 - KEX + ß-alanine, 4 - KEX + γ-amino butyric acid, 5 - KEX + δ-amino valeric acid).

than when there is no addition of the acid. As can be seen in Fig. 2, the longer the $(CH_2)n$ chain length of the amino acid is, the more favourable is the adsorption of xanthate on galena. It can be also said that within the scope of this study the xanthate adsorption on galena increases with an increasing value, dipole moment value of the amino acid.

Figures 3-6 show how xanthate adsorbs on galena with a varying concentration of amino acid and a fixed addition of xanthate, 6.24×10^{-5} mol/l, at pH 5.90 ± 0.10.

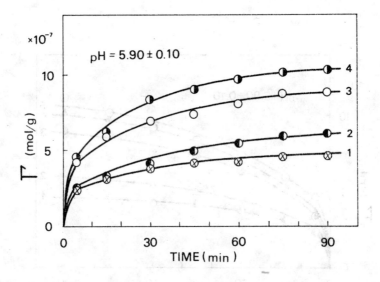

Fig. 3. Xanthate adsorption on galena with a varying concentration of glycine and a fixed addition of xanthate, 6.24×10^{-5} mol/l. (1 - no addition of glycine, 2 - 1.0×10^{-4} mol/l glycine, 3 - 2.0×10^{-4} mol/l glycine, 4 - 3.0×10^{-4} mol/l glycine).

When glycine was added in concentrations of 1.0×10^{-4} mol/1, 2.0×10^{-4} mol/1, and 3.0×10^{-4} mol/1, the xanthate adsorption at equilibrium amounted to 6.1×10^{-7} mol/g, 8.8×10^{-7} mol/g, and 1.0×10^{-6} mol/g, respectively, as shown in Fig. 3. In this case, the xanthate adsorption on galena increases with increasing glycine concentration.

Figure 4 shows that β-alanine addition causes an increase of the xanthate adsorption in the same way as in the case of glycine, and also that there is an optimum ß-alanine addition to give maximum xanthate adsorption on galena. As can be seen in

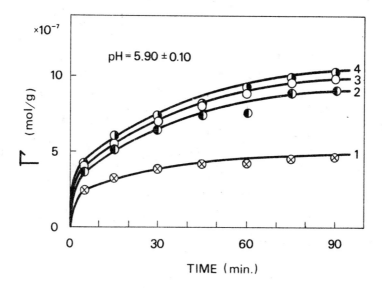

Fig. 4. Xanthate adsorption on galena with varying concentration of ß-alanine and a fixed addition of xanthate, 6.24×10^{-5} mol/1. (1 - no addition of ß-alanine, 2 - 1.0×10^{-4} mol/1 ß-alanine, 3 - 3.0×10^{-4} mol/1 ß-alanine, 4 - 2.0×10^{-4} mol/1 ß-alanine).

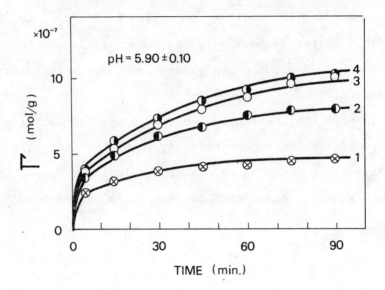

Fig. 5. Xanthate adsorption on galena with varying concentration of γ-amino butyric acid and a fixed addition of
xanthate, 6.24 x 10^{-5} mol/l. (1 - no addition of
γ-amino butyric acid, 2 - 0.5 x 10^{-4} mol/l γ-amino
butyric acid, 3 - 2.0 x 10^{-4} mol/l γ-amino butyric
acid, 4 - 1.0 x 10^{-4} mol/l γ-amino butyric acid).

Figs. 5 and 6, the addition of either γ-amino butyric acid or
δ-amino valeric acid has a similarly favourable effect on
xanthate adsorption, while the addition of each amino acid above
1.0 x 10^{-4} mol/l causes a decrease in xanthate adsorption.

It can be understood from the above facts that the longer the
$(CH_2)n$ chain length of the amino acid is, the lower the optimum
amino acid concentration required to give a maximum xanthate adsorption. The optimum amino acid concentrations are approximately
3.0 x 10^{-4} mol/l for glycine, 2.0 x 10^{-4} mol/l for β-alanine,
and 1.0 x 10^{-4} mol/l for γ-amino butyric acid and δ-amino

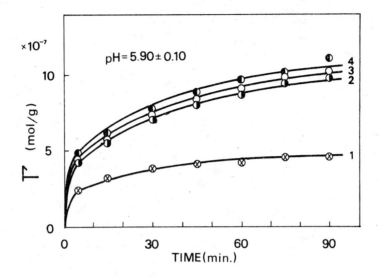

Fig. 6. Xanthate adsorption on galena with varying concentration of δ-amino valeric acid and a fixed addition of
xanthate, 6.24×10^{-5} mol/l. (1 - no addition of δ-
amino valeric acid, 2 - 0.5×10^{-4} mol/l δ-amino
valeric acid, 3 - 2.0×10^{-4} mol/l δ-amino valeric
acid, 4 - 1.0×10^{-4} mol/l δ-amino valeric acid).

valeric acid. The maximum adsorption of xanthate at the optimum

amino acid concentration amounted to $1.0 \sim 1.1 \times 10^{-6}$ mol/g in

each case.

Figure 7 shows the pH dependence of xanthate adsorption at

equilibrium on galena with a constant addition of xanthate,

6.24×10^{-5} mol/l, with addition of either 1.0×10^{-4} mol/l gly-

cine or 1.0×10^{-4} mol/l δ-amino valeric acid. In Fig. 7 the pH

dependence of xanthate adsorption on galena without addition of

amino acid is also presented for reference.

As can be seen from a comparison of the results in Fig. 7 and

Fig. 1, the pH region where the glycine addition causes an in-

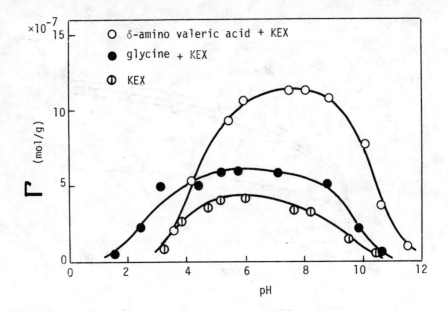

Fig. 7. The pH dependence of xanthate adsorption on galena
with a fixed addition of KEX, 6.24 x 10^{-5} mol/l, and
with addition of 1.0 x 10^{-4} mol/l glycine or 1.0 x
10^{-4} mol/l δ-amino valeric acid.

crease in the xanthate adsorption coincides with that where glycine exists as dipole ion in water. The same thing can be said
for δ-amino valeric acid, too.

Amino Acid Adsorption on Galena in the Presence of Amino Acid
and Xanthate in Water

The amino acid adsorption on galena was measured as a function of time with a 1.0 x 10^{-4} mol/l addition of each amino acid
when the addition of xanthate was at 6.24 x 10^{-5} mol/l and the
pH of solution was adjusted to 5.80 $\pm$ 0.10. Figure 8 presents the
results for glycine and δ-amino valeric acid. In the case of

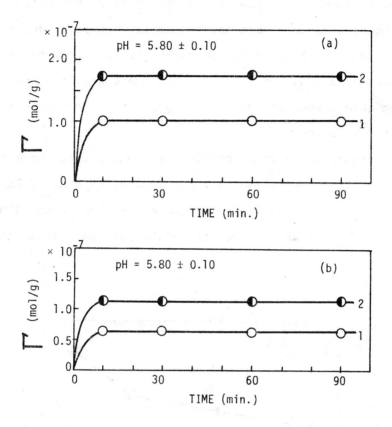

Fig. 8. Amino acid adsorption on galena as a function of time with a fixed addition of xanthate, 6.24×10^{-5} mol/l, and with addition of (a) 1.0×10^{-4} mol/l δ-amino valeric acid or (b) 1.0×10^{-4} mol/l glycine. 1 - without addition of xanthate, 2 - with addition of xanthate.

amino acid adsorption on galena, the adsorption attained to an equilibrium state within the reaction time of 10-20 min. As can be seen in Fig. 8, the adsorption of amino acid on galena is generally far less than that of xanthate; namely, 10-20% of the adsorption of xanthate. In every case the presence of xanthate

causes an increase of the amino acid adsorption on galena; i.e.,
the adsorption amount of amino acid with a 6.24×10^{-5} mol/l
xanthate addition is about one and a half times that of amino
acid without the addition of xanthate. It can be stated on the
basis of the facts shown in Figs. 2-8 that xanthate tends to
coadsorb on galena together with amino acid when they co-exist
in an aqueous solution.

Figure 9 presents the relationship between the amino acid adsorption on galena at equilibrium and the dipole moment of amino
acid. With or without addition of xanthate, the larger the dipole
moment of amino acid, the greater the amino acid adsorption on
galena.

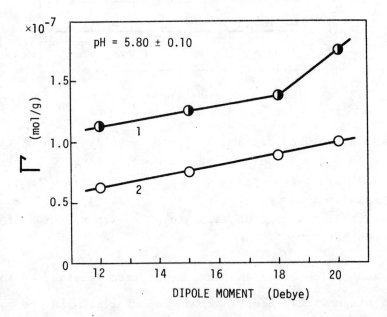

Fig. 9. Relationship between the equilibrium adsorption amount
of amino acid and the dipole moment of amino acid.
1 - with addition of xanthate, 2 - without addition of
xanthate.

Adsorption of Xanthate and Amino Acid on Quartz in the Presence
of Both Reagents in Water

Figure 10 shows the amino acid adsorption on quartz as a
function of time with a 1.0 x 10^{-4} mol/l addition of amino acid
and a 6.24 x 10^{-5} mol/l addition of xanthate, at a fixed pH
5.80 $\pm$ 0.1. The amino acid adsorption on quartz is far less than
that on galena. Furthermore, other tests indicated that there
was no measurable amount of xanthate adsorption on quartz at all

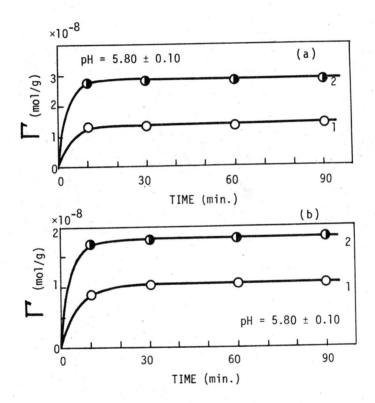

Fig. 10. Amino acid adsorption on quartz as a function of time
with a fixed addition of xanthate, 6.24 x 10^{-5} mol/l,
and with addition of (a) 1.0 x 10^{-4} mol/l δ-amino
valeric acid or (b) 1.0 x 10^{-4} mol/l glycine. 1 -
without addition of xanthate, 2 - with addition of
xanthate.

even in the presence of amino acid. Accordingly, it is assumed
that the mineral on which xanthate can adsorb more favourably
with a small addition of amino acid should be in limited cases
the mineral on which xanthate can essentially adsorb to some
extent in the absence of amino acid.

These phenomena lead to the idea where for sulphide ore with
quartz as a gangue mineral the addition of amino acid may promote the collection of sulphide mineral by xanthate without collecting quartz.

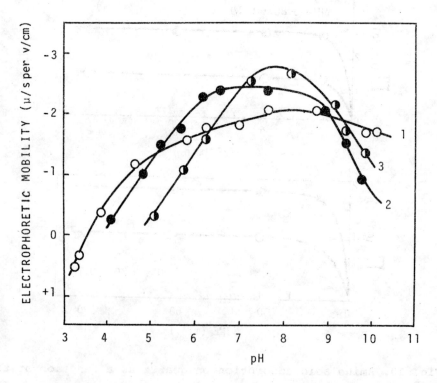

Fig. 11. The pH dependence of the electrophoretic mobility of
quartz in water with or without addition of amino
acids. 1 - in water, 2 - with glycine, 3 - with
δ-amino valeric acid.

Figure 11 presents the electrophoretic mobility of quartz as a function of pH with or without addition of amino acid. In the absence of amino acid, quartz particles are negatively charged in water in a wide pH region above pH 3.5 as shown in Fig. 11. When amino acid is added to water, the quartz particles tend to increase their negative charge slightly more in the pH region where the amino acid exists as dipole ion. The results suggest that amino acid addition may lead to an improvement of the dispersion properties of quartz slime in pH regions 5-9 for glycine and 6-9 for δ-amino valeric acid.

Flotation Tests of Galena

Table 2 and Fig. 12 show the results of flotation tests using -200 mesh galena particles as a feed, xanthate as a collector and 4-methyl-2-pentanol as a frother. In these tests, the effect of amino acid addition on the flotation recovery of galena was studied, one of the amino acids being added to the xanthate in each run. As can be seen in Table 2 and Fig. 12, within the scope of this study amino acid addition causes a marked increase in galena recovery as compared with galena collection with xanthate alone. Further, as in the case of xanthate adsorption, it may be noted that the longer the $(CH_2)n$ chain length of the amino acid, the greater the increase in galena recovery.

Flotation tests were also carried out for synthetic ore which was a mixture of -200 mesh galena and -10 μm quartz. The synthetic ore contained about 10% of -10 μm quartz by weight. Table 3 shows that the existence of quartz slime adversely affected the flota-

TABLE 2

Flotation Tests for Galena

Test No.	Product	Time (min)	Weight Wi(g)	Weight Σ Wi(g)	Recovery (%)	Conditions
1	Froth-1	1	1.697		35.0	Frother(4-methyl-2-pentanol)
	-2	1	0.216	1.913	39.5	3×10^{-5} mol/l
	-3	1	0.112	2.025	41.8	Collector(KEX)
	-4	2	0.062	2.087	43.1	6.24×10^{-6} mol/l
	-5	2	0.005	2.092	43.2	pH: 5.87
	Tailing		2.748	4.840		Conditioning time: 5 min
2	Froth-1	1	3.084		62.2	Frother(4M2P) 3×10^{-5} mol/l
	-2	1	0.295	3.379	68.1	Collector(KEX)
	-3	1	0.034	3.413	68.8	6.24×10^{-6} mol/l
	-4	2	0.056	3.469	69.9	Glycine 1.25×10^{-5} mol/l
	-5	2	0.007	3.476	70.1	pH: 6.0
	Tailing		1.483	4.959		Conditioning time: 5 min
3	Froth-1	1	3.286		66.5	Frother(4M2P) 3×10^{-5} mol/l
	-2	1	0.230	3.516	71.2	KEX: 6.24×10^{-6} mol/l
	-3	1	0.093	3.609	73.1	β-alanine: 1.25×10^{-5} mol/l
	-4	2	0.048	3.657	74.0	pH: 6.21
	-5	2	0.007	3.664	74.2	Conditioning time: 5 min
	Tailing		1.276	4.940		
4	Froth-1	1	3.327		67.4	Frother(4M2P) 3×10^{-5} mol/l
	-2	1	0.382	3.709	75.2	KEX: 6.24×10^{-6} mol/l
	-3	1	0.132	3.841	77.9	γ-amino butyric acid
	-4	2	0.059	3.900	79.1	1.25×10^{-5} mol/l
	-5	2	0.009	3.909	79.3	pH: 6.38
	Tailing		1.024	4.933		Conditioning time: 5 min

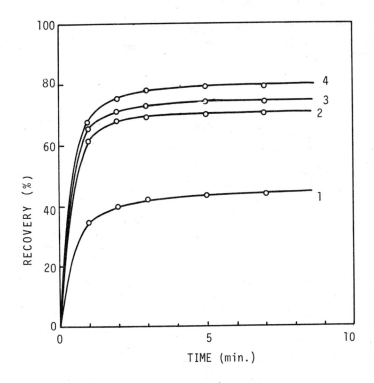

Fig. 12. Effect of amino acid addition on the flotation recovery of galena. 1 - KEX, 2 - KEX + glycine, 3 - KEX + β-alanine, 4 - KEX + γ-amino butyric acid.

tion of galena. However, it is clear that by adding glycine galena can be floated to some extent, the quartz slime being considerably depressed.

It can be seen from these facts that the suitable introduction of amino acid to sulphide ore flotation may result in the acid playing an important role in the promotion of xanthate adsorption on sulphide mineral, and simultaneously in the dispersion of slime.

TABLE 3

Flotation Tests for Synthetic Ore

Test No.	Product	Time (min)	Weight of galena Wi (g)	ΣWi (g)	Recovery (%)	Conditions
1	Froth-1	1	0.526		11.9	Quartz slime: 0.506 g
	-2	1	0.077	0.603	13.6	Frother (4M2P) 3×10^{-5} mol/l
	-3	1	0.042	0.645	14.6	KEX: 6.24×10^{-6} mol/l
	-4	2	0.038	0.683	15.4	pH: 8.55
	-5	2	0.018	0.701	15.8	Conditioning time: 5 min
	Tailing		3.728	4.429		
2	Froth-1	1	2.860		56.6	Quartz slime: 0.502 g
	-2	1	0.195	3.055	60.5	Frother (4M2P) 3×10^{-5} mol/l
	-3	1	0.050	3.105	61.5	KEX: 6.24×10^{-6} mol/l
	-4	2	0.036	3.141	62.2	pH: 8.93
	-5	2	0.014	3.155	62.4	Conditioning time: 5 min
	Tailing		1.897	5.052		Glycine: 1.25×10^{-5} mol/l

CONCLUSION

Amino acids were examined in this study to see if they promote the reaction between collector and mineral and simultaneously act as dispersing agent. The amino acids used were of
such molecular formulas as $NH_2-(CH_2)n-COOH$, where n = 1-4. Two
kinds of basic tests were tried; (1) the effect of amino acids
on the reaction between collector and sulphide mineral and (2)
the dispersing action of amino acid on slime.

In test (1) the xanthate adsorption on galena using potassium
ethyl xanthate was measured in the presence of amino acid from
the point of view of the amino acid concentration, the $(CH_2)n$
length of the amino acid and the pH of the solution. Results

showed that xanthate adsorption on galena became notably more favorable by adding amino acid, especially in the pH region where amino acid exists as a dipole ion in water. There is an optimum amino acid concentration for each amino acid which gives a maximum xanthate adsorption on galena. Within a limited concentration of amino acid, the longer the amino acid $(CH_2)n$ the more favorable the effect of amino acid addition on xanthate adsorption.

In test (2), the dispersion effect of amino acid on slime was investigated by using quartz as a slime mineral. Electrophoretic mobility measurements for quartz particles in water were made for the kinds of amino acid used and the pH of solution. It was found that there was an optimum pH range for each amino acid, where quartz particles were more negatively charged with an addition of amino acid than without amino acid addition.

Finally, flotation tests for galena alone and for a synthetic ore, a mixture of galena and quartz slime were carried out on the basis of the above basic results. It was confirmed that a suitable introduction of amino acid to sulphide ore flotation can result in the acid playing an important role in the promotion of xanthate adsorption on sulphide mineral and in its simultaneously acting as a dispersing agent for slime.

REFERENCES

1. Mukai S. and Wakamatsu T. Copper silicate mineral flotation by activation with organic copper-avid reagent. Proceedings of XI İMPC, Cagliari, 1975, 671-689.

2. Greenstein J. P. and Winitz M. Chemistry of the Amino Acids. J. Wiley, New York, 1961, 435-522.

ABSTRACT

Amino acids of such molecular formulas as $NH_2-(CH_2)n-COOH$, where n = 1-4, were examined to see if they promote the xanthate adsorption on galena and also have a simultaneous dispersing action for quartz.

The xanthate adsorption on galena became notably more favorable by adding amino acid in suitable quantity, especially in the pH region where the amino acid exists as a dipole ion in water.

Electrophoretic mobility measurements using quartz slime showed that there was an optimum pH region, 5-9, where quartz particles were more negatively charged by the addition of amino acid than without amino acid addition.

Flotation tests for galena alone and for a mixture of galena and quartz slime confirmed that suitable introduction of amino acid to sulphide ore flotation can result in the acid playing an important role in the promotion of xanthate adsorption on sulphide mineral and in its simultaneously acting as a dispersing agent for slime.

RÉSUMÉ

Les acides-aminés qui ont des formules moléculaires telles que $NH_2(CH_2)n-COOH$, où n = 1-4, ont été examinés quand ils activent l'adsorption du xanthate sur de la galène, tout en ayant, ont une action de dispersion du quartz.

L'adsorption du xanthate sur de la galène devient notablement favorable par l'addition d'une quantité convenable d'un acide-aminé, particulièrement dans l'intervalle de pH où l'acide-aminé existe dans l'eau comme un dipole.

Les mesures de mobilité electrophorétique utilisant une boue de quartz ont montré qu'il existe un intervalle optimal de pH, 5-9 où les particules de quartz sont plus négativement chargées par l'addition d'un acide-aminé que sans cette addition.

Les tests de flottation de la galène seule et du mélange galéne et boue de quartz ont confirmé qu'une introduction convenable de l'acide-aminé lors de la flottation du minerai sulfuré peut faire jouer à l'acide un rôle important, en tant qu'activateur de l'adsorption du xanthate sur le minéral sulfuré, et an même temps, en tant qu'agent de dispersion de la boue.

ZUSAMMENFASSUNG

Es wurde untersucht, ob Aminosäuren mit der Zusammensetzung $NH_2-(CH_2)n-COOH$, wobei n = 1-4 ist, die Adsorption des Xanthogenats an Bleiglanz (Galenit) fördern und gleichzeitig auf Quarz dispersiv wirken.

Die Adsorption des Xanthogenats durch Bleiglanz wirkt sich besonders vorteilhaft aus wenn der Zusatz der Aminosäure in entsprechender Menge, und im pH-Bereich erfolgt, in welchem die Aminosäure als Dipolion in Wasser auftritt.

Elektrophoretische Messungen der Ionenbeweglichkeit mit Hilfe von Quarzschlick haben erwiesen, dass der optimale pH-Wert bei 5,9 liegt, wo die Quarz-Moleküle durch einen Zusatz von Aminosäure negativer als ohne einen solchen Zusatz geladen werden.

Flotationsversuche mit Bleiglanz allein, sowie mit einer Bleiglanz-Quarzschlick-Mischung haben gezeigt, dass ein angemessener Zusatz an Aminosäure dazu beitragen kann, dass die Adsorption des Xanthogenats an einem sulfidhaltigen Mineral gefördert wird bei gleichzeitiger Dispergierung des Quarzschlicks.

РЕЗЮМЕ

Исследованы аминокислоты с молекулярной формулой $NH_2 - (CH_2)_n - COOH$, где $n = 1-4$, с точки зрения их пригодности для ускорения адсорбции ксантогената на галените и одновременного диспергирования кварца.

Абсорбция ксантогената на галените становится особо значительной при добавке аминокислоты в таком количестве и особенно в таком пределе pH, при котором аминокислота находится в воде в виде дипольного иона. Электрофоретические измерения мобильности с употреблением кварцового шлама показали, что существуют оптимальные пределы pH (5-9), в которых частицы кварца заряжены более отрицательно при добавке аминокислоты, чем без нее.

Оптыты по флотации для самого галенита и для смеси галенита с кварцевым шламом подтвердили, что соответствующее введение аминокислоты в процесс флотации сульфидной руды может повысить роль кислоты как активатора адсорбции ксантогената на сульфидном минерале и одновременно диспергирующего вещества для шлама.

SELECTIVE FLOTATION OF MOLYBDENITE: DEPRESSION MECHANISMS OF CHALCOCITE WITH SODIUM SULPHIDE, ANAMOL – D AND NOKES REAGENT

S. Castro

Departamento de Ingenieria Metalurgica, Universidad de Concepción, Concepción, Chile

INTRODUCTION

Most of the available molibdenum in the world is obtained as a by-product from porphyry copper ores. It is recovered as molybdenite (MoS_2) in grades ranging from 0.01 to 0.06% and generally associated with chalcocitic and chalcopyritic mineralizations [1].

Due to its natural hydrophobicity and its capacity to react with thiol-collectors, molybdenite is recovered together with copper in rougher circuits. The primary Cu-Mo concentrate contains between 0.2 and 1.0% Mo and 20 to 42% Cu.

The separation of molybdenite from this concentrate is performed by selective flotation employing specific depressants for Cu and Fe sulphides. The most commonly used depressants are:

Sodium sulphide and hydrosulphide,
Anamol-D or Arsenic Nokes (As_2O_3 dissolved in Na_2S),
Nokes Reagent (P_2S_5 dissolved in NaOH),
Sodium Cyanide,
Potassium ferro and ferricyanide.

181

The top three reagents are successfully employed in two thirds of the world's porphyric copper operations.

Since chalcocite   and   chalcopyrite are the most important minerals in the porphyric copper ores, various authors have studied the reaction mechanism of chalcocite with alkyl xanthates [2, 3]. In addition, the formation of dixanthogen and dithiophosphatedisulphide by means of electrocatalytic mechanisms has been the subject of special attention [4, 5, 6]. Conversely, not much has been written about the depression mechanisms of chalcocite with the above reagents [7]. Although the influence of sodium sulphide on the desorption of xanthate and the redox potential of the solution has been studied to some extent [8, 9, 10], the depression mechanisms of the Nokes reagents are still unknown.

The present investigation attempts to clarify some chemical and physico-chemical aspects involved in the depression mechanism of chalcocite with such reagents.

EXPERIMENTAL

Material and Reagents

A sample of natural chalcocite was obtained from the Chuquicamata Mine in northern Chile. The lumps were hand-sorted and ground dry in a porcelain laboratory mill. Particles of size -65   to +200 mesh were used throughout. The sample assayed 72.90% Cu, 9.25% Fe and 21.20% S. Microscopic observation revealed a very pure chalcocite sample with traces of pyrite and chalcopyrite.

A commercial sample of potassium isopropyl xanthate was purified by recrystalization from acetone and precipitation with ethyl ether.

The sodium sulphide solutions were prepared with chemical grade $Na_2S.9H_2O$ and always used within 8 h of preparation.

All other reagents (As_2O_3, P_2S_5, etc.) were Analar Grade. The pH was adjusted with either HCl or NaOH. Distilled water was used throughout the investigation.

Techniques

Since natural chalcocite is usually superficially oxidized, each sample underwent a sulphidization treatment before the experiments. Sulphidization was performed for 5 min at pH 8 on 1 g samples with 100 ml containing 500 mg/l Na_2S x $9H_2O$. After decanting, the supernatant was discarded and the residue washed repeatedly with distilled water.

Flotation tests were carried out with 1 g of sulphidized chalcocite in a 100 ml Hallimond tube, modified with a fritted glass plate. The suspension was conditioned for 5 min at pH 11 with 25 mg/l of isopropyl xanthate as collector and with 8.5 mg/l of amyl alcohol as frother. The suspension was then transferred to the cell and floated for 1 min with a constant flow of nitrogen of 40 ml/min.

The xanthate adsorption measurements were performed under the same conditions as the flotation tests. The concentration of xanthate in solution was determined from an absorbance reading at 301 nm on a Carl Zeiss model PMQII spectrophotometer.

The Eh measurements were always conducted under conditions similar to those for flotation. A platinum plate electrode, 1 cm^2 in area, was used and the reading was referred to the saturated calomel electrode. To avoid pollution the electrode was purified after each experiment, with aqua regia, followed by washing in boiling distilled water.

The mineral electrode potentials were measured using a natural chalcocite crystal as the electrode. A cut chalcocite sample was attached to the end of a glass tube with an epoxicement, contact being made with a droplet of mercury inside the glass tube. Physical polishing of the electrode surface between runs was performed using alumina. Potentials were measured by means of a Corning model 7 potentiometer.

The concentration of sulphide ions in solution was determined by using the colorimetric method described previously [11].

RESULTS

Effect of Na$_2$S. The recovery of chalcocite and the adsorption of isopropyl xanthate as a function of Na$_2$S.9H$_2$O concentration are shown in Fig. 1. This shows that recovery decreases to 65% and the adsorption density to 60% with such low concentrations as 1 mg/l sodium sulphide and contact time of 5 min. The depression and desorption are almost complete for higher concentrations. Both the depression and desorption are transient effects. The kinetics of the depression of chalcocite at different Na$_2$S concentrations was studied by measuring the potential of a chalcocite electrode. As can be seen in Fig. 2 there are two regions, one corresponding to a conditioning period followed by that corresponding to a de-

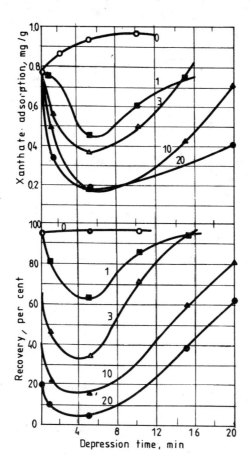

Fig. 1. Adsorption of isopropyl xanthate and chalcocite recovery as a function of   depression time, with
different sodium concentrations at pH 9.5. The
numbers placed on curves denoted Na_2S concentrations
expressed in mg/l.

pression period. This second period starts with the addition of
the Na_2S solutions to the system. A sharp drop in the potential
of the mineral electrode is observed in the presence of Na_2S.
For example, at 100 mg/l of Na_2S the potential abruptly changes
from -40 to -400 mV in 1 min.

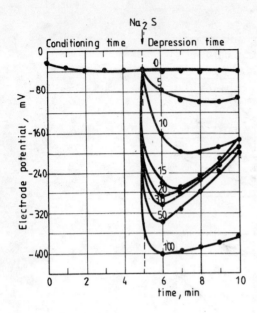

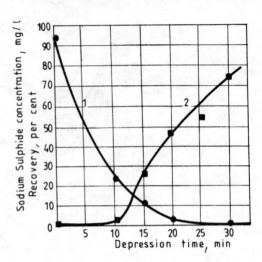

Fig. 2. Chalcocite electrode
potential as a func-
tion of depression
time, for different
additions of Na₂S at
9.5. The numbers on
the curves denote
Na₂S concentration
expressed in mg/l.

Fig. 3. Chalcocite recovery and
kinetics of sodium sul-
phide uptake by the mi-
neral, at pH 9.5.
Curve 1: Sodium sulphide
concentration. Curve 2:
Flotation recovery.

Figure 3 demonstrates the rate of consumption of the HS⁻ and
S²⁻ ions and influence of this on the recovery of chalcocite. The
concentration of Na₂S decreases from about 93 mg/l to 10 mg/l in
the 15 min before chalcocite begins to reactivate.

Figure 4 shows the recovery, the concentration of residual
sulphide, the potential of the mineral electrode and the redox
potential of the solution as a function of the initial concentration of Na₂S. Depression of chalcocite is obtained with Na₂S concentrations higher than 6 mg/l and with a moderately reducing Eh

186

(between + 120 and -35 mV). Under these conditions the electrode
potential of chalcocite varies from -40 to -250 mV.

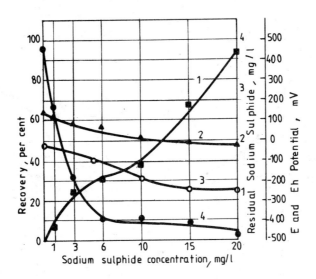

Fig. 4. Effect of sodium sulphide concentration on chalcocite
flotation, redox potential and residual sodium sulphide concentration, at pH 9.5. The potential E and Eh
were measured 3 min after the addition of the
depressant. Curve 1: Residual sodium sulphide. Curve 2:
Redox potential (Eh). Curve 3: Potential of the chalcocite electrode. Curve 4: Flotation recovery.

Effect of As_2O_3 Dissolved in Na_2S. Figure 5 indicates that the
As_2O_3 addition to the Na_2S solution reinforces its depressing
action on chalcocite. The recovery of chalcocite after depression
with 3 mg/l Na_2S is about 85%, whereas the combined effect of
3 mg/l Na_2S and 1.5 mg/l As_2O_3 reduced the recovery to only 25%.

The reactivation behaviour of chalcocite is much slower for
the combined solutions of Na_2S and As_2O_3 than for a simple Na_2S
solution. Figure 6 shows a significant difference in the

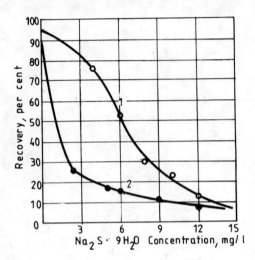

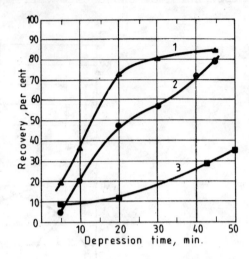

Fig. 5. Influence of arsenic trioxide on the
depression of chalco-
cite with sodium sul-
phide, at pH 9. Curve
1: Sodium sulphide.
Curve 2: Sodium sul-
phide plus 1.5 mg/l
As_2O_3.

Fig. 6. The reactivation of chalcocite as a function of
the depression time for
Na_2S and Na_2S-As_2O_3 solutions, at pH 10.5, IsopX
30 mg/l. Curve 1: Na_2S,
9.75 mg/l; Curve 2: Na_2S,
3.90 mg/l; Curve 3: 3.90
mg/l Na_2S plus 0.90 mg/l
As_2O_3.

floatability of chalcocite after 50 min depressing time with a
simple Na_2S solution and As_2O_3-Na_2S solution.

The effect of the Na_2S-As_2O_3 mixture on Eh, recovery and xanthate
adsorption is shown in Fig. 7. Eh drops to +70 and even lower to
-20 mV when the Na_2S-As_2O_3 mixture is applied in concentrations
of 1 and 2 mg/l, respectively. Similarly, the xanthate adsorption
density and the recovery of chalcocite markedly decrease with
depressor concentration.

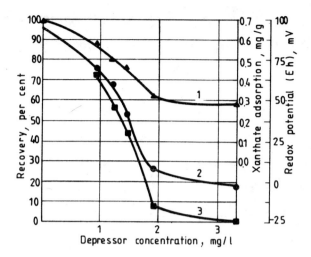

Fig. 7. Depression of chalcocite as a function of $Na_2S-As_2O_3$ concentration in solution, at pH 11. Curve 1: Xanthate adsorption. Curve 2: Flotation recovery. Curve 3: Redox potential.

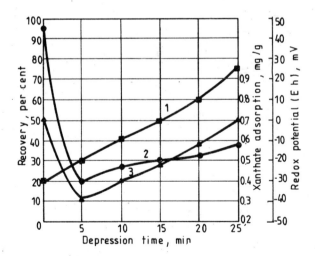

Fig. 8. Effect of   depression time on the flotation of chalcocite with 2.9 mg/l of Arsenic Nokes Reagent, at pH 11. Curve 1: Redox potential. Curve 2: Flotation recovery. Curve 3: Xanthate adsorption.

Figure 8 shows that although the readsorption of xanthate in the presence of the As_2O_3-Na_2S mixture is complete after 25 min, the floatability of chalcocite is not completely re-stored.

Effect of P_2S_5 Dissolved in NaOH. Figure 9 shows the effect of the Nokes Reagent (1.3 $NaOH/P_2S_5$ ratio) concentration expressed in mg/l of P_2S_5. Here an effective depressing action and a strong desorbing effect are observed. This behaviour is similar to that of Arsenic Nokes Reagent.

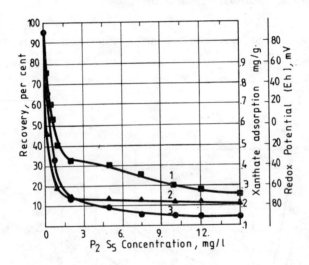

Fig. 9. Influence of the Nokes Reagent concentration, expressed as mg/l of P_2S_5, on the flotation of chalcocite,
at pH 11. Curve 1: Flotation recovery. Curve 2: Xanthate adsorption. Curve 3: Redox potential.

Chemical Study of the Nokes Reagent. Figure 10 shows the percentage of the sodium sulphide remaining after the reaction with arsenic trioxide. The addition of 20% of As_2O_3 to a sodium sulphide solution of 14.5 mg/l demonstrated that only 26.5% of this initial concentration was consumed by the arsenic trioxide.

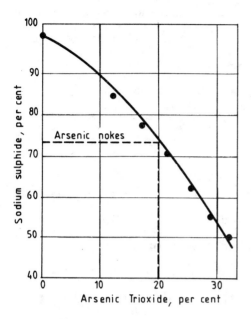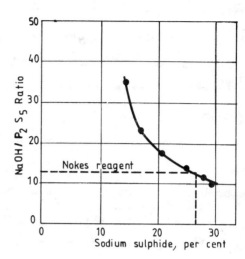

Fig. 10. Percentage of Na_2S remaining in solution as a function of the per cent of arsenic trioxide used in the preparation of the Anamol-D Reagent.

Fig. 11. Percentage of Na_2S formed in the reaction between P_2S_5 and NaOH as a function of the NaOH/P_2S_5 weight ratio.

In Fig. 11 the amount of sodium sulphide formed by the reaction between phosphorus pentasulphide and sodium hydroxide is presented for different NaOH/P_2S_5 weight ratios. These results clearly show that the Nokes Reagent (1.3 NaOH to P_2S_5 weight ratio) contains 27% of sodium sulphide.

Depression Mechanisms

Sodium Sulphide. The HS^- and S^{2-} ions resulting from the alkaline hydrolysis of $Na_2S.9H_2O$ solutions react with heavy metals to produce low solubility compounds. In addition, these ions are unstable in aerated aqueous solutions since they are easily oxidized to S^o, $S_2O_3^{2-}$, SO_3^{2-}, and SO_4^{2-} ions. These two chemical characteristics of sulphide ions must be considered in flotation systems.

The desorption of xanthate from the chalcocite surface can be explained by a chemical displacement mechanism. The sulphide ions chemisorb on the mineral surface forming a film of copper sulphide and releasing xanthate ions into the solution. The solubility product Kps, and the activity of the sulphide ions in solution govern this reaction. Thus, when the sodium sulphide concentration decreases to a critical level, the inverse reaction is favoured, namely the formation of copper (I) xanthate. Since the surface properties of chalcocite are not modified by the chemisorption of the sulphide ions, floatability behaviour can be restored.

It is well known that under strongly reducing conditions dixanthogen cannot be formed [12, 13] . Consequently, the increase of Eh with time and the reactivation of chalcocite, as shown in Fig. 4, suggest that at the end of the depressing stage, the collector coating includes both cuprous xanthate and dixanthogen.

On the other hand, the high consumption rate of HS^- ions on chalcocite is due principally to its catalytic oxidation activity [11, 14, 15]. In this way a large amount of sodium sulphide is oxidized to thiosulphate, sulphite and sulphate ions in aerated flotation pulps. This instability of sodium sulphide presents a serious problem in the selective flotation of molybdenite. Stepwise addition and rigorous control of the depressant concentration are recommended to avoid the reactivation of copper sulphide minerals.

Arsenic Nokes Reagent. The chemical factors involved in the reaction between arsenic trioxide and sodium sulphide are still not well understood. Preis et al. [16] have reported that sodium arseniate, monothioarseniate and arsenic are the principal reaction products. It can be seen that the reaction mechanism is complex and a number of arsenic-sulphur species could be formed. The reaction appears to be proceeded by the formation of either mono-, di- or trithioarseniate (III), according to the following equations:

$$As_2O_3 + 6Na_2S + 3H_2O \rightleftharpoons 2Na_3AsS_3 + 6NaOH \tag{1}$$
$$As_2O_3 + 4Na_2S + H_2O \rightleftharpoons 2Na_3AsOS_2 + 2NaOH \tag{2}$$
$$As_2O_3 + 3Na_2S + H_2O \rightleftharpoons 2Na_3AsO_2S + H_2S_{(g)} \tag{3}$$

It is interesting to note that hydrogen sulphide would be formed along with monothioarseniate.

The oxidation of these compounds into thioarseniate (V) species could proceed by a redox mechanism with the formation of arsenic, but this does not exclude the possibility that the dissolved oxygen could also play a determining role. For example, the following reaction could occur:

$$Na_3AsO_2S + 1/2O_2 \rightleftharpoons Na_3AsO_3S \tag{4}$$

Similarly other thioanions of As(V) could be produced.

It should be noted that the reactions discussed above proceed in the presence of an excess of sodium sulphide. However, NaHS can also be formed by the chemical decomposition of thioarseniate (III) or (V) ions in alkaline solutions, in accordance with the following reactions:

$$Na_3AsS_4 + NaOH \rightleftharpoons Na_3AsOS_3 + NaHS \qquad (5)$$

$$Na_3AsOS_3 + NaOH \rightleftharpoons Na_3AsO_2S_2 + NaHS \qquad (6)$$

$$Na_3AsO_2S_2 + NaOH \rightleftharpoons Na_3AsO_3S + NaHS \qquad (7)$$

$$Na_3AsO_3S + NaOH \rightleftharpoons Na_3AsO_4 + NaHS \qquad (8)$$

A similar mechanism might be valid for the thioarseniate (III) species.

Consequently, the Arsenic Nokes Reagent is expected to contain a mixture of arsenical thioanions and sodium hydrosulphide. In order to understand the processes occurring in the system, the kinetics and thermodynamics of the reactions involved need to be considered.

As has been shown the stoichiometry of the overall reaction indicates that for each mol of arsenic trioxide 2.7 moles of sodium sulphide are consumed. This can not be fully interpreted in terms of a single reaction alone. In addition, the chemical nature of the arsenical thioanions needs to be further investigated.

In consequence, a definite mechanism cannot be postulated. The following equations show some ways in which the above reactions might be explained:

$$As_2O_3 + 3Na_2S + H_2O + 1/2\ O_2 \rightleftharpoons$$
$$\rightleftharpoons Na_3AsO_2S_2 + Na_3AsO_3S + 2OH^- \qquad (9)$$

$$As_2O_3 + 3Na_2S + H_2O + 1/2\ O_2 \rightleftharpoons$$
$$\rightleftharpoons Na_3AsO_4 + Na_3AsOS_3 + 2OH^- \qquad (10)$$

However, there is no way of detecting which one is the preferred reaction.

The question arises as to how each of these species contributes to the depression of the flotation of chalcocite.

It was found experimentally that the Anamol-D Reagent, prepared with 20% arsenic trioxide, contained 60% Na_2S. The additional 40% would correspond mainly to arsenic-sulphur species. These thioanions are advantageous since they reinforce and prolong the depressing action of sodium sulphide and the readsorption of xanthate does not make the surface of chalcocite hydrophobic. Apparently they follow a different mechanism which involves a surface reaction. The surface properties of chalcocite are modified by the formation of copper thioarseniates at the surface. Quite stable compounds of this type, like enargite (Cu_3AsS_4), are found in nature. After the chemisorption of these thioanions the surface becomes hydrophylic and floatability is rendered more difficult.

The other possibility for the greater effectiveness of the Arsenic Nokes Reagent is that the thioarseniate ions act as a reservoir for the sulphide ions. In fact, this limits the rate of the catalytic oxidation of the sulphide ions and prolongs its effectiveness.

Nokes Reagent. The chemical reaction that takes place between P_2S_5 and concentrated NaOH is strongly exothermic and releases hydrogen sulphide which in alkaline medium gives rise to sulphide and hydrosulphide ions. At the same time, phosphorus derivatives of the thiophosphate type are produced. Klement [17] and Kubierschky [18] have reported that mono and dithiophosphate form.

It is expected that the alkaline hydrolysis of phosphorus pentasulphide will result only in thiophosphates (V) according to the following reactions:

$$P_2S_5 + 6NaOH \rightleftharpoons Na_3PS_4 + Na_3PO_3S + 3H_2O \qquad (11)$$

$$P_2S_5 + 6NaOH \rightleftharpoons Na_3PO_2S_2 + Na_3POS_3 + 3H_2O \qquad (12)$$

The stoichiometry of these reactions are in agreement with sample two of the original Nokes Patent [19], which indicates that a reagent prepared with 13 g (0.325 moles) of sodium hydroxide and 10 g (0.045 moles) of phosphorus pentasulphide, has a 7.2 $NaOH/P_2S_5$ molar ratio. It can be seen according to the above reactions that thiophosphates would form in an excess of sodium hydroxide. Under these conditions a decomposition in aqueous solution similar to that of thioarseniates would occur. For example, tetrathiophosphate would give rise to trithiophosphate in an alkaline solution:

$$Na_3PS_4 + NaOH \rightleftharpoons Na_3PS_3O + NaHS \qquad (13)$$

Similarly, di and mono-thiophosphate and sodium orthophosphate can be formed by the same mechanism, releasing in each step one mol of NaHS per mole of decomposing thiophosphate. In addition, reports have shown that after 1 h of reaction most of the phosphorus in the solution occurs as thioanions [20].

On the other hand, it was pointed out in the previous section that for a 1.3 NaOH/P_2S_5 weight ratio, only 27% of the reagent corresponds to sodium sulphide. This concentration is the result of the simultaneous equilibria of all the above reactions.

The mechanisms already analyzed above and concerning the depressing action of sodium sulphide are also applicable to the Nokes Reagent.

The deleterious effect of thiophosphates on chalcocite flotation can be ascribed to a surface reaction of these compounds with the cupric sites, analogous to that in the case of thioarseniate. The differing stability of aqueous solutions of thioanions and sulphide ions can also play a role in the depressing mechanism.

Finally, it is clear from this work that both Anamol-D Reagent and Nokes Reagent contain sodium sulphide and arsenic or phosphorus thioanions. In addition, it was shown that the role of these thioanions is to reinforce the depressing action of sodium sulphide.

REFERENCES

1. Sutulov A. Flotation Recovery of Molybdenite. In: 16th Annual Conference of the Metallurgist, Vancouver, Canada, August 1977.
2. Gaudin A. M. and Schuhmann R. J. Phys. Chem., 40, 257 (1936).
3. Paterson J. G. and Salman T. Trans. Canadian Min. Metall. Bull., 1 (1968).

4. Chander S. and Fuerstenan D. W. On the Floatability of Sulphide Minerals with Thiol Collectors: The Chalcocite/Diethyldithiophosphate System. In: Proc. XI International Mineral Processing Congress, Universitè di Cagliari, Cagliari, 1975, 583.

5. Kowal A. and Pomianowski A. Electroanalytical Chemistry and Interfacial Electrochemistry, 46, 411 (1973).

6. Allison S. A., Goold L. A., Nicol M. J. and Granville A. Metal. Trans., 3, 2613 (1972).

7. Castro S. Flotation of Molybdenite. In: International Molybdenum Encyclopaedia (Ed. A. Sutulov) Vol. 2, Santiago, Chile, 1979 (in press).

8. Castro S. Selective Flotation of Molybdenite from Copper Porphyric/ores. In: Investigaciones Mineras y Metalúrgicas (Ed. A. Stulov) CIMM-1976, Santiago, Chile, 1977, 94. (Spanish text).

9. Tsvetkov I. T. et al. Tsvet Metal., 10, 66 (1973) (Russian Text).

10. Frolov, Yu. M. et al. Tsvet Metal., 3, 78 (1973) (Russian text).

11. Castro S., Goldfarb J. and Laskowski J. Int. J. Miner. Process, 1, 141 (1974).

12. Abramov A. A. Tsvet. Metal., 3, 21 (1967).

13. Tolun R. and Kitchener J. A. Trans. Inst. Min. Met., 73, 313 (1963).

14. Tuwiner S. B. and Korman S. Min. Engineering. Trans. AIME, 187, 226 (1950).

15. Golikov A. A. and Shokolova V. J. Tsvet. Metal., (1972), (Intern. Bull. 4, 1, 1972).

16. Preis K. Lieb. Ann. 257, 1890, 178/203 (Gmelins Handbuch der Anorganichen Chemic No. 17, Arsen. 1965, 459).

17. Klement R. Z. Anorg. Ch. 253, 1947, 237/48, 238, 244. (Gmelins Handbuch der Anorganischen Chemic, Phosphor No. 16, 1965, 580).

18. Kubierschky C. J. pr. Ch. (2), 31, 1885, 93/111,97, 101. (Gmelins Handbuch der Anorganischen Chemic. Phosphor No. 16, 1965, 580).

19. Nokes Ch. Differential froth flotation of sulphide ores. United States Patent, No. 2, 492, 936, 1949.

20. Nickless G., Pollard F. H. and Rogers D. E. J. Chem. Soc., 11, 1721 (1967).

ABSTRACT

The depressant effect of sodium sulphide, Anamol-D (Arsenic Nokes Reagent) and Nokes Reagent on chalcocite was investigated experimentally through measurement of xanthate adsorption density, hydrosulphide uptake kinetics, redox potential of the solution (Eh), potential of chalcocite mineral electrode (E) and Hallimond tube flotation tests. These studies indicate that depression with sodium sulphide is a transient effect. As the HS^- and S^{2-} ions disappear from the solution, readsorption of isopropyl xanthate and reactivation of the mineral takes place.

It was found that the addition of 5 to 20% arsenic trioxide reinforces and prolongs the depressing action of sodium sulphide. In the presence of As_2O_3 the readsorption of xanthate does not make the surface hydrophobic. Similar conclusions were obtained for the Nokes Reagent. These results suggest that the detrimental effect of arsenic and phosphorus thioanions on chalcocite flotation involves a surface reaction.

Chemical studies demonstrated that the Anamol-D Reagent contains 60% Na_2S and that arsenic is present in it as a thioarseniate type species. These studies also showed that the Nokes Reagent contains 27% Na_2S mixed with thiophosphates.

RÉSUMÉ

L'effet depressif du sulfure de sodium, Anamol-D (Réactif Nokes Arsenic) et Réactif Nokes sur la chalcocite. A été etudié experimentallement en measurant: densité d'adsorption du xanthate, cinétique de consommation de hydrosulfure, potential redox de la solution (Eh), tension d'une electrode mineral de chalcocite (e) et en effectuant tests de flotation dans des tubes Hallimond. Cette étude indique que la dépression avec sulfure de sodium est transitoire. Dans la mesure que les ions HS^- et S^{2-} disparessent de la solution, une readsorption du isopropil xanthate une reactivation du mineral prendre place.

Il a été trouvé que l'addition de 5 a 20% de trioxyde d' arsenic reforce et prolonge l'action dépressive du sulfure de

sodium. Dans la presence de As_2O_3 la readsorption du xanthate
ne rendre pas la surface hydrophobique. Conclusions semblables
ont été obtenués pour le Reactif Nokes. Ces resultats suggérent
que l'éffect nuisible des thioanions d'arsenic et phosphore sur
la flotation de la chalcocite impliquent une reaction de surface.

Etudes chimiques ont demontré que le réactif Anamol-D contient 60% de Na_2S et que l'arsenic est present sous la forme des
especes du type thioarseniate. A été également demontré que le
reactif Nokes contient 27% de Na_2S melangé avec des thiophosphates.

ZUSAMMENFASSUNG

Der depressive Effekt von Natriumsulfid, Anamol-D (Arsen
Nokes Reagenz) und Nokes Reagenz auf Chalcosit (Kupferglanz Cu_2S)
wurde experimentell untersucht. Es wurden die Dichte der Xanthat-
adsortion, die Kinetik der Hydrosulfidaufnahme, das Redoxpoten-
tial der Losung (Eh), das Potential der Chalcositelektrode (E)
und der Hallimondflotationstest untersucht.

Die Ergebnisse lassen auf einen vorubergehenden Ubergangs-
effekt der Natriumsulfiddepression schilessen. Mit der Abnahme
der HS^- und S^{2-} Ioen findent eine Readsortion von Isopropylxan-
that und die Reaktivierung des Minerals statt. Die Zugabe von 5
bis 20% Arsentrioxyd verstarkt und verlangert die depressive
Wirkung von Natriumsulfyd. In Gegenwart von As_2O_3 wird die
Oberflache durch das Xanthat nicht mehr hydrophob. Gleiche
Ergebnisse wurden mit dem Nokes Reagenz erhalten.

Diese Ergebnisse weisen darufhin, dass der negative Effekt
der Arsen und Phosphorthiosalze auf die Chalcositflotation mit
einer Oberflachenreaktion verbuden ist.

Nach den durgefuhrten Untersuchungen enthalt das Anamol-D
Reagenz 60% Na_2S und Arsen als Thioarseniatetverbindungen und
das Nokes-Reagenz 27% Na_2S und Thiophosphate.

РЕЗЮМЕ

Исследовано депрессирующее влияние сульфида натрия, Анамола-Д (мышьяковистый реагент Нокеса), и реагента Нокеса на халькозин путем измерения адсорбции ксантогената, кинетики поглощения гидросульфида, окислительно-восстановительного потенциала раствора (E_h), потенциала халькозинового электрода (E) и проведением опытной флотации в аппарате Халлимонда. Измерения показали, что депрессирующее действие сульфида натрия имеет затухающий характер. В моменте исчезновения в растворе ионов HS^- и S^{2-} наблюдается реадсорбция изопропилового ксантогената и реакцивация минералов.

Установлено, что 5 – 20% добавка трехокиси мышьяка усиливает и продлевает депрессирующее действие сульфида натрия. В присутствии As_2O_3 реадсорбция ксантогената не вызывает гидрофобизации поверхности. Похожие результаты получены с реагентом Нокеса. Эти результаты убеждают, что вредное действие тиоанионов мышьяка и фосфора на флотацию халькозина основано на поверхностной реакции. Химические исследования показали, что реагент Анамол-Д содержит 60% Na_2S и что мышьяк выступает в этом реагенте в форме соединений типа тиоарсенатов. Кроме того, установлено, что реагент Нокеса содержит 27% Na_2S смешанного с тиофосфатами.

DISCUSSION

PAPER 4

T. P. MELOY (West Virginia University, Morgantown, USA)

Your electrostatic model of the distortion of the bubble particle flow field is excellent. I believe that in real flotation systems the bubble is rapidly and drastically being distorted by the turbulence in the cell and this distortion is one or two orders of magnitude greater in terms of velocity than the relative velocity of the bubble-particle. This in turn means new surface areas rapidly being created and destroyed. What can we learn from your experiments that apply to this model of flotation?

L. J. WARREN (CSIRO Division of Mineral Chemistry, Port Melbourne, Australia)

(1) What is the physical meaning of the hydrodynamic capture efficiency E as definied by Eq. (8). Is it, for example, an average for all initial particle-bubble orientations? Does it represent the average proportion of all possible rectilinial encounters which result in capture?

(2) The capture efficiency E varies with the initial orientation of particle and bubble. Does the range in measured E values from 0.1 to 0.7 result in different initial orientations and if not then what gives rise to the variation in values?

A. BAHR (Institut für Aufbereitung, TU Claustal/Zellerfeld, Federal Republic of Germany)

The authors on the basis of their own experiments have concluded that favourable experimental conditions necessitate
small air bubbles and the lowest possible flow rates. This does
not accord with the results of our experiments which were
carried out with the use of a pneumatic flotation cell under
the following conditions: capacity 100 m^3/h, bubble size 0.2-
1.5 mm and rate of flow up to 28 m/s.

Very good flotation results were obtained with small air
bubbles as well. The direction of air bubble motion is perpendicular to the direction of flow of the flotation pulp. Conditions in the flotation cell differ from those of Drs. Schulze
and Gottschalk. Do the authors think that these contradictory
results may be explained by the different boundary layer states
at the gas/liquid interface under their experimental condition?

PAPER 5

S. T. POLKIN (Institute of Steel and Alloys, Moscow, USSR)

There is no sense in separating cassiterite from quartz
because these minerals are easily separated by gravitation and
flotation. The most difficult task is to separate cassiterite
from ferric oxides hydroxides, from turmaline and other dark
coloured minerals (ilmenite, ilmenorutile and others). Is it
possible to use alkylpolyoxiethylene in this case?

Which reagent conditions do you recommend for the cassiterite flotation of industrial ore?

V. G. KOTLAROV (Central Research Institute of the Tin Industry, Novosibirsk, USSR)

Research trends in the interaction of non-ionic surface-active agents (of the alkyl-polyoxyethylene type) with certain known collectors, e.g., sulpho-succinic acid seem promising. Results on quartz and cassiterite separation are rather good. However, it seems to us that it is impossible to draw final conclusions at this stage. The research material is very simple in composition (quartz, cassiterite) and tin content is very high (1%). Unfortunately, the authors did not show the possibility of separating cassiterite from common accompanying minerals such as turmaline and chlorite. We suggest that the authors pursue these trends in their research.

L. J. WARREN (CSIRO Division of Mineral Chemistry, Port Melbourne, Australia)

(1) The reagent "OPEG" or Triton X-100 is sometimes used as a dispersant, and presumably acts then as a hydrophilic surfactant. Dr Van Lierde did not give any suggestions for the mechanism by which OPEG increased the flotation recovery of both cassiterite and quartz, even in the absence of Aeropromotor 840.

(2) In practice, is the activation of cassiterite by OPEG sufficiently greater than the activation of quartz to make selective separation of cassiterite from ores possible?

J. H. PIEPER (Billiton Research, Arnhem, The Netherlands)

In this contribution, cassiterite is floated with a rather wide size range, viz. 80% minus 200 mesh and deslimed at -10 µm. However, it is common practice to float cassiterite of a much finer size range, say, of less than 40 µm, above which size it is rather hard to float. I wonder if you can tell us something about the flotation response of your test material in the coarser size range?

PAPER 6

M. C. FUERSTENAU (South Dakota School of Mines, Rapid City, USA)

I am especially interested in the authors' work with unactivated sphalerite. In this work, they did not observe any adsorption of ethyl xanthate on this mineral with xanthate concentrations of 10^{-4} to 10^{-3} mole/l in slightly acid and slightly basic media.

We have found sphalerite to respond to flotation at pH 3.5 with ethyl xanthate although high concentrations (greater than 10^{-2} mole/l) are required.

It would be important to the understanding of sphalerite flotation if the authors would extend their study of this system with higher xanthate concentration and lower values of pH.

A. A. ABRAMOV (Institute of Steel and Alloys, Moscow, USSR)

The method certainly opens up new possibilities in experimental studies on the mechanism of reagent action during flotation. This has been confirmed by the results of the application of an analogous method in the U.S.S.R. (Mekhanobr Institute). The strong influence of the specimen on the properties of its surface compounds is a drawback of the method.

Both the germanium underlayer and the layers of lead, copper or zinc sulphides on top of it are typical semiconductors. That is why the results obtained should be considered as the consequence of contact between two semiconductors and not as evidence of the particular properties of every single sulphide. The results presented should be considered with the above facts in mind.

Certain unusual properties and deviation from the known data on the composition of sorption layers of the collector on the mineral surface can be explained if the interrelationships between the electrochemical characteristics of the germanium underlayer and the sulphide minerals are considered.

P. M. SOLOZHENKIN (Inst. of Chemistry, Academy of Sciences of Tadzkikskaya S.S.R., Dushanbe, U.S.S.R.)

It was with great pleasure we followed the paper presented by professor Pomianowski and his co-authors.

The products of sorption of ethyl xanthate on the surface of sulphide minerals were examined in this work by IR-ATR spectrophotometry. I would like to ask our colleagues from Poland whether they found the basic lead and copper xanthates in alkaline solutions (pH 8.0-10.3). We would also like to know if our colleagues have conducted any investigations on the definition of the spectrochemical parameters characterizing the donor-acceptor properties of xanthate.

We would like to add some data to the excellent report of our Polish Colleagues on dithiophosphates. In the application of absorption spectra the d-d transitions in the visible range are most interesting. The distance between energetic levels characterizes the ligand field intensity and determined Δ , the crystal field parameter. With an increase in Δ , ligands displace in a spectrochemical series.

A comparison of the absorption spectra of metal complexes with dithiophosphate derivatives shows that the removal of hydrogen atoms from the reagent molecules causes bathochromic displacement of the maxima in the absorption spectra [1].

In spectrochemical series dithiophosphate ions are placed after dithiophosphinates regardless of metal   type. Table 1 shows that Δ values for dithiophosphates exceed 500-1500 cm^{-1}, that for dithiophosphinates. This change of Δ value might be explained by the strengthening of the π -donor properties of the ligand with the removal of a hydrogen atom from the molecule. The greater the π -donor ability of the ligand, the lower the value of Δ [2]. K. B. Yacimirski shows that the

TABLE 1

Spectrochemical Parameters Δ (cm^{-1}) and β for the Complexes of Metals with Sulphur-Bearing Phosphoorganic Ligands

Me	$(C_2H_5O)_2PS_2^-$		$CH_3(C_2H_5O)PS_2^-$		$(C_2H_5)_2PS_2^-$	
	Δ	β	Δ	β	Δ	β
Rh^{III}	21,900	0.29	21,400	0.29	20,450	0.29
Ir^{III}	26,700	0.24	25,900	0.21	24,740	0.24
Cr^{III}	14,400	0.47			13,700	0.48
Co^{III}	14,200	0.36-0.34			13,370	0.33

π-antibonding effect Δ_π in the case of π-donor molecules is 7000 cm^{-1} for chromium diethyldithiophosphate, 7500 cm^{-1} for diethyldithiophoshinate and 5000 cm^{-1} for chromium (III) ethyl-xanthate [3]. Appreciable electron transfer from ligand to metal in dithiophoshinates as compared to dithiophosphates is confirmed by the redox potential E_o. The reducing ability of the ligand is characterized by the redox potential of the system ligand - oxidized ligand. The value of E_o is 0.255 V for the diethyldithiophosphate ion and 0.174 for ethyl-ethyldithiophosponate.

On the other hand an increase in the Δ value on introducing an oxygen atom into a ligand molecule can be caused by the strengthening of the accepting properties of ligand. This hypothesis is in agreement with the EPR results. The coefficient of the hyperfine interaction of an unpaired copper atom electron with the nuclear magnetic moments of phosphorus atoms increases from 5.5 eV in copper dialkyldithiophosphinate to 9.5 eV in copper dialkyldithiophosphate [4].

B. P. Toropova has mentioned [5] that the increase in the stability of metal dithiophosphinates compared with that of dithiophosphates can be correlated with the increase in the reduction ability of the dithiophosphate ion.

We have established that the removal of the oxygen atom from the reagent molecule sharply reduces the magnitude of the solubility product of the complex [6].

For metal complexes with phosphorus dithioacid derivatives with a parallel bathochromic shift in the absorption bands, an increase in the stability of the compounds is observed (an increase in the stability constant and a decrease in solubility).

The absorption spectra make it possible to calculate the
Racah B parameter which characterizes interaction in the complex. The value B for a free ion is always higher than for the
same ion in the complex. A reduction in the B parameter reflexes
the reduction of mutual electron repulsion resulting from the
formation of molecular orbitals. By putting β = B complex/B
free ions it is possible to place ligands in the nepheloauxetic
series according to the value of the β parameter, and this
reflects the ability of ligands to draw electrons from the
metal.

The position of phosphorus dithioacids in a nepheloauxetic
series is not so rigid as in the spectrochemical series. A very
small difference in the β values for the sulphur-bearing
ligands does not make it possible to draw strict conclusions
concerning the change in the co-valent component of the bond.

The very low values of β as shown in Table 2 indicate a
high co-valent component in the metal - sulphur bond.

TABLE 2

Solubility Products of Metal Diethyldithiophosphates and
Dithiophosphinates

Reagent \ Metal	Ag^I	Cd	Pb	Cu^I
Diethyldithiophosphate	1.1×10^{-16}	1.2×10^{-10}	7.5×10^{-12}	1.1×10^{-16}
Diethyldithiophosphinate	3×10^{-18}	8×10^{-13}	9×10^{-14}	5×10^{-18}

REFERENCES

1. Solozhenkin P. M., Usova S. and Grishina O. N. Zh. Inorg. Chem., 20, 2737-2742 (1975).

2. Jørgersen C. K. I. Inorg. Nucl. Chem., 24, 1571 (1962).

3. Yacimirskij K. B. Theoret. Eksp. Chem., 4, 728 (1968).

4. Toropova V. R., Cherkacov R. A. and Saveleva N. I. Zh. Org. Chem., 40, 1043 (1970).

5. Kakovskij I. A., Solozhenkin P. M. and Usova S. V. Zh. Inorg. Chem., 22, 3067 (1977).

PAPER 7

P. M. SOLOZHENKIN and S. USOVA (Institute of Chemistry, Academy of Sciences of Tadzhikskaya S.S.R., Dushanbe, U.S.S.R.)

Predali et al. report very interesting results on the state of the surface of sulphide minerals during flotation using ESCA spectroscopy. This method, presented at our Congress for the first time, seems very promising. It would be of interest to know whether the nature of the chemical compound formed during the sphalerite activation and the copper valency of this compound were established. I would also like to make a contribution related to the application of the ESCA method for the investigation of antimonite activation by various metals. In antimonite the energy of the $Sb3d_{3/2}$ bond corresponds to 539.1 eV and S2p to 161.6 eV. During its activation by lead salts an additional peak appears, characterized for $Pb4f_{7/2}$ by 138.1 eV. The ratio between the number of antimony atoms and lead atoms in the surface layer reaches a value of 5.3. An increase in the concentration of lead atoms in the surface layer favours

the formation of lead xanthate and an increase in antimony
sulphide flotability.

Unlike xanthates diethylaminophenylmercuroacetate (DEAPMA),
a metalorganic collector, reacts with the sulphur antimonite
ions to form the following compound:

$$\begin{array}{c} S \\ \diagdown \\ \diagup \\ S \end{array} Sb - S - Hg - \langle \bigcirc \rangle - N(C_2H_5)_2$$
$$\begin{array}{c} \diagup \\ Sb - S \end{array}$$

In the activated antomonite the energy of the $Hgf_{7/2}$ bond
is equal to 101.1 eV; the ratio between the number of antimony
atoms and the number of mercury atoms which is 1.8, together
with the peak which is characteristic of a nitrogen atom, indicates the formation of a surface compound containing mercury.

The surface of galena treated with chromium salts was investigated using the ESCA method. The energy of the $Cr2p_{3/2}$
bond was found to be in the range of 577.2-578.9 eV. It has
been established that the chromium on the galena surface has
different valencies.

The data obtained using the ESCA method for galena and
pyrite coincide with the results presented in this paper.

V. I. Niefiodov et al. have obtained the energy characteristics of atoms in the complexes of metals with sulphydric
reagents by using ESCA [1].

The influence of the metal on the character of the metal-
sulphur-bond in dialkyl dithiocarbonates, dialkyl dithiophosphates and dialkyl monothiophosphates was investigated.

The observed differences in energy levels S2p of the sulphur
atom indicates the considerable influence of the metal on the

character of a metal-ligand bond. The results obtained allow
one to conclude that the ionic component in the covalent bond
in the complexes of lead, cadmium and bismuth is higher than in
the complexes of copper, zinc and nickel. The data with the ESCA
method are in agreement with that of the infra-red spectra
(Table 1).

TABLE 1

Energy of Bond and the Covalency Component in the Metal-Sulphur
Bond in Dithiophosphates

Dithiophosphate	Zn	Ni	Cu	Cd	Pb	Bi
Degree of covalency (IR spectrum)$_2$	0.788	0.79	0.772	0.625	0.595	0.404
S2p (ESCA)	162.9	162.9	162.8	162.6	162.4	162.6

The evaluation of the ionic component in the metal-sulphur
bond in complexes is in accordance with Poling's definition:
the less the difference of electronegativity of atoms bonded,
the lower the ionic component in the covalent bond. Zinc complexes are an exception.

The values of the S2p energy characteristics of sulphur atoms
and Mn(I) metals show that the ionic component in the metal-
sulphur covalent bond in dithiophosphates is lower than that
in monothiophosphates but higher than that in dithiocarbonates.

A comparison of the estimate of the metal-ligand bond according to ESCA with the stability of complexes (stability
constants, solubility products) shows that a decrease in the
degree of covalency in the series: dithiocarbonate $>$ dithio-

phosphate $>$ monothiophosphate correlates with a decrease in the complex stability of this series, i.e., the weak bond are more ionic. It has been established that the product of dithiocarbonates solubility is considerably less than in the case of dithiophosphates [3]; the product of silver diphenylmonothiophosphate solubility (7.2×10^{-15}) is higher than that of silver diphenyldithiophosphate (7.3×10^{-19}) [4], the constant of the mercury monothiophosphate stability is less than that of mercury dithiophosphate [5].

The evaluation of the metal-ligand bond according to ESCA corresponds to flotation results. Dithiocarbonates, which give rise to metal-sulphur bonds of a lower ionic degree, are more effective flotation collectors than dithiophosphates.

The difference between the energy levels of a copper atom in dithiocarbonates and dithiophosphates indicates a high degree of electron delocalization in dithiocarbonate. This conclusion is confirmed by the fact that in contrast to other chalcophylic ligands, with which copper forms complexes of a lower valency, copper (II) dithiocarbonate is a rather stable compound.

REFERENCES

1. Zhumadilov E. K., Markova E. I. and Nefiodov V. I. Coordination Chemistry, 4, 7, 997 (1978).

2. Eremeeva T. P. and Vorsina I. A. Otd. AN SSSR, ser. khim. nauk, 3, No. 7 (1976).

3. Kakovskij I. A. In: Physical Chemistry of Flotation Processes. Publishing House "Nedra", Moscow 1972, 306.

4. Kakovskij I. A., Solozhenkin P. M. and Usova S. V. Zh. Inorg. Chem., 22, 3067 (1977).

5. Tropova V. F., Sajkina M. K., Guseva I. I., Cherkasov P. A. and Khakimov M. G. Zh. Organic Chemistry, 38, 2088 (1968).

PAPER 8

A. A. ABRAMOV (Institute of Steel and Alloys, Moscow, U.S.S.R.)

The authors suggest an interesting new method of improving the selectivity of collectors. The pecularities of amino acid abstraction by various minerals make it possible to increase the sorption of the collector on galena and at the same time to streighten the hydrophilic qualities of the gangue mineral which are depressed in flotation, that is quartz.

I would like to know the authors' points of view as regards the following questions:

(1) How does the action of the above-mentioned reagent on the surface of sulphide differ from that on the surface of silicate minerals?

(2) How can the varying character of abstraction of amino acids influence the surface properties of sulphide and silicate minerals and does this accord with the Second Law of Thermodynamics?

(3) How do the authors explain the mechanism of mutual adsorption of xanthate and amino acids on the surface of galena giving rise to a sudden increase of collector sorption on this mineral?

(4) Do the authors consider possible chemical interaction between an amino acid and a collector, as well as the formation of new compounds whose properties can explain the adsorption phenomena described?

(5) Can the ions present in the pulp neutralize the action of the amino acids during flotation of the ore?

J. J. PREDALI (Minemet Recherche, Trappes, France)

The studies were carried out with the galena comminuted down to 200 mesh from which -10 μm slimes were removed. Thus, the question arises as to why the fine galena particles were elimi- nated. Do you think that the use of amino acids might improve recovery of the fine galena particles which are known for their poor flotability? Have you carried out any experiments with galena or any other sulphides on this subject?

K. ŻMUDZIŃSKI (CUPRUM Research and Design Establishment, Wroclaw, Poland)

(1) Have you investigated the influence of amino acids on natural lead ores?

(2) Did you study any other sulphides apart from galena for example, copper or zinc sulphides. If so, what results did you obtain?

P. SOMASUNDARAN (Henry Krumb School of Mines, Columbia Univer- sity, New York, USA)

Figure 11 in the paper shows that the addition of glycine as well as δ-amino valeric acid increases the negative charge of the quartz particles, for example around pH 7. Figure 1 clearly shows that both polar heads of glycine are fully ionised in this pH-range leaving no net charge on the glycine. The fact that the adsorption of an ion with no net charge increases the mobility of particles gives an opportunity to look at the mechanisms involved in the interesting observations presented by authors. Possibilities for the increase in electrophoretic mobility include a shift of the shear etc. A shift of the shear plane towards the surface reduced adsorption of any bivalent cation etc. A shift of the shear plane is possible due to the hydrophobic environment created by the glycine adsorbed. Such alterations can also lead to enhanced adsorption of xanthates by glycine and of glycine by xanthate due to synergism, as we have observed for the calcite (oleate) starch system. Have the authors looked at the mechanism of such adsorptions using their data?

P. M. SOLOZHENKIN (Institute of Chemistry, Academy of Sciences of Tadzhikskaya SSSR, Dushanbe, U.S.S.R.)

The subject of the paper was very interesting and raised a number of questions concerning the effect of amino-acids in the process of flotation. It would be of interest to know whether the authors studied the coordination of amino acids with the cations of transistive metals and whether they considered the possibility of the formation of amino-complexes with metals on the surface of galena and quartz. The second question is related to the mechanism of the fixing of amino acids on minerals in a range of pH where they exist in the form of dipoles.

An amino acid anion contains two donor groups and a metal ion is usually connected with the carboxylic and/or with an amino group or with both groups with the formation of chelating compound.

Ions of nickel, copper and zinc seem to form chelating compounds. For example, copper bis-glycine complexes have the following structure:

$$H_2C - NH_2 \qquad 0 - C = 0$$
$$| \qquad\qquad Cu \qquad |$$
$$0 = C - 0 \qquad NH_2 - CH_2$$

Copper complexes with alanine amino-butyric acid and other amino acids have been investigated using the EPR method in a number of papers [2, 3, 4].

Glycine forms a chelating compound with chromium (III) in the form of a $[Cr/gly/_2OH]_2$ dimer. Magnesium and calcium ions form the usual salts (carboxylates) which, it seems, tend to solvate heavily in solution. Interesting results were also obtained when complexes of precious metals with amino acids were investigated. For example, in 1,2,3- $[Rh(NH_2CH_2COO)_3] \cdot H_2O$ compound the value of N1S was found to be equal to 400.4 eV using the ESCA method, which coresponds to the coordination of Rh $\leftarrow$ NH$_2$. In the $[Zr(OH)_8 (H_3CCH(NH_3)COO)_8]Cl_8$ compound the N1S energy is equal to 401.8 eV, which corresponds to the presence of a NH_3^+ group, i.e., the coordination of α-alanine in this case takes place only through a COO^- group [5].

In the $[\text{Rh}(\text{NH}_2\text{CH}_2\text{COO})_2 \ (\overset{+}{\text{NH}}_3\text{CH}_3\text{CH}_2\text{COO})\text{Cl}]$ compounds two N1S maxima with energy levels of 400.4 and 402.1 eV are observed with an intensity ratio of 2:1. This indicates the existence of two different ways of amino acid coordination in this compound. The different character of the amino acid sorbtion on galena and quartz favours an increase in flotation selectivity.

The possibility of interaction of amino acids with metal xanthates in the process of flotation should be also taken into consideration, particularly with lead xanthates. In this case even the formation of mixed metal complexes is possible.

REFERENCES

1. Williams D. Metals of Life. Publishing House "Mir", Moscow, 1975.

2. Seizo Musumi, Toshiyum Isobe and Shikricht Kimoto. Chem. Lett., 1101. (1972).

3. Hiroshi Yokoi, Mitsuri Sai, Taro Isobe and Shigeru Onsawa. Bull. Chem. Soc. Japan, 45, 2189 (1972).

4. Hiroshi Yokoi and Taro Isobe. Chem. Lett., 95 (1972).

5. Nefiedov V. I. Coordination Chemistry, 1, No. 3, 291 (1975).

AUTHORS' REPLIES

H. J. SCHULZE

In reply to comments made by Professor Meloy, I would like
to point out that disturbance of the bubble surface by the
streaming field together with additional deformations and rota-
tions, lead to permanent disturbance of the distribution of
ions in the interface and consequently to a dynamic diffusion
interface and ion double layer and a dynamic gradient of surface tension. Thus not only the hydrodynamic narrow interaction
(HNI) is affected but so is the electrostatic bubble/particle
interaction. It is generally known that HNI with the bubble
depends on whether or not the surfactant adsorption layer makes
the bubble rigid. However, hydrodynamic resistivity can increase up to 4-fold, as has been shown by the investigations
of Brenner and Happel in particular but in a way not of essential importance for the microprocess presented here. I am
still unable to describe the effect of the above-mentioned disturbances on the double-layer interaction. The hydrodynamic
surface tension ought to be near that of pure water which is
very favourable in relation to the strength of capillary forces. Bubble oscillations due perhaps to deformations can essentially determine the strength of bubble/particle aggregates.
These problems are the subject of a paper to be published by us
soon in "Aufbereitungstechnik", Wiesbaden.

220

In reply to Dr. Warren, I would like to say that the physical importance of the so-called hydrodynamic collision efficiency E is derived as follows:

E is the quotient of the number of all particles linearly transported in a streaming tube to the bubble surface per unit time, and the number of all particles flowing in a streaming tube of diameter equal to that of bubble R_B (the diameter D_m^x of the streaming tube corresponds at a great distance from the bubble to that streamline which just touches the bubble surface in its line). Consequently E can never be 0 or 1. E only takes into account rectilinear paths of approach and thus is not valid in this form in a highly turbulent field or at slower free length of path of bubble/particle interaction where there is no possibility of forming a complete streaming field around the bubble.

The extreme deviation of our values of E obtained by measuring D_m^x and R_B on photographs of the trajectories is possibly caused not by different initial orientations but by too few data.

In reply to Professor Bahr, we would like to clarify that our conclusion that it would be desirable to work with fine bubbles at slow pulp flow velocities is not quite correct because firstly, we did not stress that this relates only to turbulent pulps in classical mechanical flotation cells and, secondly, under such conditions bubble size and pulp flow velocity are not independent. We should thus stress that this conclusion is correct only from the hydrodynamic point of view which, however, characterizes only one aspect of many elemen-

SCHEMATIC DIAGRAM FOLLOWING RADOEV AND SCHULZE

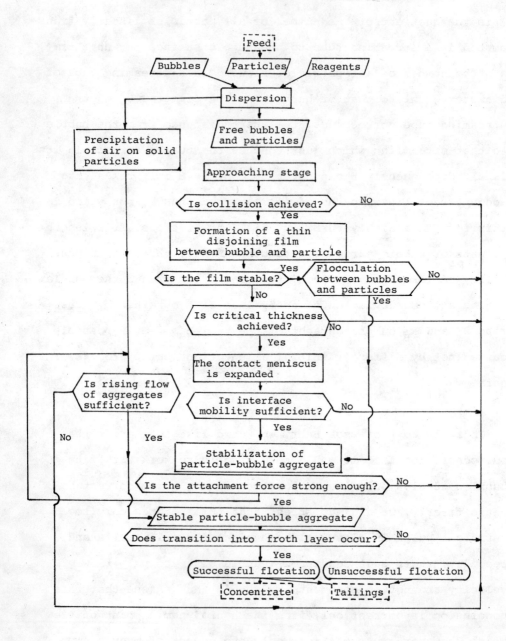

tary acts taking place in the overall process. The flotation
process cannot, then be analysed with only one phenomenon accounted for, as shown in the accompanying Figure.

Professor Bahr's remarks seem to be significant for the following reasons:

(1) It is essential to take a great number of particle -
bubble collisions into consideration;

(2) At such high relative velocities only short contact times
are realized and rupture of disjoining film occur at these
times (the problem of the stability of disjoining film is thus
still a central point in the theory of flotability - see Figure
attached);

(3) It seems to me important to look, as Professor Bahr does,
for new solutions in order, for example, to separate bulk
events from all other events in the overall process.

I do not think the properties of the gas/liquid interface to
be essential as even total absence of bubble surface circulation, inhibited by a surface-active agent, only leads to four-
fold increase in hydrodynamic resistance against movement.

A. van LIERDE

In reply to Dr. Warren we would like to say that around
pH 4-5 the OPEG adsorbs onto cassiterite through hydrogen bonding between its oxyethylene groups and OH groups of the mineral.
Flotation results from hydrophobisation due to the long hydrocarbon chain of OPEG. In the presence of sulphosuccinate hydrophobicity increases as a result of co-adsorption of both reagents. This adsorption is facilitated by the van der Waals

interactions at the solid/liquid interface of both reagents.

With regard to Warren's second question, the answer is affirmative for the ore investigated. Selective flotation of cassiterite is not, however, possible for all types of ore since some types of gangue minerals are also collected by the OPEG.

We would like to say in reply to Dr. Pieper that in our experiments we found that $-74 +15$ µm cassiterite grains flotate best. Coarser particles flotate well but with lower recovery and under conditions of vigorous pulp agitation. It is to be remembered, however, that intergrowth cassiterite-gangue particles are present in higher proportions in the $+74$ µm fractions.

In reply to Professor Polkin, the sulphosuccinate-OPEG combination was tested in the flotation of raw ore whose gangue was composed of quartz, fluorite and siderite. Under these circumstances we thought it important to carry our research aimed at the selective flotation of cassiterite from these minerals. It is obvious, then, that this collector can not be recommended for cassiterite ore as it does not permit cassiterite to be selectively flotated from quartz.

Our experimental work was not, however, limited to this system and the interaction of the OPEG with goethite, hematite, siderite, ilmenite, rutile, baryte, fluorite and pyrolusite was also studied and these results will be presented soon.

Dr. Kotlarov is to be thanked for his suggestions concerning Sn-Cu complex ores. The authors think that their reply to Professor Polkin also clarifies some of the questions raised by him.

P. NOWAK and A. POMIANOWSKI

In reply to comments made by Professor Sołozhenkin, we would like to say that our spectrophotometric investigations were restricted to the middle-infrared region. We did not carry out any measurements which might have given information on the donor-acceptor properties of the xanthate anion. Neither can we give an answer to the question concerning the formation of basic lead and copper xanthates. We tried to prepare basic xanthates of lead and copper, but we were not successfull. Therefore, we could not compare the spectra of basic metal xanthates and the samples after sorption.

Following Professor M. C. Fuerstenau's suggestion we have carried out experiments on synthetic ZnS samples and solutions of potassium ethyl xanthate of high concentration and low pH values. At a value of pH = 3.5 and a xanthate concentration of 1×10^{-3} mol/dm^3 no absorption bands were observed. At the same pH and a xanthate concentration of 1×10^{-2} mol/dm^3, a small amount of zinc ethyl xanthate was observed (below one monolayer), but at pH = 2.5 and a xanthate concentration of 1×10^{-2} mol/dm^3 again, no absorption bands were observed.

It must be noted, however, that there are many factors determining the process of xanthate sorption on a mineral surface. In strongly acidic solutions potassium ethyl xanthate is decomposed. The situation is further complicated by the possibility of zinc xanthate decomposition. In the case of natural sphalerite, activation caused by several other minerals present in the ore may be expected, thus the process of sorption of xanthate on the surface of unactivated sphalerite may be influenced by the composition of the mineral sample.

In reply to Professor Abramov we would like to point out that the influence of the semiconductor properties of sulphide minerals on the sorption of flotation collectors has been discussed for more than twenty years. Special attention has been paid to this problem in the work of Plaksin and his co-workers. It should be noted, however, that the possibility of the existence of a relation between the semiconductor properties and the flotability of the minerals has raised many objections.

We have carried out two types of experiments. Samples in the form of thin layer on the surface of a germanium reflection element have been used in some experiments while samples in the form of powdered grains have been used in other experiments. In the latter case the samples were not contacted with the germanium reflection element during the sorption process. Since we have not observed any differences in the spectra of these samples we believe that the composition of the sorption product on the two types of samples was identical. It follows, then, that the underlying germanium does not influence the properties of the sulphide layer.

It is possible that such an influence might be more pronounced in the case of the thinnest layers of sulphide. Finally, we would like to state that so far there has been no consensus of opinion in the literature as to the composition of the adsorbed layers on the surface of sulphide minerals after sorption of a collector. We hope that the results of our investigations will help to solve this problem.

J. J. PREDALI

We did not investigate the complexes formed by the metals
and various flotation collectors. It is indeed essential to
gain knowledge of the solubility products when studying electrochemical equilibria in a solution but this was not our purpose
here. Our intention was to study the surface compounds of the
sulphides in the course of conditioning, especially the nature
of those species formed with the flotation modifiers and not
with the collectors (xanthates) which cannot be detected due
to the large amount of sulphur - which in turn depends on the
sulphides under consideration.

T. WAKAMATSU

I wish to thank Dr. Zmudziński, Dr. Predali, Professor
Somasundaran, Professor Fuerstenau, Professor Solozhenkin and
Professor Abramov, who have contributed to the discussion of
my paper.

In reply to Dr. Zmudziński, I would like to say that several
tests using natural ore with amino acid were performed. For
lead sulphide ore with quartz as a principal gangue mineral,
some improvements in galena recovery have been noticed by adding
a suitable amount of amino acid. Natural ore is in general accompanied by various kinds of gangue minerals or slime minerals
apart from quartz. We have not sufficiently investigated the
action of amino acid on each of these minerals. Accordingly,
detailed studies for natural ore are to be undertaken in the
future. As to whether there is similar amino acid effect on

sulphides other than galena, we have carried out some preliminary tests. It was recognized that the amino acid addition could
promote the collection of such sulphides as chalcopyrite, pyrite, bornite and the like, on which xanthate can be strongly adsorbed.

In reply to Dr. Predali, I would like to say that the physical and chemical properties of solid material vary with its
size or fineness. In particular it is known that the flotability
of solid particles decreases abruptly at sizes around
10-5 μm, leading to the reduction of collector adsorption on
the solid. Therefore, as a first step in our tests, we deslimed
galena sample at 10 μm.   As regards the effect of amino
acid on the -10 μm   galena particles, this depends on the
exent of oxidation on galena surface. As long as the oxidation
on galena surface is not too substantial, a favorable amino
acid effect is expected for galena particles down to about
2 μm.

As Professor Fuerstenau pointed out, adsorption phenomena in
the xanthate-amino acid-mineral system which we studied are
indeed in a complex situation and this is not the stage to
present a schematic representation of the adsorption model of
related species at the solid/liquid interface. As indicated in
the introduction to the text, the dipole ion of each amino acid
has a relatively large dipole moment value compared with that
of water. Therefore, the dipole ions of amino acid can closely
approach the solid surface, and presumably bahave as counter
ions in the electric double layer. The amino acids used are
more or less hydrophobic due to the CH_2 chain between the basic

228

and acidic group in the molecule. Thus it is considered that on approaching the solid/water interface amino acid dipoles exude a water molecule layer around the solid surface to promote xanthate·adsorption onto the surface of the solid.

Further, when the dipole ions of amino acid adsorb at the solid/water interface, the zeta potential of the solid varies due to the suitable orientation of the dipoles - electrokinetic potential occurrence depends on the dipole orientation at the non-water liquid/solid interface. In this case there must be possibilities for an increase in electrophoretic mobility including a shift of the shear plane, as Professor Somasundaran suggested to us. In my opinion zeta potential variation at the solid/water interface should be closely related to the enhanced adsorption of xanthate by amino acid and of amino acid by xanthate - that is, to the cooperative effect of two kinds of adsorbates.

Amino acids are typical ligands which can coordinate to transition metal atoms or ions forming complexes. A very interesting result of an ESCA study of some amino acid-metal compounds was presented by Professor Solozhenkin, where emphasis was placed on the difference in the bond energy of an l-s electron of an N atom and different metal atoms. That amino acids behave as ligands must be another factor governing the experimental result we obtained in the amino acid-xanthate-mineral system.

My view on several comments raised by Professor Somasundaran, Professor Solozhenkin, and Professor Abramov as to the mechanism of coadsorption of xanthate and amino acid on a mineral as well as the joint effect of adsorbates on the coadsorption is as yet undecided. In order to gain a clear understanding, fundamental investigations should be continued extensively and in detail for more simplified systems.

Session 2

Fine Particle Technology

Chairmen: P. Somasundaran
J. Szczypa

THICKENING OR DEWATERING OF SLOW-SETTLING MINERAL SUSPENSIONS

Invited lecture by P. Somasundaran

Henry Krumb School of Mines, Columbia University, New York, USA

INTRODUCTION

The processing of slow-settling mineral suspensions called slimes or sludges is an industrial problem of great magnitude. A typical example of this problem is the one facing the phosphate mining industry in the southern United States. There, just an hour's drive from the fantasy land of Walt Disney, piece of colossal machinery bearing whimsical names such as Super Scooper, mine for phosphate rock. This operation, while yielding about 30% of the world phosphate required for meeting the fertilizer need for ever-increasing food production, also produces in its wake slime that has to be thickened or dewatered. This slime is currently being held in lakes covering thousands of acres of land and since it is slow-settling, the land that it covers remains unused and the billions of gallons of water that it contains remain immobilized. Similar slimes and sludges are also generated in other industries, some examples being red mud, acid mine drainage and coal slimes - all notorious for their slow-settling behavior. The annual rate of production of these slimes in the United States alone [1] gives us an indication of the enormity of the problem of their disposal. About 40 to 50 mil. t of phosphate slime, 8 to 10 mil. t of red mud, 10 mil. t of coal slimes and about 0.5 mil. t of acid sludge formed from the oxidation products of pyrite are produced every year. It has become an important task to devise methods for the dewatering of these slow-settling suspensions. The sedimentation behavior of such suspensions is not as well understood as that of coarser slurries which have been extensively studied in the past. Sedimentation theories have been adequately developed to cover the two extremes of slurry concentrations [2-11]. Thus there are theories for very dilute suspensions based on Stoke's free-settling theory and for the fixed bed systems on the basis of various models for flow through porous media. However, for the intermediate concentration systems which cover the slurries mentioned above, treatments based on modifications of Stoke's theory and the packed bed theory have not had much success. In this paper, it is the thickening or dewatering of such slow-settling slurries that will be discussed.

ROLE OF CONSTITUENT MINERALS

First of all, it is useful to identify the factors responsible for slow-settling behavior. In most cases, such settling of slimes has been attributed to the presence of clays or clay-type minerals. In the case of phosphate rock, for example, phosphate occurs along with clays and during mining and subsequent washing operations the clays are liberated from the matrix. It is mainly this clay which, when present along with other minerals, appears to be responsible for the slow-settling behavior of slimes. The role of clays has been investigated recently by Nagaraj, McAllister and Somasundaran [12] who studied the sedimentation behavior of suspensions of various combinations of major mineral components of phosphatic slime or morphologically similar materials.

The systems investigated were essentially composed of kaolinite or montmorillonite, quartz and a fibrous mineral (attapulgite, chrysotile or amphibole). Table 1 lists various the mineral systems that were studied. It was stipulated that a system should simulate the following settling characteristics of typical slow-settling slimes: (a) an initial period of gelling; (b) slow overall subsidence with a continuously changing settling rate that is typical of a network structure; (c) absence of significant segregation of mineral constituents during sedimentation; (d) a clear supernatant and a sharp slurry/supernatant interface; (e) a bulky sediment; (f) presence of tears and channels in the sedimenting structure, and (g) water exiting as microvolcanoes. A system exhibiting such characteristics can also be used as a model system for controlled studies on slow settling. The study of Nagaraj et al. [12] showed that none of the constituent minerals themselves or their binaries resembled industrial slime with respect to the above characteristics. From the various combinations of kaolinite, montmorillonite, attapulgite, quartz, chrysotile, and amphibole studied, the montmorillonite-attapulgite-kaolinite ternary and the montmorillonite-attapulgite-kaolinite-quartz quarternary were found to

TABLE 1

Mineral Systems Studied

<u>Single Minerals:</u>

Montmorillonite   Quartz

Kaolin   Chrysotile

Attapulgite   Amphibole

<u>Binary Systems:</u>

Kaolin-Chrysotile 1:1   Attapulgite-Montmorillonite 4:1 and 6:1

Kaolin-Attapulgite 1:4 and 1:1 Amphibole-Montmorillonite 4:1, 5:1 and 6:1

Kaolin-Amphibole 1:1   Chrysotile-Montmorillonite 4:1

Kaolin-Quartz 1:2

<u>Ternary Systems:</u>

*Montmorillonite-Attapulgite-Kaolin

 Montmorillonite-Attapulgite-Quartz

 Kaolin-Attapulgite-Quartz

<u>Quaternary System:</u>

*Montmorillonite-Attapulgite-Kaolin-Quartz

behave very similarly to the industrial slime. The study using

these systems also enabled us to determine the role of each

constituent. The clay minerals, montmorillonite and attapulgite,

were found to be responsible for the slow sedimentation rate

owing possibly to their peculiar morphology and swelling pro-

perties. For example, whereas montmorillonite-attapulgite-kaoli-

nite-quartz behaved similarly to industrial slime, the ternary

system kaolinite-attapulgite-quartz showed no similarity - sug-

gesting that montmorillonite does play a major role in determi-

ning the settling behavior of slimes. Similarly, systems without

attapulgite or other fibrous-type mineral were also found to

settle differently from typical slimes.

236

The clarity of the supernatant was found to be determined mostly by the surface charge properties of the mineral components. A clear supernatant resulted only when the pH was such that the minerals were oppositely charged. Evidently some type of flocculation or bridging between particles was necessary to obtain a clear supernatant.

BATCH SEDIMENTATION MODELS

Different criteria are normally chosen for the study of sedimentation of suspensions depending on the aim of the particular study. For thickening, it is mostly the solid concentration of the pulp that is important whereas for effluent treatment, the clarity of the supernatant becomes the primary criterion. In yet other processes, it can be the yield strength of the solids or moisture content that is of major concern. However, almost all the past studies on the mechanism of thickening have been generally based on changes in the solids concentration of the slurry as a function of time in a batch sedimentation process. This is usually presented in the form of a sedimentation curve, which is a graph of the interface between the slurry and the supernatant as a function of time (Fig. 1). Various sedimentation models have been reviewed recently by Somasundaran and Sresty [13] and major aspects of the review are given below. The simplest sedimentation curve is produced by a suspension made up of a narrow size fraction of hard regular particles at a volume concentration of about 10 to 25%. In this case, batch settling is characterized by a linear suspension height vs. time relationship often called the "constant. settling rate period". It is easily analysed along the lines of the modified Kozeny model for flow through porous media [14]. Here settling ends abruptly with little further decrease in height; such material is said to be incompressible.

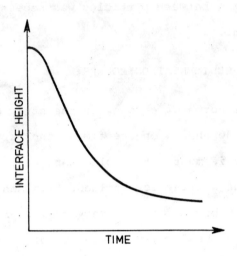

Fig. 1. Typical batch sedimentation curve.

On the other hand, when the system contains particles of different sizes, one can obtain multiple interfaces [15-17]. Davies [18] has shown that the existence of such multiple interfaces can be seen up to a critical solid concentration of about 30 to 35 vol.%. The appearance of multiple interfaces is attributed to the faster settling of the larger spheres. Above the critical concentration, this differential settling is prevented by interparticle distances that are smaller than the diameter of the smaller particles.

In contrast to the above cases, the sedimentation curves of dilute suspensions of clay-type materials display a reverse S-shape such as the one shown in Fig. 2, which is in fact so

238

TABLE 2

Major Criteria in Dewatering

Solid concentration of sediment

Volume of sediment

Settling rate

Supernatant clarity

Cake yield strength

Cake moisture

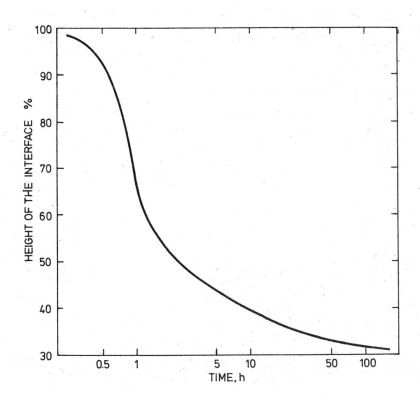

Fig. 2. Reverse S-shape sedimentation curve.

curved that no region could be described as exhibiting a constant settling rate period [19]. Moreover, settling continues in this case at an ever-decreasing rate over an extremely long time period, suggesting that the material is compressible.

The sedimentation of such clay suspensions has been studied by a number of investigators [20-23]. A noteworthy quantitative study in this area is that of Michaels and Bolger [24] who related the settling rate of flocculated particles to the micro-structure of the flocs and the properties of the surrounding medium.

The basic flow unit in the Michaels-Bolger model is a small cluster of particles called a floc, rather than the individual particle. At low shear rates, the flocs group into large clusters called aggregates, and the aggregates in turn form an extended three dimensional network. On the basis of this model three different types of settling curves are obtained, one for each solid concentration region. These are shown in Fig. 3.

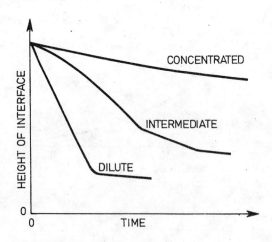

Fig. 3. Sedimentation curves for pulps of various solid concentrations [24].

240

Curve a is for dilute suspensions, curve c is for concentrated suspensions and curve b in the middle is for intermediate suspensions. For the case of dilute suspensions, the flocs are considered to settle individually on the basis of Stokes' law. The derivation is based on Richardson and Zaki's equation for the group settling rate of uniform, spherical particles

$$V_i = V_A \, \mathcal{E}^{4.65} \tag{1}$$

where V_i is the settling rate of slurry-supernatant interface, V_A is the Stokes' velocity of single aggregates and $\mathcal{E}$ is the void fraction. Equation (1) can be rewritten for initial conditions in terms of d_A, the average diameter of the aggregate. Michaels and Bolger examined the application of their expression by comparing a visually observed floc diameter with that calculated on the basis of their model for a slurry of untreated kaolin at pH 4. A value of 200 µm was obtained for the diameter of the aggregate, in fair agreement with the visually observed diameter ranging from 40 to 400 µm. Bodman et al. [25] have also similarly tested the validity of the Michael-Bolger expression for the case of the settling of industrial TiO_2 and alum mud systems. While the value obtained visually for TiO_2 was not in disagreement with those obtained from the expression, the agreement obtained for the alum mud system was rather poor.

As far as the slurries of intermediate concentrations that are of interest here are concerned, these were considered by Michaels and Bolger to settle as a coherent network. In this case, the downward movement of a control volume of the slurry in the presence of an undersupport force and a wall support force was treated on the basis of the Kozeny-Carman equation for fluid flow through pores. The expression given below relating settling rate, V, to the diameter of the container, D_c, and the initial suspension height, H_i, has been tested for kaolin suspensions, phosphatic slime, and TiO_2 and alum mud slurries.

$$V = V^\infty \left[1 - \frac{D_y}{D_c} - \frac{H_y}{H_i} \right] \tag{2}$$

where

$$V^\infty = \frac{g(\rho_K - \rho_W) \phi_K \epsilon^3}{\kappa \mu_W \tau^2 S^2} \tag{3}$$

$$D_y = \frac{4\sigma_y}{g(\rho_K - \rho_W) \phi_K} \tag{4}$$

$$H_y = \frac{\sigma_c}{g(\rho_K - \rho_W) \phi_K} \frac{H_i}{\Delta H} \tag{5}$$

V^∞ is the initial settling rate in an infinitely large container, and D_y and H_y are respectively the yield diameter and yield height. σ_c is the compressive load that exists at the boundary between the constant density zone ΔH and the underlying compressed zone, σ_y is the yield stress of the slurry network, ρ_K and ρ_W are densities of kaolin and water respectively, κ is the shape factor in the Kozeny-Carman Equation, τ is the tortuosity factor, S is the specific surface area, μ_W is the viscosity of water, and ϕ_K is the volume fraction of the kaolin. For a container of 6 cm inside diameter, the wall effect is only 0.04 and therefore the model can be considered to

242

suggest that the container diameter has a negligible effect on the settling of flocculated slurries. The effect of container diameter on the settling of a phosphatic clay suspension examined by us [26], however, showed that the diameter has a definite effect on the settling rate (Fig. 4). An increase in diameter caused a decrease in the settling rate for diameters up to about 8 cm and above that, a slight increase. This observation can, however, be explained with the help of a phenomenological model that we have developed.

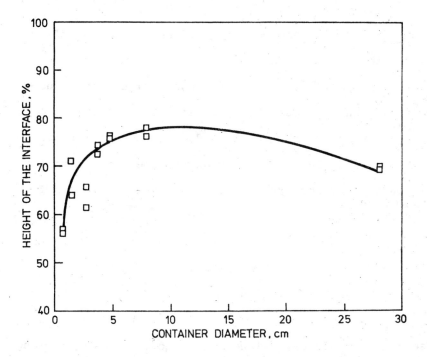

Fig. 4. Diagram illustrating the effect of container diameter on the height of phosphate slime-supernatant interface; initial solids concentration, 2.6% -37 μm slime; no additives, height of the slime column, 17.8 cm, time of settling, 8 h [20].

Our model is based on the actual visual observation of the
settling systems and the formulation of the simplest plausible
equations for the settling curves which display an S-shape with
no region exhibiting a constant settling rate period and settling continuing at an ever-increasing rate over an extremely
long time period. In fact it is in this respect, i.e., where
constant settling rate period is absent, that these systems
fail to be satisfactorily represented by the previous models of
Kynch, Richardson-Zaki, etc.

Figure 5 illustrates the observed sequence of the settling.
In the first one or two seconds after one stops mixing the
slurry, the rotational movement of the suspension ceases due to
gelling. The gelling process itself appears to be complete over
a period of several minutes, and then due to the downward movement of coarser particles and the upward movement of micro air
bubbles through the structure, fissures and tears begin to form.
Water seeps up through these tears and when the water meets
resistance to its continued transport, lenses of water are formed. Further seepage occurs when channels open up between
tears, with water finally exiting at the slurry-supernatant interface in the form of microvolcanoes. At this point one can
clearly see the interface settling down quickly and water along
with entrained particles can be seen spouting through the center of the domes of the volcanoes. Water also seeps along the
walls of the container, folding the slurry away from the wall
at the interface. The observed effect of the container diameter
on the rate of settling is in fact attributed to this seepage

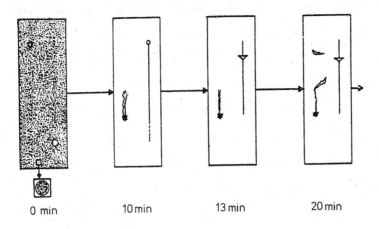

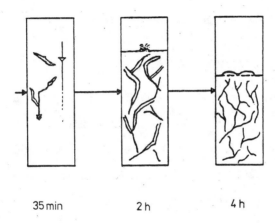

Fig. 5. Sedimentation processes for batch conditions [27],
2.6% phosphatic slimes, 0.5 g coarse graphite **tracer**.
Observations: 0 min, suspension gels almost immediately following mixing and the rotational movement
terminates; ~10 min, rising air bubbles and descen-
ding particles create vertical tears; ~13 min to
~35 min, water concentrates into lenses around the
tears; ~2 h, channeling and microvolcanoes enhance
dewatering process; ~4 h, water filaments depleted,
channels begin to close and no further significant
sedimentation.

along the walls. The advantages of using a thickener with an inclined wall is very well known. On the whole, the sediment settles as a bulky compressible mass, leaving a clear supernatant. Finally the continuous removal of water causes the contraction of the channels and as a result further subsidence becomes difficult.

If the movement of either the particles or micro air bubbles through the slurry structure is responsible for dewatering, then the addition of coarse particles to the slurry or the generation of micro-bubbles in it should enhance its sedimentation. The effect of particles and micro-bubbles have been tested and the results are discussed below.

Effect of Coarse Particle Additives

As shown in Fig. 6, the addition of different amounts of sand tailings to slime was indeed found to increase the settling rate by as much as fifty-fold. The reason for the effect of additives was investigated by conducting settling tests using particles with a wide range of specific gravities, surface properties, sizes and shapes. The effect of varying the density of the additives was studied primarily to test the possibility that the effect of coarse particles might be due to an increase in the weight of the slurry network when they are trapped in it. If the effect of the coarse particles was due to such an increase in the weight of the network, denser particles should be better additives. Results given in Fig. 7, however, show that an increase in the density of the additive produced no enhancement in settling; this suggested that the observed effects were not

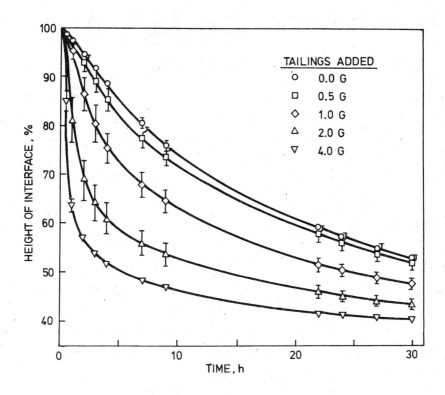

Fig. 6. Diagram illustrating the effect of addition of
quartz flotation tailings on the settling of 2.6%
-37 μm phosphatic slime, vertical bars indicate
range when larger than the symbol [26].

due to any increase in the weight of the network. It is interesting to note here that cassiterite, the heaviest mineral,
produced no effect on settling. A careful examination of the
settling suspensions showed that the heavy cassiterite particles had broken through the slurry before the slurry had a
chance to gel and trap them. Apparently, since the particles
had thus already left the slurry, it could produce no effect
on subsequent settling. Hydrophobic silicon-coated glass beads.

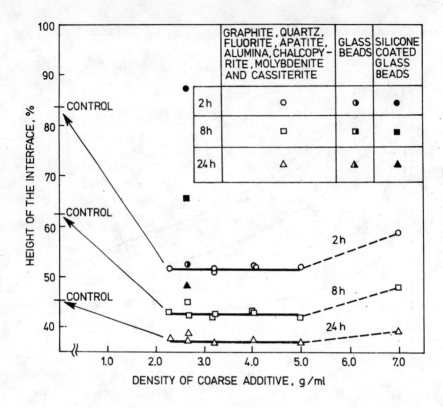

Fig. 7. Diagram illustrating the effect of density of coarse additives on the settling of 2.6% -37 μm slime [26].

which also broke through the slurry too early, similarly failed to produce any effect on settling. In contrast, uncoated (and thus hydrophilic) glass beads and quartz particles of the same size did get trapped in the slurry and were effective in enhancing the settling. Thus various hydrophilic and partially hydrophilic minerals had approximately the same effect on the subsidence, while totally hydrophobic silicone coated glass beads did not have much effect. This finding suggested that some polar interactions with the aqueous medium is necessary

to hold and trap the coarse particles in the slurry during gelling in order that there can be subsequent movements in the
slurry for the creation of tears.

In this regard, it appears that addition of certain polymers
to the whole slurry or treatment of the coarse additives with
polymers under certain conditions might be beneficial to settling. The effect of polymers could possibly be due to the enhanced bridging of particles to clay and resultant better trap-
ping of particles by the slurry. Whether such bridging occurs
or not, results of La Mer et al. [28] given in Fig. 8 do show
that addition of polymers can produce significant effects on
settling. It is to be noted, however, that while polymers may
increase the initial settling rate, the final solid content can
even be lower than where there is no such increase, often due

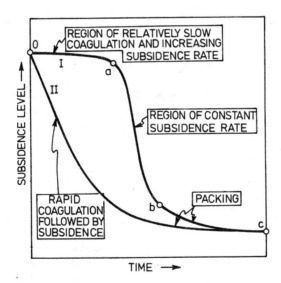

Fig. 8. Sedimentation in the absence (curve I) and in the
presence (curve II) of polymer [28].

to almost permanent entrapment of large quantities of water inside the bulky flocs that may form in the presence of polymers. In this respect, the correct choice of polymers and the proper conditioning of the slurry with it, is important.

Recently a polyethylene oxide polymer has been successfully used by the U.S. Bureau of Mines for the dewatering of Florida phosphatic clay wastes both in batch tests and in a continuous test with a trommel [27].

Effect of Air Bubbles

The experiments conducted to determine the effect of air bubbles consisted of the application of suction above a suspension of the slurry. The results obtained are shown in Fig. 9.

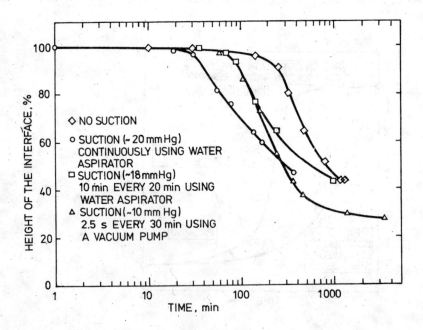

Fig. 9. Diagram illustrating the effect of air bubbles generated by suction on the settling of phosphatic slime [12].

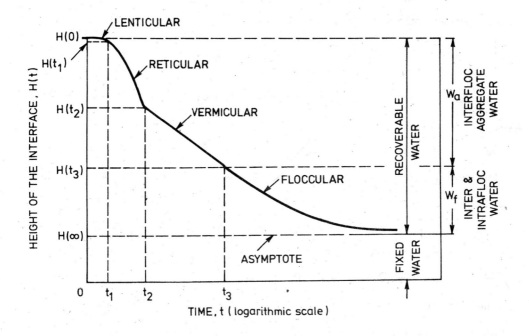

Fig. 10. Schematic representation of settling of slimes showing principal regions [27].

It can be seen from the results given in Fig. 10 that the generation of bubbles enhances subsidence significantly. Like the microbubbles that are ordinarily present in slime, these bubbles are also found to act by altering the physical features of the slurry such that water seepage becomes possible through more channels. It can also be seen that suction has no effect on settling during the initial ten to twenty minutes. Also, once the solids settle to a volume of 25 to 26%, mild suction above the suspension even for long periods produces no measurable effect. A stronger suction was found to merely disperse the sediment. The above observations suggest that generation of tiny bubbles by some means within the sediment itself might offer, either by itself or in combination with other techniques, an attractive way to enhance subsidence.

IDEALIZED SETTLING MODEL

In general, the results that have been obtained as a function of coarse particle addition, particle density, particle shape and hydrophobicity, size, container diameter, sediment height and bubble generation support the sedimentation mechanism based upon a three dimensional network model in which gelling occurs rapidly following mixing, with further settling occurring only when tears and fissures are formed for water seepage. The complex sedimentation behaviour of slimes is due to the fact that it is governed by a combination of several mechanisms, different ones predominating over each concentration range. This is illustrated in a composite sketch of the sedimentation curve shown in Fig. 10. The various stages that the suspension goes through have been named the reticular stage, vermicular stage, floccular stage and asymptotic stage. The exact nature of various processes and the magnitude of their effects would be expected to depend upon the character of the solids composing the slimes and the experimental conditions.

To summarize, the idealized settling model is presented below along with phenomenological equations describing the various stages of settling [29]. A suspension in which there is an internal structure exhibing compressibility, settles according to the action of two interrelated processes, namely gravitational expulsion of the water in the suspension and

252

internal resistive forces that oppose the gravitational expulsion. The two processes can be expressed by a phenomenological equation of the following type:

$$- \frac{dW}{dt} = c + k\phi(W) \ \psi\left[1 - f(W)\right] \qquad (6)$$

This Equation is based upon the fact that at any given time, the rate at which water passes upwards through the interface $- \frac{dW}{dt}$ depends upon the amount of water (W) contained in the slurry below the interface, while the resistance depends upon the amount of water which has already passed through the interface, i.e., 1 - f(W). In addition to these two processes, there may also be some initial incompressible settling prior to the development of resistance, and this is represented by c.

While studying the removal of water, it is important to identify the different types of waters that are present in the slurry, namely interaggregate water, interfloc water and intrafloc water. Various amounts of these waters are removed during different stages of settling.

Lenticular Stage H(O) to H(t$_1$)

In the first stage, called the lenticular stage, the gell structure develops in the suspension. There is negligible interface settling during this period. The value of c in the equation is therefore zero. Channels form during this period and water seeps up leading to the formation of lenses. When this stage is fully developed, the solids are concentrated into loosely connected aggregates of flocs interspersed with lenticular water-filled fissures.

Reticular Stage $H(t_1)$ to $H(t_2)$

In the reticular stage, lenses become interconnected so that we have continuous macrofilaments or reticules of water throughout the structure. As channels open at the interface, such interaggregate water is rapidly expelled from the sedimenting mass with the rate of dewatering finally slowing down as bridging occurs between aggregates. The simplest form of this equation has the logistic form:

$$\frac{-dW_a}{dt} = -k(1 - W_a)W_a \qquad (7)$$

The rate of expulsion of water depends upon the amount of water present and on the degree of bridging which provides a growing resistive force which in turn is proportional to the water that has already escaped.

Integration of Eq. (7) yields an expression for the descent of the slurry/supernatant interface in terms of rate coefficients r and s.

$$H(t) = \left[H(0) - H(t_3)\right] \left\{1 - 1/\left[1 + r\,\exp\left[-s(t - t_1)\right]\right]\right\} + H(t_3) \qquad (8)$$

The fit of this Equation is reviewed subsequently.

Vermicular Stage $H(t_2)$ to $H(t_3)$

In this stage bridging consolidates, further depleting the liquid filaments into a narrow vermiform structure. Settling proceeds in this stage at a decreasing rate as the water in the filaments is further expelled till the channels close. Equation (8) does describe this stage quite well though with different parameters than in the reticular stage. A better fit for the dewatering rate has been found to be given by the exponential relation (9) and it represents a moderating rate of interaggregate water expulsion as compared with that during the reticular stage.

$$\frac{dW_a}{dt} = -k \exp \alpha W_a \tag{9}$$

This Equation also can be rewritten to relate the descent of the interface to settling time in the form given below:

$$H(t) = H(t_2) - b \ln(t/t_2) \tag{10}$$

Floccular Stage $H(t_3)$ to $\sim H(\infty)$

When all the water in the macrochannels between aggregates has been expelled, the end of the vermicular stage is reached and further dewatering can take place due to the consolidation of individual flocs. Water removal at this stage, called the floccular stage, can take place due to two processes: relatively fast expulsion of interfloc water in the microchannels between flocs and relatively slow expulsion of intrafloc water from within the flocs. The forces involved are gravitational and opposing viscous forces. Each of these processes follow first-order kinetics:

$$\frac{dW_f}{dt} = -kW_f \tag{11}$$

where W_f is now the fraction of inter- and intra-floc water.

Integrated between appropriate limits and rewritten, Eq. (11) yields the following expression relating slurry/supernatant interface to settling time.

$$H(t) = m \exp\left[-p(t - t_3)\right] + n \exp\left[-1(t - t_3)\right] + H(\infty),$$

$$(q \quad p) \qquad (12)$$

Asymptotic Stage $\sim H(\infty)$ to $H(\infty)$

At the end of the intraflocc process, the system gradually approaches an equilibrium between gravitational, frictional, and electrical forces, with viscous forces falling to zero. The graph of suspension height vs. time asymptotes to a constant value in this stage.

Test of the Phenomenological Model

To determine the validity of the above phenomenological model, various rate coefficients for the above settling Equations were first tested and the resultant settling curve was compared with the experimental data. The comparison is illustrated in Fig. 11 for three slime samples. The solid lines are theoretical lines and the points are experimental data. Agreement between the model and the experimental results is evident. However, even though the model suggested has a basis in various phenomena observed during settling and fits the data quite well, the problem cannot actually be considered to have been solved till the Equations have been provided with a physical basis with all the parameters related to the physical and chemical properties of the slurry.

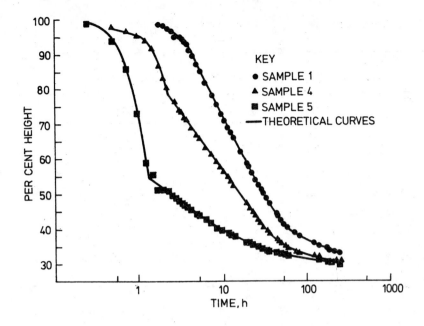

Fig. 11. Illustration of the fit of the phenomenological
model [27].

CONCLUDING REMARKS

A detailed description of behavior of slow-settling suspensions has been given here along with the mechanism by which
dewatering occurs and the mechanisms by which additives help
the dewatering process. The role of certain major factors such
as vessel diameter and the properties of additives has also
been discussed. Furthermore a phenomenological settling model
that satisfactorily represents the observed behavior of slime
has been reviewed. The problem of dewatering is very important
as it can be a very costly operation (Table 3). Depending on
the technique used, it can cost anywhere up to $50 per dry ton
and this range of expense is indeed prohibitively high.

257

TABLE 3

Cost of Dewatering of Sludges by Various Methods [30]

Technique	Capital and Operating Cost/Dry t	
	Average	Range
Lagooning	$ 2	$ 1- 5
Sand bed drying	—	3-20
Centrifugation	12	5-35
Vacuum filtration	15	8-50
Heat drying	35	25-40

Obviously there is a great need to develop new technology and to achieve this, there is also an equal need to fully advance our scientific understanding of these systems. Much more re-search certainly needs to be done before we can claim such a full understanding. Detailed and systematic experimental stu-dies in the areas discussed above, physical and chemical alike, are in dire need of the proper formulation of settling models and of full understanding of the settling behavior of slow-settling slimes and sludges, the processing of which is steadi-ly gaining in importance every day.

ACKNOWLEDGEMENTS

The support of the Particulate and Multiphase Processing Program of the National Science Foundation (ENG 78 25213) is gratefully acknowledged. Authors of References 12, 13, and 27, published from our laboratory are also acknowledged.

REFERENCES

1. Imhoff K. et al. Disposal of Sewage and Other Water-borne Wastes, Ann Arbor Sci. Pub., Inc., Ann Arbor, Mich., 1971.

2. Stokes G. G. Trans. Cambridge Phil. Soc., 9, 11 (1851).

3. Happel J. and Brenner H. Low Reynolds Number Hydrodynamics with Special Ref. to Particulate Media, Prentice-Hall, Engelwood Cliffs, 1965.

4. Lamb H. Hydrodynamics, Cambridge University Press, London, 1932.

5. Carman P. C. Trans. Inst. Chem. Engrs., 15, 150 (1937).

6. Carman P. C. J. Soc. Chem. Ind., 57, 225 (1938).

7. Mangelsdorf P. C. J. Appl. Phys., 30, 442 (1959).

8. Ergan S. Chem. Eng. Progr., 58, 89 (1962).

9. Wyllie M. R. J. and Gregory A. R. Ind. Eng. Chem., 47, 1379 (1955).

10. Coulson J. M. Trans. Inst. Chem. Engrs., 27, 237 (1949).

11. Edmundson I. C. and Tootill J. P. R. Analyst, 88, 128 (1963).

12. Nagaraj D. R., McAllister L. and Somasundaran P. Int. J. Mnl. Proc., 4, 111 (1977).

13. Somasundaran P. and Sresty G. C. Dewatering of Slow-settling Sludges, Second Handbook Volume on Particle-Fluid Separation Technology, private publication by IIT Research Institute, Chicago, 1977.

14. Carman P. C. Flow of Gases Through Porous Media, Academic Press, New York, 1956.

15. Davies R. and Kaye B. H. Particle Size Analysis Symposium, Bradford University, England, 1970.

16. Davies R. and Kaye B. H. Powder Tech. 5, 61 (1971/72).

17. Smith T. N. Trans. Inst. Chem. Engrs., 43, 769 (1965).

18. Davies R. Powder Tech., 2, 43 (1968/69).

19. Somasundaran P., Smith E. L., Jr. and Harris C. C. Effect of Coarser Particles on the Settling Characteristics of Phosphatic Slimes, Proc. 1st Int. Conf. on Particle Technology, Chicago, August 21-24, 1973, I.I.T. Research Institute, 144-150.

20. Wadsworth M. E. and Cutler I. B. Mining Eng., 8, 830 (1956).

21. La Mer V. K. and Smellie Jr. R. H. J. Colloid Sci., 12, 230 (1957).

22. La Mer V. K. and Smellie Jr. R. H. J. Colloid Sci., 12, 566 (1957).

23. Bramer H. C. and Hoak R. D. Ind. Engng. Chem. Process Design Development, 5, 316 (1966).

24. Michaels A. S. and Bolger J. C. Ind. Eng. Chem. Fundam., 1, 24 (1962, Feb.).

25. Bodman S. W., Shah Y. T. and Skriba M. C. Ind. Eng. Chem. Process Design Develop., 11, 46 (1972).

26. Somasundaran P., Smith E. L. Jr. and Harris C. C. Dewatering of Phosphate Slimes Using Coarse Additives, XIth Int. Miner. Proc. Congr. Proceedings, Istituto de Arte Minerari e Preparazione dei Minerali, Universita de Cagliari, 1975, 1301.

27. Harris C. C., Somasundaran P. and Jenson R. R. Powder Tech., 11, 75 (1975).

28. La Mer V. K. and Smellie R. H. Jr. Theory of Flocculation, Subsidence and Filtration Rates of Colloidal Dispersions Flocculated by Polyelectrolytes, Clays and Clay Minerals, 9, 1962, 295.

29. Smelley A. G. and Feld I. L. Flocculation Dewatering of Florida Phosphatic Clay Wastes, U.S. Bureau of Mines Report of Investigations, No. 9349, 1979.

30. Burd R. S. A Study of Sewage Handling and Disposal, U.S. Dept. of Interior, Federal Water Pollution Control Administration, publication WP 20-4, May 1968.

ABSTRACT

Properties of slow-settling suspensions have been described
and it was shown that clays when present along with other minerals appear to be responsible for the slow-settling behaviour
of slimes.

The mechanism by which additives help the dewatering process
has been discussed. A phenomenological settling model that
satisfactorily represents the observed phenomena has been
reviewed.

RÉSUMÉ

On a décrit les propriétés des suspensions à sédimentation
lente et on a montré que les argiles en présence d'autres minéraux sont responsables de la sédimentation lente des bones.

On a discuté le mécanisme grâce auquel les additifs aident
les processus de deshydratation. On a passé en revue les
travaux sur le modèle phénomenologique de sédimentation qui
décrit d'une manière sufficante le comportement observé des
bones.

ZUSAMMENFASSUNG

Die Eigenschaften der langsam sedimentierenden Suspensionen
werden erörtert und gleichzeitig wird gezeigt, daß der Ton in
Anwesenheit von anderen Mineralien ein langsames Absetzen der
Schlämme verursacht.

Diskutiert wird der Mechanismus, infolge dessen die Beimen-
gen den Entwässerungsprozeß unterstützen. Es wird ein Über-
blick der Arbeiten zum Thema des phänomenologischen Modells
des Absetzvorganges gegeben, daß das beobachtete Verhalten der
Schlämme vollständig beschreibt.

РЕЗЮМЕ

Описаны свойства медленно седиментирующих взвесей и показано, что глины в присутствии других минералов влияют решительным образом на медленное осаждение сузпензий. Обсужден механизм, вызывающий вспомагательное действие добавок в процессе обезвоживания. Произведен обзор работ на тему феноменологической модели осаждения, которая полностью описывает наблюдаемое поведение илов.

FLOTATION OF AN ULTRAFINE SCHEELITE ORE AND THE EFFECT OF SHEAR-FLOCCULATION

P. T. L. Koh and L. J. Warren

CSIRO, Division of Mineral Chemistry, Port Melbourne, Australia

INTRODUCTION

The flotation behaviour of very finely divided minerals is of importance, particularly with the increasing need to treat fine-grained and lower-grade ore bodies. Even with coarse-grained ores losses of ultrafines can be economically important where the valuable mineral has a tendency to slime, as in the case of scheelite. The need to utilize existing scarce resources more efficiently and the requirement to discharge cleaner tailing streams will also increase the need to treat the ultrafine fractions of ores.

Several investigators [1, 2] have analyzed the size by size flotation behaviour of pulps containing a wide range of particle sizes. The important early work of Gaudin and his colleagues [1, 3, 4] on pulps where all the particles are ultrafine was confined to suspensions prepared from single minerals and artificial mixtures (see also Koh and Warren [5]). Recently, however, Lovell [6], has reported on the flotation of a finely ground apatite ore, and this appears to be the first published study of totally ultrafine ore.

We report here results from a study of the flotation of a scheelite ore which was ground till all particles were finer than 10 μm. While in some respects the ultrafine pulp showed similar behaviour to pulps with a normal size distribution there were other effects due in particular to the fineness of the particles, e.g., the formation of voluminous wet froths, high entrainment of gangue, and slow flotation rates. These effects were explored in detail, and then tests were carried out to assess the benefit of pretreating the ore by shear-flocculation [7].

EXPERIMENTAL METHODS

Scheelite ore. A sample of ore was obtained from the ball mill feed at King Island Scheelite Ltd., Tasmania, Australia, and crushed to -24 mesh in the laboratory. Ultrafine pulps were prepared by grinding 400 g of the crushed ore for 16 h with 400 cm^3 of tap water in a steel ball mill (20 cm diameter, 5 kg ball charge : 80 balls of 2.5 cm diameter). The ground pulp was diluted with tap water to give solids contents of 1, 3.3 and 10% w/v as required.

The ground ore contained about 1.5% scheelite and 8.3% calcite. The remainder was mainly garnet (andradite) with small amounts of mica, quartz, actinolite, stilpnomelane and chlorite. The siliceous gangue will be referred to collectively as "garnet".

A photosedimentometer was used to measure the particle size distribution. Assuming an average specific gravity of 3.86 (= andradite garnet), 50% by weight of the particles had an equi-

264

valent Stokes' diameter of less than 1.2 μm, i.e. $ESD_{50} = 1.2$ μm. No particles were larger than 11 μm. The BET surface area was 18.2 m^2g^{-1}.

Scheelite and garnet. The preparation of relatively pure ultrafine scheelite (about 95% $CaWO_4$, $ESD_{50} = 1.2$ μm) has been described elsewhere [5]. A sample of ultrafine garnet (about 93% garnet, $ESD_{50} = 3.0$ μm) was prepared using similar techniques.

Analytical methods. An X-ray fluorescence technique was used to determine the amount of scheelite in the ultrafine ore and in the flotation concentrates. The amount of calcite was determined by liberating carbon dioxide with acid [8].

Flotation technique. The freshly ground scheelite ore was first conditioned for 5 min with sodium metasilicate and sodium carbonate and the pH adjusted to 10.4 (except where indicated otherwise). Sodium oleate solution, prepared by neutralizing a commercial oleic acid (Kitolene 011), was then added and the pulp conditioned for a further 2 min. Resin frother was added just before flotation in a Denver laboratory flotation machine (Model D-1) with an open impeller (diameter 72 mm) and a 1 kg cell (volume 4 1). The froth was allowed to build up for 20 s before any concentrate was removed; this period was not included in the measured flotation time of 10 min. Flotation rates were measured where required by removing the concentrate after 1, 2, 3, 5 and 10 min. No make-up water was added during flotation. The volume of concentrate (solids + water) was measured in a graduated cylinder.

Some experiments were performed using the relatively pure samples of scheelite and garnet. In these cases the fine dry mineral powders were dispersed separately by ultrasonic agitation (130 W, 20 kHz, 2 min) in sodium metasilicate solution before and after a 30 min equilibration period.

Shear-flocculation technique. Sodium carbonate (1 kg/t), sodium metasilicate (0-5 kg/t) and sodium oleate (0.5-1.5 kg/t) were added to the freshly ground ultrafine scheelite ore and the pH adjusted to 10.4. The slurry was then stirred at high speed (700-1200 rpm) for up to 60 min, during which time aggregates formed by shear-flocculation.

The effect of the geometry of the flocculation system on the degree of aggregation is still under study. The size and shape of the impeller affect the efficiency of the shear-flocculation process. With several of the designs tested, shear-flocculation was very poor. A commonly available system which produced acceptable results was the Denver laboratory flotation machine operated at 1200 rpm with the air off. In all systems it was necessary to exclude air bubbles during shear-flocculation.

The technique when using the Denver cell was to condition the ultrafine pulp for the required time at the required speed, readjust the pH to 10.4 if necessary, add resin frother and subject the flocculated pulp to flotation as described above.

RESULTS

Reagent Additions for Ultrafines Flotation

The reproducibility of the flotation techniques was calculated from a triplicate set of experiments on an ultrafine pulp of 3.3% solids content. The standard deviations of the recovery values for scheelite, calcite and garnet were 1.47, 1.77 and 0.45% for average recoveries of 29.5, 12.0 and 4.0% respectively, while the standard deviations of the grade values for scheelite and calcite were 0.56 and 1.18% for average grades of 9.5 and 19.2% respectively.

The effects of increasing concentrations of sodium oleate, resin frother and sodium metasilicate are shown in Tables 1, 2 and 3.

The reagent additions required to produce acceptable scheelite recoveries and grades varied with pulp density. The "best" flotation performances achieved with ultrafine pulps of 1, 3.3 and 10% solids are compared in Table 4.

TABLE 1

Effect of Sodium Oleate on Recoveries of Scheelite, Calcite, Garnet and Water, and Grade of Concentrate

Sodium oleate (kg/t)	Scheelite recovery (%)	Calcite recovery (%)	Garnet recovery (%)	Concentrate grade (%)	Water recovery (%)
0	8.5	3.5	2.6	4.8	3.8
0.75	25.9	11.3	4.8	6.8	3.7
1.5	32.5	17.0	5.6	7.0	3.5
3.0	32.5	15.9	5.8	6.9	3.1

Conditions: Silicate 2.5 kg/t; carbonate 1 kg/t; frother 0.2 kg/t; pulp density 3.3%; flotation speed 1300 rpm; flotation time 10 min; pH 10.4.

TABLE 2

Effect of Frother on Recoveries of Scheelite, Calcite,
Garnet and Water, and Grade of Concentrate

Resin frother (kg/t)	Scheelite recovery (%)	Calcite recovery (%)	Garnet recovery (%)	Concentrate grade (%)	Water recovery (%)
0	6.0	2.0	0.3	17.4	0.3
0.12	12.8	6.9	1.7	8.5	2.1
0.2	31.9	17.2	4.3	8.3	3.2
0.3*	32.5	17.0	5.6	7.0	3.5

Conditions: Oleate 0.75 kg/t; silicate 1 kg/t; carbonate 1 kg/t;
pulp density 3.3%; flotation speed 1300 rpm; flotation time
10 min; pH 10.4.
*Flotation speed 1200 rpm instead of 1300 rpm to avoid foaming.

TABLE 3

Effect of Sodium Metasilicate on Recoveries of Scheelite,
Calcite, Garnet and Water, and Grade of Concentrate

Sodium meta-silicate (kg/t)	Scheelite recovery (%)	Calcite recovery (%)	Garnet recovery (%)	Concentrate grade (%)	Water recovery (%)
0	23.4	19.1	4.5	6.1	3.7
0.2	24.5	20.0	4.8	6.0	5.0
1.0	25.2	27.2	4.2	6.1	3.0
2.5	25.9	11.3	4.8	6.8	3.7
4.0	21.6	6.2	3.7	7.8	3.2

Conditions: Oleate 0.75 kg/t; carbonate 1 kg/t; frother
0.2 kg/t; pulp density 3.3%; flotation speed 1300 rpm;
flotation time 10 min; pH 10.4-11.

TABLE 4

Effect of Pulp Concentration on Recoveries of Scheelite,
Calcite, Garnet and Water, and Grade of Concentrate

Pulp conc. (% w/v)	Scheelite recovery (%)	Calcite recovery (%)	Garnet recovery (%)	Water recovery (%)	Concentrate grade (%)
1	33.8	33.4	8.7	2.4	4.5
3.3	31.9	17.2	4.3	3.2	8.3
10	21.2	12.4	3.6	3.3	6.6

Conditions: 1% pulp - 5 kg/t oleate, 8.7 kg/t silicate, 3.3 kg/t carbonate, 0.63 kg/t frother, 1300 rpm, pH 11.7.   3.3% pulp - 1.5 kg/t oleate, 2.5 kg/t silicate, 1 kg/t carbonate, 0.2 kg/t frother, 1300 rpm, pH 10.7.   10% pulp - 0.5 kg/t oleate, 2.5 kg/t silicate, 1 kg/t carbonate, 0.04 kg/t frother, 1200 rpm, pH 11.7.

Foaming during Flotation

A characteristic feature of the flotation of ultrafine scheelite ore was the production of stabilized froths. After air was admitted to the flotation cell a voluminous froth of small persistent bubbles built up until it poured over the lip of the cell. Froths of this type were called "foams" and resulted in a high recovery of solids, but with little selectivity (see, for example, Test 1 in Table 5). Foaming occurred frequently with pulps of 10% solids and above, occasionally with pulps of 3.3% solids and not at all with 1% pulps. However, foaming was not simply a function of solids content but depended also on the flotation impeller speed, the concentrations of frother and sodium metasilicate and the composition of the ore.

TABLE 5

Effect of Foaming on Flotation of Ultrafine Scheelite Ore*

Test	Oleate (kg/t)	Meta-silicate (kg/t)	Resin frother (kg/t)	Flotation impeller speed (rpm)	Pulp volume (litres)	Pulp density (% solids w/v)	Scheelite recovery (%)	Concentrate grade (%)	Water recovery (%)	Anti-foam (kg/t)
1	0.75	1.0	0.3	1300	4	3.3	32.6	2.98	13.7 foam	–
2	0.75	1.0	0.3	1200	4	3.3	29.8	3.48	9.5 foam	–
3	0.75	1.0	0.1	1300	4	3.3	12.8	8.51	2.1	–
4	0.75	2.5	0.3	1200 adjusted	4	3.3	25.9	6.82	3.7	–
5	1.5	1.5	0.03	1200	4	10	40.6	2.67	9.7 foam	–
6	0.75	2.5	0.03	1200	4	10	24.5	2.70	5.6 foam	–
7	0.5	2.5	0.04 stepwise	1200	4	10	21.2	6.60	3.3	–
8	0.75	2.5	0.05 stepwise	1200–1300 adjusted	3	12.5	38.4	6.51	5.6 foam	–
9	0.75	4.5	–	1300	3	14	22.4	4.97	7.3	0.1

* Ore contains 1.5% scheelite, pH 10.5-11.5, 1 kg/t carbonate.

For example, lowering the speed of the impeller reduced the amount of "pour-over" but did not result in the foam being transformed into a froth (cf. Tests 1 and 2 in Table 5).

Foaming was sometimes prevented altogether by reducing the concentration of frother to starvation levels (cf. Tests 2 and 3). However, the transition from an extensive foam into a poor froth occurred over a relatively narrow range of frother concentrations and it was difficult to control frother additions so as to maintain a good froth without producing a foam. Adding the frother in stages rather than as a slug at the commencement of flotation was essential (cf. Tests 6 and 7). When an anti-foaming agent, Dow Corning Antifoam B Emulsion, was added in place of the frother the foam was converted into a manageable froth of relatively large bubbles but flotation performance was poorer (cf. Test 9).

Sodium metasilicate additions higher than 2.5 kg/t prevented foaming in 3.3% pulps (Table 5, Tests 2 and 4). At higher pulp densities silicate reduced pour-over but the stabilized non-selective froth persisted (cf. Tests 5 and 6).

A considerable improvement was achieved by reducing the volume of pulp in the flotation cell from 4 to 3 l (Test 8). A foam was still generated but it could be controlled in the extra space available below the overflow lip of the cell. The best recovery and grade values were obtained for 10% pulps by using a deep foam, adding resin frother in stages, adjusting the flotation impeller speed as required and maintaining a fairly high concentration of metasilicate, e.g. Test 8.

The effect of changing the ratio of scheelite:calcite:garnet in the ore was tested on samples prepared by mixing normal ore with extra calcite (collected from the King Island mine) and extra scheelite (prepared as described above). After grinding in the usual way, the calcite-rich and scheelite-rich ores were floated under the same conditions at 3.3% pulp density.

The calcite-rich ore foamed to a much greater extent than the normal ore floated under the same conditions (cf. Tests 1 and 2 in Table 6), suggesting that it was the calcite which was the primary cause of foaming. This hypothesis is supported by comparing Test 2 of Table 6 with Test 5 of Table 5 from which it is evident that foaming occurred both with a calcite-rich ore at low pulp density and with a normal ore at high pulp density. It was not, therefore, the pulp density as such which was related to foaming but rather the amount of calcite per unit volume of pulp, since this was almost the same in both experiments (7.2 and 7.5 g/l respectively).

TABLE 6

Effect of Ore Composition on Foaming

Test	Ore type	Ore composition			Flotation performance		
		Scheelite	Calcite	Garnet	Scheelite recovery	Scheelite grade	Water recovery
		(% wt)	(% wt)	(% wt)	(%)	(%)	(%)
1	normal	1.5	8.3	90.2	25.9	6.8	3.7 no foam
2	calcite-rich	1.4	21.5	77.1	58.0	1.6	29.3 10 min foam
3	scheelite-rich	10:3	7.6	82.1	33.6	28.3	7.1 sl.foam
4	scheelite-rich	17.4	7.0	75.6	36.1	34.5	11.7 4 min foam

Conditions: 3.3% pulp density, 0.75 kg/t oleate, 2.5 kg/t silicate, 0.3 kg/t frother, flotation speed 1200 rpm, pH 10.2.

Tests 3 and 4 in Table 6 show the results of increasing the
proportion of scheelite. In Test 3, the weight of scheelite per
unit volume of pulp was higher than in Test 5 of Table 5, con-
firming that in the flotation of ultrafine ore at 10% solids
foaming is mainly caused by the ultrafine calcite. In Test 4
the proportion of scheelite was increased further till the
total concentration of hydrophobic particles (calcite + scheelite) was the same as in Test 2. Under these conditions the
scheelite-rich ore foamed less than the calcite-rich ore.

Foams were not observed during the flotation of pulps consisting of 100% ultrafine garnet.

Effect of Longer Flotation Times

Several experiments were carried out in which the flotation
time was extended to 30 min. The pulp of ultrafine scheelite
ore was conditioned with silicate, carbonate and oleate in the
usual way, and frother was added after 0, 5, 15 and 25 min flotation in an attempt to maintain constant froth height and
water content in the froth.

The longer flotation time greatly increased the recovery of
scheelite but only at the expense of scheelite grade in the
concentrate (Table 7).

A specific flotation rate, defined by

$$Q = \Delta W_c / \bar{W}_p \Delta t \tag{1}$$

where ΔW_c is the increase in weight of the mineral in the concentrate during   time Δt, and $\bar{W}_p$ is the average weight of
that mineral in the pulp during time Δt, was calculated for
each of the main minerals in the ore during each of the three

time periods 0-10, 10-20 and 20-30 min (Table 8). The results show that while the specific flotation rate of scheelite decreased after the first 10 min of flotation, that of calcite rose slightly and that of garnet remained constant.

TABLE 7

Effect of Long Flotation Time on Recovery and Grade

Flotation time	Cumulative values					
	Water recovery	Scheelite recovery	Scheelite grade	Calcite recovery	Calcite grade	Garnet recovery
(min)	(%)	(%)	(%)	(%)	(%)	(%)
10	5.45	37.9	6.20	36.1	30.7	6.71
20	12.3	55.7	5.21	60.8	29.6	12.1
30	20.3	67.2	4.45	75.2	25.9	18.3

Conditions: 3.3% pulp, 1.5 kg/t oleate, 2.5 kg/t silicate, 1 kg/t carbonate, 0.4 kg/t frother, flotation speed 1300 rpm, pH 10.2.

TABLE 8

Effect of Long Flotation Time on Specific Flotation Rates

Flotation period	Specific flotation rate, $Q\ min^{-1}$		
(min)	Scheelite	Calcite	Garnet
0 - 10	0.049	0.043	0.007
10 - 20	0.033	0.048	0.006
20 - 30	0.030	0.045	0.007

Conditions: As per Table 7.

Once the flocation behaviour of ultrafine scheelite had been properly investigated, tests were then carried out to assess the benefit of pretreating the ultrafines by shear-flocculation.

Table 9 shows that the recovery of scheelite was increased significantly by shear-flocculation but that the improvement depended, among other things, upon the time of stirring and the stirrer speed. The extent of flocculation in the Denver cell increased steadily for 60 min and then decreased slowly (Fig. 1). Shear-flocculation of the very fine particles (0.1-8 µm, ESD_{50} 1 µm) required high stirrer speeds (Table 9).

Although the main object of the shear-flocculation step was to improve the recovery of scheelite, the process was even more effective in recovering ultrafine calcite. The increase in recovery or in selectivity index was greater for calcite than for scheelite (Table 9). Calcite and scheelite responded similarly to changes in stirrer speed and time of stirring.

The extent of shear-flocculation was not found to vary significantly with pulp density for pulps stirred at 1200 rpm for 60 min. Recovery of scheelite at 1, 3.3 and 12.5% solids was 49.0, 51.0 and 49.0% respectively.

The set of five experiments (Tests 1-5) reported in Table 9 were carried out with chemical parameters chosen on the basis of the flotation experiments and maintained constant in order to determine the effects of stirrer speed and stirring time. However, the experiment which produced the best scneelite recovery (Test 5) also gave the lowest grade. Water recovery was higher than normal and it appeared that for the shear-floccu-

275

TABLE 9

Pretreatment by Shear-flocculation: Effects of Stirring Time and Stirrer Speed*

Test	Stirring time (min)	Stirrer speed (rpm)	Scheelite recovery (%)	Scheelite selectivity index**	Calcite recovery (%)	Calcite selectivity index**	Garnet recovery (%)	Scheelite grade (%)	Water recovery (%)
1	0	0	31.9	2.9	17.2	2.1	4.3	8.3	3.2
2	15	700	34.9	3.0	27.6	2.9	3.8	8.9	3.6
3	60	700	37.4	2.9	32.9	3.2	4.0	8.3	3.3
4	15	1200	32.2	2.6	29.4	2.8	4.5	7.2	3.5
5	60***	1200	51.0	2.6	57.4	3.6	8.8	5.9	4.4
6	60	1200	47.7	3.4	38.9	3.4	4.4	9.3	3.6

* Denver laboratory flotation machine with air off, 3.3% pulp density, 1.5 kg/t oleate, 2.5 kg/t silicate, 0.2 kg/t resin frother (stage addition), pH 11.4.

** Selectivity index $= \left[1 + \left\{10^4 (G - W)/W(100 - G)(100 - R)\right\}\right]^{\frac{1}{2}}$, where G = concentrate grade, W = head grade, R = recovery. For scheelite, $W_s \simeq 1.5\%$; for calcite, $W_c \simeq 8.5\%$

*** Chemical conditions adjusted to: 2 kg/t oleate, 4 kg/t silicate, 0.2 kg/t resin frother, pH 10.2.

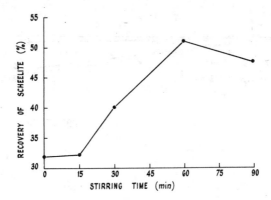

Fig. 1. Effect of stirring time on degree of shear-flocculation of ultrafine scheelite ore. 1 kg Denver cell,
1200 rpm, pulp density 3.3%, oleate 1.5 kg/t, silicate 2.5 kg/t, frother 0.2 kg/t, pH 10.4, flotation
time 10 min.

lated pulp a different set of chemical parameters was needed.
Thus, in Test 6 oleate was increased to 2 kg/t to reduce water
recovery and to counteract the effect of increasing silicate to
4 kg/t. The higher silicate level was expected to depress calcite and reduce water recovery, and also to depress garnet. The
total addition of frother was maintained at 0.2 kg/t but it was
added in smaller doses. The pH was reduced from 11.4 to 10.2 to
take advantage of the reported lower floatability of calcite in
this region [21]. As may be seen in Table 9, the combined effect
of all these changes was to produce a drier froth with low garnet content, to significantly reduce calcite recovery but to
maintain a high recovery of scheelite.

The results presented in Fig. 2 show that the rate of flotation of ultrafine scheelite was increased after pretreatment by
shear-flocculation.

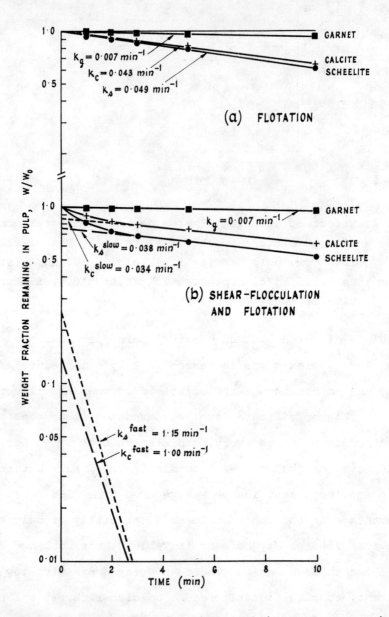

Fig. 2. Flotation rates of scheelite, calcite and garnet in
natural ore samples. (a) Flotation only. (b) Shear-
flocculation followed by flotation. ----- Fitted
first-order processes for scheelite. ———— Fitted
first-order processes for calcite.

For the dispersed ore (Fig. 2a) the flotation kinetics were described approximately by a single first-order rate process during the first 10 min of flotation. After shear-flocculation (Fig. 2b) the flotation kinetics were best described by a combination of two first-order rate processes [9]. Values of the rate parameters are given in Table 10.

TABLE 10

Flotation Kinetics - Effect of Pretreatment by Shear-flocculation

	Scheelite ore				Pure scheelite*			
	Dispersed**		Flocculated***		Dispersed		Flocculated	
	k	ϕ	k^{slow}	k^{fast}	k	ϕ	k^{slow}	k^{fast}
Scheelite	0.05	0.75	0.04	1.15	0.08	0.51	0.12	1.25
Calcite	0.04	0.86	0.03	1.00	-	-	-	-
Garnet	0.007	1.00	0.007	-	-	-	-	-

* Koh and Warren [5]

** 3.3% pulp, 1.5 kg/t oleate, 2.5 kg/t silicate, 1 kg/t carbonate, 0.2 kg/t frother, flotation speed 1300 rpm, time 10 min, pH 10.2, k = first-order rate constant.

*** As for (*) except 2 kg/t oleate, 4 kg/t silicate, ϕ = fraction of slow-floating component, k^{slow}, k^{fast} = first-order constants of slow- and fast-floating components, respectively.

DISCUSSION

Reagent Additions

Discussions of the behaviour of ultrafine particles in flotation often assume that ultrafines are inherently different from larger particles [10]. However, our results (Tables 1-3) show that at least with respect to the relative effects of varying

additions of chemical reagents on flotation performance, the
ultrafine pulp behaved similarly to scheelite ore pulps of normal particle size [11, 12]. All recovery values for the ultrafines are lower, of course, because of their slow rate of flotation, but the relative changes are the same.

Furthermore, the consumption of collector was not excessive.
Additions of about 1 kg/t sodium oleate were sufficient for
shear-flocculation and flotation of an ultrafine scheelite ore
of surface area 18.2 m^2g^{-1}. This represents a five-fold increase
in collector consumption over a typical industrial flotation
plant where 0.2 kg/t oleic acid is used to float a pulp of surface area about 2.6 m^2g^{-1}; i.e. the extra collector required was
less than the proportionate increase in surface area per unit
weight.

Causes of Foaming

Although there were similarities in chemical response between
ultrafine and normal size pulps, the finely ground pulps differed in their tendency to form voluminous, wet, small-bubble
froths or "foams" during flotation. This tendency to foam does
not appear to be the same as the "overfrothing" condition
described by Taggart [13] in which fluffy large bubbles are produced carrying little solids, nor is it the same as Gaudin's
"over-flocculated froth" which was fairly dry [14]. However,
Lovell [6] observed a similar froth condition during flotation
of a very fine apatite ore.

Whereas a good froth may be considered to consist of fairly
small spherical bubbles grading upwards into large polyhedral

280

bubbles with little water [14], in a foam the rate of coalescence is apparently reduced allowing the small bubbles to persist and to be carried up to the free air surface. Here the rate of bursting is also lowered, and the total volume occupied by froth grows rapidly till the foam overflows the flotation cell.

Thus, reducing the volume of pulp in the cell (Table 5, Test 8) would increase the residence time of bubbles in the deeper froth and allow more coalescence before bubbles reach the free air surface. The low concentrate grade observed in foams (Table 5) is explained by the fact that small spherical bubbles fill the available space less efficiently than larger polyhedral bubbles. The ratio of water to air is therefore greater in a foam and the increase in entrained gangue, mainly garnet, lowers the concentrate grade.

The problem of foaming with finely ground ores may be seen as a result of the fineness of the particles, their concentration in the pulp and their hydrophobicity. Fine particles, instead of sliding down the bubble walls like larger particles, remain distributed over the bubble surface and hinder coalescence. The concentration of ultrafines must also be large enough to form nearly complete bubble coatings. Thus, foaming was observed more often at high than at low pulp densities. It is also necessary that the particles be hydrophobic. Foaming did not occur during flotation of garnet alone, but sufficient ultrafine hydrophobic calcite or scheelite in the ore led to extensive foams (Table 6).

Livshits and Dudenkov [15] on the other hand, argued that a small hydrophobic particle would tend to bridge between bubbles, allowing their wetting perimeters to approach and the bubbles to

coalesce. This theory may be appropriate when bubble mineralization is poor and there are large particle-free patches on the
bubble surface (Fig. 3a), but when mineralization is high it is
more likely that particle-particle content will prevent bubble
coalescence (Fig. 3b). Stabilization will be even more likely
for plate-like particles where the maximum contact angle can be
developed at an edge and lateral movement of opposite particles
is hindered as the bubbles approach (Fig. 3c).

The enhanced ability of ultrafine hydrophobic calcite to
cause foaming (Table 6) is probably a result of the shape of
ground calcite particles. A large proportion of these particles,
even in the micro-meter size range, have parallel flat surfaces
as a result of the perfect rhombohedral cleavage of calcite
(Fig. 4). Ultrafine scheelite particles are more irregular in

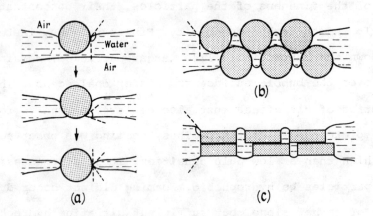

Fig. 3. Effect of ultrafine hydrophobic particles on bubble
coalescence. (a) Poor mineralization of bubbles.
(b) High mineralization of bubbles. (c) Effect of
flat particles.

shape (Fig. 5) and are not therefore as effective as calcite in preventing bubble coalescence in the froth.

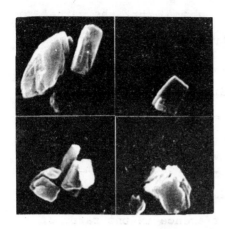 

Fig. 4. (left). Shapes of finely-ground calcite particles. Scanning electron micrograph x 16,000.

Fig. 5. (right). Shapes of finely-ground scheelite particles. Scanning electron micrograph x 9600.

The beneficial effect of sodium metasilicate in reducing foaming was probably due to its ability to depress calcite rather than to any direct chemical effect. Adsorption of silicate on the calcite surfaces made the particles hydrophilic [16] and prevented their attachment to bubbles and their stabilizing action in the froth.

Foaming was not observed in the absence of a frother. In other words, ultrafine hydrophobic particles alone do not appear to be able to stabilize the froth. The extra degree of bubble stability conferred by adsorption of the frother at the bubble-water interface is required in addition.

Entrainment and Flotation

Correlation of the mineral recoveries with the water recoveries (Koh and Warren, in preparation) showed that the garnet recovery is almost entirely due to entrainment, whereas scheelite recovery is virtually independent of water recovery. With calcite the position is intermediate. Since garnet is the major gangue mineral these results indicate clearly the importance to grade of obtaining a dry froth.

With ultrafine pulps the problem of gangue entrainment is particularly severe, because there is no classification effect due to drainage in the froth. The difference in the rates of recovery of scheelite and garnet should therefore be less the finer the particles become, leading to a reduced selectivity in ultrafine pulps.

Long Flotation Times

Despite the difficulty of floating finely divided ores, about 30% of the scheelite, of particle size 0.1-8 μm, could be recovered by a single rougher flotation step (Table 1). Concentrate grades of about 7% scheelite were obtained by avoiding foaming and by maintaining a dry froth.

The main reason for the low recovery was the slow flotation of ultrafine scheelite, e.g., the first-order flotation rate constant was only 0.05 min^{-1} (Fig. 2) compared with values of the order of 1.0 min^{-1} for the flotation of 10-100 μm particles [17]. The lower flotation rate of ultrafines can be accounted for by their lower rate of collision with bubbles and their low particle momentum, which reduces the chance of adhesion.

284

In view of the low flotation rate, improved recovery should be achieved merely by increasing the time of flotation. The recovery of ultrafine scheelite was indeed increased by extending flotation to 30 min (Table 7) but only at the expense of concentrate grade. Grade fell, because whereas the recovery rate of garnet remained essentially constant and followed the recovery of water, that of the valuable mineral steadily decreased after the first 10 min of flotation as the more floatable particles were removed (Table 8). This trade-off between grade and recovery is not unexpected, although there do not appear to be any published data for the relative variation of flotation rates over extended times. It appears to be particularly important in the case of ultrafine pulps owing to the relatively low selectivity which we consider to be due to the large part played by entrainment.

Shear-Flocculation

The object of applying shear-flocculation to ultrafine particles is to increase the effective particle size. The overall rate of attachment to bubbles should then increase because of the greater size and momentum of the flocs [17].

Koh and Warren [5] have confirmed that scheelite flocs float faster than dispersed particles (Table 10). The flotation kinetics found in the present study of natural ore samples were similar to those for pure scheelite suspensions, as may be seen by comparing the rate constants in Table 10. In particular, the rate constants of the fast-floating scheelite was almost the same in the flocculated ore as in a flocculated suspension of pure scheelite (1.15 and 1.25 min^{-1} respectively), supporting the inference that aggregates of scheelite are present in the natural ore sample after high speed agitation of the pulp.

On the other hand, the flotation rate of garnet did not change after the ore had been subjected to shear-flocculation (Table 10), and it is unlikely, therefore, that separate flocs of garnet are formed or that garnet is trapped to any significant degree in the scheelite and calcite flocs.

Calcite was also aggregated in the shear-flocculation step and its flotation rate increased considerably (Table 10). In fact, the selectivity indices in Table 9 show that calcite responded better to shear-flocculation and flotation than did scheelite. There appear to be two main reasons for this behaviour. Firstly, the zeta-potential of calcite near pH 10, with or without adsorbed oleate, is low [18, 19], and the electrostatic repulsion opposing adhesion of the colliding particles is therefore lower than for scheelite [7]. Secondly, the area of contact available between adhering calcite particles will be larger than for scheelite because of the greater number of flat surfaces on calcite grains (Figs. 4 and 5). Consequently, the free energy gain from hydrophobic association between the oleate-coated surfaces will be greater than for scheelite particles of equivalent size.

The shear-flocculation of calcite was controlled to some degree by adding sodium carbonate and sodium silicate (Table 9), thereby reducing oleate adsorption.

Shear-flocculation has been shown to depend on the size of the particles, their surface charge, their hydrophobicity, the time for which the suspension is stirred, the stirrer speed and

286

the proportion of valuable mineral in the pulp [20]. Another important variable is the geometry of the flocculation system (impeller and tank). It appears that certain types of turbulent systems favour floc formation and work is in progress to define the optimum geometrical arrangement. In the present study the hydrodynamics of the system have not been optimized, but kept constant.

Overall, the main advantage of pretreating finely ground ores by shear-flocculation is that recovery of the ultrafines can be increased without a significant reduction in concentrate grade. Thus, shear-flocculation with the present stirrer system converted about one-quarter of the ultrafine scheelite in a natural ore into a fast floating state, which increased the flotation recovery of scheelite from about 30 to 50% without loss of grade.

CONCLUSION

Consumption of the collector sodium oleate was greater during the flotation of ultrafine scheelite ore than for ores of normal particle size, but the increase was less than that expected on the basis of the increase in surface area per unit weight. Only normal additions of pH regulators, modifiers and depressants were required for flotation of the ultrafines.

A serious problem in the flotation of ultrafine scheelite ore was the formation of voluminous wet froths or foams. Bubble coalescence to produce a normal froth was prevented by a more or less complete coating of ultrafine hydrophobic particles, mainly calcite, on the bubble surfaces. The small spherical bubbles in the foam filled the available space less efficiently than larger polyhedral bubbles and allowed increased entrainment of gangue in the interbubble water.

Calcite caused foaming more easily, weight for weight, than scheelite, presumably because the many parallel surfaces on ultrafine calcite particles led to more tenacious bubble coatings. Sodium metasilicate reduced foaming by depressing the calcite.

It was essential to reduce water recovery as much as possible in order to minimize gangue entrainment during flotation of ultrafines.

Ultrafine scheelite floated slowly, and its recovery was increased by extending the time of flotation. However, concentrate grades were lowered because of gangue contamination. While the flotation rate of garnet remained constant with extended flotation times, that of scheelite steadily decreased.

If the ultrafine ore was first treated by shear-flocculation, aggregates of scheelite which floated some 20 times faster than dispersed particles were formed. The flotation recovery of scheelite increased from about 30 to 50% without loss of concentrate grade.

REFERENCES

1. Gaudin A. M., Groh J. O. and Henderson H. B. AIME Tech. Publ., No. 414, 3-23 (1931).

2. Anthony R. M., Kelsall D. F. and Trahar W. J. Proc. Australas. Inst. Min. Metall., No. 254, 47-58 (1975).

3. Gaudin A. M. and Malozemoff P. Trans. AIME, 112, 303-318 (1934).

4. Gaudin A. M., Schuhmann R. and Schlechten A. W. J. Phys. Chem., 46, 902-910 (1942).

5. Koh P. T. L. and Warren L. J. Trans. Inst. Min. Metall. Sec. C., 86, C94-C95 (1977).

6. Lovell V. M. Froth characteristics in froth flotation. (ed. M. C. Fuerstenau). In: "Flotation. A. M. Gaudin Memorial Volume", AIME, New York, 1976, vol. 1, 597-621.

7. Warren L. J. J. Colloid Interface Sci., 50, 307-318 (1975).

8. Donaldson E. M. Methods for the analysis of ores, rocks and related materials. Can. Dept. Energy; Mines and Resources, Mines Branch, Monograph 881, 1974, 161-165.

9. Kelsall D. F. Trans. Instn Min. Metall., 70, 191-204 (1960-1).

10. Klassen V. I. and Mokrousov V. A. An Introduction to the Theory of Flotation, Butterworths, London, 1963, p. 328, 372.

11. Hart J. G. Proc. Australas. Inst. Min. Metall., No. 136, 1-81 (1944).

12. Dean K. C. and Schack C. H. U. S. Bur. Min. Rept Invest., No. 6385, 15 (1964).

13. Taggart A. F. Handbook of Mineral Dressing, John Wiley, New York, 1945, p. 12-42.

14. Gaudin A. M. Flotation, 2nd edn, McGraw-Hill, New York 1957, pp. 333, 357.

15. Livshits A. K. and Dudenkov S. V. Some factors in flotation froth stability. In: Proc. 7th Int. Miner. Process. Congr., (ed. N. Arbiter), Gordon and Breach, New York, 1965, 367-371.

16. Solnyshkin V. I. and Yu-Lung Cheng. Obogashch. Rud. i Uglei, Akad. Nauk SSSR, Inst. Gorn. Dela, 1963, 147-158.

17. Trahar W. J. and Warren L. J. Int. J. Mineral Process., 3, 103-131 (1976).

18. Kumar V. Y. S., Mohan N. and Biswas A. K. Trans. SME/AIME, 250, 182-186 (1971).

19. Mishra S. K. Int. J. Mineral Process., 5, 69-83 (1978).

20. Jarrett R. G. and Warren L. J. Proc. Australas. Inst. Min. Metall., No. 262, 57-65 (1977).

21. Fuerstenau M. C., Gutierrez A. and Elgillani D. A. Trans. SME/AIME, 241, 319-323 (1968).

ABSTRACT

The batch flotation behaviour of finely ground scheelite ore ($\sim$1 µm) was investigated. Collector consumption was not excessive, and indeed was generally less than that expected on the basis of the increased surface area per unit weight. However, voluminous "foams" often formed during flotation. Foaming was explained by a reduction in the rate of bubble coalescence in the froth column, caused by coatings of ultrafine hydrophobic particles, principally calcite, on the bubble surfaces. These foams resulted in high water recovery with considerable entrainment of gangue. Foaming was controlled by a combination of methods, including depressing the calcite. Scheelite recovery was increased by extending the flotation time to 30 min but only at the expense of concentrate grade. If the slow-floating ultrafine ore was first treated by shear-flocculation, flocs of scheelite were formed and scheelite recovery increased from about 30 to 50% without loss of grade.

RÉSUMÉ

On a procédé à l'examen du maintien de la flottation en paquet du minerai de scheelite ultrafin ($\sim$1 µm). La consommation du collecteur n'était pas excessive, et à vrai dire généralement moindre que celle attendue sur la base de l'augmentation de l'aire de la surface par unité de poids. Cependant, des mousses abondantes se formaient au cours de la flottation. Le moussage est expliqué par une réduction de la vitesse de fusion des boulles dans la colonne de mousse, causée par des dépôts de particules hydrophobes ultrafines, principalement de calcite, sur la surface des boulles. Ces mousses résultaient d'une forte récupération de l'eau avec un entrainement considérable de gangue. Le moussage fut contrôlé par une combinaison de méthodes comprenant un abaissement de calcite. La récupération de scheelite fut accrue par l'extension du temps de flottation à trente minutes mais seulement au débit du concentré. Dans le cas où le minerai ultrafin en flottation lente

fut d'abord traité par coupe-floculation, des flocons de scheelite ont été formés et la récupération de scheelite est accrue
de 30 à 50% environ sans perte de qualité.

ZUSAMMENFASSUNG

Es ist das Verhalten eines feingemahlenen Scheelit-Erzes
(~ 1 µm) bei fraktionierter Flotation untersucht worden. Der
Sammlerverbrauch war nicht allzu gross, im allgemeinen geringer
als es die vergrösserte Oberfläche pro Gewichtseinheit hätte
erwarten lassen. Während der Flotation bildete sich jedoch oft
ein zähiger "Schaum". Das Schäumen lässt sich als Folge einer
Geschwindigkeits-Reduktion der Vereinigung der Bläschen in der
Schaumsäule erklären. Diese Vereinigung wird durch einen Überzug
aus ultrafeinen hydrophoben Teilchen an der Oberfläche der
Bläschen, insbesondere aus Kalkspatteilchen, verursacht.
Infolge dieser Schaumbildung war die Wasserrückgewinnung recht
gross, jedoch unter besonderem Miteinbeziehen von tauben
Gestein. Das Schäumen wird mittels kombinierter Methoden, ein-
schliesslich der Kalkspatdepression, unter Kontrolle gehalten.
Dank der Ausdehnung der Flotationszeit auf 30 Minuten konnte
das Scheelitausbringen gesteigert werden, doch auf Kosten des
Anreicherungsgrades. Wurde jedoch das aufgeschwemmte, langsam
flotierende ultrafeine Erz zuerst durch scherende Ausflockung
angereichert, so bildeten sich Scheelitflocken und das
Scheelitausbringen stieg von etwa 30% auf 50%, ohne auch nur
etwas an Qualität einzubüssen.

РЕЗЮМЕ

Исследована периодическая флотация шеелитовой раздробленной руды (ок. I µм). Расход собирателя не был высоким и по существу был ниже, чем ожидалось, исходя из увеличенной поверхности. Однако во время флотации часто появлялась обильная пена, большой объем которой объяснялся за счет уменьшения скорости коалесценции пузырьков в слое пены, вызванного слоем ультрамелкозернистых гидрофобных частиц, главным образом кальцита, на поверхности пузырьков. Эта пена способствовала высокому выходу воды при значительном уносе пустой породы. Пенообразование регулировалось несколькими методами одновременно с уменьшением кальцита. Выход шеелита возрастал при продлении флотации до 30 минут, но только за счёт качества концентрата. В том случае, когда свободнофлотируемая ультрамелкозернистая руда подвергалась вступительной скоростной флокуляции, образовывались хлопья шеелита, а выход шеелита возрастал до 30-50% без снижения качества.

NOVEL PROCESS AT YXSJÖBERG, A POINTER TOWARDS FUTURE MORE SOPHISTICATED FLOTATION METHODS

M. Gräsberg[1] and K. Mattson[2]

[1] AB Statsgruvor, Yxsjöberg, Sweden
[2] LKAB, Stockholm, Sweden

AB Statsgruvor, a member of the Swedish state-owned LKAB group, has ceased iron ore mining and is now exploiting complex sulphide and tungsten ores. Future plans mainly refer to scheelite deposits but also include other ferro-alloy metal ores.

The first scheelite mine acquired was Yxsjöberg, which when bought in 1969 was out of production. Operation restarted in 1972 with conventional processing. The treatment involved gravity concentration combined with low and high intensity magnetic separations and magnetizing roasting. The chalcopyrite and fluorspar content of the ore were recovered by flotation.

The exploitation was not successful; problems encountered were due both to inefficient mineral processing and to lack of ore reserves. It was necessary to find more ore and make better use of it.

Ore prospecting in the area has already located several other scheelite mineralizations, which now are being examined more closely. Open pit mining of a new scheelite deposit at Wigström, 25 km from Yxsjöberg, has started. The ore assays 0.30% WO_3 and is transported by truck to Yxsjöberg for concentration. Another new deposit, Sandudden, which is similar in composition will be subjected to a full operational scale test run. In addition, the Yxsjöberg concentrator is used to re-treat tailings from earlier production periods. Ore processing plans for this year include:

Raw material	Quantity, t	Grade, % WO_3
Yxsjöberg	130,000	0.38
Wigstrom	50,000	0.30
Sandudden	10,000	0.25
Tailings	25,000	0.15

Although Yxsjöberg still accounts for the major part of the throughput, sufficiently small amounts are drawn from the reserves to ensure the mine a reasonable life-time. To maintain the confidence of the staff, however, research must keep pace with production.

A new process, the main subject of this paper, has been developed and rendered production economical.

ORE COMPOSITION

The mines mentioned above belong to a cluster of tungsten deposits near Ludvika in the Bergslagen area, Central Sweden. This area is characterized by a supracrustal complex of sediments and volcanics which has been intruded by basic rocks and granitoids of precambrian age. Tungsten mineralization generally occurred along limestone horizons, preserved in places but mainly transformed into distorted bodies of skarn.

At Yxsjöberg the scheelite is associated with pyrrhotite, chalcopyrite and abundant amounts of fluorite. The main skarn minerals are hedenbergite, hornblende and biotite, together with some garnets. Hedenbergite skarn is speckled with fairly coarse-grained scheelite while hornblende skarn contains small scheelite grains fairly evenly distributed in the matrix, cf. Fig. 1. The two ore types are mined together.

The Wigström ore is almost free of sulphides but contains wollastonite, vesuvianite and scapolite in paragenesis. Normal ore, however, consists of garnet-pyroxene skarn with some amphibole and biotite. Scheelite is fairly coarse-grained and forms

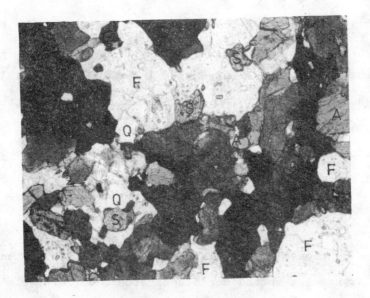

Fig. 1. Yxsjöberg amphibole skarn ore, x - nicolls, S - scheelite, F - fluorite, Q - quartz, A - amphibole, black - sulphides. The photo shows a section of an original width of app. 1.5 mm.

specks and veinlets in the ore together with large amounts of fluorite. It contains about 2% Mo in the lattice and occurs as zoned grains with increasing proportions of Mo towards the grain borders.

On average the two ores are composed as follows:

	Yxsjöberg	Wigström
Scheelite	0.5	0.45
Sulphides	6.2	0.3
Apatite	0.1	0.1
Fluorite	7.5	10
Calcite	5.1	7
Quartz	5.2	2
Felspar	15	3
Biotite	10	2
Skarn minerals	50	75

MINERAL PROCESSING

Development

After some years of struggling with limited success to improve the original flowsheet, more and more emphasis was laid upon scheelite flotation as the only means with potential to secure long term profitability. A new process had to be developed, though previous attempts to concentrate scheelite in the presence of fluorspar, calcite and apatite had failed due to the similarity of flotation properties. Thus fluorspar had been an unavoidable contaminant in such concentrates, and calcite-bearing scheelite ores had only been floated with low recoveries or had rendered low-grade concentrates. Apatite usually caused somewhat less trouble but still exerted a negative influence on the results.

The aim was preferably to produce seleable scheelite concentrates assaying at least 65% WO_3 with the highest possible recovery or else to produce lower grade concentrates and then to create a market for them or upgrade them chemically to commercial composition.

At different stages of the investigation experienced consultants such as Denver Equipment, Allied Colloids Ltd, Hazen Research Inc., KemaNord and Gränges Mineralprocesser took part in the research work. Contacts were also made with Institut Mechanobr, Leningrad, and various scheelite producers.

The test work progressed along two different lines, viz:
- Bulk flotation of calcium minerals with subsequent separation
- Direct selective scheelite flotation

Bulk flotation and separation following Petrov (1, 2) seemed for a long time to be a feasible method, as laboratory results were encouraging. The best results were obtained with an amphoteric unsaturated high molecular carboxylic acid (KemaNord Lilaflot OS) as collector. However, difficulties were encountered with this method in pilot plant tests due to the varying calcite composition of the bulk concentrate which prevented steady separation conditions. These problems have temporarily halted further development of this interesting method. It is believed that an adaption to continuous operation will become possible later on when the mechanisms involved are better understood.

Starting with the test reports from LKAB and its consultants and with information from the literature, Granges Mineralprocesser AB first of all managed to find a practically workable direct selective scheelite flotation process. This process has proved to be reliable and by far superior to other existing flotation methods for scheelite. The only disadvantage is high consumption of chemicals. As collector a common fatty acid is used.

The two processes mentioned have much in common, e.g., both utilize sodium silicate as an important ingredient to achieve selectivity. As opposed to bulk flotation and separation, however, selective scheelite flotation performed equally well as in the laboratory when tested on pilot plant scale. Commissioning in full scale operation was also easy.

Therefore, even if plants for the future may involve a comeback of bulk flotation as a supplementary method, the remainder of this paper will deal with direct selective scheelite flotation.

Application

The flowsheet of the process is shown in Fig. 2. Metallurgical results for the period January-September 1978 are given in Table 1.

Grinding: The grinding circuit consists of a rod mill ∅ 1.8 x 3.7 m and a ball mill ∅ 2.3 x 2.4 m. The rod mill is operated in open circuit, while the ball mill works in closed circuit with a ∅ 250 mm hydrocyclone.

The normal feed rate is 18 to 25 t/h. At higher throughputs, 30 to 35 t/h, half the feed is passed through a parallel rod

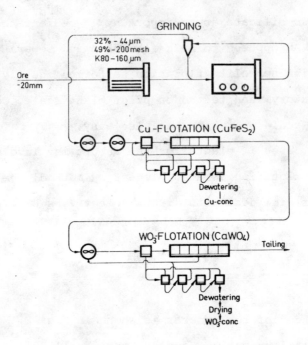

Fig. 2. Yxsjöberg flowsheet for copper and scheelite flotation.

mill of the same size. When the concentrator is operated with
old tailings, ball mill grinding is omitted to prevent overgrinding.

The hydrocyclone overflow is kept at about 50 weight % solids
and contains 50% minus 74 µm, cf. Table 2.

TABLE 1

Copper and Scheelite Flotation at Yxsjöberg, January to September 1978

Ore type product	Weight t	Assay, % (1)				Distr., %	
		Cu	WO$_3$	CaF$_2$	CaCO$_3$	Cu	WO$_3$
Yxsjöberg ore							
Feed	92,649	0.210	0.384	6.2	5.9	100.0	100.0
Cu-conc	678	22.6	0.01			79.0	0.0
WO$_3$-conc	405.3	0.01	69.9	1.8	10.7	0.0	79.4
Tailings	91,566	0.045	0.08			21.0	20.6
Wigström ore							
Feed	22,584		0.289	8.7	9.2		100.0
WO$_3$-conc	81.0		65.0	0.8	13.0		78.2
Tailings	22,503		0.055				21.8
Old Tailings							
Feed	5735	0.05	0.124	3.6	4.5		100.0
WO$_3$-conc	6.0		66.6	7.3	7.6		56.4
Tailings	5729	0.05	0.054				43.6
Total result							
Feed (2)	120,968	0.163	0.355	6.6	6.5	100.0	100.0
Cu-conc	678	22.6	0.01			77.8	0.0
WO$_3$-conc	492.3	0.01	68.8	1.7	11.3	0.0	78.8
Tailings	119,798	0.036	0.076			22.2	21.2

(1) CaCO$_3$ was determined as loss of ignition at 1000°C.

(2) Cu and WO$_3$ feed grades are calculated values. Assay gave 0.167% Cu and 0.360% WO$_3$.

TABLE 2

Fines from Hydrocyclone, Screen Analyses

Mesh width, μm	Cum. weight % passing	Mesh width, μm	Cum. weight % passing
583	100	74	50
297	95	44	32
147	77	9	6.5

Flotation: There are two flotation circuits (Fig. 3), one for chalcopyrite and one for scheelite. Copper concentrates are produced from Yxsjöberg ore only. When treating other materials, Cu-flotation is by-passed. For the time being, fluorspar is not floated.

Fig. 3. Copper and scheelite rougher circuits at Yxsjöberg.

The modifying agents used in the conditioners favour the selectivity vs. both scheelite and particularly pyrrhotite in copper flotation. Though the ore contains about 5-6% pyrrhotite, this mineral does not interfere and the concnetration ratio is unusually high, from 0.210 to 22.6% Cu or 108:1. Recovery is about 79%.

The copper content of tailings from old dumps cannot be recovered by the current method as the presence of rest reagents would cause scheelite losses to the copper concentrate.

In the scheelite flotation fatty acid serves both as collector and as frother. The low feed grade, about 0.4% WO_3 or 0.5% $CaWO_4$ corresponding to some 0.25% by volume of mineral, calls for strong accumulation of scheelite in the circuit, before a rich, self-supporting froth is obtained. Figure 5 shows a metallurgical balance calculated from simultaneous sampling of the products at various points of the treatment route. The rougher feed is upgraded almost three times by recirculated products, a fact that facilitates cleaning by providing a rougher concentrate with 35 to 50% WO_3. The flows within the cleaning circuit are consequently even smaller than could be anticipated from the crude ore assay, and only small machine volumes are necessary. Thus for the last three cleaning stages flotation machines of 100 l effective volume are used. The concentrate pump has an outlet opening of 25 mm and discharges into a Ø 18 mm rubber hose. These dimensions caused some concern and worry during the engineering period but have proved adequate.

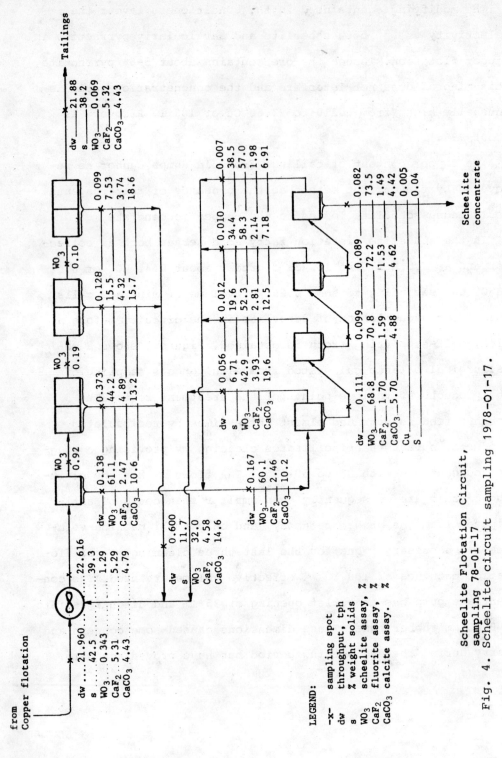

LEGEND:

-x-	sampling spot
dw	throughput, tph
s	% weight solids
WO_3	scheelite assay, %
CaF_2	fluorite assay, %
$CaCO_3$	calcite assay. %

Scheelite Flotation Circuit,
sampling 78-01-17

Fig. 4. Scheelite circuit sampling 1978-01-17.

Scheelite flotation is accompanied by intense flocculation which requires special measures in the cleaner circuit to release and discard contaminating particles from the scheelite flocs.

As scheelite floats considerably faster than most sulphide minerals, the circuit could be composed of few units. Scavenger flotation in this case is not as efficient as with sulphides, because calcite and fluorite particles become increasingly active and difficult to depress each time they are returned into the circuit. Calcite and fluorite behave differently in the circuit and their kinetics can be selectively influenced by pretreatment in a way that facilitates at least partial concentrate grade control. The behaviour of apatite is unclear as the content is low in the raw materials at hand; however, this question is of interest as the presence of phosphorus in the concentrate disturbs the subsequent production of ammonium paratungstate by reducing the tungsten recovery in the leaching process.

Fig. 5. Copper cleaner circuit at Yxsjöberg.

Other impurities in the concentrate of importance for a hydro-metallurgical treatment, such as Si, Fe, As, Sn, Bi and S are considerably lower than in the concentrates obtained by gravi-metrical and magnetic methods. Only the molybdenum content of the concentrate, 0.05% for Yxsjöberg and about 2% for Wigstrom, is not altered with the new method as the element occurs in the scheelite lattice. Molybdenite, however, could have been floated off prior to scheelite flotation.

As the process has been in operation only one year, further improvements may be expected. Already very high grade concentrates are obtained at good recoveries in a single operation. The concentration ratio for old tailings has been up to 500:1. For shorter periods, of course, better results have been achieved than those reported for the whole 9 month period. In this context, prospects for further improvements and adaptation of process parameters to other mineral combinations are bright, thus giving rise to hope of progress in separation sharpness and of an increased number of applications throughout the world.

Continued Research and Development
_____

The most important means for further process development is faster chemical analysis. Sampling is now carried out for a 24 h period and analyses are obtained the following day. Adequate process control cannot be exerted under such circumstances. Changes in the concentrator head grades therefore almost inevit-ably are reflected in poorer metallurgical results. During the summer of 1978 a quick method for calcite analysis in scheelite concentrates was introduced. Concentrate quality improved im-mediately and no corresponding decrease in recovery was noted.

It is now planned for an on-stream analyser to further speed up grade information and possibly to also economize on reagent consumption. The roles of different process variables should be easier to clarify by then.

Table 3 illustrates how the losses were distributed in the final tailings in the circuit balance study of 78-01-17. Obviously the losses in the ultrafine sizes are of importance for the overall results. Grinding and classification are the main tools to affect the amount of ultrafine slime and thus slime losses. The grinding equipment existed before reconstruction and only the hydrocyclone was introduced to the circuit.

From this point of view it would be favourable to replace the ball mill with e.g., a pebble mill but it has not been determined whether slime content reduction is likely nor have any tangible plans for the modification been established.

It is also of importance for the company to remain in a position allowing the treatment of ore from various small deposits in the area. The concentrator must be kept flexible enough to process different ore types without prior expensive pilot scale runs. The experience already gained means substantial advancement in minor deposit development and it is believed that most scheelite ores can be adapted to full scale operation after trial runs with just a few thousand tons of ore. On-stream analysis would be very valuable for quick trimming of the process.

A Theoretical Discussion

The success of a process which relies on such small differences in flotation properties as does the Yxsjöberg process balances on a thin thread. If the ruling mechanisms are not

TABLE 3

Scheelite Flotation at Yxsjöberg 1978-01-17, Sizing-sorting Assay Test

Size fraction, μm – μm	Circuit feed 21.96 t/h = 100%			Concentrate 0.083 t/h = 0.373%				Tailings 21.88 t/h = 99.627%		
	Weight %	Assay % WO_3	Distr. % WO_3	Weight %	Assay % WO_3	Distr. % WO_3	Rec. % WO_3	Weight %	Assay % WO_3	Distr. % WO_3
+250	8.0	0.13	3.0	1.1	17.5	0.3	8.8	8.0	0.12	13.7
250–125	21.7	0.13	8.3	6.9	59.2	5.6	77.0	21.7	0.03	9.3
125–75	20.4	0.25	15.0	15.3	72.3	15.3	96.0	20.4	0.010	2.9
75–45	15.9	0.39	18.2	22.9	74.3	23.4	97.4	15.9	0.010	2.3
45–26	13.0	0.48	18.3	23.6	73.5	24.0	99.0	13.0	0.005	0.9
26–9	14.4	0.51	21.5	26.0	75.8	27.2	88.3	14.4	0.06	12.4
-9	6.6	0.81	15.7	4.2	72.6	4.2	23.6	6.6	0.62	58.5
Total calc.	100.0	0.34	100.0	100.0	72.4	100.0	79.6	100.0	0.070	100.0
an.		0.343			73.5		79.8		0.069	

better understood in the future than they are to-day, sooner or later unexpected operational problems may arise despite the practical experience already gained. On the other hand a deeper penetration of the theoretical background may result in various spin-off effects, not least of which would be a new generation of more exact separation methods.

The connection between flocculation and flotation mechanisms was discovered early [1, 2]. However, not all kinds of flocculation are selective and imply favourable conditions for flotation. Thus Taggart [3] describes such flocculation as a result of selective oiling or high-speed agitation of thick pulps, explaining that only at oiled surfaces are contact angles large enough and bubble adhesion consequently strong enough to effect contact levitation or to survive violent agitation.

In recent years the connection between flocculation and flotation has been studied with new interest. Rubio and Kitchener [4] found that polymeric flocculants with hydrophobic groups can be used to flocculate hydrophobic slimes selectively away from hydrophilic ones. Consequently, conventional flotation collectors can provide the necessary basic surface differentiation of minerals before the flocculant is added. This principle provides a widely applicable method and can apparently be used either to obtain selective flocculation or to improve selectivity in flotation. Experimental results support such conclusions for systems of chrysocolla-malachite and calcite-dolomite but difficulties were encountered to achieve comparable separations with real copper ore. The problems were attributed to undesired metal ion activation of the gangue.

An unexpected feature of the system was the necessity to subject the slurry to a high rate of shear during flocculation. This is in accordance with reports from Warren [5, 6], who studied aggregation of ultrafine scheelite suspensions in turbulent flow generated by a single blade paddle stirrer in a baffled beaker. Coagulation by an indifferent electrolyte and flocculation by a polyelectrolyte produced aggregates which were broken up by intense agitation. Scheelite suspended in dilute sodium oleate solutions behaved quite differently. Aggregation occurred only at high stirring speeds, the extent of aggregation and the size of aggregates increasing the faster the suspension was stirred. Classical theories of colloid stability could not explain this shear flocculation. Warren proposes the following explanation: particles collide and with turbulent agitation the average energy of collision is much greater than the thermal energy and allows the colliding particles to approach more closely. Formation of aggregates is favoured by an energy of "hydrophobic association" which comes into effect if collisions result in the bound water molecules being removed and a direct contact between the hydrophobic particles being established. The resistance to thinning and removal of the water layers separating approaching particles is deemed likely to be weaker for hydrophobic particles than in the case of hydrophilic ones.

When shear-flocculation scheelite later was subject to flotation [5], the flocs behaved like individual particles of 10-100 μm in size.

It is not yet understood how an effect of a similar kind to that reported by Warren is obtained at Yxsjöberg with just normal, quite moderate, agitation. Apparently conditions can be created chemically that decrease the energy barrier for thinning the water layer around the scheelite particles, if such water removal is a necessary prerequisite for success.

Early patents have been found to contain all parameters of interest for a scheelite flotation process which is selective towards calcite, fluorspar and may be also apatite. The proper order of addition, the combination and the amounts of the necessary ingredients are evidently much more difficult to find as long as no theoretical predictions can be made.

Calcite, fluorspar and scheelite show similar surface properties but data in the literature reveal small differences that can systematically be utilized for separation purposes. If one accepts the hypotheses of Dr. Carl du Rietz [7], collectors are chemisorbed to the mineral surfaces, their ability to do so being ruled by the solubility of the surface ions and the collector in competition with other chemical constellations formed by substances present in the pulp. Immobile water molecules have to be screened off. With Ca^{2+} as the common surface ion, the outcome must depend on its activity in the three different minerals. This is affected by the chemical environment, e.g., temperature, pH-value, concentrations of activating and depressing agents etc.

How these factors influence actual separation and how new separations may be performed is currently being studied. However, it is significant for the present state of knowledge that no reasonable explanation can be given for the fact that in pilot plant tests calcite was easier to depress than fluorite, while in full scale operation the opposite was true. Current investigations try to explain such matters.

REFERENCES

1. Mitrofanov S. I. Solution of Some Problems Concerning the Theory and Practice of Selective Flotation in the USSR. Proc. 4th International Mineral Processing Congress, Stockholm, 1957, 441-460.

2. Klassen V. I. and Moukrosov V. A. An Introduction to the Theory of Flotation. Butterworth, London, 1963, 333-334.

3. Taggart A. F. Handbook of Mineral Dressing. John Wiley and Sons, New York, 1945, 12-101.

4. Rubio J. and Kitchener A. A. Trans. Inst. Min. Met. (Sect C) 86, C 97-100 (1977).

5. Warren L. J. J. Colloid Interf. Sci. 50, 307-318 (1975).

6. Koh P. T. L. and Warren L. J. Trans. Inst. Min. Met. (Sect C) 86, C 94-95 (1977).

7. Du Rietz C. Chemisorption of Collectors in Flotation. Proc. 11th Int. Mineral Processing Congress, Universitè di Cagliari, Cagliari, 1975, 375-404.

ABSTRACT

At the Yxsjöberg concentrator in central Sweden a new scheelite flotation process came on stream in late 1977. From a feed
containing on average 0.5% scheelite, 7% fluorspar and 5% calcite a concentrate with 68-75% WO_3 is produced at approximately
80% recovery despite the very similar flotation properties of
these calcium minerals. Prior to scheelite flotation some 0.7%
chalcopyrite in the mill head is floated off, the content of
pyrrhotite (about 5%) and scheelite remaining depressed. The
practical application of the process is described and results
are also presented for another ore. For commercial reasons all
process parameters cannot be released at this stage. The process is remarkably selective. This could be explained by con-
current flocculation and flotation mechanisms or by adequate
modifications of solubility conditions. Full understanding of
the process may create a second generation of flotation processes more exact in control and separation abilities.

RÉSUMÉ

A Yxsjöberg, en Suède Centrale, un nouveau processus de
flottation pour la scheelite a été mis en service vers la fin
de l'année 1977. A partir d'un minerai, qui contient environ
0,5% de scheelite, 7% de fluorite et 5% de calcite, le procédé
donne un concentré de scheelite contenant de 68 à 75% WO_3 avec
un rendement d'environ 80%, malgré les propriétés de flottation
trés semblables des trois minéraux de calcium. Avant, on fait
flotter environ 0,7% de chalcopyrite, en déprimant les contenus
du minerai de pyrrhotine (env. 5%) et de scheelite. L'application pratique du procédé est décrite et les résultats obtenus
avec deux minerais sont présentés. Cependant, pour des raisons
commerciales il n'a pas été possible de relever tous les paramètres du processus. La sélectivité remarquable du procédé pourrait
être expliquée soit par un concours de mécanismes de flocculation et de flottation soit par une modification propre des
conditions de solubilité dans la pulpe. Une compréhension

totale conduirait à une seconde génération de méthodes flotta-
tives plus exacte en contrôle et en écart de séparation.

ZUSAMMENFASSUNG

Ende 1977 wurde in Yxsjöberg in Mittel-Schweden ein selekti-
ves Schwimmverfahren für Scheelit in Betrieb genommen. Aus
einem Erz mit etwa 0.5% Scheelit, 7% Flusspat und 5% Kalzit
lässt sich dabei trotz der sehr ähnlichen Flotationseigenschaf-
ten dieser drei Calcium-Minerale ein Scheelittkonzentrat mit
68-75% WO_3 bei rund 80%-igem Ausbringen erzielen. Vorausgehend
werden etwa 0.7% Kupferkies bei Depression von Magnetkies
(rd 5%) und Scheelit abgeschwommen. Es wird praktische Anwendung des Verfahrens beschrieben und das Ergebnis für zwei Erz-
sorten vorgelegt. Alle technische Einzelheiten dagegen werden
aus kommerziellen Gründen nicht mitgeteilt. Die ungewöhnliche
Selektivität des Verfahrens wäre entweder mit gleichzeitiger
Flockung und Flotation oder mit geeigneter Veränderung der
Löslichkeitsverhältnisse in der Trübe zu begründen. Volle
Erkenntnis der betätigten Mechanismen kann zu einer zweiten
Generation von Schwimmverfahren führen, welche bessere Ueber-
wachung und schärfere Trennungen ermöglichten.

РЕЗЮМЕ

В Уксёберской обогатительной фабрике по переработке вольфрамовых руд в центральной Швеции в 1977 г. введена в эксплуатацию новая схема флотации шеелита. Из руды, содержащей 0,5% шеелита, 7% флюорита и 5% кальцита получают концентрат с 68 – 75% WO_3 при извлечению около 80% не смотря на очень похожие флотационные свойства кальциевых минералов.

Перед флотацией шеелита из руды флотируется ок. 0,7% халькопирита при депрессии пиротина (ок. 0,5%) и шеелита.

Описывается практическое применение процесса, кроме того приведены результаты для другой руды, однако коммерчеким причинам не все параметры процесса могут быть опубликованы в настоящее время.

Процесс является чрезвычайно селективным, что можно объяснить за счет одновременной флотации и флокуляции, а также соответствующей модификации условий растворимости.

Полное изучение процесса может привести к развитию второй генерации современных процессов флотации, более легко контролируемых и с высшей степенью сепарации.

A NEW REAGENT SYSTEM FOR THE SELECTIVE FLOCCULATION OF RUTILE

G. Rinelli and A. Marabini

Consiglio Nazionale delle Ricerche, Laboratorio per il Trattamento dei Minerali, Roma, Italia

INTRODUCTION

There has been a marked upsurge of interest in selective flocculation in recent years, not least because this process provides one of the few ways of tackling the problem of the treatment of very fine materials by purely physical methods. However, there still remain many points to be cleared up regarding the chemical principles which result in the coalescence of just one mineral in a multimineral system, and also the mechanics of floc formation and the separation of flocs from particles not affected by flocculation.

This latter aspect is all important as regards the practical application of the process, as it has a decisive influence on the index of separation [1]. It is therefore necessary to produce flocs with such physical characteristics as to permit:

316

(1) Minimum entrapment of undesired minerals within the floc,

(2) Easy separation of the flocs from the particles that remain dispersed.

The use of the high molecular weight compounds commonly adopted for flocculation is often unproductive because flocs formed by long-chain polymers always contain mechanically entrapped extraneous particles, while the very high consistency of the flocs formed makes it difficult to subsequently purify them by simple countercurrent washing.

The investigations reported here were designed to study what happens with a reagent system which polymerizes autonomously when it goes into action, with a view to influencing floc formation and consistency during the process.

Rutile was chosen for the study because it is known that analytical chemists make use of a reagent system consisting of tannic acid and antipyrine for the selective precipitation of titanium from acid solutions with the formation of flocs [2]. It was thus considered reasonable to investigate the same system of reagents for the selective flocculation of rutile according to different principles from those pertaining in the case of classical polymers. Rutile is also of special interest because when it occurs in cohesive rock deposits it is particularly difficult to concentrate owing to the presence of numerous associated minerals. This entails the need for fine-grinding processes that result in the production of large quantities of fines. There have been few studies on the selective flocculation and/or coagulation of TiO_2, and all of these have been on synthetic titania [3, 4, 5].

Quartz and hematite, as a siliceous matrix base and iron-bearing mineral respectively, were chosen to be separated from the rutile.

EXPERIMENTAL PROCEDURE

Determination of Flocculating Power on Pure Minerals

Procedure. The samples used in the tests on individual minerals were:

Rutile, 98% pure, kindly provided by the French B.R.G.M.

Hematite, pure, from the Isle of Elba,

Quartz, pure, Carlo Erba Company.

The rutile and the quartz were ground to minus 15 μm in a Boulton vibrating mill using porcelain grinding bodies. The hematite was also ground to minus 15 μm in a mill with steel grinding bodies. The ground minerals were stored as aqueous pulps constituted with deionized water; these formed the bulk stock from which the samples were taken for test purposes.

The following reagents of analytical grade (Carlo Erba Company) were used:

Tannic Acid (TA)
Antipyrine (AP)
H_2SO_4

Before every test the mineral pulp was shaken to ensure complete homogenization and the density was checked. A quantity of pulp containing 1 g of mineral was transferred to a 100 ml measuring cylinder and diluted with deionized water to about 80 ml. The pH was adjusted by addition of H_2SO_4. Tannic acid in 5% aqueous solution was then added and the pulp was condi-

tioned by stirring for about   5 min,   after which the
volume was made up to about 100 ml and antipyrine added, also in
aqueous solution, and after a further   30 s   stirring
the suspension was allowed to settle.

Flocculation efficiency was evaluated by the turbidimetric
method, measuring optical transmittance at regular time intervals using a photometer with a polychromatic source.

In this series of tests on pure minerals the aspects examined were:
- The influence of the absolute concentrations of reagents on
  rutile flocculation;
- The sedimentation rate of rutile, quartz and hematite in the
  presence and absence of the reagent system;
- The influence of pH on the flocculating action of the TA-AP
  system on rutile, quartz and hematite;
- The influence of the TA/AP concentration ratio on the process.

Influence of Reagent Concentration on Rutile Sedimentation

Starting from pointers which were derived from the analytical
method regarding the reagent quantities needed to precipitate
titanium quantitatively in an acid medium (H_2SO_4), a first
series of tests was run to assess what the best level of concentration of the two reagents might be.

Systematic tests were initially made at a pH of about 1.6
keeping the quantity of TA unchanged at 1.2 g/l and varying the
amount of AP. Figure 1 illustrates the transmittance values
read after 10 min sedimentation. It is apparent that the flocculating effect is at a maximum at AP concentrations of over
2 g/l.

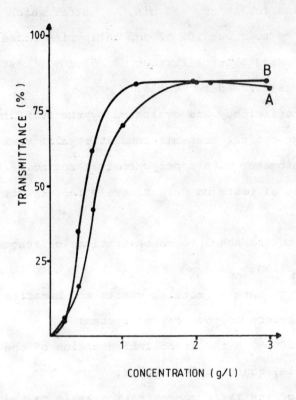

Fig. 1. A - Effect of Antipyrine addition on flucculation of
a rutile suspension (tannic acid, conc. = 1.2 g/l,
pH = 1.6), B - Effect of Tannic Acid addition on
flocculation of rutile suspension (Antipyrine conc.=
2.4 g/l, pH = 1.6).

Sedimentation tests were then run keeping the quantity of AP
constant at 2.4 g/l and varying the quantity of TA, again at a
pH of 1.6. Figure 1 illustrates the transmittance values found
in these tests. It was confirmed that the flocculating effect
of the reagent system peaks at a TA concentration of 1.2 g/l
and remains constant even when more TA is added.

A maximum flocculating effect on rutile was thus ensured
with TA and AP concentrations of 1.2 and 2.4 g/l, respectively,

320

and so these concentrations were selected for all subsequent
tests on pure minerals.

Flocculating Power of the TA-AP System on Rutile, Quartz and Hematite

The flocculating power of the TA-AP system (1.2 and 2.4 g/l,
respectively) in a sulphuric acid pulp (pH = 1.6) on rutile,
quartz and hematite was evaluated by measuring the transmittance
of the suspensions at regular time intervals.
The values obtained are shown by the A curves in Fig. 2.

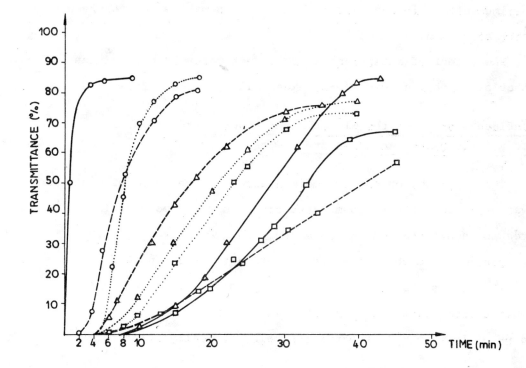

Fig. 2. Sedimentation rates of a rutile, quartz, hematite
        suspension. ──── - rutile,──── - quartz,······ - he-
        matite. O- with TA (1.2 g/l) and AP (2.4 g/l) -
        pH = 1.6.   Δ- with AP only (2.4 g/l) - pH 1.6.
        □- with H_2SO_4 only - pH = 1.6.

Also indicated on these diagrams are the transmittance
values as a function of time at pH 1.6 in the presence of AP
only (Curve B), and without any reagent addition at all (Curve
C). There are no sedimentation curves with only TA present,
since this did not result in the flocculation of any of the
three minerals.

It emerges from an examination of Fig. 2, 4 and 5 that the
TA-AP system acts energetically as a flocculant on rutile,
while its effect is much less marked in the case of quartz and
hematite. Rutile settles out completely in 3 min, while the
maximum effect in the case of quartz and hematite was observed
only after about 15 min.

The effect of antipyrine alone is not markedly better than
that of sulphuric acid alone, except in the case of quartz.

Influence of pH on the Flocculating Power of the TA-AP System
on Rutile, Quartz and Hematite

The effect of pH on the sedimentation of the three minerals
was examined under the same test conditions as above as far as
reagent concentration is concerned. The transmittance of the
suspension of each mineral was recorded after 3 min (Fig. 3).

It follows that there exists the possibility of separating
rutile from quartz and hematite by selective flocculation at
a pH of less than 2, the results being virtually quantitative.

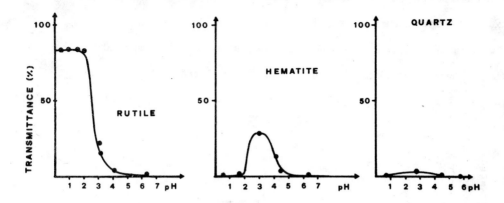

Fig. 3. Effect of pH on flocculation of suspensions of pure
minerals (TA = 1.2 g/l, AP = 2.4 g/l, pH = 1.6)
Transmittance observed after 3 min.

Influence of TA/AP Concentration Ratio on Flocculating Power
where the Three Pure Minerals are Concerned

The results obtained regarding the influence of reagent concentration on the sedimentation of rutile (Fig. 1), showed that
it was possible to obtain the maximum flocculating effect even
with TA and AP concentrations higher that those used in all the
previous tests. It was therefore decided to examine the influence of the concentration ratio of the two reagents on the stability of the individual mineral suspensions to ascertain
whether there are any other ratios which are more advantageous
as regards selectivity.

The TA/AP concentration ratio was varied from 0.5, used in
all the previous tests, up to 10. The TA concentration was kept
constant at 2.4 g/l.

The TA concentration was doubled as compared with the previous tests to permit variation of the TA/AP ratio without

going below the critical AP concentration needed to maintain maximum flocculant effect.

Figure 4 illustrates the transmittance after 3 min and after 10 min sedimentation with four different TA/AP ratios, namely 0.5, 1, 5 and 10.

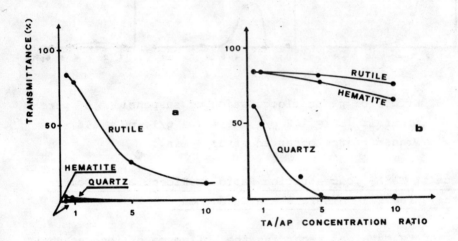

Fig. 4. Effect of TA/AP concentration ratio on flucculation of suspensions of pure minerals (TA = 2.4 g/l, pH = 1.6)
(a) Transmittance observed after 3 min
(b) Transmittance observed after 10 min.

It can be seen that the flocculating power with rutile and hematite remains virtually the same as the TA/AP ratio is increased to the point where the AP concentration is only one tenth that of the TA. In the case of quartz, on the other hand, there is a complete absence of flocculation when the quantity of AP drops below one fifth that of TA.

During the initial three-minute period the flocculating action of the TA-AP system is nil for all four concentration ratios where hematite and quartz are concerned.

After 10 min rutile and hematite are almost completely flocculated at all TA/AP ratios, while quartz remains completely
dispersed on decreasing the amount of AP to less than one fifth
the TA. This bears out the fact that tannic acid has some action
in dispersing quartz, as was shown repeatedly during the course
of the tests.

The results indicate that in the case of separation of rutile
from quartz it is also possible to work on times of around
10 min, provided that a TA concentration of 2.4 g/l is used and
that the TA/AP ratio is reduced to below one to five.

Observations on Results for Selective Flocculation of Rutile

During the tests made on the individual minerals it was observed that the physical characteristics of the flocs of rutile
vary depending on the conditions under which they were formed,
in accordance with the working hypothesis.

The results of the observations can be condensed as follows:

| | Conditions | | Floc consistency |
pH	TA concentration g/l	TA/AP ratio	(Largeness, weight, resistance to shear stress)
1.6	2.4	0.5	++++
1.6	2.4	1	+++
1.6	2.4	5	++
1.6	2.4	10	+
1.6	1.2	0.5	+++
1	1.2	0.5	+

Flocs consistency is greatest at a TA concentration of
2.4 g/l and a TA/AP ratio of 0.5. Though selective flocculation
of rutile from quartz and hematite is favoured by a pH of 1 and
a high TA/AP ratio, the resulting flocs lack consistency, and
this makes separation difficult, especially in the case of
rutile-hematite separations owing to the high specific gravity
of the iron mineral.

What are presumably the most efficient conditions for ensuring selective flocculation of rutile from quartz and hematite
have been derived from the whole series of tests made, and observations run, on the mechanical behaviour of the flocs. These
may be summarized as follows:

Rutile-Quartz Selective Flocculation

Conditions (a) pH = 1.6

TA concentration = 2.4 g/l

TA/AP ratio = 5

Rutile-Quartz and Rutile-Hematite Selective Flocculation

Conditions (b) pH = 1.6

TA concentration = 2.4 g/l

TA/AP ratio = 0.5

Selective Flocculation Tests

Procedure. The minerals used for the selective flocculation
tests were:
- Natural rutile ore grading 77%, with siliceous gangue, kindly
  supplied by the French B.R.G.M.
Hematite and quartz as in the tests on individual minerals.

The selective flocculation tests were run on binary and ternary mixtures of the three minerals, using a total quantity of 4 g of mineral. The first conditioning with TA was performed using a volume of 30 ml so that in the final AP conditioning it was possible to vary the solid content of the pulp from 10 to 100 g/l. Having completed the conditioning, the pulp was poured into a 4-cm diameter, 60-cm tall separating column. Water was led into the lower end of the column at a flow rate varying from 20 ml/min (slow washing), to 80 ml/min (fast washing), depending on the test. The liquid overflowing the top end of the column contained the gangue, while the flocculate was extracted from the bottom of the column and analysed.

Rutile-Quartz Separation Tests

Table 1 gives the results of the selective flocculation tests on rutile-quartz mixtures performed as per conditions (a). Tests 1, 2, 3 and 4 were performed at diverse solid/liquid ratios; this enabled the best concentration of solids for the final conditioning stage to be ascertained; namely, 5%. Tests 5 and 6 were performed under the same conditions as Tests 3 and 4, but using a washing rate three times higher. In Test 7 the flocculate obtained in Test 3 was re-washed.

TABLE 1

Results of Selective Flocculation Tests on Rutile-Quartz Mixtures

Test No.	% solid	Water flow rate ml/min	pH	TA concentr. g/l	TA/AP	Head mixture g		Head mixture %		Flocculate Grade		Flocculate Recovery	
						Rutile	Quartz	Rutile	Quartz	Rutile	Quartz	Rutile	Quartz
1	1	20	1.6	2.4	5	1.54	2.46	38.5	61.5	61.6	38.4	98.1	38.2
2	2	20	1.6	2.4	5	1.54	2.46	38.5	61.5	61.3	38.7	91.0	36.6
3	5	20	1.6	2.4	5	1.54	2.46	38.5	61.5	65.5	34.5	94.8	31.3
4	10	20	1.6	2.4	5	1.54	2.46	38.5	61.5	52.0	48.0	77.3	46.7
5	5	80	1.6	2.4	5	1.54	2.46	38.5	61.5	74.0	26.0	64.9	14.2
6	10	80	1.6	2.4	5	1.54	2.46	38.5	61.5	62.4	37.6	63.3	19.1
7	5	20	1.6	2.4	5	1.31	0.69	65.5	34.5	75.9	24.1	67.2	40.6

TABLE 2

Results of Selective Flocculation Tests on Rutile-Quartz and Rutile-Hematite Mixtures

Test No.	% solid	Water flow rate ml/min	pH	TA Concentr. g/l	TA/AP	Head mixture (g)			Head mixture (%)			Flocculate Grade (%)			Flocculate Recovery		
1	5	50	1.6	2.4	0.5	Rutile 1.54	Quartz 2.46		Rutile 38.5	Quartz 61.5		Rutile 72.7	Quartz 27.3		Rutile 83.1	Quartz 19.5	
2	5	50	1.6	2.4	0.5	TiO_2 1.54	Fe_2O_3 2	SiO_2 0.46	TiO_2 38.5	Fe_2O_3 50	SiO_2 11.5	TiO_2 67.5	Fe_2O_3 27.2	SiO_2 5.3	TiO_2 67.9	Fe_2O_3 21.1	SiO_2 17.8

TABLE 3

Results of Selective Flocculation Tests on Rutile-Quartz-Hematite Mixture

% solid	Water flow rate ml/min	pH	TA Concent. g/l	TA/AP	Head mixture						Flocculate					
					g			%			Grade			Recovery		
					TiO_2	SiO_2	Fe_2O_3	TiO_2	SiO_2	Fe_2O_3	TiO_2	SiO_2	Fe_2O_3	TiO_2	SiO_2	Fe_2O_3
5	50	1.6	2.4	0.5	0.61	2.99	0.4	15.2	74.8	10.0	70.7	24.0	5.3	81.2	5.6	9.3

Rutile-Quartz, Rutile-Hematite and Rutile-Quartz-Hematite Separation Tests

Table 2 sets forth the results obtained on rutile-quartz and rutile-hematite mixtures using the conditions (b). In all these tests conditioning was done with 5% solids.

Table 3 gives the best result obtained on a rutile-quartz-hematite mixture.

DISCUSSION OF RESULTS

The results obtained show that, generally speaking, the reagent system studied is suitable for separating rutile from quartz and hematite by selective flocculation. However, the separation indexes are very dependent on operating conditions, as regards chemical and mechanical parameters alike.

In the case of the rutile-quartz separation, it is apparent from Table 1 that by adopting chemical conditions favouring separation - particularly as regards the quantity of tannic acid and the TA/AP ratio - it is possible to obtain good rutile recoveries, but with flocculate grades not exceeding 65% if the countercurrent washing is performed at low flow rates which is necessary because the consistency of the flocs is poor. If one wishes to increase the rutile grade of the flocculate, it is necessary to have a higher wash-water flow rate, but then the weakness of the flocs results in some of them being destroyed and in part of the rutile being dragged over with the over-flowing quartz; where the flocculate grading is 74% rutile, recovery is only 65%. However, it is possible to upgrade a weak-floc concentrate by passing the flocculate through the column a second time, as was done in the case of the Test 3 concentrate. The result (Test 7) shows that the flocculate grade can be improved, but at the expense of a considerable drop in overall efficiency.

Generally better results are obtained by operating under Table 2 conditions instead, where chemical conditions may be less favourable for rutile-quartz separation but the ensuing flocs are stronger. This gives flocculates grading 72% rutile with 83% recovery, operating at a medium wash-water flow rate.

As far as rutile-hematite separation is concerned, this is greatly hindered by the high specific gravity of the iron mineral. In this case it is always necessary to have strong flocs (test reported in Table 2), and though the rutile grade of the flocculate was 67.5%, i.e., similar to that obtained under the same conditions in the rutile-quartz separation, recovery was only 67.9%.

However, much better results were obtained with the rutile-quartz-hematite mixture (Table 3) where a flocculate grading 70.7% TiO_2 was obtained (i.e., a ratio of concentration of better than 4 : 1), with 81% recovery. In this case, too, the elimination of quartz was much better than that of hematite.

It has thus been demonstrated that the proposed reagent system, whose operative mechanism will be examined below, can be considered as a flocculating complex of great flexibility as regards the formation of flocs having a variety of physical characteristics. So when separating different minerals it is possible to adjust conditions to achieve the best results either by altering the concentration ratio of the two reagents or by appropriately using different countercurrent washing techniques. This is a great advance compared with the situation where classical high molecular weight polymers are used; there is only one critical concentration which gives optimal flocculation and yet the only way of controlling floc consistency is by varying the amount of polymer.

The work reported here was limited to that required to check one principle; it must be widened greatly to examine all the possibilities offered by the use of different floc separation techniques which cannot always be parametrically reduced to a systematic form.

It is, however, worth observing that the tests on mixtures involved natural rutile ore grading 77% TiO_2. In the best tests the flocculate grades were very close to that figure and recoveries were reasonably high. This means that the entrapment of extraneous particles was reduced to a minimum.

Mechanism of Tannic Acid-Antipyrine System in Rutile Flocculation

Though the TA-AP system is used in analytical chemistry for the quantitative precipitation of Ti in the presence of numerous interfering elements including Fe^{3+}, no studies appear to have been performed on the chemical mechanisms involved. However, by considering the structural and chemical properties of the various substances involved, it is possible to advance a hypothesis on the interactions which occur between titanium, tannic acid and antipyrine.

The Ti^{4+} ion has an electronic configuration of the inert gas type. However, it tends to attain a more stable configuration by completing the s and d levels through acceptance of twelve electrons from six lone-pair donors, with the formation of complex compounds [6].

The ionization potential of the Ti^{4+} ion is so high that it cannot be stable in aqueous solution in the free state. In the presence of nucleophilic anions, such as occur in aqueous solutions of titanium sulphate (and titanium surface ions of TiO$_2$ in the presence of H$_2$SO$_4$), anionotitanates of the type $[Ti(SO_4)_3]^{2-}$ are formed [7]. In the case of the addition of organic compounds containing lone-pair electron donor groups, the Ti^{4+} ions also tend to form complex compounds. Lacking d electrons, it particularly tends to form its most stable compounds with anionic ligands containing oxygen [8]. The reagents used in the colorimetric analysis of Ti are generally of a phenolic nature and together with Ti they form compounds ranging in colour from yellow to orange-red depending on the reagent concentration and the reaction pH. As the pH is varied the formation of complexes occurs stagewise and the ligand/Ti ratio varies widely, reaching a maximum at the highest pH values.

Hexacoordinated compounds with an octahedral structure where the concentration ratio is 1 : 2 are most common, but octacoordinated compounds with a dodecahedral structure also occur [7].

Tannic acid is a polyphenolic derivative formed by the union of a molecule of glucose with five molecules of meta-digallic acid, i.e., it is a penta-m-digalloyl-glucose with the formula:

334

```
                         CH₂  - 0 - Ar
                          |
                  ┌──────CH
                  │       |
                  │      CH   - 0 - Ar
                  │       |
              0   │      CH   - 0 - Ar
                  │       |
                  │      CH   - 0 - Ar
                  │       |
                  └──────CH   - 0 - Ar
```

where Ar stands for the meta-digallic acid radical whose formula

is:

The large number of -OH groups (which are not hydrolyzed in
very acid solutions), plus the presence of carbonyl groups explains why the TA molecule can combine with titanium by coordination bonds where the 0 is the long-pair electron donor element. Because of the presence of the phenolic groups in the
ortho position, is is also likely that chelating rings are formed which render tha Ti-TA complex more stable.

The ratio according to which Ti and TA link up to form complex compounds may vary, of course, depending on reaction conditions and in particular, on pH. The number of TA molecules
which take part in the formation of complexes may become very
large both because of the numerous attachment sites in the TA
molecule and because of the ease with which tannin molecules
can bond together [9] once they are fixed on the first attachment points, consisting of the Ti^{4+} ion.

As with all vegetable tannins, TA has the property well
known in tanning chemistry of linking up with peptide groups
characterized by the presence of -CO-NH- groups, such as those
found in proteins, $-NH_2$ groups, etc. In this case, too, the
phenolic hydroxyls of tannin participate in the bond, but with
a hydrogen-bridging formation mechanism.

Thus, in the system considered in the present investigation
antipyrine is a compound that can link up with the phenolic
hydroxyls of tannin which have remained free after complexing
with the titanium.

Antipyrine is a 2, 3-dimethyl-1-phenyl-3-pyrazolin-5-com-
pound with the formula:

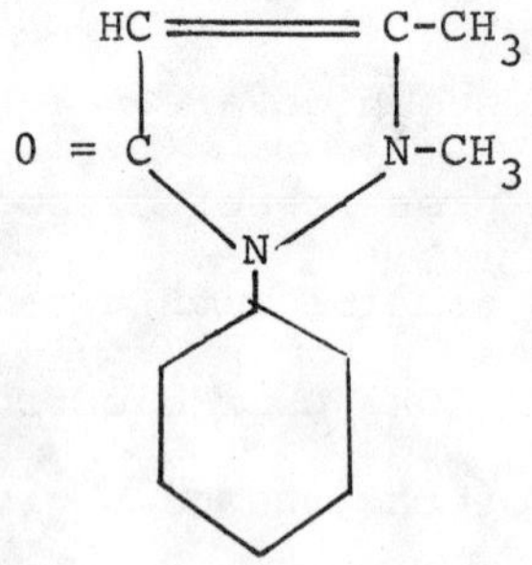

The ketonic and amminic groups present in the antipyrine molecule can take part in the formation of hydrogen-bridging with
the tannic acid molecules. Because of the great number of phenolic groups present in the tannic acid molecules there are
numerous attachment sites and various steric possibilities of
combination with the antipyrine molecules.

Hence the -OH groups which remain free in the Ti-TA complexes and which, as such, ensure that the complexes themselves
are highly soluble, link up with the antipyrine molecules;
these thus act both as an insolubilizing element and also as a

336

means to fix the previously complexed TA molecules and to hold them stably together[*].

This is very probably the mechanism govering the formation of the hydrophobic macromolecular organic structures that bind the rutile particles with the selective formation of flocs in the suspension studied.

Reaction between Ti and TA in Solution

Some tests on the way TA reacts with solutions of Ti^{4+} ions were run to obtain confirmation of the hypothesis framed above. The tests were performed on standard solutions of titanium sulphate by varying both the TA concentration and the pH.

The results show that when TA is added gradually to the titanium solution a compound is formed which colours the solution and partially precipitates, remaining in unstable equilibrium with the solution. The intensity of the colour increases as the concentration of TA and the pH increase. When the amount of TA is increased further the precipitate completely redissolves. The quantity of precipitate is at a maximum for pH values above 3.8. Under these conditions the TA/Ti molecular ratio also exceeds the maximum possible coordination number of the Ti^{4+}.

These observations provide initial confirmation of the hypothesis regarding the TA-Ti reaction mechanism. The appearance of colour indicates an alteration of the ligand-field strength and a shift of the α-α transition bands towards the longer wavelengths of lower energy values. This shows that the

---

[*] The phenomenon is similar to that which occurs in the case of vegetable tannins and animal proteins in leather tanning [10].

TA molecules have substituted nucleophilic anions like $(HSO_4)^-$ or $(SO_4)^{2-}$ and the water molecules present in the coordination shell of the titanium. Comparison of the ultraviolet and visible absorption spectra performed on solutions of titanium sulphate and on solutions of the Ti-TA compound reveals the shift of the absorption band from the ultraviolet (188 nm) to the visible (420 nm).

The variation in the colour intensity of the complex compound indicates a different degree of substitution by the TA of the ligands existing in the initial solution of titanium sulphate and confirms that the TA can link up with the Ti in different concentration ratios, while the increase of the TA/Ti ratio observed at pH values of over 3.8 indicates that an association of TA molecules among themselves can occur during the formation of the complex compound.

The partial solubility of the Ti/TA complex in water shows that a large number of hydroxyls still remain free after the formation of the compound itself.

Formation of the Ti-TA-AP Compound

The addition of AP to the solution in which the Ti-TA compound is present leads to the quantitative precipitation of the complex, thus leaving the aqueous solution colourless. As the quantity of AP is gradually increased the precipitate tends to form larger and larger flocs of increasingly greater consistency, eventually becoming a single gummy mass. This is completely in line with what was observed in the flocculation tests (with a TA/AP ratio of 1/10 the mineral particles bond together as a single gummy agglomerate).

338

It is thus evident that antipyrine exerts a stabilizing effect where the complexed tannic acid molecules are concerned, and causes coalescence of the macromolecules of the TA-Ti complex. The formation of the interparticle aggregates during rutile flocculation is precisely the result of this phenomenon.

We wished, however, to check the formation of the Ti-TA-AP compound on the surface of the rutile particles by an infrared study performed using a Perkin-Elmer Model 577 spectrophotometer.

Adsorption tests were run on the pure rutile used in the tests on individual minerals. One gram of sample was treated with an aqueous solution (50 ml) containing 0.5 g TA and 1 g AP, adopting the methods used for the flocculation tests. The suspension was centrifuged initially and the solid residue was

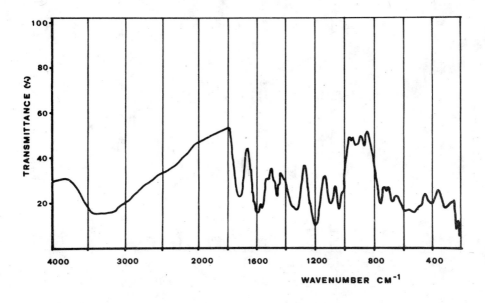

Fig. 5. Infrared spectrum of the rutile after the reaction with tannic acid and antipyrine.

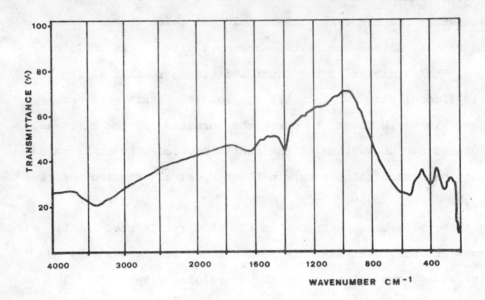

Fig. 6. Infrared spectrum of the untreated rutile.

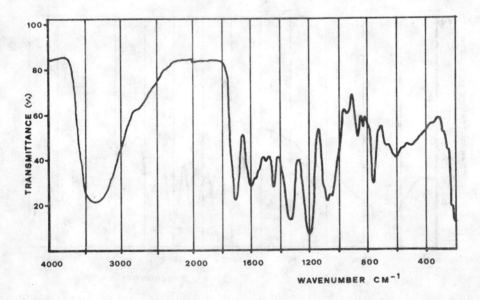

Fig. 7. Infrared spectrum of the compound formed in solution between Ti^{4+}, tannic acid and antipyrine.

washed with water and recentrifuged. The infrared examination
was then carried out (Fig. 5) adopting the usual technique involving KBr pellets. At the same time infrared spectra of untreated rutile (Fig. 6) and of the compound formed in solution
between Ti, TA and AP (Fig. 7) were also examined.

It is apparent that the complex formed on the surface of the
rutile sample is the same as that formed in solution.

CONCLUSIONS

The study shows that the problem of selective flocculation
can be tackled in a manner which has so far received little attention. The common use of true polymers raises problems of
selective adsorption and of floc consistency control which are
of decisive importance as regards the possibility of mechanical
separation of the flocs. The interparticle bonds are formed
either by hydrogen-bridges or by hydrophobic bonding.

The use of a binary system of reagents in the investigations
reported here results in the breakdown of the flocculation process into two successive and distinct stages: (1) the complexing of the metal element by a nucleophilic compound; (2) the
aggregation of the surface-conditioned particles by means of a
second compound which renders the particles hydrophobic and
causes them to coalesce. This process is somewhere between
hydrophobic bonding and polymer bridging, and may be defined
as selective flocculation by "molecular bridging".

It is clear that as two reagents are involved, the process
is much more flexible than when only one polymer is used. The
complexing agent (which in the present case can be taken to be

any tannin) can be chosen from among those which are most selective towards a given cation in relation to its molecular structure, even if the surface compound formed on the particles may still be soluble and hydrophilic. The flocculating agent, which has to eliminate the residual hydrophily and exert a bridging action between the particle complexes, can be diversified over fairly wide limits. In the case considered here, any compound containing e.g., $-CO-NH-$, $-NH_2$, $= CO$ groups could be considered in place of antipyrine.

The possibilities opened up by this twofold choice, especially as regards being able to alter the concentration ratio of the two reagents, broadens the chemical basis of the selective flocculation process, enabling control to be exerted over the progress of floc formation - which can be matched to suit the mechamism adopted for separation of flocs from particles that are still dispersed.

Further research is needed and the studies must be extended to other minerals in order to explore more fully the possibilities of applying this process. However, the results obtained in the case reported here are certainly encouraging, particularly as regards the rutile-hematite separation, where the specific gravity of the two minerals certainly does not favour separation.

ACKNOWLEDGMENTS

The Authors wish to thank Mrs. M. A. Esposito and Mr. C.Cozza for their valuable contribution to the performance of the experimental tests, and also Prof. M. Maltese of the Institute of

Inorganic Chemistry at Rome University for most useful discussions on the chemical interpretation of the phenomena.

REFERENCES

1. Yarar B. and Kitchener J. A. Trans. Inst. Min. Met., Sec. C, 79, C 23 (1970).

2. Vogel A. I. Text-Book for Quantitative Inorganic Analysis. Longmans, London, 1968, 544.

3. Pugh R. J. and Kitchener J. A. J. Colloid Interface Sci., 35, 656 (1971).

4. Friend J. P. and Kitchener J. A. Chem. Eng. Sci., 28, 1071 (1973).

5. Pugh R. J. Colloid and Polymer Sci., 252, 400 (1974).

6. Ballhausen C. J. Introduction to Ligand Field Theory. Mc Graw-Hill, New York, 1962, 227.

7. Pascal P. Nouveau Traité de Chimie Minérale. Masson Et. Cie. 1956, Vol. IX, 127.

8. Perrin D. D. Organic Complexing Reagents, Structure, Behavior, and Application to Inorganic Analysis. Intersc. Publish., New York, 1964, 314.

9. Haslam E. Chemistry of Vegatable Tannins. Acad. Press, London, 1966, 7.

10. Kirk-Otmer. Encyclopedia of Chemical Technology. Intersc. Publish. New York, 1956, Vol. 12, 303.

ABSTRACT

A new reagent system consisting of tannic acid and antipyrine
has been investigated for the selective flocculation of rutile.
The flocculating power of the system was observed on rutile,
quartz and hematite in relation to reagent concentration and pH.
A separation test was carried out on binary and ternary mixtures
of the three minerals. The results obtained were related to the
effect of the chemical and mechanical conditions on the nature
of the flocs.

The mechanism of action of the two reagents was investigated
and interpreted as a "molecular-bridging" in which the tannic
acid acts as a complex-forming compound with the Ti^{4+} and the
antipyrine exerts a stabilizing and aggregating effect.

RÉSUMÉ

Un nouveau système de réactifs, composé d'acide tannique et
d'antipyrine, a été étudié pour la flocculation sélective du
rutile. La puissance de flocculation du système a été observée
sur du rutile, du quartz et de l'hématite, en fonction de la
concentration des réactifs et du pH. Un test de séparation a
été effectué dur des mélanges binaires et ternaires de ces trois
minéraux. Les résultats obtenus ont été comparés à l'influence
des conditions chimiques et mécaniques sur la nature des flocons.

Le mécanisme d'action des deux réactifs a été étudié et est
interprété comme un "pont moléculaire", dans lequel l'acide
tannique agit en tant que composé formant un complexe avec du
Ti^{4+} et l'antipyrine procure un effet de stabilisation et
d'agrégation.

ZUSAMMENFASSUNG

Es wurde ein neues, aus Tannin und Antipyrin bestehendes
Reagenzien-System untersucht, das sich zur selektiven Ausflockung von Rutil eignet. Die Flockungsfähigkeit dieses Systems
ist an Rutil, Quartz und Hämatit hinsichtlich der Konzentration
der Reagenzien und des pH-Wertes untersucht worden. Trennungs-

proben wurden mit Zwei- und Dreikomponentengemischen dieser
drei Minerale durchgeführt. Die erzielten Ergebnisse wurden
mit dem Einfluss chemischer und mechanischer Bedingungen auf
die Beschaffenheit der Flocken in Zusammenhang gebracht.

Der Mechanismus der Einwirkung beider Reagenzier wurde
untersucht und als "molekulare Brücke" interprätiert, wobei
das Tannin komplexierend auf Ti^{4+} wirkt, während Antipyrin
einen stabilisierenden und sammelnden Effekt ansübt.

РЕЗЮМЕ

Исследована новая система реагентов, состоящая из танина
и антипирина, для селективной флокуляции рутила. Сила флокуляции
системы наблюдалась на рутиле, кварце и гематите в зависимости
от концентрации реагентов и pH. Опыты по разделению проводились
на двойных и тройных смесях трёх минералов. Полученные результаты были объяснены влиянием химических и механических условий
на характер флокул. Исследован механизм действия двух реагентов,
интерпретированный как "молекулярный мост", при котором танин
действует как комплексообразующее соединение с Ti^{4+}, а антипи-
рин оказывает стабилизирующее и собирательное действие.

THE EFFECTS OF THE PHYSICAL VARIABLES OF CARBOXYMETHYL CELLULOSE REAGENTS ON THE DEPRESSION OF MAGNESIA BEARING MINERALS IN WESTERN AUSTRALIAN NICKEL SULPHIDE ORES

M. K. Rhodes

Australian Selection PTy Ltd., Kalgoorlie, Australia

INTRODUCTION

Depression of talc and other readily floatable magnesia bearing minerals in nickel flotation, has been carried out for many years, particularly in Canada[1], and southern Africa[2]. Polysaccharides in the form of natural gums and starches, and nigrosene dextrin type compounds have been the most commonly used depressants.

The use of carboxymethyl cellulose reagents in copper-nickel flotation has been known since the early 1950's when research was conducted in the U.S.S.R. by Vaneev[3]. Carboxymethylcellulose reagents had, however, been used in the food, textile, paper, cosmetics, and oil well drilling industries for much longer.

The first nickel sulphide orebody in Western Australia was found in ultramafic rocks in 1966[4]. Since then seven nickel mining operations have commenced. Carboxymethylcellulose reagents have been used in the treatment of five of the ores, as depressants for readily floatable magnesia bearing minerals.

The most comprehensive paper on C.M.C. depressants[5], was published in 1964. Information on Western Australian ores is restricted to two papers[6, 7]. Most of the testwork carried out to date has been performed by operating companies and the results have not been published.

In this work the effects of the physical variables of C.M.C. reagents on the flotation performance was studied with particular respect to the resulting magnesia level in the concentrates. The variables studied were: degree of polymerisation; C.M.C. content; degree substitution; structural variation and dosage. The effects of C.M.C. solution temperature were also investigated.

CHARACTERISTICS OF CARBOXYMETHYLCELLULOSE REAGENTS

Preparation

These reagents are cellulose ethers, and are prepared by the action of monochloroacetic acid or its sodium salt on alkali celluloses

$$RONa + ClCH_2COONa \rightarrow ROCH_2COONa + NaCl \qquad (1)$$

(R - anhydroglucose molecule).

The sodium carboxymethyl groups (CH_2COONa) replace a proportion of the hydrogen atoms associated with the hydroxyl groups of the glucose units which form the cellulose molecule (Fig. 1). Sodium chloride and some sodium glycolate

(HOCH$_2$COONa) are formed as by-products.

The control of the reaction conditions determines the physical properties of the resultant reagents. These are discussed below. As is the case with most organic polymers, the values of the physical parameters are only average values.

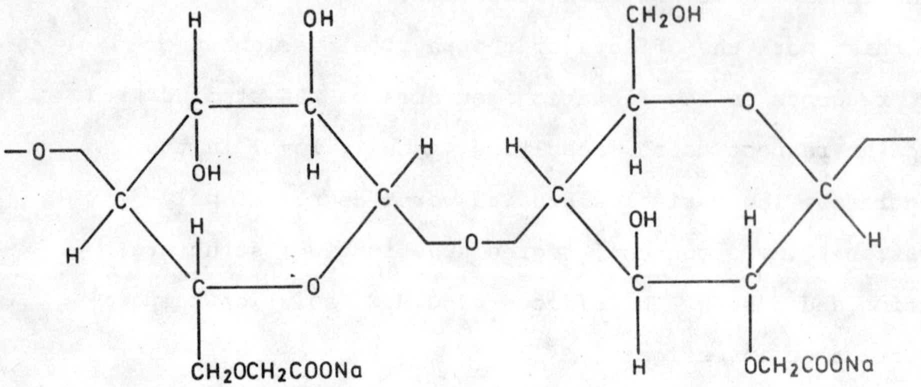

Fig. 1. Sodium carboxymethyl cellulose (Degree of substitution - 1.0).

Properties

Degree of Substitution (DS). This is the average number of carboxymethyl groups introduced into one glucose unit. For commercial qualities of C.M.C. the DS varies between 0.4 and 1.5.

C.M.C. Content. This is the degree of purity of the product, and is measured as the percentage of sodium C.M.C. present.

Degree of Polymerisation (DP). This expresses the average
number of glucose units per cellulose ether molecule, and is
a function of chain length, and therefore molecular weight.
Increasing the DP increases the viscosity of an aqueous
solution of sodium carboxymethylcellulose[8], and the solution viscosity is therefore used as a variable because it is
more easily measured than DP.

Structure. The structure of the C.M.C. molecule varies
with degree of substitution and degree of polymerisation.
However, for reagents with the same DS and DP it is possible
to introduce further variations by repositioning the substituted radicals. For instance the DS would be 1.0 if two
radicals were substituted on every other unit but the structure would be different.

C.M.C. Solution Temperature. The viscosity of a C.M.C.
solution drops with increasing temperature, but the effect is
reversible if the solution is not heated above $80^{\circ}C$ or for
lengthy periods.

ORE SAMPLE DESCRIPTION

The samples tested were from Selcast Exploration Ltd's
Andrews Shaft (Mine 1), and from the Redross Mine managed by
Anaconda Australia Inc. (Mine 2). Both mines were underground
operations situated in the Eastern Goldfields region of
Western Australia.

Head analyses of the samples from each mine are given in
Table 1. Because of problems with the oxidation of the nickel

349

sulphides, the samples were stored in a nitrogen atmosphere.

TABLE 1

Average Chemical Analysis of the Ore Samples

| Sample Origin | Content % | |
	Ni	MgO
Mine 1	3.4	21
Mine 2	3.4	14

Mineralogy. Some silicate minerals, which have plate like structures, tend to float readily when subjected to the flotation process. Minerals of this type which contain magnesia have been grouped together under the term "readily floating magnesia-bearing minerals". Four such minerals, talc, chlorite, phlogopite and serpentine were identified in the samples tested. In addition fibrous forms of tremolite and actinolite were also identified, and these could also float. Table 2 gives the average proportions of these minerals in the samples tested.

TABLE 2

Mineralogical Analysis of the Ore Samples

| Sample Origin | Readily floatable mineral content Wt% | | | | |
	Talc	Chlorite	Amphiboles	Serpentinite	Phlogopite
Mine 1	16	17	12	4	2
Mine 2	36	10	10	-	-

The opaque minerals present were pentlandite, violarite, pyrrhotite, pyrite, chalcopyrite and magnetite.

350

EXPERIMENTAL DESIGN

In the initial phase of the testwork factorial design was used to investigate four variables at two levels. Yates analysis[9] was used to calculate the effect of each treatment combination, and an internal estimate of error variance employed.

Three series of test were conducted to study the variables, which were degree of substitution, C.M.C. content, degree of polymerisation, and dosage. Each level was selected within a short range because the C.M.C. samples had similar but not identical characteristics.

The dosage rates were similar to those used in plant practice, and the two levels were selected so that the "total contained C.M.C. addition" (dosage x content) was the same for the high dosage-low content and low dosage-high content treatment combinations. This allowed the eight tests in each series with similar total contained C.M.C. additions to be analysed as 2[3] factorial experiments with DP, DS and content as variables.

TABLE 3

Variables Used in the Factorial Experiments

| Factor | Variable | Level | |
		Low	High
A	Degree of polymerisation	200-300	450-550
B	Degree of substitution	0.5-0.6	0.75-0.85
C	C.M.C. Content	60%	99%
D	Dosage Mine 1	180g/t	300g/t
	Mine 2	330g/t	550g/t

Based on the results of the factorial testwork, subsequent investigations were confined to variations in dosage, and degree of polymerisation. In addition the effects of C.M.C. structure and temperature were studied.

The mesh of grind and reagent additions other than C.M.C. were similar to those used in plant practice and were kept constant. In each test only an extended roughing stage was performed, and contentrates were removed at various time intervals. Extra frother was added after 210 s in each test.

The concentrates and final tailings were assayed for nickel and magnesia.

Response Level

The magnesia (MgO) content in the concentrates was selected for determining the effect of the C.M.C. reagents. However, as the depressant should depress gangue without hindering the flotation of the nickel minerals, the response level took into account nickel metallurgy as well as the magnesia content.

This was achieved by determining the magnesia content for a given value of "the weight of concentrate per 100 units of nickel" (unit weight). This value is a parameter used in release analysis [10, 11]. It represents a quantity of concentrate, and is given by cumulative recovery %/fractional concentrate grade. The magnesia contents were determined at two levels of "unit weight in each test.

RESULTS

Factorial Experiments

Total contained C.M.C. addition was the only factor which significantly (95% confidence) affected the magnesia content of the concentrates in all experiments.

Degree of polymerisation, and the degree of substitution were significant at only one level of "unit weight" for the two Mine 1 samples, and the Mine 2 sample, respectively.

There were no significant interaction effects, so single variable tests were conducted in the subsequent investigations.

Effect of Variation in Total Contained C.M.C. Addition

Two groups of tests, one on a sample from each mine were performed to determine the optimum addition. All the tests were carried out using a high purity C.M.C. with a DP of 250 and a DS in the range 0.75-0.85. The results are presented in Fig. 2.

Effect of Variation in Degree of Polymerisation

Reagents with DP values ranging from 250 to 1150 were tested. The equivalent viscosity range for 2% aqueous solutions of these reagents at $25^{\circ}C$ was 56-32,000 cp. Figure 3 shows the relationship between the DP value and the magnesia content of the concentrates.

During the investigation it was noticed that the tailings had flocculated in the tests using reagents with DP values of 1000 and 1150.

353

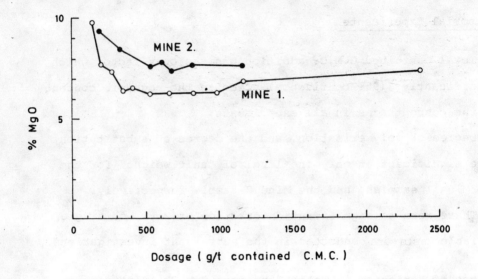

Fig. 2. Effect of total contained C.M.C. addition on
the magnesia content.

Effect of Temperature

Plant practice with ore from both mines had indicated that
variations in ambient temperature affect either the magnesia
content of the concentrates or the depressant demand.
An investigation showed that the air temperature in the
Eastern Goldfields varied between -2°C and 45°C, with pulp
temperatures 5°C inside these limits.

At 3 [2] factorial experiment was used to study the effect
of pulp and solution temperatures in this range for Mine 1 ore.

C.M.C. solution temperature was not a significant variable
at the 5% level, but the pulp temperature was a highly
significant variable (> 99% confidence) for the linear effect.

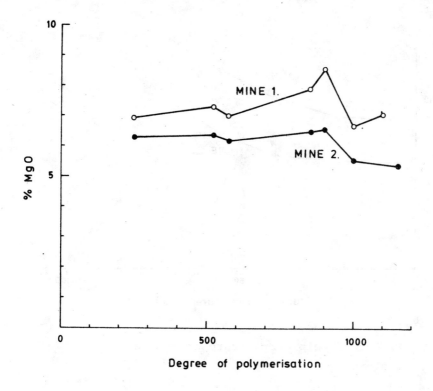

Fig. 3. Effect of degree of polymerisation on the
magnesia content.

Pulp temperatures of 55° and 70°C were also investigated
and the increase in magnesia content of the concentrates
(Fig. 4) was almost exponential. In addition the nickel
recovery dropped. These results were confirmed on Mine 2 ore.

Effect of C.M.C. Structure Variation

One C.M.C. reagent was obtained in which the structure was
altered so that the carboxymethyl groups were substituted in
clusters rather than distributed evenly along the chain.

355

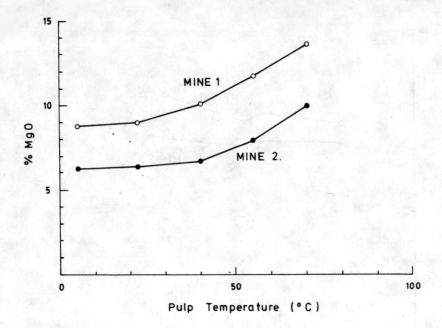

Fig. 4. Effect of pulp temperature on the magnesia
content.

Table 4 details the results. The optimum total contained
C.M.C. addition was lowered by 15% for Mine 1 ore, and 40%
for Mine 2 ore.

PLANT OPERATIONS

Carboxymethylcellulose reagents were used in both operations. For Mine 1 ore the C.M.C. addition was controlled so
that the concentrate produced contained less than 5% MgO.
The lowest magnesia content was required in the Mine 2
operation to ensure that the final nickel concentrate grade
was as high as possible.

TABLE 4

Effect of C.M.C. Structure on the Magnesia Content

Sample Origin	C.M.C. Structure	Addition (g/t contained C.M.C.)	Response Level (%MgO)
Mine 1	Standard	300	9.0
	Altered	180	9.4
	Altered	250	9.0
	Altered	300	8.9
Mine 2	Standard	550	4.5
	Altered	550	4.4
	Altered	330	4.3

Variation in Degree of Polymerisation

The reagent with a DP value of 1150 was tested on the Mine 1 ore. The addition rate was reduced by 13% whilst the magnesia content of the concentrate remained constant (Table 5). This confirmed the laboratory testwork which showed that this reagent was equivalent, or better than, the lower DP ones. The reagent, however, showed no economic adventage.

Altered Structure

This reagent was tested on both ores, and details of addition rates costs are given in Table 5. Plant trials were carried out for a total of eleven days on Mine 1 ore, and fifteen days on Mine 2 ore. In both cases the dosage was reduced in similar proportions to the reduction in optimum dosage in the laboratory testwork. An average of 17% in the plant vs. 15% for Mine 1, and 44% vs. 40% for Mine 2.

TABLE 5

Plant Trials

Ore	Reagent	Dosage g/t CMC	%MgO in conc.	%Reduction in dosage	Ratio of cost	%Reduction in cost
Variation of D.P.						
Mine 1	Standard (D.P.250)	375	4.4	–	1	–
	Test (D.P.1150)	328	4.5	13	1.21	-8
Structure Variation						
Mine 1	Standard	475	4.4	–	1	–
	Altered	391	4.3	17	1.14	3
Mine 2	Standard	447	2.9	–	1	–
	Altered	249	1.6	44	1.14	37

The cost benefit from using this reagent was marginally positive for Mine 1 ore, but for Mine 2 ore the reduction in depressant cost at 37% was such that the reagent was subsequently used on a permanent basis.

Effect of Temperature

A comparison was made between pulp temperature and C.M.C. addition for Mine 1 ore over a year. Figure 5 shows the relationship between pulp temperature, C.M.C. addition needed to maintain the MgO content below 5%, and time in four weekly periods. Although there were changes in ore type treated during the period which resulted in varying depressant demand, there was a definite trend towards increasing C.M.C. additions with increasing temperature.

358

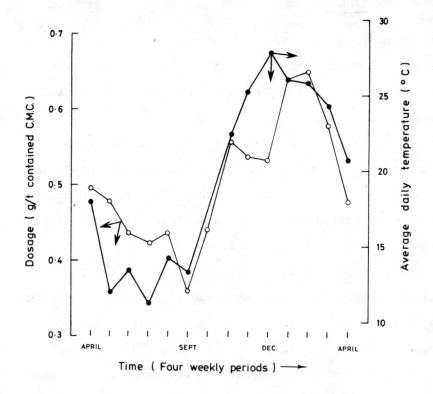

Fig. 5. Comparison of C.M.C. dosage and average daily temperature.

DISCUSSIONS AND CONCLUSIONS

The main objective of the investigations was to determine whether any of the physical variables of C.M.C. reagents affected the depression of readily floatable magnesia bearing minerals associated with nickel bearing sulphide ores. No work was specifically carried out to determine mechanisms of depression, however, some general comments have been made in this regard.

Practical Implications

Total contained C.M.C. addition should be used in the comparison of pure and technical grade C.M.C. reagents, as this was the only significant variable in all the factorial experiments.

After an optimum addition for the depression of magnesia had been reached, further additions within a normal operating range did not affect the nickel recovery. This is in contrast to some natural gums which depress sulphides with dosages of approximately 15-20% above the optimum [12].

In Western Australian nickel treatment plants the C.M.C. reagents which have been used have had DP values ranging from 300-600. The laboratory testwork confirmed that of the low DP reagents this was the most suitable range. Scope, however, exists for the use of reagents with DP values of greater than 1000, as this type was technically successful in both the laboratory and the plant.

Up to $40^{\circ}C$, C.M.C. solution temperature did not affect the magnesia content of the concentrates, consequently the solution can be stored under the conditions experienced in the Eastern Goldfields, without affecting the flotation response.

Theoretical Considerations

C.M.C. reagents are polymers which have ether groups substituted on alkali cellulose. Unsubstituted hydroxyl groups are retained in the macromolecule.

360

Bakinov et al.[5] postulated that hydrogen bonding was
the determining mechanism in the adsorption of carboxymethylcellulose reagents on readily floating silicates. This
mechanism has also been suggested in the guar gum molecule [12].
It has also been stated [13] that 2 phenyl, 2 propanol can
absorb onto the surface of talc by means of its hydroxyl
groups through hydrogen bonding.

If the depression was achieved by hydrogen bonding it
could be expected that increased C.M.C. addition would lead
to non selective adsorption when the total energy became too
high. A slight drop in nickel recovery did occur at approximately five times the optimum dosage, which is consistent
with the postulated mechanism. If hydrogen bonding occurs
between unsubstituted OH groups and surface oxygen atom sites,
the broken edge structures of the layer silicates might
provide suitable sites. The anionic groups would render the
subsequent surface hydrophilic.

When the chain length of the polymer increase more OH
groups are contained in each molecule, and the hydrogen bond
adsorption energy would be expected to increase. Reagents
with a high DP might be expected to adsorb onto the valuable
minerals and depress them. An increase in the magnesia content of the concentrate for a given value of "unit weight"
did occur when reagents in the DP range 800-900 were used,
and with both ores the nickel recovery into the first timed
concentrate was also lower, which indicated that depression
of the sulphides was occurring. For reagents with a DP above
1000 there was still a drop in nickel recovery, but the

magnesia content was on average lower than for the other C.M.C.'s. During the testing of these high DP reagents flocculation of the silicates was evident in the tailings, whereas this was not the case with the reagents with DP values less than 1000. The cause of the improved depression with these reagents, which have a molecular weight or approximately 250,000, was possibly due to selective flocculation.

The process of selective flocculation has been described by other authors [14-16]. Basically high molecular weight polymers are selectively adsorbed onto specific minerals which are flocculated and the flocs separated from the non flocculated material.

If the C.M.C. reagents did adsorb onto the readily floating silicates by hydrogen bonding, the extra chain length of the reagents with a high degree of polymerisation was probably sufficient to allow polymer bridging to occur and cause the flocculation which was observed. Because of the weak hydrogen bond adsorption mechanism, the carboxymethylcellulose reagents might have tended to scrub off the depressed minerals, due to the agitation during flotation, and allowed them to refloat. The flocculation could have reduced any tendency to refloat. Table 6 shows that the recovery of magnesia into the last timed concentrate was lower for the two high DP reagents, and this supports the postulation of reduced reflotation. Flocculation of the silicate minerals could also have reduced the amount of mechanical entrainment in the froth.

362

TABLE 6

Recovery of Magnesia into 3.5-7.5   min Concentrate vs.
Degree of Polymerisation

Degree of polymerisation	Recovery (MgO%) Mine 1	Mine 2
250	5 3	12 6
520	4 9	10 5
1000	4 5	6 7
1150	4 3	6 9

Carboxymethylcellulose reagents have been used for selective flocculation of gangue previously, prior to the flotation of chromite [17].

Increasing the temperature of a C.M.C. solution from 5° to $40^{\circ}C$ reduces the viscosity by more than half. As C.M.C. solution temperature did not affect the magnesia content of the concentrates, the effects observed with reagents of different viscosities were due to the parameters such as degree of polymerisation which change the viscosity, not the solution viscosity itself.

The reasons for pulp temperature affecting the magnesia content of the concentrates could be twofold. Either the magnesia minerals float faster or the sulphides slower. Analysis of the results at 55° and $70^{\circ}C$ showed that the magnesia minerals floated faster throughout the tests and that the nickel recoveries were lower. As xanthates decompose more rapidly with increasing temperature [18], this might have contributed to the lower nickel recovery. The reason for the faster flotation of the magnesia bearing minerals has not been established.

The optimum dosage of the altered structure reagent was substantially reduced without increasing the magnesia content in the concentrates. This suggests a more efficient adsorption onto the magnesia bearing minerals. The substitution of the carboxymethyl radicals in cluster, probably achieved this by reducing the effects of electrostatic repulsion caused by the anions.

ACKNOWLEDGEMENTS

The author wishes to express his gratitude for the help given with this work by various members of the staffs of: Australian Selection (Pty.) Ltd., Selcast Exploration Ltd., Agnew Mining Company (Pty.) Ltd., Anaconda Australia Incorporated, and to the metallurgical staff of the Western Australian School of Mines. The help of the various representatives of C.M.C. manufacturing companies, who supplied samples and technical data, is also acknowledged.

REFERENCES

1. The milling of Canadian ores. Proc. 6th Commonow. Min. Metall, Cong., Canada, 1957, pp. 259 and 266.

2. Personal communication with South African reagent manufactures.

3. Vaneev I.I. Non-ferrous Metals, Moscow, No. 11 (1957).

4. Woodal R. and Travis G.A. The Kambalda nickel deposits, Western Australia. Proc. 9th Commonow. Min. Metall. Cong. London, 1969, Pap. 26, 17pp.

5. Bakinov K.G., Vaneev I.I., Gorlovsky S.I., Eropkin V.I., Zashikin R.V. and Koney A.S. New methods of sulphide concentrate upgrading. 7th Int. Min. Proc. Cong., New York, (Gordon and Beach, New York, 1964,) 227-238.

6. Eltham J.A. and Tilyard P.A. Aust. Inst. Min. Metall. Annual Conf., 417-429, 1973.

7. Draper N., Quadrio J.S. and McHunter A.M.W. Aust. Inst. Min. Metall. Annual Conf., 431-432, 1973.

8. Batdorf J.B. Sodium carboxymethylcellulose. In: Industrial Gums. (ed. Whistler R.L.), Academic Press, New York, 1959, Ch. XXVII.

9. Yates F. The design and analysis of factorial experiments. Imperial Bureau of Soil Science, Harpanden, 1937.

10. Dell C.C. Release analysis, a new tool for ore dressing research. In: Recent Developments in Mineral Dressing. Inst. Min. Metall. London, 1953, 75-84 and 94-97.

11. Dell C.C. Bunyard M.J., Picketon W.A. and Young P.A. Trans. Inst. Min. Metall. 81, C89-96, (1972).

12. Anon. "Acrol" gangue depressants in base metal sulphide and oxide flotation. (Trochem. Pty. Ltd. Johannesburg, S. Africa).

13. McHardy J. and Salman T. Trans. Inst. Min. Metall., Sec. C, 83, C25-29 (1974).

14. Usoni L., Rinelli G., Marabini A.M. and Ghigi G. Selective properties of flocculants and possibilities of their use in the flotation of mine minerals. 8th Int. Min. Proc. Congr. Leningrad, 1968 (Institute Mekhanobr Leningrad, 1968) paper D-13.

15. Yarar B. and Kitchener J.A. Trans. Inst. Min. Metall. Sec. C, 79, C23-33 (1970).

16. Read A.D. and Whitehead A. Treatment of mineral combinations by selective flocculation. Proc. 10th Int. Min. Congr. (London 1973) Inst. Min. Metall., London 1974, 949-957.

17. Sher P., Miloshevic M. and Bulatovich P. Anionic flotation of chromite in an alkaline media without preliminary desliming. 8th Int. Min. Proc. Congr. Leningrad, 1968, (Institute Mekhanobr, Leningrad 1968), paper D-16.

18. Klassen V.I. and Mokrousov V.A. An introduction to the theory of flotation. Butterworth, London, 1963, 238.

ABSTRACT

The effects of the carboxymethylcellulose (C.M.C.)
reagents were studied with respect to the magnesia content of
the concentrates produced. Total contained C.M.C. addition
(dosage x C.M.C. content of the reagent) was the most significant variable which affected the magnesia content. Low
magnesia levels were obtained with two types of C.M.C.
reagents not previously used in nickel sulphide flotation.

These were reagents with a DP value of more than 1000,
and those with an altered molecular structure. It is postulated that selective flocculation acted as an additional
depressing mechanism for the high DP reagents. Equivalent
depression with up to 40% lower additions of C.M.C. was
produced using reagents with an altered structure.

During summer, pulp temperatures up to 40°C are experienced, and higher dosages of C.M.C. are required to prevent an
increase in the magnesia content in the concentrate. Data are
presented on laboratory and plant studies.

RÉSUMÉ

Des études portant sur les effets de la carboxyméthylcellu-
lose (C.M.C.) furent entreprises, en relation avec la quantité
de magnésie contenue dans les concentrés résultants. La variable
la plus significantive sur la teneur en magnésie est le total
de C.M.C. (dosage x contenu C.M.C. du réagent) ajouté. Des bas
niveaux de magnésie furent obtenus avec deux types de réagents
C.M.C. qui n'avaient pas été utilisés auparavant pour la flotation des sulfures de nickel. C'étaient des agents ayant une
valeur de D.P. de plus de 1000 ou avec une structure moleculaire
changée. Admettous comme postulat qu'une flocculation sélective
ait augmenté, avec des réagents D.P. élevés, le rôle d'un
mécanisme déprimant. Une dépression équivalente a été obtenue
par une addition de C.M.C. allant jusqu'à 40% de moins lorsque
les réagents utilisés avaient une standuse changée. En été, la

température des poulpes peut atteindre 40°C et des dosages de
C.M.C. plus élevés sont requis pour restreindre une augmentation
du contenu en magnésie du concentré. On présente des données
établies soit en laboratoire soit en pratique.

ZUSAMMENFASSUNG

Untersucht wurde der Einfluss von Karboxymethylzellulose,
(C.M.C.) auf den Magnesiumoxidgehalt der hergestellten Konzen-
trate. Ein voller Zusatz von C.M.C. (Gesamtdosis x C.M.C. -
Gehalt des Reagens) stellte die bedeutendste Variable dar, die
den Magnesiumoxidgehalt beeinflusste. Geringe Magnesiumoxidge-
halte ergaben sich durch zwei Arten von C.M.C.-Reagenzien, die
bisher in der Flotation von Nickelsulphiden noch jeine Anwendung
gefunden hatten. Es waren Reagenzien mit einem DP-Wert von über
1000, und Reagenzien mit veränderter Struktur. Es wird hier
vorausgesetzt, dass im Falle hochwertiger DP-Reagenzien eine
selektive Flockung sich depressiv auswirkt. Eine äquivalente
Depression stellt sich ein wenn bis zu 40% niedrigere Dosen
C.M.C. mit veränderter Struktur zugesetzt werden. Im Sommer
liessen sich Temperaturen bis zu 40°C feststellen, bei denen
grössere Mengen von C.M.C. notwendig waten um einem Ansteigen
des Magnesiumoxidgehalts im Konzentrat vorzubeugen. Genauere
Zahlenangaben sind in den Ergebnissen von Laboruntersuchungen,
sowie von Untersuchungen in situ zu finden.

РЕЗЮМЕ

Изучались влияния карбоксилированных метилцеллюлозных (КМЦ) реагентов на содержание магнезии в концентратах. Общее количество добавки КМЦ (доза x содержание КМЦ в реагенте) является самой значительной переменной величиной, влияющей на содержание магнезии. Низкие концетрации магнезии, полученные с КМЦ реагентами двух типов, необходимы прежде всего для флотации сульфидов никеля. Эти реагенты со значительной степенью полимеризации, выше 1000, являются реагентами с измененной молекулярной структурой. Принимается, что в случае реагентов с высокой степенью полимеризации селективная флокуляция действует как дополнительный депрессор флотации. При применении реагентов с измененной молекулярной структурой достигается такое же подавление флотации, но со снижением расхода КМЦ на 40%. Летом, когда температура пульпы достигает 40°C, необходимо увеличить дозы КМЦ, чтобы преупредить повышение содержания магнезии в концентрате. Представлены данные по лабораторным и производственным опытам.

BENEFICIATION OF FINELY DISPERSED ORES BY SELECTIVE FLOCCULATION AT HIGH SALT CONCENTRATIONS

V. P. Kuznetsov, M. L. Volova, E. I. Lyubımova, L. M. Shishkova,
V. E. Lifirenko and Yu. F. Sokolov

All-Union Institute of Mineral Raw Materials, U.S.S.R.

INTRODUCTION

The application of selective flocculation for the recovery
of finely dispersed ores is considerably complicated by the
negative effect of salt composition in the water and pulp which
leads to the reinforcement of the coagulation of the particles.
For this reason, ın elaborating conditions for selective flocculation, the physical and chemical dispersion of the pulp, as
well as its interrelation with the subsequent interaction of
mineral particles with the flocculant, become increasingly important.

The present paper considers some principles of the physical
and chemical dispersion and selective flocculation of bauxites,
one of the most complicated types of highly dispersed raw
materials, characterized by high dispersion of basic materials
(boehmite, gibbsite, kaolinite, hematite).

Earlier studies demonstrated the theoretical possibility of
selective flocculation of bauxite suspensions. It was found that

one of the necessary conditions is that one obtain a high degree of suspension dispersity characterized by the content of fine fraction (-0.5 μm). The suggested physicochemical method of dispersion consists of preliminary precipitation of the pulp ions into poorly soluble compounds with sodium carbonate and hydroxide. The pulp is subsequently dispersed by sodium hexamethaphosphate or sodium lignosulphate.

Selectivity of flocculation by hydrolyzed polyacryloamide (PAA) was observed only when the initial concentration of calcium in the liquid phase did not exceed 20-30 mg/l [1]. Only detailed studies of the interrelation between the reagents and the ions in the liquid phase, as well as the surface exchangeable ions made possible the elaboration of the conditions of selective flocculation at higher concentrations of salts which are characteristic of bauxite suspensions.

Effect of Salt Composition on Flocculation

Investigations were carried out with two types of bauxite, kaolinite-boehmite (sample 1) and hematite-boehmite (sample 2). Indices of beneficiation were estimated according to the content of Al_2O_3, SiO_2, Fe_2O_3 in the products and a silicon modulus (M = Pct. Al_2O_3/ Pct. SiO_2). The size distribution of the fine-particle fraction of bauxites (-44 μm) after their mechanical dispersion is presented in Table 1.

Ca^{2+}, Mg^{2+}, SO_4^{2-}, Cl^- and other species are found in aqueous solution. The first bauxite is characterized by a high content of Ca^{2+} and SO_4^{2-} in aqueous solution; the concentration of Ca at a solid-liquid ratio 1:10 is equal to 230 mg/l. The exchange capacity

TABLE 1

Granulometric Composition of Bauxite Suspensions

Bauxite	Kaolinite-Boehmite					Hematite-Boehmite			
Particle size, μm	Yield %	Content, % Al_2O_3	SiO_2	M	Yield %	Content, % Al_2O_3	SiO_2	Fe_2O_3	M
−44+20	4.9	55.2	13.5	4.1	3.4	27.8	15.6	35.6	1.8
−20+10	17.5	50.0	19.1	2.6	3.6	28.9	21.4	26.7	1.3
−10+ 5					5.6	40.7	17.6	19.6	2.1
− 5+ 2	15.6	52.0	18.2	2.9	20.4	57.9	8.9	14.3	6.5
− 2+ 1	19.7	58.1	14.2	4.1	18.5	59.7	8.1	19.4	7.4
−1+0.5	13.3	57.4	15.1	3.8	21.3	48.3	8.5	28.2	5.7
− 0.5	29.0	39.6	24.2	1.6	27.2	18.8	11.9	52.9	1.6
Initial product	100	50.1	18.7	2.7	100	42.5	10.7	30.2	4.0

for Ca, determined after treatment with 1 N KCl was equal to 2.6 mequiv./100 g of bauxite. The second bauxite contained few soluble salts, the ion content of the liquid phase approximated the composition of natural water, the calcium concentration in a liquid phase equaled 35 mg/l (in water 25 mg/l). The exchange capacity for Ca was equal to 6.5 mequiv./100 g of bauxite. In the present paper, the main emphasis is placed on the reagent interaction with calcium, for the latter is found to be a basic coagulating ion.

A pipette method of sedimentation analysis was used for estimating the physicochemical conditions for producing stably dispersed suspension and flocculation. For the first sample, the degree of dispersity was equal to 100% at 29% yield of

-0.5 µm size fraction and at 27% yield for the second sample. Flocculation was estimated according to the characteristics of the sediment obtained (+20 µm size fraction).

Table 2 shows the influence of the initial concentration of Ca in a pulp on the bauxite flocculation in the first sample.

TABLE 2

Effect of Initial Ca Concentration in a Liquid Phase
on the Flocculation of Bauxite Suspensions
by Hydrolized Polyacryloamide

Concentration, mg/l					Size fraction +20 µm				Dispersion degree according to the size fraction −0.5 µm %
Ca	Na_2CO_3	NaOH	Sodium hexa-metha-phos-phate	PAA	Yield %	Concentrate, % Al_2O_3	SiO_2	M	
15.6	200	250	300	−	5.0	55.0	12.0	4.6	95
15.6	200	250	300	2	52.4	60.5	12.1	5.0	95
38.7	400	300	400	2	50.8	56.1	17.6	3.2	42
230	400	500	400	2	78.8	50.9	19.1	2.7	4.0
230	400	500	800	2	35.4	55.5	18.4	3.0	70
230	400	500	1600	2	6.0	58.2	13.6	4.3	97.5
230	400	500	1600	10	5.2	59.1	13.4	4.4	98

The Ca concentration in a liquid phase was controlled by the dilution of the pulp by soft water, followed by the extraction of a liquid phase influencing the concentration of other ions in a liquid phase. To achieve a high degree of dispersity indicated by content of a 0.5 μm size fraction in practically complete absence of calcium removed in poorly soluble compounds precipitated by sodium carbonate and sodium hydroxide at the high initial concentration of calcium in the pulp the great must be the amount of sodium hexamethaphosphate added. The interaction of the flocculant with the mineral surface at a calcium concentration of 230 mg/l takes place either in a non-selective way or polyacryloamide does not flocculate the pulp.

The relationship between selective flocculation and initial concentration suggests that the interaction between the flocculant and the surface of mineral is greatly influenced by the quantity and character of the products of the reaction between reagents and ions in the pulp. These ions are formed in the liquid phase and on the mineral surface when physicochemical dispersion takes place. Considerable attention is devoted to this problem in the present paper.

Factors Determining Physico-Chemical Dispersion and Flocculation of Bauxite Suspensions

Interaction of the reagents with ions in the pulp, basically with calcium, was considered in a model system, represented by a liquid phase of a bauxite suspension, obtained after mechanical dispersion of bauxite in distilled water (content in aqueous phase, mg/l: Ca - 166, Mg - 5, SO_4 - 435, HCO_3 - 46.4). The reactions were evaluated from the change of optical density of the solution and the final concentration of reagents after the separation of poorly soluble reaction products on the colloidal filter.

X-ray examination and infra-red spectroscopy show that with the addition of sodium hexamethaphosphate or sodium carbonate to the solution in alkaline medium (pH 8-10), amorphous polyphosphates and calcium carbonates are formed respectively (Fig. 1, curves 1 and 2). In the first case, the structure of the slowly coagulated suspension reveals no change. In the second case, a calcite structure is formed in 5 to 6 min after the addition of the reagent. Sodium hexamethaphosphate which is introduced one minute after the addition of soda, greatly influences the character of its interaction with the ions of the solution. This is the main reason for the adsorption of the polyphosphate anion on the surface of a newly formed solid phase, causing the dispersion and stabilization of poorly soluble products of the reaction (curve 3). It is possible that the ions absorbed on the growing crystals block the active centres, retard or suppress the growth of crystals and in this way encourage stabilization.

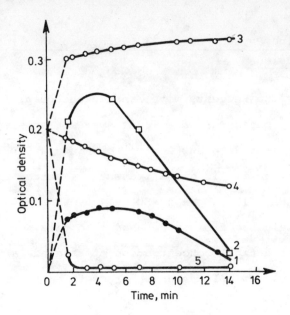

Fig. 1. Change of optical density of solution with time.
1 - only sodium hexamethaphosphate 500 mg/l, pH -
10.3, 2 - only Na_2CO_3 750 mg/l, sodium hexamethaphosphate, mg/l: 3 - 100-400, 4 - 1000, 5 - 1500.

X-ray examination and IR spectroscopy revealed that in the
presence of sodium hexamethaphosphate, the structure of calcium
carbonate depends on the order in which reagents are added to
the solution, their ratio, the reaction time between the solution and reagents, etc. If the preliminary interaction time of
the ions in the solution with the soda is not sufficient to
form a calcite structure, then the subsequent addition of
sodium hexamethaphosphate makes the formation of the given
structure difficult.

At high concentrations of sodium hexamethaphosphate (> 1000
mg/l) another property of polyphosphate compounds was revealed,
namely, the complexing ability which allows the conversion of
the insoluble compounds of multivalent metals into soluble

376

compounds (curves 4 and 5). Furthermore, the addition of sodium lignosulphonate also causes the dispersion and stabilization of poorly soluble products.

As is shown below, investigation of the reaction character on the model system makes it possible to confirm the important role of the poorly soluble products of the reaction in physico-chemical dispersion of bauxite suspensions. In this case, the interaction between the reagents and the surface of mineral should also be taken into consideration.

Figure 2 shows the influence of sodium hexamethaphosphate on the yield of a -0.5 µm fraction, adsorption of polyphosphate

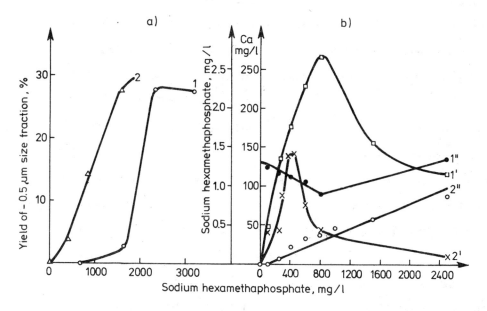

Fig. 2. Effect of sodium hexamethaphosphate on weight of -0.5 µm class kaolinite-boehmite bauxite (a), its adsorption on solid phase (b, 1', 2') and residual concentration of Ca in filtrate (b, 1", 2"). Initial concentration of calcium - 142 mg/l. 1,1',1" - only sodium hexamethaphosphate, 2,2',2" - Na_2CO_3 - 625 mg/l, NaOH - 375 mg/l.

anion on a solid phase and residual concentration of calcium in a liquid phase. These were determined after the filtration of the pulp on a colloidal filter. The amount of sodium hexamethaphosphate adsorbed on the solid phase was determined by subtracting the amount left in the liquid phase from the initial amount applied. In the obtained values the adsorption of reagent on the surface of poorly soluble products is included, retained by the colloidal filter.

Two cases in which a high degree of physicochemical dispersion of bauxite suspension can be achieved are suggested for consideration. The first case is characterized by the addition of sodium hexamethaphosphate alone into the pulp. At its low concentrations, the final concentration of calcium in the liquid phase is somehow decreased (curve 1") with a substantial increase in sodium hexamethaphosphate uptake on the solid phase (curve 1'). This is due to the formation of amorphous calcium polyphosphates in the bulk liquid phase and on the surface of the solid phase. Reaction in the pulp does not result in physicochemical dispersion of the suspensions. With an increase in sodium hexamethaphosphate concentration, some complex compounds are formed; the final concentration of calcium in the filtrate increases with a subsequent decrease of the quantity of sodium hexamethaphosphate on the surface of the solid phase. A high degree of dispersity of -0.5 μm fraction is observed at a concentration of sodium hexamethaphosphate exceeding 2000 mg/l (curve 1). These data suggest that the formation of a complex compound with a subsequent decrease in the number of active centres on the surface of the minerals, prevents the coagulation of mineral particles.

The second case is characterized by the addition of sodium carbonate, sodium hydroxide and sodium hexamethaphosphate into the bauxite suspension. Physicochemical dispersion starts at a sodium hexamethaphosphate concentration of 300 mg/l, at which point its dispersive and stabilizing action on the poorly soluble products of the reaction is clearly revealed (Fig. 1). This is evidently related to the adsorption of a polyphosphate anion on the surface, of minerals and poorly soluble products of the reaction. Adsorption increases with increasing sodium hexamethaphosphate concentration, but to a lesser extent than mentioned in the first case (Fig. 2, curve 2'). At the same time the final concentration of calcium in the filtrate increases parallel to the concentration of sodium hexamethaphosphate (curve 2"). A high degree of dispersity was obtained at a sodium hexamethaphosphate concentration of more than 1000 mg/l (curve 2); in this case, along with poorly soluble products of the reactions, a major portion of calcium was represented by complex compounds.

The action of sodium lignosulphonate differs substantially from the effect of sodium hexamethaphosphate (Fig. 3a). It is impossible to achieve stably dispersed bauxite suspension by the addition of sodium lignosulphonate itself, even at high concentrations (curve 1). In such a case uptake by a solid phase is quite high (curve 1'), and the concentration of calcium in a liquid phase is practically unchanged (curve 1"), i.e., the coagulating ability of calcium is not decreased in the considered system. The degree of dispersion   as given by the yield of -0.5 μm fraction   can be achieved with the pre-

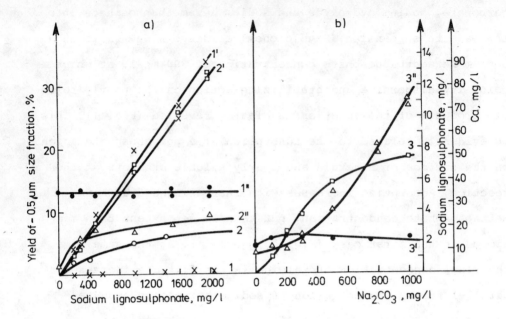

Fig. 3. Effect of sodium lignosulphonate (a) and Na_2CO_3 (b)
on weight of -0.5 μm class hematite-boehmite bauxite
(1, 2, 3), adsorption lignosulphonate on solid phase
(1', 2', 3') and residual concentration of Ca in
filtrate (1", 2", 3"). Initial concentration of calcium - 35 mg/l. 1,1',1" - only sodium lignosulphonate; 2,2',2" - Na_2CO_3 - 300 mg/l, NaOH - 200 mg/l;
3,3'3" - NaOH - 300 mg/l, sodium lignosulphonate -
300 mg/l.

liminary addition of sodium carbonate and sodium hydroxide into

the suspension, where the dispersion and stabilizing action of

sodium lignosulphonate on poorly soluble products becomes si-

gnificant (curve 2). In this case a certain increase in calcium

concentration is observed (curve 2"). With an increase in

sodium carbonate concentration, when redistribution between the

solid and liquid phases becomes more evident (Fig. 3b, curve 3"), the yield of a -0.5 μm fraction increases (curve 3). According to the UV-spectrophotometry data, a part of the exchangeable calcium from the complex compounds passes into solution..

Thus, when physicochemical dispersion of bauxite suspensions occurs in the presence of sodium carbonate, sodium hydroxide, sodium hexamethaphosphate or sodium lignosulphonate, the following processes take place:

(a) Precipitation of the ions from the liquid phase and the exchangeable ones in poorly soluble compounds in the presence of sodium carbonate and sodium hydroxide followed by the dispersion and stabilization of the reaction products as a result of interaction with sodium hexamethaphosphate or lignosulphonate;

(b) Formation of complex compounds, leading to a decrease in the number of active centres on the mineral surface.

In accordance with the principles of colloid chemistry, the nature and number of exchangeable ions greatly influence the electric double layer and the thickness of hydrated films on the surface of the minerals, respectively.

Dispersion of poorly soluble products of the reaction, due to the adsorption of sodium hexamethaphosphate or lignosulphonate, is accompanied by an increase in hydration and the number of centres binding water. It may be assumed that the disjoining pressure of hydrated layers then increases, causing the bauxite suspension to be stably dispersed.

Addition of the flocculant inevitably causes its interaction with poorly soluble products of the reactions. Polyacryloamide does not flocculate the calcium carbonate that is formed (Fig. 4, curve 1 and 2). Its interaction with calcium carbonate

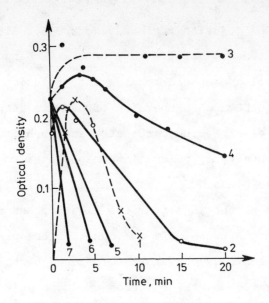

Fig. 4. Change of optical density of solution in dependency
of time of preliminary agitating with sodium hexamethaphosphate 250 mg/l. Na_2CO_3 - 625 mg/l. 1, 2 -
Na_2CO_3, 3-7 - Na_2CO_3, sodium hexamethaphosphate,
1, 3 - without flocculant, 2, 4-7 - polyacryloamide
- 4 mg/l. Time of preliminary agitating with sodium
hexamethaphosphate, min: 4-1, 5-5, 6-10, 7-15.

changes substantially when sodium hexamethaphosphate is first

added to the solution; hexamethaphosphate greatly influences

on   the structure of calcium carbonate. A certain induction

period has been observed, after which flocculation starts prac-

tically at once, i.e., the optical density approximates zero

when mixing has stopped. If the time of the preliminary mixing

of the solution with sodium hexamethaphosphate is shorter than

the induction period itself, neither flocculation nor partial

flocculation is observed. The longer the period of mixing of

the solution with the flocculant, the larger aggregates are

formed and, respectively, the lower is the optical density of the solution (curves 3-7). The data presented demonstrate the decisive role of the structure of poorly soluble products of the reaction during their interaction with the flocculant. This problem needs more detailed investigation.

Poorly soluble products of the reaction that are formed in the liquid phase and on the surface of mineral particles can provide adsorption centres for the flocculant and make possible non-selective flocculation of bauxite suspensions. Separation which takes place at low concentrations of calcium in the liquid phase (Table 2) shows that the role of poorly soluble compounds in relation to boehmite, kaolinite and hematite is not the same.

A large number of poorly soluble compounds are formed on the surface of minerals at high concentration of calcium in a liquid phase and high exchange capacity. These compounds conceal the surface properties of the minerals and selective flocculation then drops. It is impossible to reduce the interaction of the flocculant with the surface of kaolinite at a sodium hexamethaphosphate concentration which ranges from 200 to 400 mg/l. With high concentrations of sodium hexamethaphosphate, when poorly soluble reaction products are dissolved and calcium is almost fully represented by complex compounds, the existing active centres are not enough for flocculant adsorption and polyacryloamide does not flocculate the suspension, as is shown in Table 2.

In connection with this, in order to increase selectivity it is necessary to strengthen the dispersive action of sodium hexamethaphosphate on poorly soluble reaction products, and in this way create the conditions for their irregular fixing on minerals. An acoustic treatment was tried and is described in the next section.

Effect of Acoustic Treatment on Flocculation of Bauxite

Acoustic treatment was carried out either by supersounds (at a frequency of 22 kHz), or on a rotor type laboratory disperser (sound frequency range) [3]. The latter device strengthens the dispersive action of sodium hexamethaphosphate in reactions with poorly soluble products (Fig. 5a, curves 1 and 2). It can

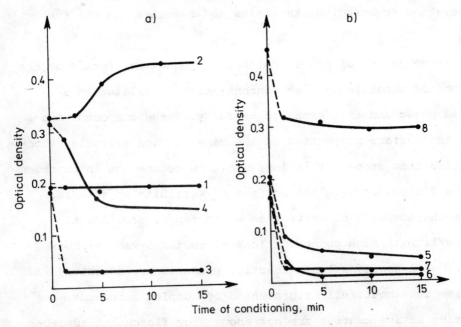

Fig. 5. Effect of acoustic treatment upon flocculation of poorly soluble products of reaction (a) and powders - Al(OH)$_3$ (b, 5, 6) and SiO$_2$ · nH$_2$O (b, 7, 8). Na$_2$CO$_3$ - 625 mg/l, sodium hexamethaphosphate - 100 mg/l, polyacryloamide - 5 mg/l. 1, 3, 5, 7 - treatment by reagents in agitator; 2, 4, 6, 8 - acoustic treatment; 1, 2 - without flocculant; 3-8 - with flocculant.

be seen that the greater the dispersity of the compound formed, the poorer the flocculation effect of hydrolized polyacryloamide in the system considered (Fig. 5a, curves 3 and 4).

To show the effect of acoustic treatment on the interaction between the flocculant and various minerals in the presence of poorly soluble compounds, we have used the following model system: highly dispersed powders of $Al(OH)_3$ and $SiO_2 \cdot nH_2O$ (solid concentration 2.5 g/l) were added to a liquid phase of a bauxite suspension. Hydrolized polyacryloamide does not flocculate powders in the system under discussion. Intensive flocculation of both powder was noticed only where sodium carbonate, sodium hydroxide and sodium hexamethaphosphate were added to the suspension, i.e., a great number of adsorption centres were created for flocculant adsorption (Fig. 5b, curves 5 and 7). If any additional acoustic treatment of the suspension was carried out after the addition of the reagents, the interaction of the powders with the flocculant changed essentially (Fig. 5b, 6 and 8). Acoustic treatment practically entirely prevents the flocculation of $SiO_2 \cdot nH_2O$, while $Al(OH)_3$ flocculates intensively under the same conditions. This fact confirms that the attractive energy between poorly soluble compounds and the mineral surface depends on the mineral.

Acoustic pulp treatment greatly increases the efficiency of the physicochemical dispersion of bauxite suspensions; a high degree of dispersion as indicated by the yield of a -0.5 µm fraction is achieved at considerably lower concentrations of sodium hexamethaphosphate (200-400 mg/l); treatment with the reagents only in a mixer leads to poorer results (Fig. 6a,

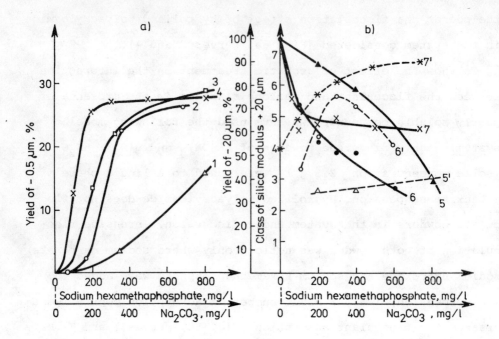

Fig. 6. Effect of sodium hexamethaphosphate (1, 2, 3, 5, 6)
and Na$_2$CO$_3$ (4, 7) on weight of -0.5 μm class in
dispersing (a), +20 μm class in flocculation of
bauxites by use of hydrolyzed polyacryloamide (b,
5, 6, 7) and its silica modulus (5', 6', 7').
1, 2, 3, 5, 5', 6, 6' - kaolinite-boehmite bauxite,
Na$_2$CO$_3$ - 400 mg/l, NaOH - 400 mg/l; 4, 7, 7' -
hematite-boehmite bauxite, NaOH - 300 mg/l, sodium
lignosulphonate - 300 mg/l; 1, 5, 5' - treatment in
agitator; 2, 3, 4, 6, 6', 7, 7' - acoustic treatment.

curves 1-3). The application of the mixer makes possible the
achievement of a high degree of dispersity as indicated by the
yield of a -0.5 μm fraction in the presence of sodium sulphonate (curve 4). In accordance with the above-mentioned facts
the effect of acoustic treatment can be ascribed to the formation of new additional adsorption centres for water, promoting

TABLE 3

Selective Flocculation of Bouxites

Bauxite	Product	Yield %	Content, %			M	Recovery, %		
			Al_2O_3	SiO_2	Fe_2O_3		Al_2O_3	SiO_2	Fe_2O_3
Kaolinite-Boehmite	Bauxite concentrate	49.4	60.3	12.3	3.6	4.9	59.3	33.5	28.1
	Semi-product	26.0	45.4	22.9	5.8	2.0	23.6	22.7	20.8
	Kaolinite (flocculant overflow)	24.6	35.0	25.0	13.1	1.4	17.1	33.8	51.1
	Raw material	100	50.2	18.2	6.3	2.7	100	100	100
Hematite-Boehmite	Bauxite concentrate	64.5	53.6	8.2	20.4	6.5	81.4	49.8	43.7
	Semi product	7.1	28.5	18.6	30.9	1.5	4.8	12.4	7.3
	Hematite- (flocculant overflow)	28.4	20.6	14.2	51.9	1.5	13.8	37.8	49.0
	Raw material	100	42.5	10.7	30.1	4.0	100	100	100

the hydration of mineral surfaces and consequently the stabilization of bauxite suspensions.

The high degree of dispersity of bauxite suspensions at
lower reagent concentrations and irregular coverage of different minerals by insoluble reaction products created by the reagent and acoustic treatment of pulp, greatly increase the
selectivity of interaction of flucculants with minerals and the
indices of beneficiation at high salt concentrations, accordingly (Fig. 6b).

The positive effect of the acoustic treatment on the selective flocculation of fluorite slimes was shown in a paper by
S. Stoev and B. Kintisheva [4].

Thus, simultaneous application of both reagent and acoustic
treatments is a promising method for the regulation of ion as
well as colloidal composition of the pulp in the concentration
processes of finely disseminated ores.

Selective flocculation has been suggested for the beneficiation of low-grade bauxites (Table 3).

Scale-up of the Process

Selective flocculation of bauxites is characterized by some
specific features. That is why it is important to check its
basic stages in a continuous test. For this purpose a pilot
plant was constructed which included some industrial-type
devices, where the basic parameters of the process were checked
(Fig. 7). The flowsheet includes the stages of preliminary
mechanical dispersion, classification, physicochemical dispersion and flocculation. The feed size is below 10 mm, and the
pulp volume is of 25-30 l.

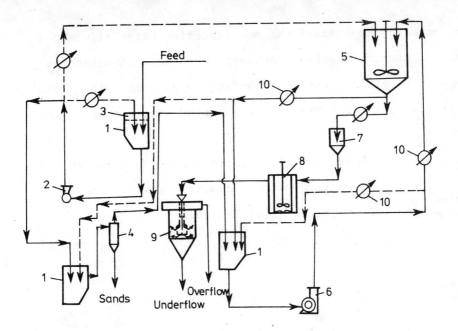

Fig. 7. Pilot set for selective flocculation. 1 - sump,
2 - sand pump, 3 grid, 4 - hydraulic cyclon, 5 -
agitator, 6 - acoustic apparatus, 7 - buffer container, 8 - agitator for treatment with flocculant,
9 - separator, 10 - cock.

A NP-2 type pump was used for the mechanical dispersion of
bauxites. For separation of coarse particles, a screen Ø 1 mm is
placed in the sump of the pump. Ø 30 mm hydrocyclones at separation
size of $d_{50} = 20 \div 40$ µm are used for the classification of pulp.
The unit for physicochemical dispersion consists of a mixer for
pulp treatment with reagents and a rotor-type vibrating apparatus for the acoustic treatment in a sound frequency range,
working in a closed cycle [5]. The unit for selective flocculation comprises a mixer, a container with an overflow outlet to
maintain continuous flocculation, a conditioner for introducing
the flocculant into a pulp, and a cylinder-cone separation

389

device enabling to discard the sedimentating material without additional disruption. Two processes take place simultaneuosly in separator: classification according to particle size (rate of overflow is 1.2-2.5 m/h) and thickening (solid content is 40-45%).

The investigations on a pilot installation in a continuous cycle revealed the optimum reagent conditions and parameters of the process of selective flocculation.

ABSTRACT

The principles of physicochemical dispersion and selective
flocculation considered in the present paper have both theoretical and practical significance for the development of the
separation processes of finely disseminated and fine-dispersed
ores and slimes. The decisive role of poorly soluble products
in selective flocculation has been established and some methods
of influencing the ion as well as the colloidal state of disperse system have been suggested. The application of both reagent and acoustic pulp treatments in the sound frequency range
seems to be one of the methods of the future. The acoustic
treatment of the pulp intensifies the dispersive and stabilizing effects of sodium hexamethaphosphate and lignosulphonate
on the poorly soluble products of the reaction. This makes
possible their irregular distribution on the surface of different minerals, and consequently controls the selectivity at high
salt concentrations in the pulp.

The ways of controlling the ion and colloid composition of
mineral disperse systems which were worked out allow the application of natural waters with high salt content in flotation
and other mineral beneficiation processes.

RÉSUMÉ

En prenant l'exemple des bauxites finement dispersees on a
étudié la corrélation entre les conditions de la dispersion
physiquo-chimique et la floculation sélective avec une concentration élevée de sels en pulpe. On a montré le rôle principal
des composants peu solubles, comme le resultat de la réaction
des réactifs et des ions en pulpe dans le processus de floculation sélective.

L'interaction sélective du floculant et des minéraux domi-
nantes dépend de la quantité, la dispersité et la structure des
produits difficiles à dissoudre de la réaction, qui sont dans
les conditions définies des centres d'adsorption du floculant.
On a étudié un procédé de floculation sélective de bauxite avec

le traitement de la pulpe par des réactifs et un traitement
acoustique dans la game sonore des fréquences avant l'introduction du floculant.

Le traitement acoustique de la pulpe renforce l'action de
dispersion et de stabilisation de l'hexametaphosphate et du
lignosulfonate de sodium sur les produits peu solubles de la
réaction et contribue à la distribution non uniforme sur la
surface des minéraux principaux, que définit la sélection avec
une concentration élevée de sels.

On a construit un grand appareil de laboratoire contenant
un dispositif rotor-vibratoire pour le traitement acoustique
de la pulpe et un epaissiseur pour la séparation des flocules.

ZUSAMMENFASSUNG

Es wird an Bauxiten mit hoher Dispersion der Hauptmineralien
die Beziehung   zwischen den Bedingungen der physikalisch-che-
mischen Dispergierung und der selektiven Flockung bei hohen
Salz-Konzentrationen in der Trübe untersucht. Gezeigt wird hier
der Haupteinfluss von schwerlöslichen, während der selektiven
Flockung als Folge einer Reaktion zwischen den in der Trübe
befindlichen Reagenzien und Ionen gebildeten, Verbindungen.

Die Selektivität der Zusammenwirkung des Flockungsmittels
mit den Hauptmineralien hängt von der Quantität, Dispersion
und Struktur der schwerlöslichen Reaktionsprodukte, die unter
den bestimmten Bedingungen zum Adsorptionszentrum des Flockungsmittels werden.

Es wurde ein Verfahren der selektiven Flockung von Bauxiten
erarbaitet,welches vor Einführung des Flockungsmittels eine
Bearbeitung der Trübe mit Reagenzien und akustischem Schall
vorsieht. Die akustische Bearbeitung der Trübe verstärkt die
Dispergier- und Stabilisierwirkung des Natrium-Hexametaphos-
phats und des Natrium-lignosulfonats gegenüber schwerlöslichen
Reaktionsprodukten und trägt der ungleichmässigen Verteilung
derer auf der Oberfläche der Hauptmineralien bei.Diese bestimmt
die Selektivität bei hohen Salz-Konzentrationen.

Es wird eine grosse Laboranlage gebaut, welche ein Rotor-
Vibrogerät und einen Verdichter zur Flockentrennung eischliesst.

РЕЗЮМЕ

На примере бокситов, характеризующихся высокой дисперсностью основных минералов, рассмотрена взаимосвязь условий физико-химического диспергирования и селективной флокуляции при высоких концентрациях солей в пульпе. Показана определяющая роль в процессе селективной флокуляции труднорастворимых соединений, образуемых в результате реакции реагентов с ионами пульпы.

Селективность взаимодействия флокулянта с основными минералами зависит от количества, дисперсности и структуры труднорастворимых продуктов реакций, являющихся в определенных условиях центрами адсорбции флокулянта. Разработан способ селективной флокуляции бокситов, включающий обработку реагентами и акустическую обработку пульпы в звуковом диапазоне частот перед введением флокулянта. Акустическая обработка пульпы усиливает диспергирующее и стабилизирующее действие гексаметафосфата и лигносульфоната натрия на труднорастворимые продукты реакции и способствует их неравномерному распределению на поверхности основных минералов, что определяет селекцию при высоких концентрациях солей.

Создана укрупненно-лабораторная установка, включающая для акустической обработки пульпы роторно-пульсационный аппарат, для разделения флокул – сгуститель.

MOTION AND INTERACTION OF PARTICLES
IN A POLYDISPERSED SUSPENSION

H. J. Steiner

Institut für Aufbereitung und Veredlung, Montanuniversität Leoben, Austria

The motion of particles in suspension is determined not only
by the field of force and the properties of the liquid but also
by neighbour particles. Under definite boundary conditions the
interaction of particles may be a dominant factor in the process. This is particularly evident in dense liquid separation
where some portion of the material is raised against the force
of gravity under the influence of finely dispersed suspension.

Due attention has not been paid in the professional literature to the interaction of particles as a problem of utmost
importance for the process of separation in dense media. The
reason for this was probably the known model of suspension
i.e., a pseudo liquid of uniform density and viscosity, which
did not permit prolonged consistent considerations of such apparently simple notions as pulp density or viscosity. But
relatively simple questions are involved here by means of
which we can reveal the weak points of the pseudo-liquid model.

These questions are as follows:

- what results can be expected from measuring density and viscosity if the size of measuring equipment in relation to the measuring system approximates the size of the dispersed particle?
- will the buoyancy of suspension increase in relation to a definite size fraction if coarse particle-fractions are introduced, thus increasing the suspension density?
- does the density of separation in heavy media depend also on the volume and the average density of the separated material?

Formulation of the Problem

In monodisperse systems the settling of particles is determined by the impulse exchange between neighbour particles as well as by the contraction of the streamlines, cf. $\begin{bmatrix}1, & 3, & 4, & 5, & 7\end{bmatrix}$. However, in polydisperse systems one observed additional interactions caused by neighbour particles that manifest themselves as apparent changes in the properties of the liquid.

In principle, all the physical properties of the liquid are subject to those interactions. The present paper deals with the influence of suspended particles on the basic properties i.e., density and viscosity. Since the properties of the liquid are revealed mostly in the terminal settling velocity of particles, this work also deals with the present state of art in this area.

The Properties of Medium

Effective Concentration. The notion "medium" means a hypothetical liquid which, in relation to a definite size fraction, will act in the same way as a real suspension. Thus, medium

has been defined as a liquid of an equivalent effect. In order
to find the relationships governing the interaction of neighbour
particles, a model of suspension of monodisperse particles i
into which a particle k has been introduced is presented in
Fig. 1 (particle size k > i).

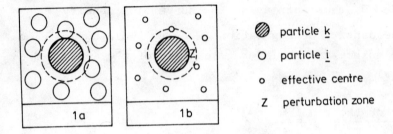

Fig. 1. Diagram of perturbation zone caused by particle k
at uniform configuration of particles i.

To explain the relations in the system the particles i
have been brought to the so-called effective centres (see
Fig. 1b). Note that the effective centres of particles i cannot
approach fully the surface of particle k. Thus, each particle k
produces a perturbation zone free of effective centres in a
statistically uniform system of particles i. The heterogeneity
of particle concentration accounts for the fact that the influence of particles i as compared with that of particle k is not
fully revealed but is weakened to a degree determined by the
effective factor. To derive a proper correlation, a real particle should be replaced by particle surface thus eliminating the
internal space of the particle (see Fig. 2) which, with respect
to interaction, is equivalent to the external space of the
grain. This transformation of the problem is possible in view
of Archimedes' buoyancy theorem.

396

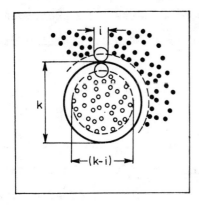

k size of particle <u>k</u>

i size of particle <u>i</u>

• effective centres of real particles <u>i</u> in the external space of particle

o effective centres of hypothetical particles <u>i</u> in the internal space of particle

Fig. 2. The transformation of the problem from the real space of particle to a hypothetical internal space of particle.

In Fig. 2 the surface of particle k has been replaced with a separating surface that brings the possible residing space of hypothetical particles <u>i</u> to the internal space of the particle exactly in the same proportions as the external particle space.

The relation of this possible space of particle <u>i</u> residence in the internal region of the particle to the total volume of particle internal space can be interpreted as an effective factor $a_{i,k}$ which, when multiplied by total <u>i</u> particle-size fraction, gives the effective volume of this fraction of particles <u>i</u>.

For spherical and cubic particles the following Equation holds:

$$a_{i,k} = \left[1 - (i/k)\right]^3 \geqslant 0 \qquad (1)$$

Equation 2 is a generalized relation for the volume fraction c_i of <u>i</u> particle-size fraction in suspension where the volume of water is w and the volume of solid particles is v_i.

The notion "effective concentration" should be understood as the concentration of fine-size and monodisperse-size fractions affecting the size of particle $\underline{k}$ just as the whole fraction of particle $\underline{i}$ considered.

If we take into account the definition of the effective factor then Eq. (3) follows from Eq. (2) as the Equation of effective concentration $c_{i,k}$ of $\underline{i}$ particle-size fraction in relation to the size of particle $\underline{k}$. The combination of Eqs. (2) and (3) leads to Eq. (4) by means of which the calculation of effective concentration boils down to the total concentration and to effective factors

$$c_i = v_i / (w + \sum v_i) \tag{2}$$

$$c_{i,k} = v_i \cdot a_{i,k} / (w + \sum v_i \cdot a_{i,k}) \tag{3}$$

$$c_{i,k} = c_i \cdot a_{i,k} / (1 - \sum (1 - a_{i,k}) \cdot c_i) \tag{4}$$

Discussion of Eqs. (1-4) shows, among other things, that the introduction of particles of size $> k$ does not cause any change in the effective concentration c_i,k. When $k \gg i$, all effective factors approach 1 thus Eq. (4) becomes Eq. (2) i.e., effective concentrations become equal to total concentrations.

Effective Density

The notion "effective density" should be understood as the ratio: specific volumetric buoyancy (gravitational acceleration) assigned to a definite size of particle $\underline{k}$. By definition, effective density is a function of particle size.

398

The starting point for the Equation of effective density is the general relationsphip of Eq. (5) for density δ_T of the suspension containing liquid with density δ_f and solid particles of volumetric concentration c_k with density δ_i.

$$\delta_T = \delta_f + \sum (\delta_i - \delta_f) \cdot c_i \qquad (5)$$

If the total concentrations c_i in Eq. (5) are substituted by effective concentrations then in accordance with (6), pulp density δ_T is replaced by the required effective density δ_k:

$$\delta_k = \delta_f + \sum (\delta_i - \delta_f) \cdot c_{i,k} \qquad (6)$$

Figure 3 gives the results of computer calculations of effective density. The particle size distribution is that of the GATES-GAUDIN-SCHUHMANN (GGS functions). From the GGS index the influence of a given particle size distribution on the function of effective density can be clearly seen.

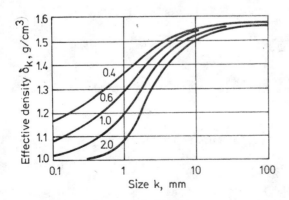

Fig. 3. Effective density functions. Calculation example with GGS index of particle size distribution as a parameter. Maximum size k_{max} = 1 mm, solid density = 2.65 g/cm, solid content = 35% by volume.

Effective Viscosity

The Einstein Equation and Its Modification. It is well known that the Equation for the viscosity η_E of a suspension as developed in 1906 by Albert Einstein cannot explain absolute values of viscosity of coarse polydisperse suspensions. According to Einstein's Equation the particle size distribution in suspension would not affect viscosity, which is unmistakably contradictory to experience in the process of separation.

In author's opinion, the Einstein Equation can also be applied to polydisperse suspensions used in concentration techniques if its validity is limited to monodisperse systems. In polydisperse suspensions we have to consider the fact that the particles do not move in liquid but in a medium the properties of which are determined by the presence of neighbour particles as already shown by the effective factors. As in the case of effective density, "effective viscosity" η_k can be defined as the viscosity of a suspension containing particles of size k. Each size fraction is such that $k > i$ causes an increase of the viscosity according to its effective concentration and its assigned effective viscosity η_i.

It also increases the viscosity by affecting the effective viscosities of all the remaining viscosity-relevant size fractions. From the Einstein Equation the relative change of viscosity $\Delta\eta$ in Eq. (7) is proportional to the total solids-concentration c multiplied by liquid viscosity η_f Eq. (8)

$$\Delta\eta = \eta_E - \eta_f \tag{7}$$

$$\Delta\eta = K \cdot c \cdot \eta_f \tag{8}$$

400

In accordance with the above relationships Eq. (9) gives the contribution term $\Delta \eta_{i,k}$ from the particle size fraction $\underline{i}$ to the effective viscosity η_k.

$$\Delta \eta_{i,k} = K \cdot c_{i,k} \cdot \eta_i \qquad (9)$$

From the boundary conditions "effective viscosity in relation to the minimum size of particle = liquid viscosity" and by summation of the contributions to viscosity due to particular size fractions $\underline{i}$ we can express both direct and indirect contributions to effective viscosity η_k in the form

$$\eta_k = \eta_f + K \cdot \sum c_{i,k} \, \eta_i \qquad (10)$$

Despite the relative simplicity of the above Equations it takes many computational steps to calculate specific cases. In practice, this can only be done by means of computer programmes.

Viscosity Coefficients

There is a definite relationship between the viscosity coefficient K and the shape of the particle in suspension. If we assume the numerical value for the viscosity coefficient given by Einstein for a sphere to be a lower limiting value, then for a polyhedral particle it may be assumed that $K > 5/2$.

A comparison of computational results with those given by the majority of authors as to the relationship between viscosity and solids concentration leads to the conclusion that the correcting constants of the viscosity coefficient in relation to Stokes drag coefficient always have the same order of magnitude.

In the range of higher solids concentrations it can clearly be seen that the liquid fraction needed for the creation of the velocity gradient is smaller than the total fraction of liquid in suspension.

If we assume that at solid fraction g_{max} the dump behaves as a solid-structure body and that this determines one of the boundary conditions for the viscosity value, then the term expressing the ratio of real solid concentration $\bar{g}$ to $(g_{max} - \bar{g})$ serves as a correcting coefficient that permits one to fit the viscosity values obtained according to Eq. (9) to the viscosities observed for higher solid concentrations.

Figure 4 gives the results of calculations of effective viscosity of the suspension characterized by the data given in Fig. 3.

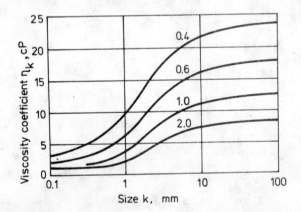

Fig. 4. Effective viscosity: computational examples with GGS index of particle-size distribution as parameter. Viscosity coefficient K = 7.0. For other conditions see Fig. 3 and text.

Figure 4 shows the effect of a particle-size distribution characterized by the GGS index on effective viscosity.

Pulp Density and Pulp Viscosity

As it can be seen from Fig. 3, with an increase in size of the reference particle k, the effective density curves asymptotically approach the limiting value which is identical to the suspension density. The density of suspension is thereby the effective density in relation to an infinitely large body. Similarly, Fig. 4 shows that with an increase in particle size the curves of effective viscosity approach the limiting values which may be referred to as suspension viscosity or "pulp viscosity". Accordingly, sufficiently precise experimental determination of density and viscosity is only possible if the respective dimensions of the device system would much exceed the size of the coarsest particles.

CONCLUSION

On the basis of the results discussed in the previous sections it may be concluded that neither the properties of the liquid nor system-constant features of pulp density and viscosity are sufficient for the calculation of the motion of particles in polydisperse suspensions. Fundamentally, it is always the properties of the medium which are dependent on the size of particle i.e., effective density and effective viscosity, that affect the motion of particles.

Present State of Art. An attempt to arrange all the observations within the range of Re $< 10^4$ (Re - Reynolds number) which is important for ore treatment processes leads to the conclusion that an exact solution of the question concerning steady settling in unlimited media is known only for infinite Reynolds numbers. These are boundary cases determined by the Newton or Stokes Equations. In Newton's range (Re $\rightarrow \infty$) it is only the forces of inertia of the particles that are of any importance. Resistance to flow in suspension is proportional to: the square of size of particle k, the square of relative velocity v_e and the effective density δ_k of the suspension.

In Stokes' range (Re $\longrightarrow$ 0) only the friction forces caused by the viscosity of the medium are important. Resistance of flow in suspension is proportional to: the size of particle k, relative velocity v_e and the effective viscosity η_k of the suspension.

The resulting force (gravity minus buoyancy) as a component of steady settling motion in suspension is proportional to the third power of particle size k, to gravitational acceleration g and to the term "solid density δ_s minus effective density". By comparing driving and drag forces, the coefficients for extreme cases according to Newton (Eg. 11) or to Stokes (Eg. 12) are:

$$C_N = k^3 \cdot g \cdot (\delta_s - \delta_k)/(k^2 \cdot v_e^2 \cdot \delta_f) \qquad (11)$$

$$C_S = k^3 \cdot g \cdot (\delta_s - \delta_k)/(k \cdot v_e \cdot \eta_k) \qquad (12)$$

Most applications in mineral processing involve a range of conditions which is intermediate between laminar and turbulent flow and the theory for these conditions is not fully developed. We will here ignore the conventional methods of determining the terminal settling velocity by means of approximated equations or diagrams.

New Approach

Required Dimensionless Coefficients. The forces operating in the system can be interrelated by dimensionless numbers:

$$Re = k \cdot v_e \cdot \delta_k / \eta_k \tag{13}$$

$$Fr = v_e^2 / (k \cdot g) \tag{14}$$

$$Ri = (\delta_s - \delta_k) / \delta_k \tag{15}$$

The Reynolds number defines the hydrodynamic behaviour that is the relation between inertial resistance and buoyancy and, the Rittinger number, Ri, the relation between the total resistance and buoyancy.

Further dimensionless numbers, e.g., the Archimedes number, can be defined as

$$Ar = Re^2 \cdot Ri / Fr \tag{16}$$

$$Ar = k^3 \cdot g \cdot \delta_k \cdot (\delta_s - \delta_k) / \eta_k^2 \tag{17}$$

By means of the Archimedes and Reynolds numbers we can reduce the particular Newton and Stokes Equations to the clear cases:

405

Newton's limit case $\qquad C_N \cdot Re^2 = Ar \qquad\qquad$ (18)

Stokes' limit case $\qquad C_S \cdot Re = Ar \qquad\qquad$ (19)

The Principle of Superposition

The force of inertia and the friction force overlap in the intermediate region between limiting cases. Generally speaking, overlap of the above forces can be represented as the sum of inertia and drag. Yet all available observations lead to the conclusion that the real drag to flow is always bigger than the sum of drag forces calculated from Newton's and Stokes' Laws (See Eq. 20).

$$C_N \cdot Re^2 + C_S \cdot Re > Ar \qquad\qquad (20)$$

The coefficients C_N and C_S of particular limiting cases should be replaced by variable coefficients C_N^x, C_S^x, if the equations are to be valid for real conditions. In relation to the methods of creating the new coefficients, overlap becomes the basic relationship for the steady settling motion in the whole range of $Re > 10^4$.

Equations

Equation 21 expresses that the total drag consists of the forces of inertia according to Newton and the friction forces according to Stokes

$$C_N^x \cdot Re^2 + C_S^x \cdot Re = Ar \qquad\qquad (21)$$

Equation 22 describes the tendency of the system to reach a balance between the forces of inertia and friction

$$c_N^x \cdot Re^2 - c_S^x \cdot Re = Min! \tag{22}$$

Equation 23 defines the coefficient of Newton's limiting case as the lowest value for the effective-equivalent coefficient of inertial drag:

$$c_N^x \geq c_N \tag{23}$$

Equation 24 defines the coefficient of Stokes' limiting case as the lowest value for the effective-equivalent coefficient of frictional drag:

$$c_S^x \geq c_S \tag{24}$$

Equation 25 relates the above equivalent-coefficients to the coefficient of limiting cases and to a new constant S:

$$(c_N^x \cdot c_S^x)/(c_N \cdot c_S) = S \tag{25}$$

The numerical value of the constant S has been found by matching with experimental results for the sphere $S = 3\pi/4$. For the coefficients of limiting cases: $c_N = 1/3$, $c_S = 18$.

COMPARISON WITH EXPERIMENTAL RESULTS

The curve in Fig. 5 was calculated on the basis of Eqs. (21, 22, 23, 24, 25) and on numerical values of the constant S which have already been presented. The points marked on the diagram show the experimental results of Allen, Arnold, Liebster, Lunnon, Wieselsberger as quoted in [1] and [6].

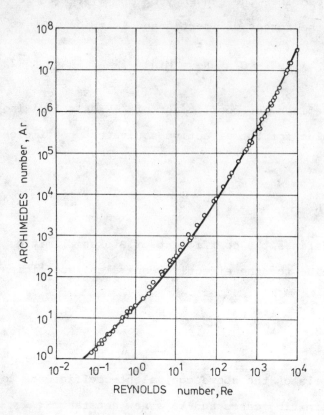

Fig. 5. Archimedes-Reynolds function of the steady-
state   settling. The curve was calculated by
means of Eqs. (21-25). For experimental points,
see text.

The almost-perfect compatibility of experimental results
with the new set of Equations leads one to suppose that the
relationships presented go beyond the limits of formal similarity - they point to a physical similarity.

CONCLUSIONS

The ratio of C_S^x to C_N^x has the character of Reynolds' number. The extreme values which are possible according to the above set of Equations distinguish the Re-regions which can be defined as the regions of Stokes, Allen and Newton. In the intermediate range between Stokes' and Newton's regions, this set of Equations is reduced to a particular solution which, strangely enough, is identical in form to the approximate Equation of Allen.

On the basis of Eqs. (21-25) a generally valid criterion of the equisettling can also be derived.

PROSPECTS

Due to the relationships between such properties of the medium as "effective density" vs. "effective viscosity" and by means of the set of Equations for steady-state settling, some fundamental problems concerning the theory of particle motion in polydisperse suspensions have been clarified.

On the grounds of theory, technical applications can now be considered. The process of separation in dense media and in particular, a way of extending the range of application of this method to fine size fractions provides a good example of the above.

The relationships presented allow one to reconsider the interactions in the system formed by the separated mineral and the particles of heavy suspension as quasi-continuun and then, for example, to analyse the influence of these interactions on

the separation and the size of separated particles in relation
to the particle-size of heavy suspension.

LIST OF SYMBOLS

k — as variable: size of particle k; As index: indication
of the size fraction k,

i — as variable: size of particle i. As index: indication
of the size fraction i,

$a_{i,k}$ — effective term of size fraction i in relation to size
fraction k,

w — water volume in suspension,

v_i — total volume of i particle-size fraction,

c_i — concentration of i particles as a fraction of the total volume of suspension,

$c_{i,k}$ — effective concentration of i particle-size fraction
in relation to k particle-size fraction,

δ_f — liquid density,

δ_i — average density of particles of size i,

δ_T — suspension density ("pulp density")

δ_k — suspension effective density in relation to k particle-size fraction,

η_f — fluid viscosity,

η_E — liquid viscosity according to Einstein,

$\Delta\eta$ — relative change of viscosity,

$\Delta\eta_{i,k}$ — contribution of particle size i to the relative change
of viscosity of k particle-size suspension,

η_k — effective viscosity of suspension in relation to k
particle-size fraction,

410

η_i - effective viscosity of suspension in relation to i particle-size fraction,

K   - viscosity coefficient in the Einstein Equation,

g   - gravitational acceleration,

Re   - Reynolds number,

Fr   - Froude number,

Ri   - Rittinger number,

Ar   - Archimedes number,

v_e - terminal velocity of steady state settling ("terminal settling velocity"),

C_N - coefficient in the Newton Equation,

c_S - coefficient in the Stokes Equation,

c_N^x - effective-equivalent coefficient in inertia term of Eq. (21),

c_S^x - effective-equivalent coefficient in friction term of Eq. (21),

S   - constant relating the drag coefficients.

REFERENCES

1. Brauer H. Grundlagen der Einphasen- und Mehrphasenbestimmungen Aarau 1971, Sauerländer AG, p. 353-395.

2. Einstein A. Ann. Physik, 19 , 289 (1906); 34, 589 (1911).

3. Fomenko T. G. Gravity concentration methods. Publishing House "Nedra". Moscow, 1966.

4. Hawksley P. C. W. The Effect of Concentration on the Settling of Suspensions and Flow Through Porous Media. Edward Arnold, London, 1951, p. 114-135.

5. Gaudin A. M. Principles of Mineral Dressing, McGraw Hill, New York, 1939.

6. Gaudin A. M. In: Flotation, McGraw Hill, New York 1957, 343 pp.

7. Schubert H. Aufbereitung fester mineralischer Rohstoffe, VEB Deutscher Verlag fur Grundstoffindustrie, Leipzig 1975, 258 pp.

ABSTRACT

The interaction of particles in a polydispersed suspension makes it necessary to characterize its properties as a function of particle size rather than of single values of density and of viscosity respectively.

Particles in a polydispersed suspension produce heterogeneities in a uniform distribution of smaller neighbour-particles. The influence of neighbour-particles is thus reduced from their total concentrations to so-called effective concentrations. An expression to calculate the effective concentrations is derived from the geometry of the system.

The function of the effective density is the result of a linear superposition of the effective concentrations and of coordinated solid-densities respectively.

The function of the effective viscosity is a non-linear combination of all the effective concentration values of the system.

The new restriction, together with the consideration of the interaction of different size classes make the Einstein equation now applicable to polydispersed suspensions of a higher solids concentration.

The limiting values of the effective density/effective viscosity functions at infinite particle size are recognized as the common values of pulp density and apparent pulp viscosity. The hitherto unsolved problem of calculating the terminal velocities of particles by means of an expression of uniform structure and validity in the whole Reynolds numbers range is solved by a new set of equations which replace the empirical relationship between the Reynolds number and the Archimedes number by a mathematical expression.

The effective density function, the effective viscosity function and the Archimedes function together provide a basis for the calculation of the motion of particles in a polydispersed suspension.

413

RÉSUMÉ

L'interaction des particules dans une suspension multidispersée rend nécessaire la caractérisation de ses propriétés
en fonction de la taille des particules plutôt qu'en fonction
de simples valeurs de densité et de viscosité.

Les particules dans une suspension multidispersée produisent
des inhomogénéités dans une distribution uniforme de particules
voisines plus petites. L'influence des particules voisines est
ainsi réduite de leurs concentrations totales à des concentrations dites effectives. Une expression pour calculer les concentrations effectives est dérivée de la géomètrie du système.

La fonction de la densité effective est le résultat d'une
superposition linéaire des concentrations effectives et des
densités solides coordonnées respectivement.

La fonction de viscosité effective est une combinaison non
linéaire de toutes les valeurs de concentration effective du
système.

Une nouvelle restriction simultanée à la considération de
l'interaction des différentes classes de taille rend l'équation d'Einstein, désormais applicable à des suspensions multi-
dispersées de plus haute concentration de solide.

Les valeurs limites des fonctions (densité effective)/
(viscosité effective) des particules de taille infinie sont
reconnues comme valeurs communes de la densité de la pulpe et
de la viscosité apparente de la pulpe. Le problème jusqu'ici
non résolu du calcul de la vitesse extrême des particules par
l'intermédiaire d'une expression de structure uniforme et
valable dans tout le domaine des nombres de Reynolds est résolu
par une nouvelle série d'équations qui remplacent la relation
empirique entre le nombre de Reynolds et le nombre d'Archimede
par une expression mathématique.

La fonction de densité effective, la fonction de viscosité
effective et la fonction d'Archimede réunies fournissent la
base de calcul du déplacement des particules dans une suspension multidispersée.

414

ZUSAMMENFASSUNG

Die Eigenschaften einer polydispersen Suspension sind wegen der Wechselwirkung der Teilchen nicht diskrete Werte, sondern Funktionen der jeweils betrachteten Korngrösse. Es sind dies die Funktionen der Wirkdichte und der Wirkwiskosität.

Jedes Teilchen einer polydispersen Funktion verursacht eine Störungszone in Bezug auf die räumliche Verteilung der jeweils kleineren Nachbarteilchen. Auf Grund dieser Störungszonen beeinflussen sich Kornklassen nicht entsprechend ihrer Absolutkonzentrationen, sondern abgeschwächt nach Massgabe sogenannter Wirkkonzentrationen. Die Beziehung zur Berechnung der Wirkkonzentrationen ergibt sich aus der Systemgeometrie.

Die Wirkdichte-Funktion ist das Ergebnis einer linearen Überlagerung der Wirkkonzentrationen bzw. der zugeordneten Feststoff-Dichtewerte.

Die Funktion der Wirkviskosität ist eine nichtlineare Verknüpfung aller im System auftretenden Wirkkonzentrationen. Den Ansatz zur Berechnung der Wirkviskosität liefert die Einstein-Gleichung, die durch eine neue Randbedingung und durch Berücksichtigung der Wechselwirkung nun auch für polydisperse Suspensionen höheren Feststoffgehaltes Bedeutung erlangt.

Die bisher ungelöste Frage einer strukturell einheitlichen Erfassung der stationären Fallbewegung wird durch einen neuen Gleichungsansatz beantwortet, der den bisher nur empirish bekannten Zusammenhang zwischen der Reynolds-Zahl und der Archimedes-Zahl durch eine exakte Beziehung ersetzt.

Mit der Wirkdichtefunktion, der Wirkviskositätsfunktion und der Archimedes-Funktion sind die Voraussetzungen für eine Berechnung der Partikelbewegung in polydispersen Suspensionen gegeben. Als besonders interessantes Anwendungsbeispiel für die abgeleiteten Beziehungen kann die Schwertrübescheidung gelten.

РЕЗЮМЕ

Взаимодействие частиц в полидисперсной суспензии создаёт необходимость характеризования ее свойств в виде соответствующих функций размера частиц, а не только на основании отдельных значений плотности и вязкости пульпы.

Частицы в полидисперсной суспензии создают неоднородности в равномерном распределении меньших соседних частиц. Благодаря этому влияние соседних частиц уменьшается от их полных концентраций до так называемых эффективных концентраций. Выражение для расчёта эффективных концентраций выведено из геометрии системы.

Функция эффективной плотности является результатом линейного наложения соответственно эффективных концентраций и плотности координированных твёрдых веществ.

Функция эффективной вязкости является нелинейной комбинацией всех значений эффективных концентраций системы.

Новое ограничение с учетом взаимодействия разных классов зерен, дает возможность от настоящего момента применять уравнение Эйнштейна к полидисперсным суспензиям более высоких концентраций твёрдого. Предельные значения функции: эффективная плотность, /эффективная вязкость при бесконечно крупных частицах, считаются общими значениями плотности и кажущейся вязкости пульпы.

Нерешенной до сих пор проблемой расчёта конечных скоростей частиц при помощи выражения с равномерной структурой и действительности в целом пределе чисел Рейнольдса, решается при помощи новой системы уравнений, которые заменяют эмпирические зависимости между числом Рейнольдса и числом Архимеда математическим выражением.

Функция эффективной плотности, функция эффективной вязкости и функция Архимеда совместно являются основой для расчёта движения частиц в полидисперсной суспензии.

ON THE EFFECTS OF THE FLUID RHEOLOGICAL AND FLOW PROPERTIES IN THE WET GRAVITATIONAL CLASSIFICATION

K. Heiskanen[1] and H. Laapas[2]

[1] *Mine Technical Group, Outokumpu, Oy, Finland*
[2] *Department of Mining and Metallurgy, Helsinki University of Technology, Otaniemi, Finland*

INTRODUCTION

The use of new wet gravitational cone classifiers in milling circuits as secondary classifiers to increase the accuracy of classification has necessitated research into these devices.

Details of the cone classifier (Fig. 1) are given elsewhere[1]. The working principle comprises (a) overflow control comprising radial vanes where the pulp flows upwards, and (b) underflow control involving sand washing, washed material recirculation and sand discharge sections. Essential in sand treatment is high pulp density. If the sand discharge works well, the overflow can be controlled by regulating its flow rate and density.

It was found that only limited data has been published on the rheological and flow properties of moving fluids in an industrial environment.

The study was divided into three parts. The first part was the investigation of the rheology of real ground and classified

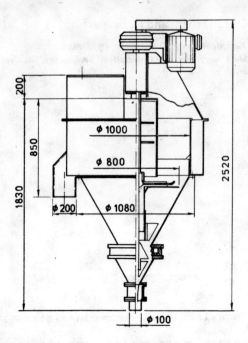

Fig. 1. The Hukki cone classifier.

pulps. The main features of interest were pulp behaviour, dynamic viscosity and the yield stress value as a function of pulp
density and fineness. The second part of the study involved the
verification of some theoretical flow pattern models on experimental patterns. The last part of the study mainly served the
purposes of classifier control by experimentally estimating the
effects of different variables.

THEORETICAL FLOW IN DUCTS

The simplified Navier-Stokes Equation [2]

$$\nabla^2 v = (1/\mu)\,dp/dx \tag{1}$$

can be used to characterize the upward pulp flow in a duct. A
cone classifier having, for example, 30 vanes can be approximated by a rectangle duct with side lengths a and b. This simpli-
fies the solution of the Navier-Stokes Equation to

$$v = \Delta py(a-y)/2\mu L + \sum_{m=1}^{\infty} \sin(m\pi y/a) \{A_m \cosh(m\pi z/a) +$$

$$+ B_m \sinh(m\pi z/a)\} \tag{2}$$

in which

$$A_m = (2a^2 \Delta p)/(\mu m^3 \pi^3 L)(\cos m\pi - 1)$$

$$B_m = -A_m(\cosh(m\pi\eta)-1)/\sinh(m\pi\eta)$$

which is a modified Poiseuille equation giving a parabolic flow
velocity distribution. The rising velocity can also be given as
a function of mean rising velocity

$$v = v_m \{(y(a-y)/2 + \sum_{m=1}^{\infty} \sin(m\pi y/a)(A_m'\cosh(m\pi z/a) +$$

$$B_m'\sinh(m\pi z/a)))/(a^2 + b^2)/24 - 8/(ab\pi^5) \tag{3}$$

$$\sum_{n=1}^{\infty} (1/(2n-1)^5)(a^4\tanh((2n-1)\pi b/2a) + b^4\tanh((2n-1)\pi a/2b)))\}$$

in which

$$A_m = (\Delta p/\mu L)A_m'$$

$$B_m = (\Delta p/\mu L)B_m'$$

From this Equation it can be seen that the shape factor of
the duct

$$\eta = b/a \tag{4}$$

affects the flow rate (constant pressure difference), the flow velocity distribution and the probability of particles reporting to overflow. This shape factor can be changed by adding more vanes to the classifier. The effect of vane addition could not be measured as a decrease in flow rate. The difference was compensated for by a higher pressure difference as the pulp level in the feed tube rose slightly.

Theoretical changes in the flow pattern are larger. The flow pattern is equally symmetric in both directions for a square duct. The transversal flow pattern changes only by becoming lower at the peak flow velocity, always maintaining a parabolic distribution when the shape ratio decreases. The smaller the ratio, the smaller is the end wall effect . The limit flow, when wall effects are neglible, is the well-known plane-Poiseuille flow

$$v = \triangle py\,(h-y)/2\mu L \tag{5}$$

In the longitudinal direction the diminishing effect of end walls when the shape ratio decreases is shown as a flattening of the flow velocity distribution. Because of this flattening of the velocity distribution, the ratio between the maximum and mean flow velocities decreases. As a result of these changes the equivelocity contours in a duct move towards the wall as the shape ratio decreases at the end walls, and towards the center, as the shape ratio decreases at the side walls (Fig. 2).

Let us consider one settling particle in a homogeneous pulp column which has a rising velocity distribution $v(y,z)$. If the settling velocity of the particle, v_s, exceeds $v(y,z)_{max}$, the particle cannot report to the overflow. If $v_s < v(y,z)_{max}$, the probability of reporting to overflow depends on whether $v_s <$ or $> v(y,z)$, i.e., on the position of the particle.

As an approximation, the probability of reporting to overflow can be said to be equal to the ratio of the area where the fluid rising velocity exceeds the particle settling velocity, to the total duct area. This excludes the rotation of particles caused by differential fluid velocity at different sides of the particle which causes the particles to move closer to the center.

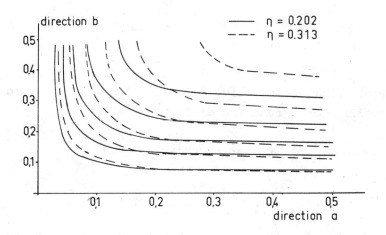

Fig. 2. Constant flow velocity curves in the duct.

As can be seen from the equal-velocity contours the area ratio mentioned cannot be estimated by any simple mathematical formula. The equations resulting from substituting any estimates of overflow reporting probability to Eq. (3) leads to Equations so complex that only a graphical solution is useful. The graphical solutions (Fig. 3) show that the duct shape affects this probability so that the thinner the duct, the smaller the size with zero probability. As an approximation of this probability

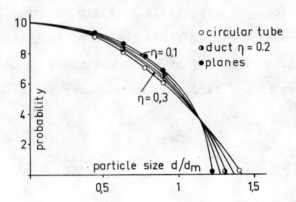

Fig. 3. Probability of relative particle sizes to report to
overflow as a function of duct shape.

the respective value of circular duct can be used

$$F = 1 - (d/d_m)^2/2 \qquad (6)$$

This form is useful on sizes up to 1.2-1.3 times d_{50}. This leads
to the hypothesis that a narrower duct would be better from the
point of view of classification accuracy.

EXPERIMENTAL

The plant experiments were partly carried out at Outokumpu
Oy's Hammaslahti mine where a CC125 cone classifier was installed. All flow tests were performed there, including a number of
feed density-overflow density-rising velocity tests and capacity
tests. Experiments with lower viscosities were also performed in

this industrial establishment, which provided all pulp samples for the viscosity measurements. Only very brief tests with high viscosity overflows were possible due to difficulties caused by too coarse overflows.

To test this classification on a laboratory scale a smaller, one-to-one scale single duct unit was built. Pulps obtained from primary classification were used as test material. These laboratory tests and all the viscosity measurements were carried out at the Helsinki University of Technology.

The difference between industrial and laboratory classifiers lay in the fact that with the laboratory classifier the pulp flowed upwards in the whole area, which was not always the case with the industrial unit. This caused some difference in calculated rising velocities, which were higher for constant d_{50} in the laboratory classifier.

Measurement of Pulp Rheology

General. Water suspensions of fast-settling solids are generally [3, 4, 5, 6] regarded as fluids, which means that they are irreversibly deformable (flow) under stress (shear stress). The fluid deformation is usually expressed [3] as the correlation of shear rate and shear stress, the resulting graph being called the flow curve. Both the shear rate and the shear stress are reported at the wall of the measuring instrument.

Figure 4 shows flow curves for various ideal rheological bodies [3] which all are time-independent fluids (the shear stress is independent of time for a given shear rate and fluid temperature). The shear rate is [7]

$$du/dy = f(\tau) \tag{7}$$

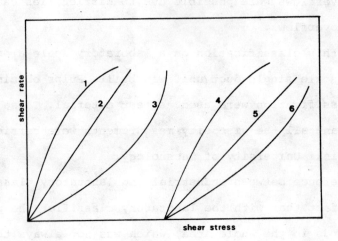

Fig. 4. Flow curves for some fluids. (1) dilatant fluid, (2) Newtonian fluid, (3) pseudoplastic fluid, (4) dilatant fluid with a yield stress, (5) Bingham plastic fluid, (6) pseudoplastic fluid with a yield value.

Equation (7) can be solved for Newtonian fluid, e.g., water, to give

$$\tau = \mu du/dy \qquad (8)$$

The term μ in Eq. (8) is called the coefficient of viscosity. The rheological properties of a Newtonian body can be merely described by μ.

Water suspensions of fast-settling solids are found to be Bingham plastic (with a yield stress) or pseudoplastic in nature [4, 5, 6, 8]. Bingham plastic fluids follow the Eq. (7)

$$\tau - \tau_o = \mu du/dy \qquad (9)$$

424

The second term on the left side of the equation is called the yield stress, which is the stress value which must be exceeded if fluid deformation is to commence. The values of both μ and τ_o are needed to define the rheology of a Bingham plastic.

A pseudoplastic body is a subgroup of fluids called power law fluids [7]

$$\tau = K(du/dy)^n \qquad n > 1 \text{ for pseudoplastic fluids} \qquad (10)$$

The coefficient K is called the fluid consistency. The higher the fluid viscosity, the higher the value of K. The exponent n, called the flow index, is a measure of the degree of departure from Newtonian behaviour on the part of the fluid. The rheological properties of a pseudoplastic fluid can be described by the terms K and n.

A term "apparent viscosity" is also frequently used in connection with non-Newtonian fluids [7]. The apparent viscosity is defined as follows:

$$\mu_a = \tau/(du/dy) \qquad (11)$$

For Bingham plastic and pseudoplastic fluids the apparent viscosity is generally higher than the true viscosity or consistency.

Measuring Apparatus. The flow curves of non-Newtonian fluids can be determined with either a rotational or capillary tube viscometer [3, 4, 7, 8]. The advantages of a capillary tube viscometer are

(a) - a wide measuring range,

(b) - uncomplicated construction and

(c) - easy mathematical treatment of data.

Figure 5 shows the modified capillary tube viscometer developed for this investigation. It consists of (1) a pulp head tank with an overflow lip to provide a constant pulp head, (2) a pulp circuit with a pulp tank and a small centrifugal pump which feed the head tank, (3) a capillary tube (class) 1.5 m long with a bore of 2.2 mm, (4) a graduated measuring tube (class) to deter-

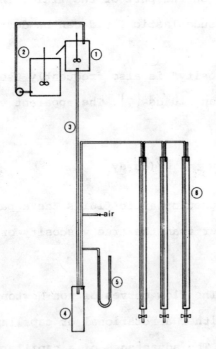

Fig. 5. Modified capillary tube viscometer.

mine the volume flow of the pulp through the capillary tube,
(5) a mercury manometer to measure the counter pressure in the
measuring tube, (6) a bubble tube (a series of three) to create
counter pressure.

The shear stress at the wall of the capillary tube [3] is

$$s_w = \Delta PR/2L$$

$$\Delta P = \Delta P_{meas} - \Delta P_{corr} \qquad (12)$$

The decrease (ΔP_{corr}) in measured pressure difference
(ΔP_{meas}) is due to entrance effects and kinetic energy losses
at the exit of the capillary tube, and has been evaluated
(Bingham plastic fluids) [3, 9] as

$$\Delta P_{corr} = 2.1\rho Q^2/\pi^2 R^4 \qquad (13)$$

The expression for shear rate of a general fluid at the tube
wall [3] is

$$(dv/dr) = \{(3+b)/4\} \{4Q/\pi R^3\} \qquad (14)$$

$$b = \{d\log(4Q/\pi R^3)\}/\{d\log(\Delta PR/2L)\}$$

For Bingham plastics, so-called pseudo-shear diagrams are
drawn which express the term $4Q/\pi R^3$ as a function of shear
stress. The resultant flow curve is described by the Buckingham
Reiner Equation [3]

$$4Q/\pi R^3 = (s_w/\mu) \{1 - 4/3(\tau_o/s_w) + 1/3(\tau_o/s_w)^4\} \qquad (15)$$

which can be simplified by omitting the last right hand term to
give

$$s_w = \mu(4Q/\pi R^3) + 4/3\tau_o \qquad (16)$$

When $4Q/\pi R^3$ is plotted against shear stress, viscosity becomes the reciprocal of the linear portion of the curve and its intercept with the shear stress axis multiplied by 3/4 gives the yield stress.

Results. The flow curves of four different classifier overflow samples were measured in a modified capillary tube viscometer within a pulp density range of 10-60% solids by weight. The specific surface areas of these samples (by permeametry) are given in Table 1.

TABLE 1

The Specific Surface Areas of Samples I-IV

Sample Number	Specific Surface Area cm^2/g
I	1047
II	1334
III	2539
IV	3916

All measurements showed the samples to be Bingham plastic in nature and to have a yield stress. Figure 6 gives the flow curves for sample I.

Figure 7 shows the pulp viscosity μ vs. the specific gravity of the pulp of samples I-IV. The viscosities were found to be independent of the fineness of the material up to an approximate pulp specific gravity of 1400 kg/m^3, after which it is clear that the higher the specific surface area of the sample, the greater the increase in viscosity. Figure 7 also includes a

428

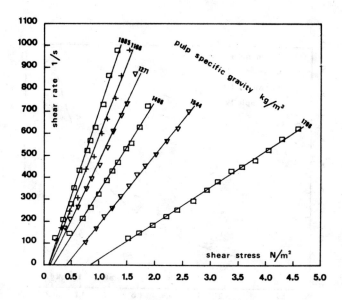

Fig. 6. Pseudo-shear diagrams for sample I.

graph in modified equation for suspension viscosity found in [7] namely

$$\mu = 1 + 2.5\phi + 14.1\phi^2 + 0.00273e^{16.6\phi} \qquad (17)$$

Figure 7 shows that up to a pulp specific gravity of 1400 kg/m^3 Eq. (17) fits all experimental data relatively well and with higher pulp densities it follows the viscosities of the coarse overflow samples. When it was found that production of classifier overflows with both high specific surface area and high pulp density was impossible, it was clear that Eq. (17) can quite satisfactorily be used to describe the overflow pulp

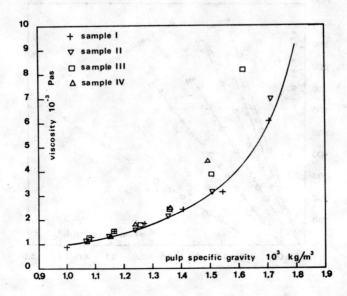

Fig. 7. The viscosity of samples I-IV vs. pulp specific
gravity. The curve is a graph of Eq. (17).

viscosities. Therefore, by measuring the pulp specific gravity
it was easy to calculate the viscosity of any overflow studied.

Figure 8 gives the pulp yield stresses vs. the pulp specific
gravity of samples I-IV. The individual yield stress values are
much higher than the viscosities affected by the fineness of
the material. All the experimental data follow the Equation

$$\tau_o = Ae^{B\rho}$$

(18)

$$A = f(S), \quad B = f(S)$$

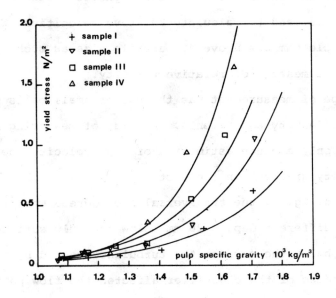

Fig. 8. The yield stress of samples I-IV vs. the pulp
        specific gravity. The curves represent a graph
        of Eq. (18).

To calculate the yield stress by means of Eq. (18) both the
pulp specific gravity and the approximate fineness (specific
surface area) of the material must be known.

Experimental Flow in Ducts

Flow experiments were carried out using two different methods.
First, the pulp was sampled at different points in the duct.
This was done by drawing the sample at approximately the same
velocity as the rising velocity of the pulp column. The method

431

was quite coarse, because the sampler end diameter measured 10 mm to provent choking. From the samples, the pulp densities and particle sizes were determined. In cases where the Reynolds flow number did not exceed 2000 and the Reynolds particle number, 4, Stokes law was used to calculate relative velocities. With Reynolds particle numbers above 4, particle size as such was directly used as a measure of relative velocity.

Another type of measurement was the use of small balls with different pulp density equivalents. This way of measuring rising velocity gave only a crude estimation of flow velocity due to the pulp density gradient in the duct.

According to Fig. 9, the transversal flow agreed well with Eq. (3)   at different depths 20 mm below the pulp surface. At depths 200 mm below the surface the turbulence caused by the rotating feed disc of the classifier affected the flow pattern to the extent that no parabolic distribution was found.

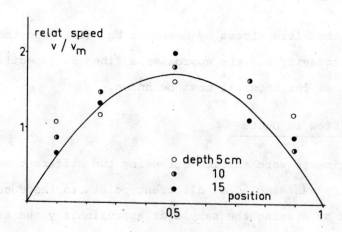

Fig. 9. Transversal flow in the duct.

The flow profile in a longitudinal direction was in only partial agreement with Eq. (3). The overflow weir end of the pattern fitted the theory. The shape of distribution was not symmetrically flat, as the theory predicted, but slowly decreased. At the ducts feed tube end the flow was reduced to very small values, and at low viscosities even to negative values (Fig. 10).

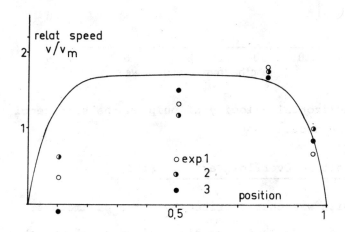

Fig. 10. Longitudinal flow in the duct (experiments 1-3).

The flow profile from the surface to a depth of 20 mm was characterized by highly reduced rising velocities, where the flow patterns were not found to be parabolic. The reduced upward flow caused a sharp increase in fineness in this region. It can be said that these last millimeters were essential for good classification. The main flow direction was towards the overflow weir. Figure 11 gives the surface velocities in a duct showing accelerating flows.

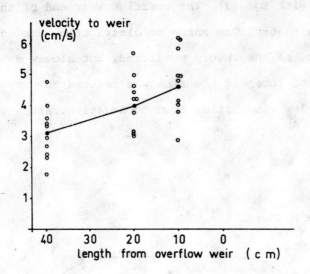

Fig. 11. Horizontal velocity of pulp on the surface of
the duct.

Variables Affecting Overflow Particle Size

Particle size was characterized by three parameters: the separation size d_{50}, which is the size having equal probability of reporting to both products, and two relative sizes, two times d_{50} and five times d_{50}. Efficiency of separation was tested by these relative sizes. The smaller the probability, the better the separation. The variables investigated were

(1) rising velocity

(2) feed pulp density

(3) duct shape

(4) Reynolds flow number

(5) viscosity

These variables were not independent. Since the total rising area was constant, the number of vanes affected the Reynolds flow number. At a constant rising velocity, viscosity and feed pulp density were compatible as can be seen from Fig. 12.

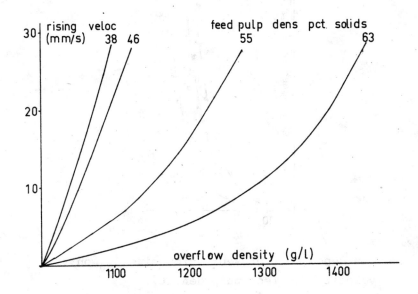

Fig. 12. The dependency of overflow pulp density on rising velocity and feed pulp density.

Separation Size. Figure 13 shows the rising velocity-separation size dependency. The relationship conforms to Stokes' law. The Reynolds flow number did not have a very great effect - not even at very high values. Another significant variable is feed pulp density. For different densities, a different value of separation size was found at a constant rising velocity. Multiple regression also showed viscosity to be a significant variable, but Fig. 13 does not, however, support this result. This

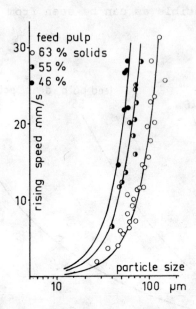

Fig. 13. The dependency of separation size d_{50} on rising
velocity and feed pulp density.

contradiction is due to the aforementioned feed density-visco-
sity dependency at constant rising velocities.

There are two different ways of controlling separation size
according to these dependencies. A variation of apex valve size
changes the rising velocity and hence the separation size. A
change in water feed changes the feed pulp density and also
affects the rising velocity. Of these two methods the latter is
by far the better; it is fast and has less influence on the
effectiveness of separation.

Relative Sizes Two Times d_{50} and Five Times d_{50}. Duct shape had no effect on particles over five times d_{50}. It is also evident from Table 2 that the effect of duct shape was most marked on sizes between 1-5 times d_{50}. At two times d_{50}, the calculated regression coefficient was 0.83, indicating that a narrower duct shape gives less coarse material to overflow. This is in fair agreement with theoretical deductions. It also appears from the

TABLE 2

The Influence of Duct Shape on the Probabilities of Relative Sizes to Report to Overflow

Experiment number	Ratio $\eta = b/a$	Viscosity 10^{-3} Pas	N_{Re}	d_{50} μm	Probability %	
					$2 \times d_{50}$	$5 \times d_{50}$
1	0.174	1.46	922	74	2.6	0.0
2	0.174	1.33	891	56	3.0	0.4
3	0.174	1.25	521	46	2.0	0.6
4	0.174	1.15	517	27	3.0	0.2
7	0.202	1.41	858	61	5.0	0.0
8	0.202	1.23	553	36	5.5	0.3
11	0.246	1.38	610	49	9.0	0.2
14	0.313	1.56	629	68	7.5	0.0
15	0.313	1.53	416	62	9.5	0.0
25	0.246	1.37	1063	57	8.0	0.2

theoretical probability curves in Fig. 3 that duct shape does not affect very coarse particles. The differences between theory and practice as to sizes which are not affected by duct shape are due to the shape and density distribution of particles in real pulps. The discrepancies found in the flow pattern must also have some effect.

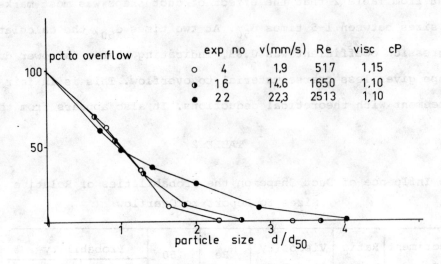

Fig. 14. Probability of relative sizes to report to overflow
as a function of rising velocity.

A comparison between tests carried out with equal pulp viscosities but different rising velocities (Fig. 14) shows that the
increased probability of coarse particles to report to overflow
is most marked with particles 1-3 times d_{50}. The effect on very
coarse particles is, however, neglible. From a regression analysis, the partial correlation coefficient between particles of
two times d_{50} and rising velocity is 0.68, the rising velocity
having a t-ratio of 3.11 in the multiple correlation.

Pulp viscosity was the main variable affecting the probability of coarse particles reporting to overflow. Its effect on
particles at two times d_{50} was clear, but was not dominant compared with other variables. For all test data the partial correlation was only 0.45, but in a multiple regression the t-test

value was as high as 5.7. In contrast to other variables, viscosity also affects very coarse particles, i.e., five times d_{50}.
Figure 15 shows the difference in probabilities for various viscosities. The correlation between viscosity and coarse particle probability was 0.64.

In multiple correlations the Reynolds flow number was usually excluded from the analysis due to low t-test values.

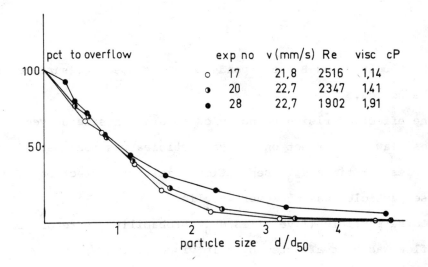

Fig. 15. Probability of relative sizes to report to overflow as a function of viscosity.

CONCLUSIONS

The flow patterns inside the classifier duct were found to be in fair agreement with the flow distributions given by a modified Poiseuille Equation. The flow just below the pulp-air interface was complex and significantly affected the overflow particle size distribution.

The flow curves of the classifier overflow samples, determined with a modified capillary tube viscometer, showed all these samples to be Bingham plastic in nature. The viscosities depended on the pulp density obeying the modified equation for suspension viscosity

$$\mu = 1 + 2.5\phi + 14.1\phi^2 + 0.00273e^{16.6\phi}$$

The yield stress value was also found to be a function of pulp specific gravity according to Equation

$$\tau_o = Ae^{B\rho}$$

in which both A and B are dependent on the specific surface area of the solids.

The effect of rising velocity on separation size obeyed Stokes' law. Its effect on coarse particles was most marked in particles 1-3 times d_{50} (separation size). The effect on very coarse particles was, however, neglible.

Coarse particle (five times d_{50}) probability to report to overflow was most affected by pulp viscosity.

The narrower the duct shape, the better the separation sharpness at 1-3 times d_{50} but not at five times d_{50}.

In conclusion it can be said that the best results in obtaining constant capacity with a cone classifier can be achieved with dilute pulps and fairly high velocities rather than with highly viscous pulps and lower velocities.

LIST OF SYMBOLS

a	duct length in direction y
b	duct length in direction z
d	particle size
d_m	separation size
ϕ	solids volume fraction
K	fluid consistency
L	duct depth or capillary tube length
n	flow index
η	shape ratio = b/a
$\triangle p$	pressure difference
$\triangle P$	pressure difference
dp/dx	pressure difference in upward direction
Q	volume flow
R	capillary tube radius
ρ	pulp specific gravity
S	specific surface area
s_w	shear stress at the wall
τ	shear stress
τ_o	yield stress
du/dy	shear rate at y
v	rising velocity
v_m	mean rising velocity
$(dv/dr)_w$	shear rate at the wall
μ	coefficient of viscosity
μ_a	apparent viscosity
∇	Laplace operator

REFERENCES

1. Hukki R. T. High sharpness of size separation-the basis for improvement in closed circuit grinding. E/MJ 178 April (1977).

2. Happel J. and Brenner H. Low Reynolds number hydrodynamics. Noordhoff International Publ. Leyden, 1973 (2nd ed.).

3. Van Wazer J. R., Lyons J. W., Kim K. Y. and Colwell R. E. Viscosity and flow measurement. Interscience Publishers. New York, 1966. (2nd ed.).

4. Devaney F. D. and Shelton S. M. Properties of suspension media for float- and sink-concentration. United States Department of Interior, Report of Investigations, 1933.

5. Kirchberg H., Topfer E. and Scheibe W. The effect of suspension properties on separating efficiency of mechanical classifiers. Proc. XI IMPC, Universide di Cagliari, 1975, 219-244.

6. Schack C., Dean K. C. and Molloy S. M. Measurement and nature of the apparent viscosity of water suspensions of some common minerals. United States Department of Interior, Report of Investigations, 1957.

7. Wasp E. J., Kenny J. P. and Gandhi R. L. Solid-liquid flow. Slurry pipeline transportation. Trans Tech Publications, 1977 (1st ed.).

8. Gronfors T. An investigation on the operational principles of a hydraulic cone classifier. Licentiate Thesis, Helsinki University of Technology, 1964 (Finnish text).

9. Streeter V. L. (ed.). Handbook of Fluid Dynamics. McGraw-Hill, 1961 (1st ed.).

ABSTRACT

Research into wet gravitational classification has so far,
with few exceptions, usually concentrated on technical operation studies and little attention has been paid to the influence of different basic fluid variables of the classification
unit itself. Very little is known about the rheology of the
fluid medium as a function of particle size, shape and density,
and as a function of pulp density and fineness in real ore
pulps. Neither are the effects of fluid movement and particle
shape on settling rates very well-known.

Only few data, if any, are available concerning the flow
distribution in a duct when classifying pulps showing non-Newtonian behaviour. The authors have not found any experimental
data concerning flow phenomena at the air-pulp interface.

These little-known phenomena have been investigated on a
laboratory and industrial scale with a Hukki cone classifier.

The real sulphide ore pulps studied showed definite Bingham -
type plastic behaviour with increasing viscosity and yield
stress on increasing pulp density and fineness. A critical pulp
density was also discovered above which pulp viscosity, particularly in the case of very fine pulps, increased drastically.

The flow inside the classifier duct agreed fairly well with
the flow distributions given by a modified Poiseuille Equation.
On the other hand, the flow just below the air-pulp interface
was found to be complex.

The effects of pulp density and viscosity, pulp rising velocity and Reynolds flow number on the separation were also
studied.

RÉSUMÉ

La recherche d'une classification gravitationelle hydrau-
lique, est généralement, jusqu'à présent et à peu d'exceptions
près, concentrée sur les études des operations techniques;
en revanche mais on a très peu attiré l'attention sur l'influence des variables fondamentales du fluide et sur l'unité même

de classification. On connait peu la rhéologie du médium fluide en fonction de la taille, de la forme, de la densité des particules, et en fonction de la densité de la pulpe et de la finesse des pulpes réelles des minerais. Aucun effect, que ce soit celui du mouvement du fluide ou celui de la forme des particules sur le degré de sédimentation, n'est très bien connu.

On dispose seulement de quelques données, peut être d'aucune, au sujet de la distribution de l'écoulement dans le conduit quand on fait la classification des pulpes présentant des propriétés non-Newtoniennes. Les auteurs n'ont trouvé aucune investigation expérimentale des phénomènes du flux à l'interface de l'air-pulpe.

Ces phénomènes, très peu connus, ont été étudiés dans le classificateur cônique de HUKKI à l'échelle du laboratoire et à l'echelle industrielle.

Les puples de minerai sulfuré étudiées présentent une nature plastique de Bingham définie, dont la viscosité et la résistance unitaire intrinsèque à la déformation augmentent avec un accroissement de la densité et de la finesse de la pulpe.

On a également découvert une densité critique de la pulpe dont le dépassement provoque une augmentation dractique de la viscosité de la pulpe, particulièrement dans le cas de pulpes très fines.

L'écoulement dans le conduit du classificateur correspond bien aux répartitions du flux données par l'équation modifiée de Poiseuille. D'autre part, on a trouvé que l'écoulement juste en dessous de l'interface air-pulpe est complexe.

On a également étudié les effets de la densité et de la viscosité de la pulpe, sa vitesse et son nombre de Reynolds sur la séparation.

ZUSAMMENFASSUNG

Als Gegenstand der Untersuchungen über die nasse Schwerkraftklassierung dienten hauptsächlick technische Operationen, während dem Einfluss wichtiger veränderlichen Flüssigkeits-Parametern sowie dem Einfluss der Klassiergeräte selbst nur wenig Aufmerksamkeit gewidmet worden ist. Wenig ist über die

Rheologie flüssiger Medien als Funktion der Grösse, Form und Dichte der Teilchen, sowie als Funktion der Schlammdichte und Kornfeinheit in wirklichen Erztrüben bekannt. Ebenso wenig wissen wir über den Einfluss der Flüssigkeitströmung und über die Form der Mineralteilchen auf die Sedimentationsgeschwindigkeit.

Nur wenige Zahlenangaben, wenn es überhaupt welche gibt, stehen uns zur Verfügung hinsichtlich der Strömungsverteilung in der Leitung während der Klassierung von Trüben mit nicht-Newtonischem Verhalten. Insofern es sich um Strömungserscheinungen in der Luft/Trübe-Grenzphase handelt, haben die Verfasser des vorliegenden Vortrages keinerlei experimentelle Untersuchungen vorgenommen.

Die hier erwähnten, wenig bekannten Erscheinungen sind sowohl im Labor als auch in situ mittels eines Hukki'schen Kegelklassierers untersucht worden.

Rein sulfidische Erztrübe weist bei zunehmender Schlammdichte und Kornfeinheit mit wachsender Viskosität und Zähigkeit entschieden plastischen Charakter auf. Es ist auch eine kritische Schlammdichte ermittelt worden, über die hinaus die Schlamm-Viskosität, besonders im Falle sehr feinkörniger Trüben, drastisch ansteigt.

Die Strömung durch den Klassierer stimmte ungefähr mit der errechneten Strömungsverteilung nach der modifizierten Gleichung von Poiseuille überein. Andererseits aber ist festgestellt worden, dass unmittelbar unterhalb der Grenzphase Luft/Trübe die Strömung komplex verläuft.

Der Einfluss der Schlammdichte und Schlammviskosität, der ansteigenden Geschwindigkeit der Trübe und der Reynolds'schen Zahl auf die Trennung von Mineralien ist ebenfalls untersucht worden.

РЕЗЮМЕ

До настоящего времени исследования по гравитационной мокрой классификации были обычно сконцентрированы, за некоторыми исключениями, на технико-эксплуатационном анализе, а влиянию переменных основных параметров на жидкую среду и на классификационное устройство уделялось мало внимания. Очень мало известно о реологии жидкой среды в зависимости от размеров частиц, их формы и плотности, а также от плотности пульпы и степени измельчения в промышленных пульпах руд. Также недостаточно хорошо известно влияние движения жидкости и размеров частиц на скорость осаждения.

Почти не существуют или существуют очень скупые данные относительно распределения течения в канале при классификации пульп с неньютоновскими свойствами. Авторы не обнаружили сведений относительно каких-либо опытных исследований на тему явлений, возникающих при течении на поверхности соприкосновения: воздух-пульпа.

Эти малоизвестные явления были исследованы в конусном классификаторе типа Гукки в лабораторном и промышленном масштабе.

При исследованиях промышленной сульфидной руды обнаружен известный пластический характер Бингама, отличающийся возрастающей вязкостью и напряжением течения при увеличении плотности и степени измельчения пульпы. Определена также критическая плотность пульпы, превышение которой вызывает значительное увеличение её вязкости, особенно в случае очень размельченных пульп.

Течение внутри канала классификатора вполне соответствует распределениям течения, приведённым в модифицированном уравнении Пуаселля. С другой стороны, течение непосредственно под поверхностью соприкосновения: воздух — пульпа, оказалось сложным.

Исследовано также влияние плотности и вязкости пульпы, возрастающей скорости течения пульпы и числа Рейнольдса на сепарацию.

STUDIES ON COMPOSITION AND BENEFICIATION
OF A FINE-GRAINED ALUMINA-RICH INDIAN ORE

B. Gururaj[1], N. Prasad[2], T. R. Ramachandran[1] and A. K. Biswas[1]

[1] Department of Metallurgical Engineering, Indian Institute of Technology, Kanpur, India
[2] Research and Development Centre, Steel Authority of India Ltd., Ranchi, India

INTRODUCTION

The total calculated iron ore reserves of India exceed 12,000 mil t assaying on the average over 52% iron [1]. A substantial proportion of these reserves is hematitic and high-grade in terms of iron content. However, the problem with Indian iron ore is two-fold. One is the high content of gangue materials, particularly aluminium-containing minerals, the other being the relatively soft nature of the ore which generates fines on handling. Alumina is believed to exist in Indian iron ore particularly in the form of lateritic clay, formed by the decomposition of basic rocks under tropical conditions.

Indian iron ore contains 1-7% Al_2O_3 which increases the viscosity of the slag in the blast furnace. To counteract this, large quantities of dolomite stone and quartzite have to be added. This in turn results in an increase in the coke rate, contamination level and silicon in the. hot metal. The ore deposits in India normally have a Al_2O_3/Fe ratio of around 0.05-0.08 or more. It has been estimated [2] that for a drop of 0.01 in the Al_2O_3/Fe ratio in the beneficiated ore, the cost per ton of hot metal produced is reduced by approximately Rs. 7.50 through increased production of hot metal in the blast furnace and reduced coke consumption. For efficient blast furnace operation, it is also necessary to keep the Al_2O_3/SiO_2 ratio to a low value.

India iron ore is relatively soft, and the introduction of mechanization and heavy blasting into the mines is generating larger quantities of fines [3-6]. The proportion of -10 mm fines from Indian mines is never less than 35% and sometimes reaches 50-60% [6]. Blast furnace technology needs exact sizing of the lump ores. Classification, preferably wet, generates a substantial quantity of fines which contain a significant quantity of iron apart from increased percentages of silica and alumina. There are also large deposits of blue dusts or natural fines in the lower layers of the deposits. Non-utilization of the large quantities of fines would amount to national wastage. On the other hand, such fines should be beneficiated before pelletization or sintering to produce agglomerates which are suitable as blast furnace burden material. Attempts to wash Indian iron ores for the purpose of removal of alumina have met with only limited success [3, 4, 7, 8]. Most attempts have resulted in the preferential removal of SiO_2 so that in spite of some lowering of the Al_2O_3/Fe ratio, the Al_2O_3/SiO_2 ratio in the beneficiated product tended to increase.

The general Indian problem as stated above is a challenging one meriting deeper scientific investigation. It was felt that

448

a basic solution could be found only if the mode of occurrence of aluminium in the ore was established. This information is not available at present. The specific minerals containing aluminium, their grain sizes, mesh of grind for liberation ets. should be determined, and some beneficiation technique applicable to fine particles-such as selective flocculation-should be adopted. This approach was undertaken in the present investigation and applied to the Barsua Iron mine samples, which represent a very typical Indian case.

Owned by the Rourkela Steel Plant (the geographical location of Rourkela in Orissa, India, is $22^{\circ}25'$ N and $85^{\circ}00'$ E), the Barsua iron ore deposit is located about 100 km from Rourkela and supplies 2 mil t of iron ore to the steel plant annually. A part of the R.O.M. is fed to the washing plant (about 700 t/h) which produces 34% + 10 mm lump material, 37% -10+2 mm. fine suitable for agglomeration and more than 24% slime [2]. A typical feed to the beneficiation plant assays 57.8% Fe, 2.8% SiO_2 and 7.2% Al_2O_3, the washed + 10 mm lump: 60.9% Fe, 1.9% SiO_2 and 4.9% Al_2O_3 and the slime approximately assays 53.5% Fe, 6.5% SiO_2 and 9.2% Al_2O_3. Thus, the Al_2O_3/Fe ratio is brought down from 0.12 to 0.08 (which is not low enough) and the Al_2O_3/SiO_2 ratio does not shift appreciably from 2.6. The slime contains a considerable quantity of iron oxide, the separation of which from alumina presents a challenging problem. Even the dumping of such a large quantity of material - a quarter of the feed to the Washing and Beneficiation Plant - year after year poses civil engineering and economic problems [2, 6]. Barsua iron ore thus present a typical problem associated with fine grained alumina-rich Indian Iron ores.

The present investigation deals with chemical and mineralogical analysis - with emphasis on X-ray and electron optical techniques - of Barsua iron ore samples and preliminary attempts to beneficiate high alumina slime by the selective flocculation technique.

MATERIALS, EQUIPMENT AND TECHNIQUE

Representative samples of Barsua Iron ore and the slimes generated in the washing and beneficiation plant were obtained by courtesy of the Rourkela Steel Plant.

Iron, silica and alumina were analysed by conventional wet chemical methods. The other detected elements viz., Chlorine, Manganese and Potassium were estimated by the $AgNO_3$ method, the permanganate colorimetric technique and flame photometry respectively.

Petrographic information regarding the samples was furnished by the SAIL [2]. X-ray diffraction studies on the powdered samples (-200 mesh size) were carried out by the Debye-Scherrer technique and using a GEC X RD-6 diffractometer and Cr $K\alpha$ radiation. On account of the unsatisfactory results from the X-ray investigation, which were due to the low proportions of fine grained aluminium - containing minerals, electron microscopic and microprobe studies were considered as essential and therefore were undertaken.

The characterization of very fine grains in the Barsua iron ore sample was carried out using the Cambridge Stereoscan and the JEM 120C electron microscope fitted with the ASID-4D (ultra-high resolution) scanning stage and Kevex Energy Dispersive

analyser. 10 g of the crushed ore were suspended in 100 ml acetone and subjected to ultrasonic vibrations in an ultrasonic
cleaner for 15 min. After allowing the suspension to settle, a
drop of the supernatant liquid was introduced on a thin (~500 Å)
carbon film supported by a 3 mm diameter 100 mesh size copper
grid. The latter was mounted in the specimen (high resolution
goniometer) stage of the JEM 120C electron microscope for studying the distribution of particles and identification by electron
diffraction. For the micro-analytical investigation, a few drops
of the supernatant liquid were deposited on a graphite support
and the latter mounted in the stereoscan or in the ASID-4D stage.

Secondary emission images of the particles were obtained in
the stereoscan at magnifications of up to x5000. At higher magnifications the images of the particles were poorly defined. The
distribution of the elements in the particles was obtained by
X-ray mapping of the regions containing particles using the
wavelength dispersive crystal spectrometer attached to the
Stereoscan (WDS) It was not possible to carry out a chemical
analysis using the WDS as the count rates for the elements Al,
Si and K were very low (~1 to 3/100 s). Secondary emission
images of the particles were obtained with the ASID-4D stage at
accelerating voltages of 20 and 40 kV. Chemical analysis of the
particles, using this stage, was carried out by tilting the
specimen holder to between 30° and 45° with respect to the
electron beam and employing an electron probe (~200 Å), the
finest one provided by the equipment. The typical X-rays emana-
ting from the particles were characterized by the Kevex analyser and the results of intensity vs. energy displayed on a TV
screen or processed by a computer for arriving at the integra-

ted intensities corresponding to various elemental peaks. A time count of 100 s was employed in all experiments. X-ray intensities from standards in the form of pure elements were used for atomic number, absorption and fluorescence corrections. About thirty regions and over 400 grains were scanned in order to characterise particle size distribution and elemental composition and to identify the phase constituting Aluminium-containing minerals in the sample.

Transmission electron microscopy was carried out at an accelerating voltage of 100 kV and micrographs of areas containing particles were recorded at magnifications x 10,000-20,000. The corresponding diffraction patterns were recorded at camera lengths of 76 and 120 cm. Sufficient care was taken to avoid photographing artefacts on the carbon film. The diffraction patterns obtained show the presence of both single and polycrystalline particles in the region covered by the diffraction aperture (an area of $\sim$0.23 μm diameter); occasionally fuzzy rings indicating the presence of amorphous phases were encountered. The values for interplanar spacings, d, were obtained from measurements of the radius R of the rings in the case of polycrystalline samples or the distance R of the individual diffraction spots from the central spot for single crystal patterns and where the value of the camera constant, $L\lambda$, for the microscope was obtained with the help of an evaporated gold film.

Some heavy media separation experiments were performed to evaluate the industrial applicability of such a technique and to determine the mesh of grind for appropriate liberation. The representative sample was ground in large quantities and sieved

to different fractions. 10 g of specific sieve size range fractions were mixed with heavy liquid such as bromoform (sp.gr.
2.5) or acetylene tetrabromide (sp.gr. 2.96) in 75 cc. test tubes and kept for 15 min for settling. Float and sink parts were
separated, filtered, dried and weighed. The fractions were analysed in terms of elemental composition and specific gravity.

Selective flocculation experiments were performed initially
with Barsua Run of Mine ore and later with the 'slimes' generated in the Washing Plant. Flocculants used were Magnafloc 140
and 292 (cationic polyacrylamides) and Magnafloc 139 and 155
(anionics) supplied by Allied Colloids Limited, U.K. and also
starch. A few other commercial polyacrylamide flocculants, which
were tried and did not give satisfactory results, are not being
referred to in this paper. NaF, Na_2SiO_3, $Na_4P_2O_7$ were used as
electrolytes in some of the experiments. Versicol W 13, a commercial dispersant, was also used in some experiments.

The flocculation experiments were performed in a cylindrical
vessel of 11 cm internal diameter and 24 cm height i.e., of a
capacity slightly more than 2 1. Samples were prepared such
that the material settling in the vessel within 5 min (the duration of a flocculation expt.) was eliminated as too coarse,
and ultra-fine slimes (not settling even in 2 h) were also eliminated. The concentration of this sized sample (typically 1
to 30 μm) was held at around 4 g/l for the flocculation experiments.

A typical experiment was carried out by mixing specific doses
of dispersant, electrolyte and fine particles of iron ore or
slime in 2 1 of aqueous suspension. The pH range was kept around

the normal equilibrium value i.e., 7-8. A specific quantity of strong flocculant solution was added and the system thoroughly agitated at a high number of r.p.m. After 7 min, the r.p.m. was reduced and flocs allowed to settle for 2-5 min. Flocculated and non-flocculated portions were separated in single-stage experiments for de-watering, drying and chemical assay.

In the multistage flocculation experiments, the flocculated portion in the first flocculation experiment (F_1) was separated from the residue (NF_1). F_1 was re-dispersed and reflocculated using more dispersant and flocculant, giving F_2 and NF_2. F_2 was similarly processed in the third stage to give F_3, the floccula-ted part, and NF_3. NF_1, NF_2 and NF_3 were combined and subjected to the final or scavenging stage of flocculation yielding F_4 and NF_4. There were thus three ultimate products: F_3, F_4-the middle and NF_4 - the final non-flucculated fraction, labelled as 'A' 'B' and 'C' respectively in Table 5.

RESULTS

A large number of composite analyses of Barsua Run of Mine ore gave results such as Fe 58-64%, SiO_2 1.5 to 2.0% and Al_2O_3 4-6%. The 'slime' assayed Fe 52-55%, SiO_2 5-7% and Al_2O_3 8-12%. The composite R.O.M. sample also contained app. 0.024% chlorine, 0.66% potassium and 0.046% manganese.

Long exposure was allowed to obtain a powder diffraction photograph and to identify trace minerals present (Fig. 1). A standard conversion table was used to obtain the corresponding values of 'd' for each 2θ measured from the film. Hematite was found to be the major element. Small amounts of goethite and

454

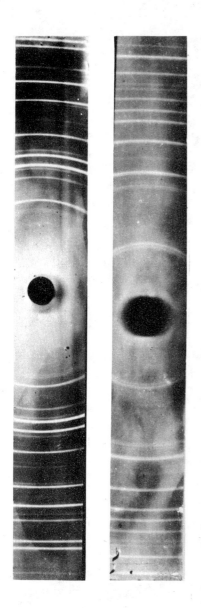

Fig. 1. Powder diffraction photograph of a Barsua ore sample. Fe target; 40 kV; 20 mA.
Exposure 20 h (with Mn filter). Top photograph 2θ = 0; bottom photograph 2θ = 180.

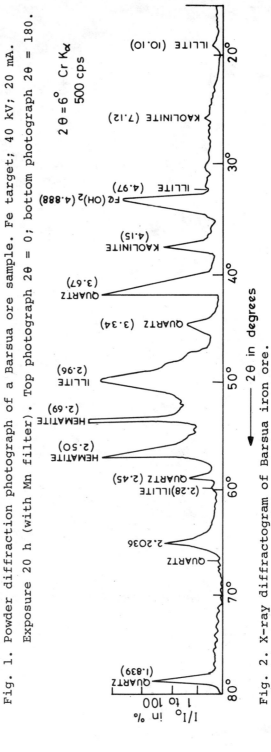

Fig. 2. X-ray diffractogram of Barsua iron ore.

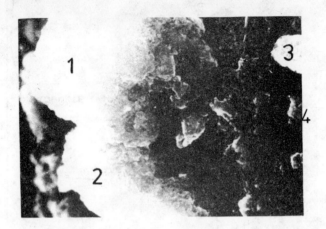

Fig. 3a.   Electron micrograph of Barsua iron ore. Magnification X 10,000. Grain 1 analyses for Al, Si, K and
Cl in addition to large proportion (peak) of iron.
Grain 2 seems to be pure iron oxide. No. 3 contains Fe, Al, Si and K and number 4 shows only Si
(probably SiO_2).

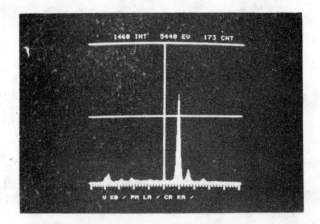

Fig. 3b.   Elemental X-ray intensity peaks for grain No. 1
in Fig. 3a showing, from left to right, the peaks
for Al and Si (combined), Cl, K, FeK_α (large) and
FeK_β.

Fig. 4a.   Electron micrograph of another zone. Magnification
x 10,000. Analysis using ASID 4D stage and the KEVEX
analyser shows a strong iron peak and additional
peaks due to Al, Si, K and Cl in grain No. 1. Grain
No. 2 shows only Al and Si and No. 3, a very promi-
nent Al peak on the left (vide Fig. 4b below) followed by a FeK$_\alpha$ peak. Grain No. 4 contains Al, Si
and K.

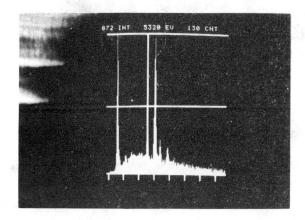

Fig. 4b.   Strong elemental X-ray intensity peak for aluminium
in grain No. 3 as shown in Fig. 4a.

traces of gibbsite and quartz were detected. This did not add anything to the petrographic information provided by SAIL [2], which did not mention any specific mineral-containing aluminium.

The relative intensity vs. diffraction angle (starting from $2\theta = 6°$) curve or diffractogram (Fig. 2) indicated the presence of hematite, kaolinite, quartz and illite. Some peaks were unidentified and a hump region indicated the presence of amorphous clay minerals.

Electron microanalytical studies and electron diffraction patterns provided conclusive information regarding minerals containing aluminium. A typical micrograph (Fig. 3a shows distinct grains with specific elements, such as No. 1 containing Al, Si, K, Cl, apart from iron. The elemental X-ray intensity peaks for this particular grain (No. 1) are shown in Fig. 3b.

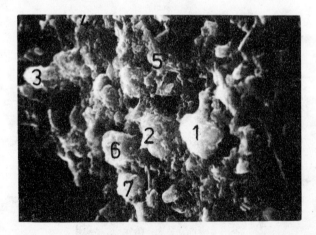

Fig. 5. Electron micrograph of a third zone. Magnification x 10,000. Shows grains 1 and 2 containing Al, Si and K, 3 and 4 containing Al and Si, 5 containing only Al and 6 and 7 containing Fe only.

Figures 4 and 5 show two other typical micrographs in which
elemental compositions of specific grains have been identified.
Grain No. 3 in the electron micrograph shown in Fig. 4a has a
strong Al peak (Fig. 4b).

Fig. 6. Electron micrograph
(x 10,000) showing a
zone containing Si, Al,
K and Mg in 5:3:1:1
weight proportion.
Illite is a possible
mineral in this zone.

Fig. 7. Electron micrograph
(x 10,000) showing a
zone containing Si
and Al in 1:1 weight
proportion. Kaolinite
is a possible mineral
in this zone.

The typical micrograph illustrated in Fig. 6 shows particles
with peaks for Si, Mg, K and Al apart from the inevitable and
strong Fe peaks. The elemental composition of the particles was
5:3:1:1 for the weight ratios of Si, Al, K and Mg respectively.
It may be noted that the composition of illite, though widely
variable, may typically be 6.1:2.43:1.38:1 for the weight ratio
of the above four elements. Figure 7 shows the regions where

459

peaks were obtained for Fe, Si and Al only. The Fe:Si:Al weight ratio was found to be 7:1:1. Excluding iron, the Si:Al ratio was 1:1. In kaolinite, the corresponding ratio is very close to 1:1.

Figures 8 and 9 show an electron micrograph and the corresponding electron diffraction pattern respectively. The "d" values calculated from the rings tally with the standard values

Fig. 8. Electron micrograph of particles (x 33,000 magnification).

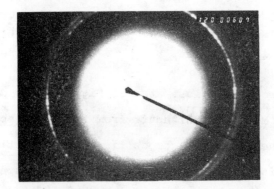

Fig. 9. Electron diffraction pattern corresponding to the previous micrograph (Fig. 8) suggesting the presence of kaolinite and illite. Diaspore and gibbsite are also suspected.

for kaolinite and illite. The presence of diaspore and gibbsite
are also suspected. Figures 10 and 11 demonstrate the additional
diffraction patterns in two other zones establishing the presence of quartz, montmorillonite, diaspore and illite as specific
minerals in the sample. .

Fig. 10. An electron diffraction pattern indicating the presence of quartz, montmorillonite and diaspore (?)

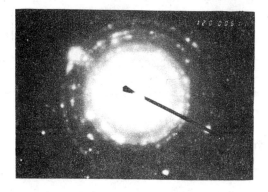

Fig. 11. An electron diffraction pattern indicating the
presence of illite and quartz.

Tables 1 and 2 summarize the collated information regarding sizes, elemental composition and phase characteristics of typical grains containing aluminium, solicon etc. in the Barsua mine sample.

TABLE 1

Size and Elemental Composition of Some Typical Grains

Reference	Grain No.	Size in μm	Elemental Composition
Fig. 3a	1	6.2 x 4.3	Al, Si, K and Fe
	2	5.0 x 3.5	Fe (probably Fe_2O_3)
	3	1.0 x 0.7	Al, Si, K
	4	0.9 x 0.8	Si (probably SiO_2)
Fig. 4a	1	2.4 x 3.0	Al, Si, K
	2	2.4 x 2.1	Al, Si
	3	4.2 x 2.1	Al (probably Al_2O_3)
	4	1.9 x 1.1	Al, Si, K
Fig. 5	1	2.1 x 1.35	Al, Si, K
	2	1.9 x 1.4	"
	3	1.5 x 1.1	Al, Si
Fig. 6			Si:Al:K:Mg is 5:3:1:1
Fig. 7			Si:Al is 1:1

Densitimetric sub-fractionation experiments showed that none of the size fractions could be sub-fractionated by bromoform (density 2.5) in which everything sank. Acetylene tetrabromide or tetrabromoethane (density 2.96) was not adequate in fractionating particles coarser than 150 mesh. Therefore, substantial liberation is considered unlikely with sizes greater than 104 μm. However, as the Barsua Washing plant data suggest, differential

TABLE 2

Size and Phase Composition of Typical Grains

Reference	Size in µm	Mineral Phase
Fig. 8	0.3 to o.7	Kaolinite, Illite Diaspore(?) Gibbsite(?)
Micrograph (not shown) Corresponding to Fig. 10	0.3 to 0.6	Quartz, Montmorillonite Diaspore(?)
Micrograph (not shown) Corresponding to Fig. 11	0.5 to 1.67	Illite, Quartz
Micrograph not shown	0.3	Quartz, Kaolinite
"	1.1 to 1.8	Montmorillonite, Illite

or preferential grinding resulting in some liberation at coarser sizes is not ruled out.

Some typical acetylene tetrabromide fractionation results are given in Table 3.

TABLE 3

Results of Densitimetric Fractionation with Acetylene Tetrabromide

Sieve Size (mesh)	Sink				Float			
	Wt. %	g/cm^3	Al_2O_3 %	Fe_2O_3 %	Wt. %	g/cm^3	Al_2O_3 %	Fe_2O_3 %
-150+200	82.5	3.7	5.1	91.0	17.5	1.83	17.33	78.8
-200+325	63.3	3.66	-	-	36.6	2.11	-	-
-325	42.1	3.64	-	-	55.4	2.23	-	-

TABLE 4

Single Stage Flocculation Results

(Expt. 1. 8.5 g ROM in 2 l suspension. 1 ml of 0.1 g/l Cationic Magnafloc 292 solution pH 8.0 No additional electrolyte. Expt. 2. As in 1 except 0.6 ml of 0.1 g/l. Anionic Magnafloc 155 pH 7.8. Expt. 3. 8 g/l of slime (1-30 µm) 1 ml of 0.2 g/l. Cationic Magnafloc 140. pH 7.9. 400 ppm Versicol W13, 800 ppm NaF added as 0.5 M solution).

Expt. No.	Wt% Flocculated	Analysis of Floc.		Analysis of Non-floc.		Al rejection p.c in tail
		%Al_2O_3	%SiO_2	%Al_2O_3	%SiO_2	
1	27.0	8.8	2.6	4.4	2.5	57.6 (in F[*])
2	36.0	6.8	2.86	7.36	2.3	60.2 (in NF[*])
3	28.8	22.2	10.0	15.8	8.3	36.6 (in F[*])

[*]F —— Flocculated; NF —— Non-flocculated. Aluminium rejection values are not high enough.

TABLE 5

Multiple Stage Slime Flocculation Results

(Expt. 4: Cationic Magnafloc 140 0.2 g/l solution added in 4 stages: 2.5, 2.0, 1.5 and 2.5 ml. Versicol W13 and NaF as in Expt. 3. Expt. 5 Anionic Magnafloc 139 0.6 g/l solution added in 4 stages: 2, 1, 0.5 and 1.5 ml. Also 800 ppm NaF, 400 ppm $Na_4P_2O_7$ and 50 ppm Versicol W13. Expt.6 Same as in Expt.5 except $Na_4P_2O_7$ replaced by Na_2SiO_3. Expt. 7 Same as Expt.6 except Magnafloc 139 replaced by Starch 0.01 g/ml solution added in 4 stages: 3, 2, 5 and 6 ml)

Expt. No.	Fractions	Wt (g)	Assay in percentages			Recovery in percentages		
			Fe_2O_3	Al_2O_3	SiO_2	Fe_2O_3	Al_2O_3	SiO_2
4	A	2.57	65.6	26.0	8.4	15.8	24.1	13.4
	B	11.41	70.4	15.6	10.8	73.0	63.6	77.8
	C	1.74	69.6	19.2	7.8	11.2	12.3	8.8
5	A	3.20	68.8	3.4	6.3	20.8	9.1	13.1
	B	9.07	67.2	5.6	12.4	57.6	42.5	73.1
	C	3.44	66.4	16.8	6.2	21.3	48.4	13.9
6	A	8.12	67.2	3.6	11.8	51.9	19.5	53.5
	B	3.57	70.4	17.8	11.2	23.9	42.3	22.3
	C	4.05	62.8	14.2	10.7	24.2	38.2	24.1
7	A	3.07	68.8	14.8	10.5	33.6	24.6	28.8
	B	5.48	66.8	19.9	11.8	58.4	59.5	57.8
	C	0.905	55.5	32.3	16.6	8.0	15.9	13.4

Below 150 mesh, float and sink fractions with substantial differences in specific gravity were obtained. Liberation improves with finer sizes as is evident from the higher proportion of float with particles of finer sizes. However, it was not possible to obtain iron-free float and aluminum free sink even with -325 mesh material.

Some single stage flocculation experiments were performed with ROM and slimes. The results are provided in Table 4. Better results were obtained through the use of electrolytes and dispersants. Table 5 contains some selected data on multiple stage flocculation. Both anionic and cationic flocculants seem to achieve some separation between mineral constituents. Electrolytes containing highly charged anions e.g., silicate and pyrophosphate as well as organic dispersants, show appreciable efficacy in the removal of some aluminium-bearing minerals from hematites through preferential dispersion.

DISCUSSION

Phase characterization is the first and most important step prior to any mineral beneficiation study. An attempt has been made for the first time to elucidate the nature of the occurrence of aluminium in typical Indian iron ore. It has been established that some phases are essentially alumino-silicates and some contain Al, Si as well as K and Mg (Table 1). Kaolinite, illite and montmorillonite are the most probable phases (Table 2). Most of the alumino-silicate minerals in the iron ore sample are extremely fine-grained. Grain sizes are in the neighbourhood of a few microns and there are also sub-micron grains (Tables 1 and 2). The present investigation illustrates the application of electron microscopy, microprobe and electron diffraction techniques in the study of fine-grained mineral samples for which petrography and X-ray techniques are inadequate.

The data in Table 3 shows that perfect liberation was not achieved even with a 325 mesh size. The sink fraction had a specific gravity much below that of pure Fe_2O_3, and contained substantial amount of Al_2O_3. Similarly, the float retained a significant quantity of Fe_2O_3. Thus, ore bodies of this nature need very fine grinding for adequate liberation prior to any beneficiation step. Fortunately for specialists in fine particle technology, industrial slimes provide good opportunities to test their ability, even though the entire ore body may not be used for uniform fine grinding. It may be mentioned in this connection that the oxidized iron formation at the Tilden Mine, owned by Cleveland Cliffs Iron Company, U.S.A., has a grain size of less than 25 um, and this crude ore is being commercially reduced to approximately 85% minus 500 mesh (25 um) prior to a beneficiation step involving selective flocculation [9].

Selective flocculation is one of the most promising avenues for beneficiating fine particles [10] which cannot be processed by conventional techniques such as gravity separation, flotation etc. Some basic studies have been made on binary systems of pure minerals and the separability of pure minerals by selective flocculation [11, 12]. However, it is acknowledged that an ore body is a much more complex system and the results from the studies on binary systems should be translated into plant prac-

tice with great caution. In this connection, precise mineralogical characterization of an ore body becomes a matter of paramount importance. Clayey minerals containing aluminium are
easily dispersible with electrolytes containing polyvalent
anions. It has been seen in the present investigation that appropriate dispersion of the above minerals by electrolytes and
dispersant is a very crucial step. Selective flocculation is
possible with cationic polymer (flocculating negatively charged
clayey particles) or with anionic polymer (flocculating more of
the iron-bearing minerals). Starch is a promising flocculant.
Multiple stage flocculation has its obvious merit [10]. Preliminary selective flocculation experiments show distinct pro-
mise. Intensive efforts are being made towards the achievement
of greater selectivity and scientific rationalization of the
results so achieved.

ACKNOWLEDGEMENTS

The authors are grateful to the R and D Centre of the Steel
Authority of India Ltd., (SAIL) for supporting the present investigation, and for permission to publish some of the results
of the investigation. They would also like to thank Prof.
J. Burke of University College, Swansea, U.K., for extending
electron microscopy facilities. The powder diffraction photographs were provided by the Mineral Physics Division of the
Geological Survey of India.

REFERENCES

1. Gokhale K. V. G. K. and Rao T. C. Ore Deposits of India, Thomson Press (India) Ltd. 1973.

2. Steel Authority of India Ltd., Private Communications.

3. Viswanathan S. and Paranjpe. Trans. Indian Inst. of Metals, 21, 71 (1968).

4. Narayanan P. I. A. and Ramakrishna Rao G. S. Trans. Indian Inst. of Metals, 21, 79 (1968).

5. Irani J. J. and Viswanathan S. Considerations on the Sizing of Blast Furnace Raw Materials. TISCO Journal, pp. 119-126, October, 1971.

6. Sen P. and Misra D. D. NML Technical Journal, 14, 47-55 (1972).

7. Banerjee S. K. and Narayanan P. I. A. Indian Mining Journal, 1-11 Sept. (1958).

8. Yu A. T. Min. Engg., 20, No. 11, 70 (1968).

9. Paananen A. D. and Turcotte W. A. Factors influencing selective flocculation - desliming practice at the Tilden Mine, Paper presented at the 1978 AIME Annual Meeting, Denver, Colorado, U.S.A. Also vide Engng. Mining J., 175, 140-142 (1974).

10. Read A. D. and Hollick C. T. Minerals Science Engng., 8, 202-213 (1976).

11. Yarar B. and Kitchener J. A. Trans. Instn. Min. Metal. Sec. C, 79, C23-33 (1970).

12. Read A. D. Trans. Instn. Min. Metall. Sect. C, 80, C24-31 (1971).

ABSTRACT

Studies have been made of a typical Indian high-alumina iron
ore which is fine-grained, and thus offers a challenging opportunity in the field of fine particle technology. For the first
time electron microscope and microanalytical studies have been
undertaken to characterize the aluminium-containing minerals
and grains in such a sample. Preliminary selective flocculation
experiments establish the feasibility of this beneficiation
technique for obtaining a concentrate assaying more in iron and
less in alumina.

RÉSUMÉ

Des études ont été faites sur un minerai de fer, typique des
Indes, riche en alumine, qui est à grains fins, et offre ainsi
une possibilité de choix dans le domaine de la technologie à
particules fines. Des études avec microscope électronique ainsi
que des études micro-analytiques ont été entreprises pour la
première fois, afin de caractériser les minéraux et les grains
contenant de l'aluminium, dans un tel échantillon. Des expériences préliminaires sur la floculation sélective établissent
la possibilité d'utiliser cette technique avantageuse, afin
d'obtenir un concentré contenant plus de fer et moins d'alumine.

ZUSAMMENFASSUNG

Es wurde ein typisches indisches Eisenerz mit hohem Aluminiumoxidgehalt untersucht, das dank seiner Feinkörnigkeit
geradezu herausfordert, auf dem Gebiet der Mikromolekular-
technik ausgewertet zu werden. Erstmalig sind Untersuchungen
mit Hilfe eines Elektronenmikroskops wie auch mikroanalytische
Untersuchungen vorgenommen worden, um aluminiumhaltige Minerale
und die darin enthaltenen Körnchen zu charakterisieren. Präliminäre selektive Ausflockungsversuche haben die Zweckmässigkeit
des Anreicherungsverfahrens zur Erlangung eines Konzentrats mit
höherem Eisen dafür aber geringerem Aluminiumoxidgehalt bestätigt.

РЕЗЮМЕ

Проведены исследования типичной индийской железной руды
с высоким содержанием окиси алюминия, которая является мелко-
зернистой и создает большие возможности в области технологии
обогащения тонких шламов. Впервые проведены микроаналитические
исследования и исследования при помощи электронного микроскопа
для характеристики минералов и зерен, содержащих окись алюминия.

Вступительные опыты по селективной флокуляции позволили определить пригодность этого метода обогащения, цель которого
заключается в получении концентрата с повышенным содержанием
железа и низшим содержанием окиси алюминия.

THE POSSIBILITY OF MAGNETIC FLOCCULATION OF WEAKLY MAGNETIC MINERALS

V. Hencl[1] and J. Svoboda[2]

[1] *Mining Institute of the Czechoslovak Academy of Sciences, Prague, Czechoslovakia*
[2] *Ore Research Institute, Prague, Czechoslovakia*

INTRODUCTION

Current design of magnetic wet separators for dressing weakly magnetic minerals is based on the presence of ferromagnetic bodies of various shapes (balls, grooved plates, rods, steel wool etc.), called matrices, in a magnetic field. A high-intensity magnetic field with high gradient is induced on the surface of such bodies which facilitates the development of a magnetic force strong enough to attract even weakly magnetic particles to their surface and thus to separate them from non-magnetic particles.

The common disadvantage of all such magnetic separator designs is the fact that the presence of a ferromagnetic matrix introduces the problem of keeping the matrix clean and passable long enough in industrial conditions. Industrial slurries contain always various extraneous bodies (wood, plastics, tramp iron from mills, etc.) and often other strongly magnetic minerals, oversized grains, etc. are also present. Filtration of such admixtures is usually not very effective and the matrix must be cleaned or replaced within a short time.

In order to solve this problem, separators employing special arrangements of magnet coils (e.g., quadrupole) capable of producing the desired magnetic field heterogeneity are being developed. Such an arrangement, however, has a disadvantage in the fact that it is not possible to use the entire volume of a magnet and the magnetic field gradient is smaller compared to conventional separators. Separation occurs solely in a relatively small volume of a narrow channel, which substantially reduces the throughput.

One of the interesting possibilities of matrixless systems is represented by the application of magnetic flocculation to the separation of magnetic and non-magnetic components. The application of magnetic flocculation has been limited to strongly magnetic minerals, particularly magnetite, placed in a weak magnetic field. According to existing theories, the value of magnetic field required for flocculation of paramagnetic materials is so high, that it precludes industrial application of this process.

This paper presents a critical analysis of current theories and outlines some possibilities of magnetic flocculation of weakly magnetic minerals which result from the experimental data.

THEORETICAL SURVEY

A suspension of magnetic particles in an external magnetic field produces flocculation forces between particles. Although such flocculation or coagulation of ferromagnetic minerals like magnetite is a well established fact, attempts to develop a reasonable theory which would be able to reliably explain this phenomenon have more or less failed. There exist a number of different approaches (1-3) to this multi-body-problem. Each approach takes only a limited number of competing forces into account and neglects other interactions which could be crucial for the explanation of this effect.

To our knowledge the only report of magnetic flocculation of paramagnetic particles is that of Watson [4]. In his theoretical treatment, Watson compared magnetic interaction with the energy produced by thermal motion and obtained a limiting value of the magnetic field in which magnetic flocculation may occur. This field, in which particle aggregates begin to be formed, is expressed as:

$$B = \left(\frac{2\ k_B\ T \eta_0}{\pi^2 \varkappa^2\ R^3} \right)^{1/2} \tag{1}$$

where k_B is the Boltzman constant, T the absolute temperature, η_0 the permeability of the vaccuum, $\varkappa$ the volume magnetic susceptibility of the particles, and R the particle radius.

Although this relation can perhaps serve as a first approach to the problem, its application to paramagnetic ores of standard dimensions (up to, say, 300 μm) yields unreasonably low magnetic fields necessary to induce flocculation. For example, siderite slurry with a magnetic susceptibility value of $\varkappa = 4.7 \times 10^{-3}$ (SI) and mean radius R-50 μm, should begin to agglomerate in a field of the order of 2 μT, which is certainly substantially lower than the experimental results indicate.

As might be expected, the process seems to be much more complicated than may appear from the above Equation. Apart from Brownian motion, particles in suspension experience mutual repulsion due to the electric double layer, which is counteracted by weak attracting non-polar van der Waals forces. In addition to these forces, one must consider magnetic interparticle forces, hydrodynamic drag, and gravitational and inertial forces.

Early reports on the coagulation of magnetite used the magnetostatic Coulomb law to describe magnetic interaction between particles (1), disregarding all other competing forces:

$$F = \frac{\varkappa^2 H^2 S^2}{kr^2 (1 + \varkappa N)^2} \tag{2}$$

where $\varkappa$ is the volume magnetic susceptibility, H the external magnetic field intensity, S the particle cross-section, r the interparticle distance and N the demagnetization coefficient.

If we apply this Equation to a weakly magnetic ore, e.g., siderite, and if we assume the flocculation field of magnetite is 20 mT, then such a field for siderite (under the same conditions as in Eq. (1)), resulting from Eg. (2), is of the order of 18 T, which is considerably higher than the experiment indicates.

Maryuta et al. [2] tried to obtain a more realistic picture by using the well-known expression for the magnetic force acting between particles derived from the theory of magnetic separation:

$$\vec{F} = -\mu_o \varkappa \vec{H} \text{ grad } \vec{H} \tag{3}$$

The expression for H, derived from geometrical considerations can be used along with Eq. (3) to estimate the magnitude of magnetic force. Comparison of this force with the hydrodynamic drag acting against particle movement for a typical siderite particle indicates that in a magnetic field of the order of 2 T, hydrodynamic drag is   higher than the magnetic force by several orders of magnitude. This could actually have been anticipated since grad H generated by the particles themselves is very low compared e.g., with gradients produced by matrices in magnetic separators.

A similar approach was adopted by Eyssa and Boom [3], who derived the following relation for the magnetic force:

$$F = 3.9 \, D \, M^2 R^2 \, (1 - \epsilon)^{4/3} \qquad (4)$$

where D is the demagnetization factor, ϵ is the porosity of the suspension, R the particle radius, and M is the magnetization of the particle given by:

$$M = \frac{\mu - 1}{4\pi + D\epsilon \, (\mu - 1)} \cdot H$$

where μ is the permeability of the particles. Comparison of Eq. (4) with hydrodynamic drag yields a better estimate of the flocculation field than the preceding Eqs. (1), (2) and (3). For instance, for a spheric siderite particle of radius 50 μm in a magnetic field 2 T, with a slurry concentration of 0.06 and particle velocity equal to 0.01 m/s (settling velocity), the magnetic force is approximately equal to the hydrodynamic drag and thus we may expect the coagulation effect. Although the flocculation field is still higher than the experimental

476

value, we reached the realm of industrially feasible magnetic fields.

It is evident that the interactions causing the flocculation of weakly magnetic particles are much more complicated than may appear from the simplified models discussed. However, a full understanding of this process is crucial in view of the importance of magnetic flocculation and work on this subject is underway in our laboratory.

FACTORS INFLUENCING MAGNETIC FLOCCULATION

As has been mentioned above, both magnetic flocculation and magnetic separation are the product of a number of forces. Magnetic flocculation occurs under the condition where the sum of forces of attraction is greater than the resulting repulsion force. Assuming sufficiently high magnetic induction, the magnetic force of attraction between approaching particles rapidly increases and reaches a maximum at their point of contact.

Besides magnetic field induction, the main factors influencing the process of magnetic flocculation are the properties of the flocculated material, i.e., its magnetic susceptibility, grain size, period of magnetization, and slurry density. In order to guarantee the formation of flocs with a sufficiently high content of magnetic component, it is imperative to optimize the magnetic field induction B. With an increase in B, flocculation proceeds in three stages.

In the first stage, flocs are uniformly formed in low quantity; their grade is high and thus this phase is called "selective flocculation".

In the second stage, numerous flocs of lower grade are formed, owing to the entrapment of non-magnetic components in the flocs. This stage is termed "avalanche flocculation". A further increase in the magnetic field leads to non-uniform formation of low-grade flocs and a high degree of flocculation is attained, constituting the "total flocculation" stage.

. Floc grade can be further influenced either chemically, e.g., by adding electrolytes which inhibit the formation of the dipolar layer or mechanically, by a suitable chosen hydrodynamic mode, e.g., by vibration.

Selective magnetic flocculation is a relatively novel process and its industrial application has been limited to strongly magnetic minerals e.g., magnetite [5, 6]. The first attempts to employ this process [7] were based on the fact that a slurry stirred in a magnetic field forms linear chain structures with characteristic changes of magnetite concentration which depend on the magnetic field and the stirring rate. With an increasing magnetic field the concentration of magnetic particles in the structures also increases and mobile voluminous structures are formed. These structures settle under given conditions and they can be separated from non-magnetic components.

EXPERIMENTAL

Features of Test Sample

For the experimental verification of the theoretical models given in section 2, an ore sample from the Rudňany plant was used. The main ingredient of the ore is manganese sideroplesite containing 83% $FeCO_3$, 11% $MgCO_3$, 5% $MnCO_3$, and 1% $CaCO_3$ in pure form and with a specific magnetic susceptibility value equal to $7.5 \times 10^{-7} \, m^3/kg$. The theoretical content of Fe as pure mineral is 42.2%; the sample used in our study contained 29.4% Fe. Gangue minerals are represented by schist as, for example, mica-quartz-feldspar, mica-chlorite-quartz, mica-quartz and mica-graphite, often sideritized, and quartz. In addition, the mineral contains baryte and small amounts of tetrahedrite, sulphides of non-ferrous metals and chalcopyrite. The sample was ground to particle sizes described by the granulometric analysis given in Table 1.

Size fraction, $-\mu m$	% weight
+ 80	4.9
+ 63	5.6
+ 40	13.4
+ 30	14.18
+ 20	11.32
+ 10	19.02
+ 5	14.18
- 5	17.4

Experimental Apparatus

A schematic diagram of the apparatus employed is shown in Fig. 1. It consists of a non-magnetic vessel (1) of circular cross-section, in the upper part of which a collecting trough (2) is placed. The bottom of the trough descends towards the outlet (3), located in the lower section of the trough. The lower section of the vessel is tapered and terminates in a discharge nozzle (4).

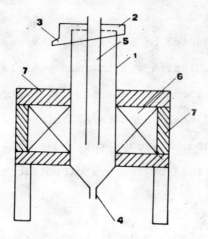

Fig. 1

Slurry is fed from the top through the tube (5), also made of non-magnetic material, and placed in the centre of the vessel and extending down to the zone where the magnetic field is generated. A homogeneous magnetic field was produced by a standard magnetic SALA-Magnetics circuit, model 4-6-1M-19. This circuit consists of an electromagnetic winding (6) and iron return frame (7), the inner diameter of the air gap being 100 mm. The magnet was fed from a dc source with an input power of 120 kVA and produced magnetic field of up to 2T in the air gap.

The slurry flowed into the apparatus from a perspex holding tank; both separation products, i.e., the overflow from the outlet (5) and sand from the nozzle (6) were fed together into the vertical pump and then returned to the holding tank which ensured a constant hydrostatic pressure and consequently a constant slurry flow through the apparatus. Flow was controlled by a valve located between the apparatus and holding tank.

Experimental Results

The apparatus shown in Fig. 1 consists of two sorting stages functioning according to different principles. The first stage is represented by a tapered space, in which only a short path is available for the slurry before it settles on the tilted walls along which it slides into the outlet nozzle. The coarser fraction in this space is in contact with the ascending flow of the rising slurry which also brings coarse grains in its train. The flow velocity decreases in the upper cylindrical section, but it still has a turbulent character even though the single flows are in first approximation laminar due to circular cross-section of the vessel. With a turbulent flow, the velocity changes from zero in the close vicinity of the vessel wall to a maximum value in the centre. Although the partial flows are quasiparallel, there is an additional flow which allows the coarse grains carried in the train of a partial flow to get into slower partial flows and then to settle down. In the opposite situation, the same applies to fine grains so that a very sharp sorting occurs. This conclusion is valid under the condition that the flow velocity in the cylinder does not fall below 0.0026 m/s where the turbulent flow turns into a laminar flow.

Our results were obtained with a closed slurry cycle using a pump which fed the separation products back into the holding tank. Following flow stabilization, the suspension was sampled at equal time intervals and the appropriate parameters were registered (slurry density, flow volume, weight yield, grade, and recovery). After sampling, additional slurry was added into the closed cycle to keep the hydrostatic pressure constant and thus to avoid changes in slurry flow through the apparatus.

Figure 2 shows the dependence of overflow density on magnetic field induction for velocities of 0.005, 0.012 and 0.026 m/s (curves 1, 2, and 3 respectively) at a constant siderite ore suspension density of 100 g/l. It follows from Fig. 2 that in a given range of rising flow velocity, the solid content in the overflow decreases with increasing magnetic field and flocs with small fractions of magnetic component are formed and that these flocs appear in the lower fraction.

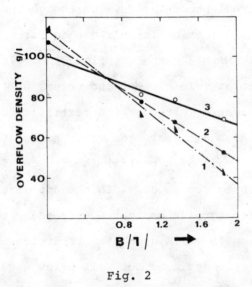

Fig. 2

Figure 3 depicts the dependence of the weight yield of the separation products upon total slurry flow at various values of magnetic induction. Curves 1 and 1a represent the weight yield of the lower fraction and overflow respectively, at zero magne-

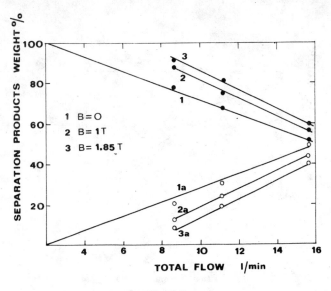

Fig. 3

tic field. Curves 2, 2a and 3, 3a describe the same dependence
for magnetic inductions 1 T and 1.85 T, respectively. While
curves 1 and 1a follow the classical pattern and intersect the
y-axis at 100 and 0% of weight yield respectively, curves 2 and
2a 3, and 3a reflect quite clearly the influence of the magnetic field. The increasing flow velocity simultaneously diminishes the effect of the magnetic field as a result of rising
mechanical forces, so that for a flow of about 16 l/min, the
experimentally determined differences between yield at non-zero
and zero magnetic fields are not very pronounced. A flow of
16 l/min represents a throughput of 205 m^3/h of slurry per 1 m^2
of crossection, which should be considered as the limiting
throughput in given conditions.

Figure 4 shows the dependence of the grade of individual separation products obtained under the same conditions as those
in Fig. 3, upon magnetic field induction. Curves 1, 2, and 3

483

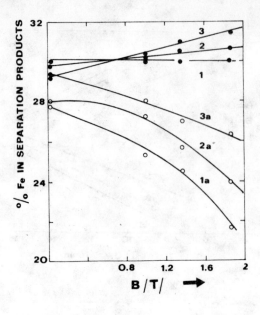

Fig. 4

express the change of Fe content in the lower fraction for flows 15.7, 11.2 and 8.7 l/min respectively, and curve la 2a and 3a describe the change of Fe content in the overflow for identical flows. The Fe content in the lower fraction increases with increasing flow rate, while the Fe content in the overflow decreases. Owing to the greater velocity of the rising flow, the Reynolds number also increases and the flow becomes more turbulent, which leads to an enhancement of the Fe content in the lower fraction. The Fe content in the overflow, however, also increases, since with increased velocity, fine non-flocculated magnetic grains are carried into the overflow.

Figure 5 shows the influence of magnetic field on Fe recovery in separation products. Curves 1, 2, and 3 correspond to flows of 8.7, 11.2 and 15.7 l/min respectively (lower fraction), while

484

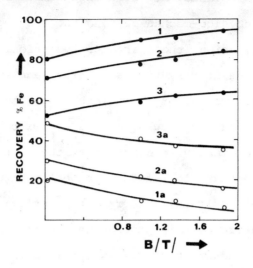

Fig. 5

curves 1a 2a and 3a describe the Fe recovery in the overflow for identical flows. One can see that the maximum Fe recovery in the lower fraction is obtained with a minimum flow.
With a rising magnetic field, the recovery of Fe increases for
the lower fraction while it decreases for the overflow.

All the above results indicate that the magnetic field affects the properties of a water slurry prepared from paramagnetic siderite ore in such a way that the magnetic flocculation
of weakly magnetic components occurs in a relatively weak magnetic field. The low selectivity of the process which is shown
in the curves in Fig. 4 is due to the fineness of the feed (the
size of most grains being 40 um) and to the non-optimized condition of the process. The suspension, e.g., was not dispersed
so that coagulation of micron-sized particles could occur,
causing a decrease in selectivity. As preliminary experiments
have shown, the magnetic flocculation process depends not only

on the magnetic field value, but also on a number of other factors, such as the physico-mechanical and the rheological properties of the suspension (the character and velocity of the rising flow, slurry density, hydrodynamic drag) and other factors.

The aim of these preliminary tests, which are still underway in our laboratory, and the results of which will be reported at this conference, was merely to demonstrate the possibility of the application of selective flocculation to weakly magnetic materials and to compare the results with current theoretical models.

The salient feature of this process in the possibility of working without an induction matrix, with all advantages that this entails, as has been mentioned in the introduction. It is possible to employ a homogeneous field of an industrially feasible magnitude and the rate of the process is relatively high. While the sedimentation of fine-grained suspensions involves rates of the order of tenths of cm/s, magnetic flocculation can proceed at rates which are one order of magnitude higher, which enables us to obtain high specific throughputs per unit cross-section area of the flocculation zone.

CONCLUSIONS

From a comparison of experimental results with theoretical predictions, it is possible to infer the following conclusions:
(1) Current theoretical models of the process of the magnetic flocculation of paramagnetic minerals and consequently the values of magnetic field calculated according to Eqs. (1) to (4), do not correspond to experimentally determined values.

(2) The model described by Eq. (4) gives the best estimate. However, even here the calculated magnetic field value is still higher than the experimental value. For instance, the magnetic induction required for the flocculation of siderite which has a magnetic susceptibility of $\varkappa = 4.7 \times 10^{-3}$ (SI), a grain size of 100 µm and a slurry concentration of 0.06, is at least 2 T, as follows from Eq. (4). However, according to the experimental results, flocculation of siderite slurry with an average grain size of 30 µm commences with a field of, at most, 1 T.

(3) We can conclude from these experimental results, that the magnetic flocculation of paramagnetic minerals is influenced by other factors which either do not enter the process of the flocculation of ferromagnetic minerals or affect it quite negligibly.

It is imperative to investigate these factors in order to make the process suitable for industrial application.

REFERENCES

1. Berdičevskij P. I. and Karmazin V. V. Obogaščenije Rud, No. 1 41 (1968).

2. Marijuta A. N., Mladeckij I. K. and Novickij P. A. Fiz.- techn. Probl. Razrab. polez. Iskop., AN SSSR, 3, 93 (1974).

3. Eyssa Y. M. and Boom R. W. Internat. J. Min. Proc., 3, 1 (1976).

4. Watson J. H. P. In: Proc. 6th Internat. Cryog. Eng. Conf. London, 1976, p. 223.

5. Alejnikov N. A., Usačev P. A. and Zelenov P. I. In: Obogaščenije Bednych Rud, Nauka, Moskva, 1973, p. 111.

6. Zelenov P. I., Alejnikov H. A. and Usačev P. A. Gornyj Zh.,
10, 64 (1974).

7. Zelenov P. I. et al., Aufbereitungs-Technik, 6, 315 (1975).

ABSTRACT

The paper deals with the basic principles of the magnetic
flocculation of weakly magnetic materials. The advantages of
the process of magnetic flocculation, hitherto applied solely
to strongly magnetic minerals on an industrial scale, are numerous (e.g., magnetite in weak magnetic fields). It allows one
to employ the entire working volume of a magnet, no gradient of
magnetic field is required and the rate of the process is sufficiently high.

The basic principles of the process are given and the possibility of the flocculation of weakly magnetic materials is investigated according to the theoretical models of the process.
Theoretical models are compared with the experimental results
of the flocculation of siderite slurry in apparatus described
below. The possibilities of the application of magnetic flocculation in industry are outlined in the final section of the
paper.

RÉSUMÉ

Cet article traite des principes fondamentaux de la flocculation magnétique des matériaux à faible magnétisme. Les avan-
tages du processus de la flocculation magnétique, appliquée
jusqu'à présent à l'échelle industrielle seulement aux minéraux
à fort magnétisme par exemple à la magnétite dans des champs
magnétiques faibles, sont nombreux. Cela permet d'utiliser la
pleine capacité de l'aimant, sans qu'un seul gradient du champ
magnétique ne soit exigé. La vitesse du processus est suffisa-
ment grande. Les principes fondamentaux du processus sont
donnés, et la possibilité de la flocculation des matériaux à
faible magnétisme est étudiée d'après les modèles théoriques
du processus. Les modèles théoriques sont comparés aux résultats expérimentaux de la flocculation de la pulpe de sidérite
dans l'appareillage décrit ci-dessous. Les possibilités d'utilisation de la flocculation magnétique dans l'industrie sont
esquisseés dans la dernière partie de cet article.

ZUSAMMENFASSUNG

Der Beitrag erörtert die Grundprinzipien der magnetischen
Ausflockung schwachmagnetischer Stoffe. Die Vorteile der magnetischen Flockenbildung, die bisher industriell nur im Falle
stark magnetischer Minerale Verwendung gefunden hat, z.B. bei
Magnetit in schwachen magnetischen Feldern, sind mannigfaltig.

Die magnetische Ausflockung ermöglicht es nämlich das gesamte
Arbeitsvolumen eines Magneten auszunutzen, ohne dass eine Steige-
rung des Magnetfeld-gradienten erforderlich wäre. Dabei verläuft
ein solcher Prozess genügend schnell. Die Grundprinzipien des
Prozesses werden angeführt, und die Möglichkeit der Ausflockung
schwachmagnetischer Stoffe wird anhand von theoretischen Modellen
eines solchen Prozesses untersucht. Die theoretischen Modelle
werden mit experimentellen Ergebnissen der Ausflockung von
Eisenspatschlick in einer eigens dazu bestimmten Einrichtung die
auch beschrieben wird, verglichen. Die Möglichkeiten der Anwendung magnetischer Ausflockung in der in dustriellen Praxis sind
im Letzten Abschnitt umrissen worden.

РЕЗЮМЕ

В докладе обсуждаются принципы магнитной флокуляции слабомагнитных материалов. Преимущества процесса магнитной флокуляции, применяемой в промышленном масштабе до настоящего времени
исключительно для сильномагнитных минералов, например магнетита,
в слабых магнитных полях, весьма многочислены. Флокуляция
позволяет использовать целый рабочий объём магнита, нет потреб-
ности в градиенте магнитного поля, а скорость процесса доста-
точно высокая.

Проведены основные принципы процесса и исследована возможность проведения флокуляции слабомагнитных материалов на основании теоретических моделей процесса. Теоретические модели срав-
нивались с опытными результатами флокуляции шлама сидерита в
описанном устройстве. В последнем разделе доклада показаны возможности применения магнитной флокуляции в промышленной практике.

DISCUSSION

PAPER 11

H. J. SCHULZE (Forschungsinstitut für Aufbereitung, Akademie
            der Wissenschaften, Freiberg, DDR)

(1) In the case of shear-flocculation there must be an equilibrium between floc formation and floc destruction (break-up).
I would be interested to know under which conditions floc
formation occurs.

(2) How large are the resulting flocs?

(3) Has the inclusion of air bubbles in the flocs been
observed or even been promoted?

(4) Could you say whether flotation might be impossible
with a certain particle size? Can you achieve a certain flotability without flocculation?

D. W. FUERSTENAU (Berkeley University, USA)

The concept of shear-flocculation in particle enlargement is
most interesting. However, considerable energy is expended in
the process. Have you made an estimate of the economic cost of
carrying out the shear-flocculation operation.

V. D. TOKAREV (Institute of Steel and Alloys, Moscow, USSR)

In your paper, the topical problem of flotation beneficiation of ultrafine scheelite ore was considered. Could the authors of this interesting paper answer the following questions?

(1) Is the choice of fineness of grind determined by the liberation size of the valuable component or the requirements of flocculation conditions?

(2) It would be interesting to know how it was possible to achieve selective flocculation with such fine particles and have you investigated the influence of pulp composition?

P. M. SOLOZHENKIN (Institute of Chemistry, Academy of Sciences of Tadzhikskaya SRR, Dushanbe, USSR)

The authors of papers 1 and 2 touched on a number of important problems in the treatment of difficult complex scheelite ores. The Soviet Union has enormous experience in the beneficiation of such ores. We ought to mention the work of the Gorukh-Dairon plant in Tadzhikistan and Tyrny-Auz in the Caucases. The authors noted these achievements when they described Petrov's method and listed the Soviet literature.

I would like to ask our colleagues from Australia and Sweden to answer some of our points.

I would like to ask Dr. Warren whether he established the role and the influence of nonsaturation in fatty acids in the flocculation and flotation processes.

The paper gives the results of the calculation of the first-order rate constants for slow and fast floating components. I would like to know what method was used in the determination and calculation of the constants.

How do the authors explain the difference between scheelite and calcite behaviour in the flotation process despite the fact that both minerals have the same calcium cation and that in both cases calcium oleate and a certain amount of physically attached collector are formed on the surface of the minerals?

I would like to mention that in order to study the changes in the physical and chemical states of the surface layers it would be useful to use electron paramagnetic resonance and spin labelling of the fatty acid as molecular detectors and probes.

What is the structure of the resin frother?

Z. SADOWSKI (Laboratory of Mineral Processing, Technical University of Wrocław, Wrocław, Poland)

In connection with the very interesting paper of Dr. Warren I would like to share some experimental results obtained during an investigation of shear-flocculation.

Three types of minerals were investigated: quartz, calcite and magnesite. The granulometric composition of fine ground materials shows that about 80% of the particles have dimensions within the range 5-10 μm. For the investigation of the shear-flocculation process the apparatus described by Dr. Warren in Trans IMM, 84, 99-104, was used. The initial mineral concentration in the liquid phase was 8 g/l. For evaluating the conditions of shear-flocculation the pipette method of sedimentation analysis (Andreasen pipette) was used.

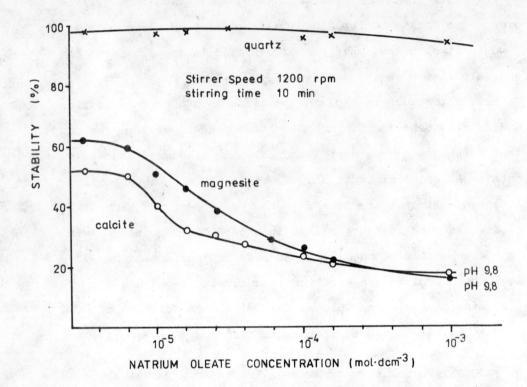

Fig. 1

Figure 1 shows the results of the experiments on the influence of the concentration of sodium oleate on the shear-flocculation process. One can see that in the case of sodium oleate concentration of 10^{-4} mol/l the process of shear-flocculation occurs in a suspension of calcite and magnesite. However, under these conditions the quartz suspension does not flocculate.

Figure 2 gives the results of the experiments into the influence of the pH on the process. One can see that within the range pH 8-9.5 shear-flocculation occurs in suspensions of calcite and magnesite. The Ca^{2+} and Mg^{2+} ions have also a great influence on the shear-flocculation process.

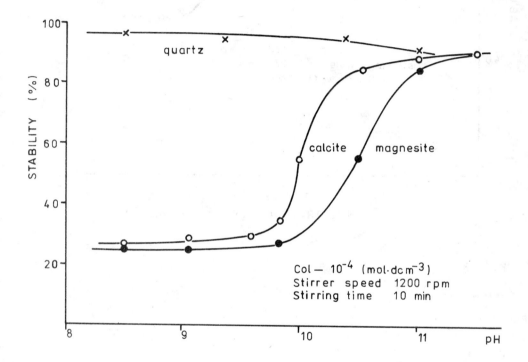

Fig. 2

Figure 3 shows the influence of the concentrations of the Mg^{2+} ions on the shear-flocculation of a quartz suspension. The results shown support the conclusions of Dr. Warren and indicate that it may be possible to separate quartz from calcite and magnesite.

495

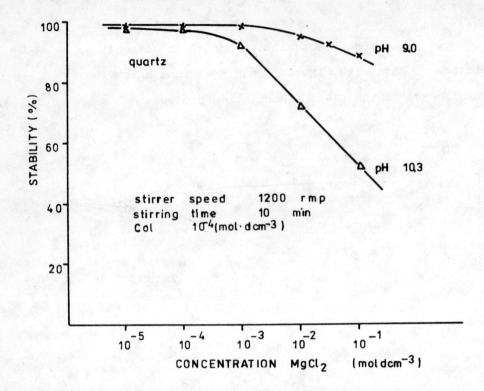

Fig. 3

PAPER 12

E. LARRIBAU (Elf-Aquitaine, France)

(1) Have you examined the mineralogical character of your scheelite ore and especially the size and spatial distribution of both valuable constituents and unwanted phases? Could you provide some data on liberation?

(2) Could you provide some information on the conditions and the type of reagents used: pH regulators, depressants and

the agent that seemed essential for the selective flocculation of fine scheelite particles?

(3) Is the method patented?

I. R. M. CHASTON (Charter Consolidated Service Ltd., England)

(1) Could the authors say if the pulp is heated during the scheelite conditioning process or elsewhere in the circuit?

(2) The results shown in Table 3 indicate that the major loss of scheelite occurs in the slime fraction. Do the authors think that it would reduce the amount of slime production if the rod mill product was cycloned before the ball mill?

(3) The same Table shows that little recovery is made in flotation of the +250 μm material. Would it not improve the operation to screen the feed to scheelite flotation at, say, 150-200 μm and regard the average?

(4) Am I right in assuming that the pyrrhotite in the ore is fully depressed through both the copper and scheelite flotation?

L. J. WARREN (CSIRO Division of Mineral Chemistry, Port Melbourne, Australia)

Gräsberg, Mattson and the ZKAB group are to be congratulated on a remarkable piece of mineral processing. At least part of their success seems to be due to careful design, monitoring and control of the flotation. Such thorough analysis is unfortunately lacking in many mineral processing plants.

The development of a large recirculating load was stated to be a key feature of their process. It is interesting to note that an Australian scheelite processing mill operated for many years with an incredibly large recirculating load. I would like to ask Dr. Mattson if it was found necessary, in practice, to thicken the feed to scheelite flotation because of the diluting effect of recirculating streams and wash waters.

With regard to the observed flocculation of scheelite in the cleaner circuit, I would like to ask the authors whether they examined the flocs closely enough to decide whether they were aeroflocs, that is, mixed bubble-particle aggregates or non-aerated aggregates of the type I believe formed by shear-flocculation.

The extent of aggregation of hydrophobic scheelite particles also depends on the size of the particles. Whereas 1 μm particles require intense agitation, 10 μm particles need only moderate shear rates and 30-40 μm particles are too large to maintain stable aggregates even under gentle agitation. With these size effects, and the effect of attrition, it is difficult to say whether significant shear-flocculation would be expected in the Yxsjöberg conditions, though I suspect some aggregation would have occurred.

I. M. CASES (E.N.S.G., Nancy, France)

You have delivered an excellent paper on beneficiation of low-grade scheelite ores. The results presented are very interesting indeed and that is why we should congratulate you.

However, the better the results, the more interest is aroused. Thus, on entering the discussion I feel like a puppy in front of a large lump of meat.

My question is: can you possibly give us some more details on the reagents used and their concentrations, pH, etc. which would enable us to understand the phenomena involved during the treatment of the ore?

E. FORSSBERG (University of Lulea, Sweden)

I would like to congratulate the authors on a very interesting process. I do think this is a very important contribution towards better utilization of tungsten deposits. However, it is a pity that the authors have not been free to reveal any details of their process not even the numbers of the US patents which are the foundation for the actual process.

Among future developments suggested on page 144 in the preprint there is the suggestion that autogenous or pebble milling might be employed. I do think this is a rather surprising statement since losses in the slime fraction are of paramount importance. I do think efforts should be concentrated on obtaining a better classification, for example by employing a Hukki classifier on the hydrocyclone underflow.

P. M. SOLOZHENKIN (Institute of Chemistry, Academy of Sciences of Tadzhikskaya SSR, Dushanbe, USSR)

(1) Apatite and sulphur bearing minerals are found in certain amounts in the ores being processed at the Yxsjoberg plant.

How are such harmful impurities as P and S removed from $CaWO_4$ concentrates and what is the limit of the amount of these impurities in the concentrate?

(2) The authors mentioned that they used common acids. In the Soviet Union bioxyr* has been suggested as a collector of non-sulphide minerals. These reagents are better than common fatty acids in the processing of scheelite ores and it seems to me that this could also be tried in Sweden.

H. KELLERWESSEL** (KHD Humboldt-Wedag A.G., Köln, Federal
                    Republic of Germany)

From Table 3 on page 144 of the preprint, it can be gathered that nearly 60% of the WO_3 losses is accounted for by the size fraction finer than 9 μm.

As to the size fraction coarser than 250 μm, recovery is also poor. The obtained results could be improved if the entire ore were ground to a somewhat greater fineness in connection with which efforts should also be made to further reduce the formation of slime and, above all, to avoid the "overgrinding" of scheelite which because of its high density, causes sufficiently fine scheelite to be recycled from the cyclone to the mill.

In this connection I should like to make the following two suggestions.

_____

* bioxyr is a product of the microbiological transformation of hydrocarbons and lipids extracted from biomass of various micro-organisms and mushrooms.

**Contributed remarks

(a) If cyclone classification is replaced by screen classification, the material will indeed be classified according to
grain size but not according to falling velocity. Scheelite of
sufficient fineness would then no longer be returned to the
mill. Otherwise one could also proceed such that cyclone classification is supplemented by screen classification: the cyclone
is adjusted to the size of cut desired for the gangue minerals.
Then scheelite is separated at a finer size of cut. The cyclone
underflow is fed onto a screen where the fine particles of
higher specific gravity are screened off - only the screen
reject is passed on to the mill for further grinding.

This arrangement possibly carried with it the disadvantage
that for carrying out screen classification water would possibly still have to be added, and this has to be removed by
thickening afterwards. For screening the use of steep-angle
screens, e.g. curved screens, Rapifine or Humboldt microscreens,
would be a possibility. This classification should take place
after the first grinding stage in order to prevent at the
outset a sufficiently fine product entering the second grinding
stage.

(b) When using rods as grinding media instead of balls or
cylpebs, in most cases the ground material shows a considerably
narrow particle size distribution; i.e., slime formation is
reduced. Rods have a "calibrating" effect. This is why rod
mills are preferably employed if increased formation of slime
("overgrinding") is to be avoided. A degree of fineness of the
ground material of less than approx. 0.3 mm is hardly achievable
in rotating rod mills. In the case of two-stage grinding, a rod

mill is generally used for the first stage, which, for example, grinds down to a fineness of less than 0.5 or 0.3 mm; in the second stage, however, ball mills are employed for finish grinding to flotation fineness (as in the present case). We have found that when using vibrating tube mills with rods as grinding media, the material can easily be ground down to flotation fineness, i.e., finer than 200 μm, 150 μm or even 100 μm. To fully utilize the "calibrating" effect of the rods it is therefore adviseable to use vibrating tube mills of the Palla 65 U type for the second grinding stage. A disadvantage of these mills, however, is that they cannot be built to any desired

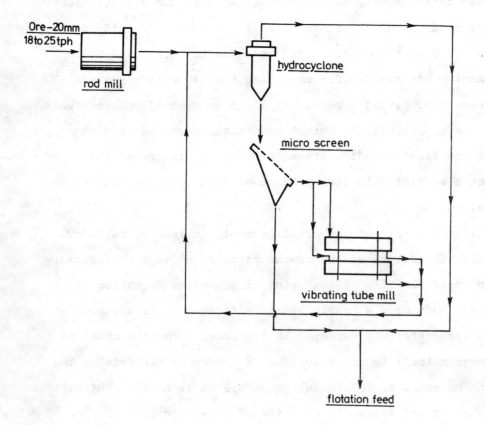

Fig. 1

size. Depending on how much finished material the rotating rod mill already produces, two or three vibrating mills would be required for finish grinding.

In the flowsheet attached both suggestions have been taken into consideration.

PAPER 13

M. C. FUERSTENAU (South Dakota School of Mines, Rapid City, USA)

With regard to the mechanism of tannic acid adsorption on hematite, adsorption of this reagent occurs in the pH range in which Fe^{2+} hydrolyzes to $FeOH^+$ i.e., from pH 2.5-3.5. This phenomenon has been observed in other insoluble oxide-polymer systems, and provides insight into both the mechanism of adsorption and pH range of application.

Have you observed this phenomenon in other systems in which you have worked?

V. D. TOKAREV (Institute of Steel and Alloys, Moscow, USSR)

Professor Rinelli has investigated in detail the conditions of selective flocculation of rutile in the presence of quartz and hematite. The investigations made it possible to achieve some technological effects but at the same time addditional questions arose which still have to be explained.

(1) What is the optimum particle size in the process presented and what does it depend on?

(2) Rather low-molecular weight compounds were utilized in the process under discussion and they render mineral particles

hydrophobic. Thus, the question is whether the "bridging theory" can explain the aggregation of particles, or whether this is hydrophobic flocculation.

(3) Have the authors tested their technology on real ores? At low pH values unfavourable phenomena connected with a change in surface properties of minerals can complicate the system and the processes.

(4) What can you say about the future for the industrial application of the technology presented if the high consumption of reagents is taken into account.

PAPER 14

A. MARABINI (Laboratorio per il Trattamento dei Minerali, C.N.R.,
            Roma, Italy)

Poly-hydroxyl reagents, like polysaccharides, have been largely used as depressants in many practical processes. Nevertheless, their mechanism of action has not been thoroughly studied and completely clarified. Therefore, as we are particularly interested in this field, I would like additional information from the author on the following points:

(1) The mechanism responsible for selective depression of Mg-silicates is presented as an "hydrogen bonding" between hydrogen and the strongly electronegative atoms of sulphur.

(2) What, in the author's opinion, is the role of the carboxylic groups on the depression of magnesia-bearing minerals? The effect of the degree of substitution of carboxymethyl groups has in fact been studied, but the results have not been re-

ported. In this respect I think that an ion exchange mechanism between these groups and Mg atoms may occur, being responsible for the selectivity towards Mg minerals.

(3) What does the author think about the influence of the structure of the CMC molecule on the depression of Mg-minerals?

L. J. WARREN (CSIRO Division of Mineral Chemistry, Port
            Melbourne, Australia)

(1) I would like to ask Mike Rhodes if there is any evidence that carboxymethylcellulose was depressing talc more, or less, than the other magnesia-bearing minerals. Talc is often said to be naturally floatable and might be expected to have a different surface chemistry from the other silicates - at least the mechanism of bonding might be different.

(2) Secondly, has any consideration been given to introducing a preliminary flocculation-thickening step to capitalise on the apparently selective flocculation observed with reagents with a high degree of polymerisation. The economics of using high DP material may then improve.

J. H. A. PIEPER (Billiton Research, Arnhem, Netherlands)

Was carboxymethylcellulose with altered structure used on other ore samples, and if so what were the results? Furthermore, how was this product prepared?

Ir. T. KATER* (Industrial Colloids, Enka (AKZO), Arnhem,
Holland)

The results as reported by Mr. Rhodes in his paper are very interesting as he touches an important but neglected aspect of carboxymethylcellulose (CMC) when this polymer is applied as a depressant for talc and other readily floatable magnesium-bearing minerals in nickel flotation.

So far, the only paper on the basic parameters of CMC depressants ever published [1] describes the influence of the average degree of substitution (DS) and the degree of polymerization (DP) on depressant efficiency. However, also important are parameters such as the distribution of the substituted carboxylic groups over the cellulose chain - as discussed by Mr. Rhodes - and the point at which the substitution has taken place on the glucosidic unit.

The reaction of the carboxylic groups on cellulose may take place at the 6-position of the glucosidic unit but also at the 2- and 3-positions (Fig. 1).

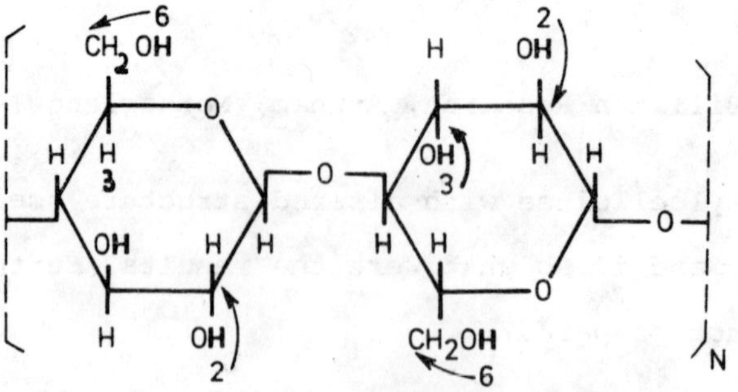

Fig. 1. Cellulose molecule.

_____

* Contributed remarks

Consequently, the variation in positioning of the carboxylic groups over the cellulose chain is large even when the degree of substitution is kept constant [2].

For example, Figure 2 shows a simple CMC molecule with DP = 3 and constant DS = 1.0. This relatively simple molecule already has 47 different combinations, resulting in 47 different CMC types.

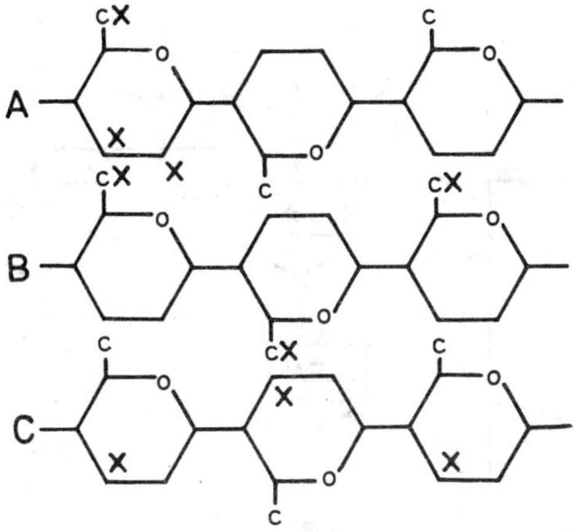

Fig. 2. Some variations of CMC with DP = 3 and DS = 1.0.

The molecule in Fig. 2A has an irregular distribution. In Fig. 2B as well as in Fig. 2C the molecules have regular distributions but the molecule in Fig. 2B has a 6-position, whereas the molecule in Fig. 2C has a 3-position distribution. These three CMC molecules, notwithstanding the fact that they have the same DP and DS, will show different behaviour in the adsorption as well as in the hydration of the mineral surfaces to be depressed.

The depression of readily floatable silicates will be more efficient not only with a specially adapted distribution of the carboxylic groups over the chain (as mentioned by Mr. Rhodes) but also when substitution has taken place at certain points on the glucosidic unit [3].

Figure 3 shows the results of floating a low grade nickel ore in a laboratory cell with two CMC products having the same DP but differing in molecular structure. These tests were carried out as batch flotation tests, using the locked cycle test procedure as presented in the Figure.

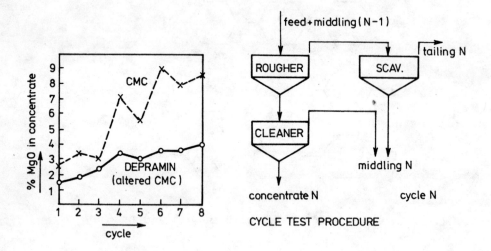

Fig. 3. Flotation test results of a CMC with an altered structure.

The CMC product with altered structure was more effective. This product is now produced by Industrial Colloids (Enka) under the trade-name DEPRAMIN.

We are glad to learn that the plant results of Mr. Rhodes have confirmed our laboratory test work.

The observation of Mr. Rhodes that high molecular weight CMC types are far more effective as depressants, is a very

interesting point. His explanation that desorption of low molecular weight CMC may occur is not supported by the results of
our research.

The energy of a hydrogen bond is low (5-7 kcal/mol) but - in
case the adsorption of CMC takes place through the hydroxyl
group - enough bonding places are available to ensure firm adsorption, even if the CMC in question has a low DP. Our adsorption measurements, using radio-active labelled CMC, have shown
that desorption does not occur.

The flotation of particles which were originally depressed,
might be explained by the creation of fresh mineral surfaces as
a result of severe agitation of the pulp in the flotation cell.
In light of this we tend to accept Mr. Rhodes' second explanation regarding selective flocculation.

Mr. Rhodes postulated that bonding between CMC and the
broken edges of the layer silicates renders the subsequent surface hydrophylic. However, the atoms in the talc layer are
covalently bonded. Brekage of such a talc layer creates an edge
with strong, unsaturated covalent remnant bonds, making the edge
highly hydrophylic. Therefore, hydration by a depressant is not
necessary. In this context we wonder whether the author means
that adsorption of the depressant onto the edge of the layer
silicate prevents subsequent adsorption of collector molecules
onto the magnesium ions in the broken edge. Or is the author of
the opinion that adsorption does not take place onto the hydrophobic front of the talc layer, but that the broken edges
provide a suitable anchorage for the CMC molecules (probably as
a result of an interaction of the carboxylic group of CMC and

the magnesium ions) and that consequently depression occurs by encapsulation of the hydrophobic surface of the talc layer.

Regarding the adsorption of CMC we are of the opinion that the hydroxyl groups and the carboxyl groups of the CMC molecule are involved. There are indications that the distribution of the carboxyl groups controls the adsorption onto the silicates and that the location of the substituents on the glucosidic unit has a major effect on the hydration - i.e., the depressing action of the CMC - and on the adsorption onto the sulphide minerals - i.e. the selectivity of the depressants.

An infrared spectroscopy investigation [1] has shown that a part of the carboxyl groups is in chemical interaction with cations on the surface of the silicate minerals. As the talc crystal itself only has oxygen ions at the outside of the layer, these cations are a result of a defect in the talc lattice. This implies that each ore requires an optimal type of depressant and that in this regard tailor-made CMC depressants are to be preferred.

REFERENCES

1. Bakinov K. G. et al. New Methods of Sulphide Concentrate Upgrading. Proc. VII IMPC, New York 1964, 227-238.

2. Mulderink J. J. M. Natürliche Polymere in Bergbau, Aufbereitung und Metallurgie. Erzmetall, 29, 560-565 (1976).

3. Roorda H. J. et al. Aktuelle Probleme der Aufbereitung niedrigwertiger Nickelerze. Erzmetall, 30, H 7/8, 287-292 (1977).

K. TKAČOVA (Mining Institute, Slovak Academy of Sciences,
          Košice, Czechoslovakia)

Professor Steiner's paper is a most interesting and unusual attempt to describe the properties of polydisperse suspensions as a function of particle size.

In talking about the surface of mineral particles exhibiting a specific influence on the properties of the system, would it not be more appropriate to use physico-chemical concepts which allow the expression of the full complexity of the surface effects, instead of using geometrical terms. Geometrical terms make it possible to account for the size and the shape of particles. However, interaction between real particles depends on the surface energy to a large extent. This can be responsible for the formation of microstructure.

My remarks are supported by the results obtained by us while working on various ferro-silicon size fractions and especially the relationship between its "geometrical surface" (S_G) and specific surface area (S_A) measured by means of the BET technique.

The relationship obtained is linear and the angle coefficient in this relation is in the range of 2 to 60, depending on the dispersion of the ferro-silicon suspension.

R. VARGANOV (Institute of Physical Chemistry, Bulgarian Academy
          of Sciences, Sofia, Bulgaria)

Why do not you take into account the drag forces as defined
by Taylor and Reynolds? It is known from the literature that
where distances between two particles are shorter than the
radius of the particles Stokes' drag force cannot be used. However, the drag forces as defined by Taylor and Reynolds enable
us to investigate the hydrodynamic interactions among the particles in the suspension in detail.

In your calculations have you also used dimensionless numbers whose values depend on the local field around the particle,
or have you only used the values directly connected with the
particles?

H. SCHUBERT* (Bergakademie Freiberg, German Democratic Republic)

(a) In the chapter entitled "Effective concentration" the
author has introduced the centre of activity for grain i in
order to determine the buoyancy of particle k, brought about by
the grains i surrounding it. The effect of a grain i upon the
buoyancy of particle k exists, but it results from its relative
position to particle k and its volume at a given mass. According
to the expression

$$\vec{F}_A = \oiint p \, \vec{dA}$$

(p - pressure at the surface of particle k; A - surface area of
particle k), buoyancy cannot be influenced by the intersection

---

* Contributed remarks

512

of the spheres of action. The conception "effective concentration" therefore becomes rather problematical.

(b) In the chapter "Effective density" it was pointed out that

$$\text{effective density} = \text{volumetric specific buoyancy/field acceleration}$$

and that this depends on particle size. However, as neither volumetric buoyancy nor field acceleration depends on volume, they cannot be a function of particle size.

The "effective density" δ_k, calculated further on the basis of effective concentration c_{ik}, becomes incomprehensible by virtue of the objections put forward in § (a).

(c) In the chapter "effective viscosity" the author assumes, on the basis of the Einstein relation that the viscosity of <u>one</u> particle size is linearly dependent on the concentration of other particle sizes. How can such linearity be caused?

Apart from this, it should be noted that Einstein's statement applies only to certain strictly defined assumptions, though these have since been somewhat extended (cf. for instance Vand V.: Viscosity of Solutions and Suspensions, <u>J. Phys. Coll. Chem.</u>, <u>52</u>, 277-314 (1948),   and that such statements are the more inadmissible, the finer the particles of the solid and the greater its percentage by volume. In such cases, the non-Newtonian behaviour of the suspensions becomes more and more conspicuous.

(d) In the chapter "Steady-state settling" the author has calculated the Reynolds number on the basis of the extreme principle (Eq. 22). Which fundamental law justifies such a demand? Or is this only a supposition, as might be gathered from the assertion concerning Fig. 5 (cf. the text immediately following Fig. 5)?

PAPER 17

I. M. CASES (E.N.S.G., Nancy, France)

You have pointed out that an increase of pulp density beyond a certain critical value causes a sharp increase in pulp viscosity. Such a result is well known to those working with clay minerals and, depending on the solid, occurs at various solid concentrations, for instance at 30% of solid in the case of kaoline, but even at 5% of solid in the case of hectorite.

Explanation of such behaviour on the part of concentrated suspensions was usually based on the properties of solids, but recent findings seem to indicate that a change in water properties is also being responsible for the observed phenomena. In this connection I would like to ask what your opinion is about such explanations.

J. MAGER (Laboratory of Mineral Processing, Technical
        University of Wrocław, Wrocław, Poland)

The results of the rheological measurements obtained by Heiskanen and Lappas especially those concerning the relation between the Bingham yield value τ_B and pulp density ϱ (Fig. 8), are very interesting. My results for concentrated quartz sand suspensions are similar.

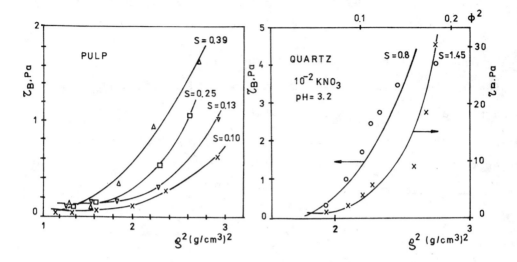

Fig. 1. Relation between the square of suspension density and the Bingham yield value for pulp (calculated from Fig. 8 in Heiskanen and Laapas) and quartz sand. S-specific surface area in m^2/g.

By analogy to the Goodeve-Gillespie Equation, the Bingham yield value is denoted as a function of the square of the volume concentration of solids. The slope of this curve is a measure of the energy dissipated by the collisions between particles.

It seems to me (and it is a question I would like to discuss) that in the high concentration region (above 20 vol.%) the Bingham yield value is a measure of multiparticle interactions which lead to the formation of a periodic colloid structure as defined by Efremov*.

_____

* I. F. Efremov, Periodic Colloid Structures, in "Surface and Colloid Science", E. Matijevic Ed., Wiley, New York 1976, vol. 8, p. 85.

PAPER 18

M. K. RHODES (Seltrust Mining Corporation Pty. Ltd., Perth,
        Australia)

Although you mentioned that other selective flocculation
studies will be the subject of another paper I would be interested to hear of your work with starch and modified starches.
In particular, whether any specific modified starch gave
better results than others, and whether starches in general were
better than cationic or anionic polyacrylamides.

PAPER 19

Bo ARVIDSON (AMAX Extractive, USA)

The problem of plugging the matrix in the matrix-type high
intensity magnetic separators is not as serious as one might
expect. There are a number of simple preventive techniques that
can be applied. Of much greater importance is that the potential
use of magnetic selective flocculation allows utilization of
electromagnets of very simply design, like the one used in the
study reported here. The need to turn off the current and the
associated decay times and dead time for valve operation would
be eliminated.

(1) Have the authors observed any influence of retention
time; what is the effect of the number of passes through the
separator?

516

(2) Has any comparative test been carried out with the separator equipped with a collecting matrix? If so, what result was obtained?

(3) As far as I can see Fig. 4 contradicts the discussion in the text. Maybe there is a typographical error?

(4) The discussion about hydrodynamic drag forces does not seem to be relevant as particles are not trapped. The competing forces would primarily be electrostative forces (as measured as zeta-potential) and shear forces due to a difference in settling velocity for different sized particles. The latter would be of less significance.

(5) How does the variation of slurry density influence the selective flocculation? Carrying out the tests, the slurry density was kept constant at 100 g/l according to the paper.

AUTHORS' REPLIES

L. J. WARREN

Dr. Schulze has raised some interesting questions. With regard to the formation of flocs by shear-flocculation we have proposed the following mechanism: (1) under turbulent agitation the average energy of collision is much greater than thermal energy, allowing the particles to approach more closely than they would in a Brownian collision, (2) the formation of flocs is favoured by an energy of "hydrophobic association" which comes into effect if the collisions result in direct contact between the hydrophobic particles, and (3) it is likely that the resistance to thinning and removal of the liquid separating the approaching particles is less for hydrophobic particles than for colliding hydrophilic particles.

Thus the conditions under which floc formation occurs will depend on the size of the particles, their surface charge and their relative velocity during an encounter as well as on the degree of hydrophobicity of the surfaces and the shapes of the particles. For a suspension of scheelite particles in 10^{-4} M sodium oleate, stirred in a baffled beaker, an impeller speed of 850.rpm caused shear-flocculation of particles 5-20 μm. At 1700 rpm the size range undergoing shear-flocculation shifted to smaller sizes, about 1-12 µm. Particles larger than 35 um were not observed to form aggregates at either stirrer speed. Although the larger particles collided with sufficient energy to cause shear-flocculation they were immediately redispersed by the separating shear.

In practice, with a poly-dispersed pulp, a given turbulence regime will not necessarily cause aggregation of particles of all sizes. Of course under these conditions, slime coating and heteroflocculation are also possible.

The floc size depends on the diameter of the original discrete particles, the shear regime, the time of agitation and, last but not least, on the method of measurement. Particles of diameter about 1 µm may be shear-flocculated to produce aggregates with cross-sectional diameters 10-100 µm, depending on the conditions chosen. Because of their open structure the equivalent Stokes diameter of these flocs is less, and ranges from 3-15 µm.

Care is taken to exclude air entrainment during shear-flocculation and no bubbles have been observed in the flocs. If bubbles are present, and we do not think they are, they must be extremely small.

In our experience there is no critical size below which particles do not float. Rather there appears to be a continuous fall in flotability, at least down to 0.5 µm. Thus ultrafine particles will float, but slowly and often with poor selectivity. Pretreatment by shear-flocculation is one means by which the flotation of ultrafine particles may be improved.

Professor D. W. Fuerstenau has identified one of the key questions to be answered before shear-flocculation can be applied in practice. We recently ran a pilot plant test of the process using finely ground scheelite ore, and we found that the value of the extra tungsten recovered by including shear-flocculation in the flotation circuit was more than four times the incremental running cost of the shear-flocculation tanks.

In answer to Dr. Tokarev, we ground the scheelite ore very finely in our laboratory experiments to simulate pulps produced either from ores with finely disseminated components or from rejection of the ultrafines fraction present after the normal grinding of flotation feeds.

The shear-flocculation of ultrafine scheelite particles appears to be about as selective as the flotation of larger particles i.e., the selectivity is conferred by the choice of reagents already used in flotation. Pulp composition affects both the recovery and grade achieved during shear-flocculation and the pH, oleate concentration and silicate concentration were chosen to give optimum performance.

Professor Solozhenkin asked about the influence of non-saturation of the fatty acid on the degree of shear-flocculation. We have not studied this aspect of the problem.

In calculating the first order flotation rate constants for "slow" and "fast" floating components of the pulp we followed the method of Kelsall (Ref. 9 in our paper). As shown in Fig. 2, the rate constant for the slow component is obtained by drawing a tangent to the experimental curve at long flotation times. The rate constant for the fast component is then calculated by difference.

Calcite and scheelite both float when an oleate collector is used. Calcite is partially depressed on addition of sufficient sodium metasilicate to the pulp, whereas scheelite flotability is virtually unaffected (see Table 3). Possible reasons for the action of silicate and the role of sodium carbonate (which is also present in our solutions) have been discussed by Solnyshkin and Yu-Lung Cheng (Obogashch. Rud i Uglei, Akad. Nauk SSSR, Inst. Gorn. Dela, 1963, 147-158).

The resin frother is supplied as an aromatic translucent solid, but we do not know its structure.

Dr. Sadowski has turned the shear-flocculation of calcite to advantage - it was merely a nuisance to us in the treatment of scheelite ores. The relatively low zeta-potential of calcite, even when coated with oleate, should make it amenable to aggregation at low stirrer speeds. Further, the results of Fig. 2 presented by Dr. Sadowski suggest their pH adjustment may effect a partial separation of magnesite from calcite.

G. RINELLI and A. MARABINI

In reply to Professor M. C. Fuerstenau's question, we did not observe the phenomenon in other metal oxide/polymer systems. However, in our case and also in the case of TiO_2 the maximum flocculating power of the tannic acid/antipyrine system occurs in the pH range below 2, where Ti^{4+} hydrolyzes to $Ti(OH)^{3+}$. It is hence possible to advance the hypothesis that this ionic species is responsible for tannic acid adsorption on a rutile surface.

With regard to Dr. Tokarev's remarks we would comment as
follows:

(1) From the point of view of reagent adsorption, the particle
    dimensions do not have any significant influence. It is
    well known that very fine grinding results in the amorphi-
    zation of the particle surface, but this phenomenon does
    not affect the chemisorption of tannic acid, since active
    sites consisting of Ti^{4+} ions are always present. The
    influence of particle size is more important when we con-
    sider the selectivity of the process. The probability of
    the formation of flocs with a large amount of unwanted
    entrapped minerals increases with the fineness of the feed.
    In this respect optimum particle dimensions do exist, but
    can be determined only on experimental basis.

(2) The formation of the flocs of rutile particles with the
    tannic acid/antipyrine system may be generally considered
    as hydrophobic flocculation. The definition of "molecular
    bridging" takes into account that in our case flocculation
    is not initiated by a single reagent as is usual, but by
    the action of more than one organic substance. Tannic acid
    is directly adsorbed on the rutile surface but flocculation
    cannot occur without the antipyrine which links the partic-
    les to each other.

(3) We have not carried out experiments on real ores. We agree
    that the interaction of different ions present in the
    solution may affect the process in practice.

(4) At present, it is not easy to predict what the possibilities of industrial application are. The aim of our work is only to demonstrate the advantage of extending the research on selective flocculation beyond the classical use of mono-reagent systems.

M. K. RHODES

With regard to Dr. Warren's first question, no specific work was done in this area but recently a study was initiated comparing the electrophoretic mobility of readily floating minerals using different C.M.C. reagents. This study is not yet complete but may yield information on the mechanisms involved and on the surface chemistry.

Preflocculation has not been tested, but an attempt was made to maximise the flocculation effect by using column type cells. The results, however, were inconclusive.

With reference to Prof. Marabini's questions, no specific work was done to determine the mechanisms responsible for the depression. The comments made refer to previous studies made by others and quoted in the reference section.

The effect of degree of substitution was studied in the initial factorial design series, but was only significant at one unit weight level for one sample.

The influence of the structure of the C.M.C. molecule is important when the total number of substitutional variations is considered. As mentioned previously, the determination of the mechanisms was outside the scope of this project.

The altered structure reagent has been tested on other ores but not by the author, and I do not have access to the results. The reagent is a proprietary brand and as such I am not conversant with the exact details of preparation.

With regard to the contribution from T. Kater, I have the following comments. The results he gives are most interesting and in many cases confirm the results of my own work.

I accept that creation of new surfaces in the cell would allow the reflotation of previously depressed particles.

The radioactive labelled C.M.C. adsorption measurements could find many uses in this type of investigation. In particular, it could possibly be used to study where the C.M.C. molecules adsorb onto the talc particles, an area which is still open to individual interpretation rather than proven data.

H. J. STEINER

Dr. Tkačova quite correctly emphasized the pronounced influence of particle morphology on certain properties of a suspension. Referring to the surface measurements cited by Dr. Tkačova, it may be recalled that a direct connection seems to exist between the various shape coefficients of fluid resistance, viscosity and specific surface respectively, which were introduced by several authors for the benefit of correlating experimental results with theory.

The type of interaction Dr Varganov seems to have in view may also occur in monodispersed suspensions and is therefore - as outlined in the paper's second chapter - not the subject of the author's present paper. The questioned dimensionless numbers are defined by Eqs. 13-16. They are in accordance with the common definitions, except that the properties of the fluid are replaced by the properties of the suspension, i.e., the particle size dependent values of effective density and effective viscosity respectively.

The answer to Prof. Schubert's questions calls for more space and may be opened with the remark that to deny the significance of the term "effective density" would, for example, mean the denial of the very simple fact that all particles of a monodispersed suspension are subjected to the true density of the fluid while a comparatively large particle, after being immersed into the said suspension, will encounter the density of the suspension. From this obvious difference in volume-specific buoyancy it follows directly that Prof. Schubert must be wrong in believing that the ratio buoyancy/volume has a constant, i.e., particle size independent, value. The introduction of the term "effective concentration" originates in the need to link the effective density and the total concentrations of different particle size classes. A comparable procedure is standard practice in physical chemistry, where "concentrations" are replaced by "activities" to make the mass law applicable.

In answer to question (c): In the limiting case of the diminishing value of solid concentration, the linear dependence of viscosity upon the concentration of a single size fraction follows directly from the Einstein Equation. The variation of the disposable part of the fluid (see page 348 of the preprint) explains the non-linear dependence of viscosity at higher solid concentration values.

And in reply to question (d): The new relation between inertial forces and frictional forces of resistance as expressed in the statement preceding equation 22 was discovered by the author some years ago. From that postulate and the restrictions expressed by Eqs. 23-24 it follows conclusively that the effective coefficient c_S^x of frictional resistance is constant (= c_S) in the Stokes range, increasing in the Allen range and reaching its maximum value $S \cdot c_S$ at the transition point between the Allen and Newton ranges. The effective coefficient c_N^x of inertial resistance is constant (= c_N) in the Newton range, increasing (with falling Re-numbers) in the Allen range and reaching its maximum value $S \cdot c_N$ at the transition point between the Allen and Stoke ranges.

The Reynolds numbers at the said transition points are $c_S/(S \cdot c_N)$ and $S \cdot c_S/c_N$ respectively. The extremum principle (minimum principle), as expressed by Eq. 22, is fulfilled to the utmost in the Allen range, where the total set equations is reduced to $2 \cdot \sqrt{S \cdot c_N \cdot c_S} \cdot Re^{(3/2)} = Ar$.

K. HEISKANEN and H. LAAPAS

In response to Professor Cases' question, the critical density in our experiments was found to be the greatest in sample IV. The phenomenon can also be seen in sample III and even in sample II to some extent. The samples had permeametric surface areas

```
sample  I            3 140 cm$^2$/cm$^3$
   "      II           4 002  "
   "      III          7 617  "
   "      IV          11 748  "
```

which show that the samples are coarse as compared with kaolin, bentonite or other mineral powders used in the industries mentioned by Prof. Cases.

The surface areas also show quite modest changes in particle size between successive samples. Our opinion is that these experiments show the critical density to be a function rather of particle size than of water properties.

We agree with Mr. Mager that in the region of high solids concentration the interaction of particles is increased and thus there are drastic changes in viscosity and in yield value. The colloid structure may be true in very fine, nearly colloidal pulps, but not in fast settling suspensions.

All our samples, except for sample IV (Fig. 8), were much coarser and their yield value was not a function of square root of the solids volume concentration.

A. K. BISWAS

In reply to Mr. Rhodes' question regarding modified starches, our recent experiments show that starches in general have better selectivity with regard to the separation of hematite from clay minerals by selective flocculation than do polyacrylamides. This is attributed to the specificity of adsorption of starch on hematite. The phosphoryl group in starch molecules seems to have a positive effect although conclusions on modified starches are not definitive.

Our answers to Dr. Arvidson's questions are as follows:

(1) The retention time does have an influence on the process of magnetic flocculation as is seen in Figs. 1 to 4, since the retention time varied for various flowrates. Dependence on number of passes was not investigated as this matrixless process was run continuously.

(2) A number of experiments was carried out in a magnetic separator with a matrix made of similar material, and the experimental data indicate that recovery and grade are better than in the case of magnetic flocculation. This could have been anticipated anyway since our coagulation tests were carried out in order to show that the effect does occur with moderate magnetic fields. In order to obtain the most favourable conditions it will be necessary to optimize the process by varying all parameters which influence the selectivity of the process. Such a program is under way in our Institute.

(3) The numbering of the bottom three curves in Fig. 4 is reversed, as is the numbering in the appropriate Figure caption. The error appeared during the retyping of the paper.

(4) We feel that hydrodynamic drag does influence the process of magnetic flocculation, it more or less decreases the rate of the process. However, owing to the complexity of the interacting system, the competing short-range forces, such as the repulsive interaction due to the electric dipolar layer and London-van den Waals forces, the

Brownian thermal motion could not be evaluated. A detailed study of parameters playing a crucial role in the coagulation of colloidal systems, including the measurement of the zeta potential is being carried out in our Institute.

(5) We did not study the influence of slurry density, but the effect of density variation may well be very pronounced owing to the strong dependence of interacting forces on the distance between particles.

Session 3

Comminution

Chairmen: H. J. Steiner
K. Żmudziński

AUTOMATIC MINERALOGICAL MEASUREMENTS
IN MINERAL PROCESSING

Invited lecture by M. P. Jones

Department of Mineral Resources Engineering, Imperial College, London, United Kingdom

INTRODUCTION

In the past a simple chemical analysis was often deemed sufficient to characterize a rock or an ore. Nowadays, however, it is becoming increasingly clear that we must also obtain large amounts of accurate mineralogical information before we can design suitable mineral separation processes. Such information is also vital for optimizing existing treatment operations.

The kind of information most useful to the mineral engineer is that which allows him (or her) to predict the behaviour of rocks and minerals (See Table 1).

In the past much of this information could only be obtained by slow, and often tedious, manual methods. However, in recent years many attempts have been made to speed up these methods using semi-automatic, or even fully automatic techniques. Considerable success has been achieved with automatic image analyses in which measurements are made on two-dimensional sections

TABLE 1

Mineralogical Information Required by
the Mineral Processing Engineer

(a) mineral structures i.e., crystallography and crystallinity.

(b) mineral compositions and stoichiometry.

(c) mineral proportions

(d) particle and grain size distributions.

(e) particle shapes.

(f) textural characteristics of unbroken material.

(g) particle compositions of broken material.

(h) textural characteristics of broken fragments.

(i) other mineral properties: density, magnetic, thermal, etc.

(j) variation of mineral properties laterally and with depth
in a deposit.

(k) variation of mineral properties with time (e.g., during
storage or transportation).

---

through a specimen in a manner analogous to the traditional
manual methods of point-, line-, or area measurement.

Methods of Mineralogical Analysis

Traditional methods of mineralogical analysis can be divided
into:

(a) Physical methods of measurement.

(b) Optical examination methods.

Physical methods have been used mainly in the study of
coarse-grained materials. These methods include the identification of minerals by determining their specific gravity, bulk
chemical analysis etc: mineral proportions are commonly determined by separating the minerals by hydraulic, magnetic, chemi-

cal, and other methods: particle* sizes are usually determined
by screening or classification whilst grain* sizes cannot ordinarily be measured: particle shapes are estimated from the
ratios of selected particle dimensions: and particle compositions are determined by chemically analysing individual particles, by heavy liquid separations, or by small-scale simulation
of plant processes.

In the optical methods an image of a specimen is generally
viewed and measured using a suitable microscope. Since images
of rocks and minerals are almost invariably complex, their
quantitative assessment is inherently difficult and is also
inevitably slow when carried out by manual methods. Furthermore, the results are often of dubious accuracy and "too close
an adherence to a particular view may encourage the observer
to look mainly for details which .....would support (that
view) and to ignore or become subconsciously blind to other
detail ....." [1].

With the optical methods minerals are identified on the
basis of their optical properties; mineral proportions are
established by grain, point or line counts; grain and particle
sizes are compared against suitable graticules; shapes are
calculated from the ratios of linear dimensions; and liberation is estimated from the examination of sections through
mineral particles.

---

* A particle is a free fragment that may, or may not, consist
of a single mineral. A grain consists of a single mineral
and is not necessarily free.

More and more information of this kind is urgently required. However, the physical methods of analysis are not slow but are very difficult to speed up or to automate. In addition, their application is limited by restrictions on particle size, the availability of heavy liquids, particle complexity, etc. [2]. Fortunately, some optical measurements that were previously carried out by manual methods lend themselves quite readily to automation. Automatic equipment, called image analysers, are very rapid and they release the mineralogist and the engineer from the tedium of making repetitive measurements. In addition, they tend to eliminate operator bias. Although they cannot be used in all circumstances (See Table 2) there are an increasing number of situations when only automatic devices will provide the required detail in the time available - for example, the routine examination of large numbers of specimens for process control purposes. Furthermore, there are other measurements that are so tedious to make that an automatic system is the only practicable way of providing the necessary data (e.g., the distribution of inter-granular distances).

Automation of Image Measuring Methods

These automatic methods generally involve the study of either thin-, or polished-sections in a manner analogous to traditional manual microscopic methods. The ideal automatic image analysing system would distinguish any specified mineral in a group of other minerals; it would have a spatial resolution of 1 μm or less; it would be comparatively cheep to buy and to run; it would produce accurate results with great speed; it would be

536

TABLE 2

Criteria for Selecting an Image Analysing System

Criterion	Measurement System			
	Automatic Area	Automatic Line		Semi-Automatic
Signals	Optical	Optical	X-rays	Optical
Typical System	T.V. System	Densitometer	Microanalyser	Planimeter
Specimen Preparation	Demanding	Demanding	Less demanding	Less demanding
Specimen viewed in:	air	air	vacuum	air
Mineral discrimination	Fair	Good	Very good	Excellent
Speed	Very fast (about 1 s/field)	Fast 1–10 ms/observation	Slower 10 ms/observation	Very slow 1 s/observation
Information provided	0,1, or 2-D	0-, or 1-D	0-, or 1-D	1-D or 2-D
Stereological transformations	Now always available for 2-D measurements	more often available for 1-D measurements	more often available 1-D measurements	not always available
Nature of material to be measured	simple: optical discrimination easy	optical discrimination more difficult	optical discrimination difficult or impossible	complex materials: discrimination very difficult
Cost/Specimen	Small	Large	Still larger	Large

reliable and versatile; and, it would be capable of being set in operation by well-trained, but not necessarily highly-qualified, personnel.

Image analysing devices that meet many of these requirements are now available commercially and fall into two main categories:

    (a) area-measuring

    (b) line-measuring

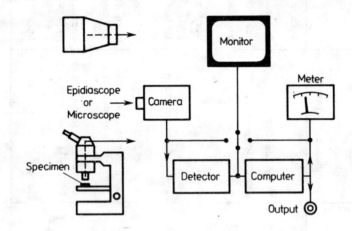

Fig. 1. Simplified block diagram of the apparatus.
The quantimet.

Most area-measuring systems are based on television scanning techniques (Fig. 1). An image of a specimen is viewed either under a beam of light or under an electron beam. Where a beam of light is used the various minerals are identified by their optical "brightness" and, it is possible, in theory, to distinguish a large number of minerals in a single specimen. In practice, birefringence (or bireflectance) effects and surface defects introduced by specimen preparation techniques limit the

538

number of mineral that can be discriminated automatically. Where electron beams are used the minerals are generally distinguished by the intensities of the back-scattered electron signals. These signals are also greatly affected by the quality of the surface of a specimen but electronic signal processing devices can cancel out the effects of minor differences of topography.

A single field of view (or measuring frame) is sub-divided into about 500,000 contiguous small areas or "picture points". The signal intensity (or brightness) of each "point" is measured in a few micro seconds and a complete frame is examined in about a second. Individual "point" values are stored sometimes for only a few milliseconds in a temporary internal memory or more rarely, on an external tape or disc, and are used to make the following basic measurements:

(a) the number of separate features, (or grains) of a
    specified mineral;

(b) the "sizes" of these features;

(c) the proportion of the frame occupied by the features;

(d) the perimeter lengths of individual features. These basic data are also used to classify the features according to 2-D shape; for example, the ratio of grain area to grain perimeter length; or the ratio of maximum observable length to the maximum breadth (at right angles to the length). In fact, the information that can be collected from an image is only really limited by the resolution of the instrument, the programming and computing capacity, and the time available.

Some systems automatically correct for small variations in the intensity the incident light over the image; they also reposition a specimen if there are small variations in the level of its surface.

Semi-automatic optical systems are available in which mineral discrimination is greatly improved by interaction with a skilled observer. The required feature is delineated by the observer and the measurements are then carried out automatically by the equipment. In this way minerals that differ only very slightly in "brightness" can be differentiated and it is even possible to distinguish a mineral or feature by its shape, its size or its association. Such a combined system can readily distinguish polishing scratches and other artefacts which can be ignored during the measurement procedure. Unfortunately, the speed of an interactive system of this kind is limited by the presence of the observer and this is a disadvantage where information is needed very rapidly.

In line-measuring systems the dense array of "points" used in the area-measuring devices is replaced by a broadly-spaced, linear arrangement of contiguous sampling "points" on the specimen surface. The specimen (or a suitable image) is usually moved in small steps across a narrow beam of light or electrons (Fig. 2). The signals from the specimen (optical, electron-optical, or X-ray) are first used to discriminate the various minerals and are then used to determine proportions, sizes, shapes, etc. in a similar manner to the area-measuring systems.

Line-measuring systems are generally slow but the extra time is used to provide better discrimination of minerals than on the area-measuring devices. Discrimination is especially good in the X-ray instruments but a single observation may take about 10 ms and an examination of a complete specimen can take 1-2 h.

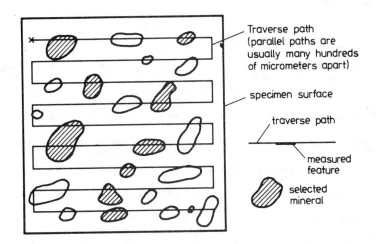

Fig. 2. Traversing system used in a Geoscan-Minic linear-measuring system.

The spatial resolution of line-measuring devices depends on the size of the illuminating beams and the distance moved between successive measurements: optical systems have resolutions of 0.5 to 1 μm whilst X-ray systems have resolutions of 1 to 2 μm.

Selecting a Measuring System

One should select the simplest system that will provide the required information in the time available. If there is little or no difficulty in optically distinguishing the minerals then the great speed of optical, television-type equipment will be an attraction. On the other hand, if the minerals are difficult to distinguish then the better discrimination (and the reduced speed) of semi-automatic or line-measuring instruments may have to be used. Other selection criteria are given in Table 2.

Sampling Considerations

The features that are measured on an image must be properly representative of the equivalent features in the bulk material and care is needed to ensure that they are not destroyed or altered by the sampling procedure. Thus, when mineral grain size is being measured, that size must be retained during the sampling and specimen preparation stages. Similarly, in the study of mineral textures the spatial relationships must not be changed by the preparation procedure.

Area-measuring instruments can, if necessary, measure the complete specimen surface and, therefore, no sampling errors need arise during the measuring stage. Line-measuring equipment, on the other hand, sample the specimen surface along a pre-arranged linear traverse. The orientation of the traverse must not be parallel to the textural features of the specimen and the length of the traverse must produce an adequate number of observations for the provision of statistically viable results. This is usually done by covering the whole specimen surface with a diffuse array of parallel lines (See Fig. 2). The minimum number of observations needed in certain circumstances to achieve a stated accuracy can be calculated by the application of Binomial Probability (See Appendix 1). In general, the sampling errors during measurement vary with $\frac{1}{(\sqrt{N})}$, where N is the number of observations of a particular feature.

Specimen Preparation

Automatic image analysers cannot readily distinguish mineralogical features such as grain boundaries from scratches and
other polishing artefacts introduced during specimen preparation. Great care is, therefore, needed to minimise the production of such artefacts. The preparation of adequate specimens
can sometimes take longer than the measuring procedure and the
preparation stage becomes the "rate-controlling" step in an
analysis. Specimens prepared by careful, traditional polishing
techniques are usually adequate but a much higher quality of
surface finish is needed for optical methods than for analysers
using X-ray data. Therefore, X-ray devices may be preferred to
optical methods where speed is especially important.

The performance of an optical image analyser can sometimes
be improved by specialized specimen preparation techniques such
as etching or staining.

Measurement Errors

The minimum error when measuring a linear dimension with an
optical, T.V.-based instrument is about 1 μm. The relative
error when measuring areas is often much less than 1%. The precision of linear measuring systems is also about 1 μm and this
is controlled by the size of the step used to move the specimen
and by the effective size of the illuminating beam.

The results obtained by automatic measuring systems compare
favourably with results obtained from the same specimens by
skilled, conscientious manual observers [3, 4]. It is not easy
to establish the absolute errors of either method because it is

543

difficult to prepare standard sections of known characteristics. However, the mean value for the proportion of a mineral calculated from measurements on a number of sections through a single artificial specimen agreed closely with the known bulk composition [5]. The reproducibility of automatic measurements is good [5] (See Table 3) and is often much better than can be achieved by manual measurements.

TABLE 3

Reproducibility of Automatic Mineralogical Measurements

Duplicate measurements from a single section
obtained by linear analysis

Intercept length (L) - μm	First run	Second run
2*	61	78
2-4	25	29
4-6	27	24
6-10	47	53
10-16	64	70
16-25	108	103
25-40	198	198
40-63	117	114
63-100	13	13
100-160	2	1
Total (N)	601	605
Sum of (L) - μm	16576	16183
Total traverse length - μm	450,000	450,000
Mean intercept length i.e., $\frac{\text{sum of (L)}}{\text{Total (N)}}$ - μm	27.6	26.8
Volumetric percentage = linear percentage = $\frac{\text{Sum of (L) x 100}}{\text{Total traverse length}}$	3.68	3.60

*
Values below 2 μm are largely due to electronic "noise" and to minute polishing artefacts and are ignored in all the calculations.

544

Stereological[*] Considerations

Image analysis does not seek to provide detailed, local descriptions of single features in a specimen but, instead, determines statistical values that can be correlated with the physical characteristics of the specimen. Automatic image analysing equipment make zero-, one-, or two-dimensional measurements on two-dimensional images: the presence or absence of a feature is determined by point analysis; the length of that feature in a predetermined direction(s) is determined by linear analysis; and the area of the feature is measured by area analysis. However, the mineral processing engineer is mainly interested in three-dimensional data such as volumetric mineral proportions, 3-D size and shape, volumetric particle compositions, etc. Thus, individual zero-dimensional measurements are valueless for determining grain sizes; 1-D and 2-D measurements invariably under-estimate 3-D sizes and always over-estimate the degree of liberation of mineral particles; two dimensional images cannot (with a few trivial exceptions) show more than one continuous phase (Fig. 3) even though any number of those phases can exist in the bulk specimen; lamellae of uniform thickness appear to vary in thickness depending on the angle of the section; the contiguity of two features may be difficult, or impossible, to establish; the continuity, or otherwise of pores is not apparent, etc. Consequently, all the measured values must be con-

---

[*]Stereology is the study of the relationships between the structure as seen on a random section or projection plane and the true spatial qualities that these represent.

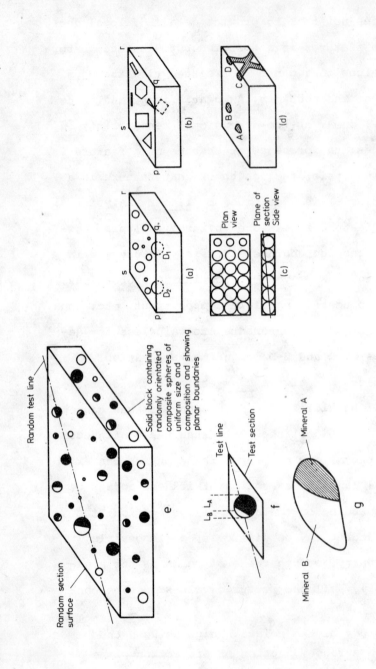

Fig. 3. Effects of random sectioning on size, shape, contiguity and connectivity of granular materials: (a) uniform-sized spheres distributed at random in space and cut by plane pgrs; (b) uniform-sized cubes distributed at random in space and cut by plane pgrs; (c) effect of sectioning contiguous, uniformly sized spheres; (d) effect of sectioning connected features — C and D are part of a single feature; are A and B connected? Relationship between volumetric, areal and linear estimates of mineral liberation (e) measurement of linear grade (f) and typical profile (g).

verted into 3-D values; this can be done occasionally by comparison with standard materials [6], but more usually it can
only be done by mathematically transforming the measured values
into 3-D values using stereological principles [7, 8, 9].

On a few rare occasions the transformation of low dimensional data into 3-D values is quite simple: the volumetric proportion of a mineral in a bulk specimen is, within experimental
error, numerically the same as the proportions obtained by
zero-, one-, or two-dimensional measurements; i.e., $P_p = L_1 =$
$A_a = V_v$ where P_p = point proportion, L_1 = line proportion
A_a = area proportion and V_v = volume proportion.

Other transformations are more complex [8, 9]; for example,
the relationship between the measured random intercept lengths
across a feature and the equivalent mean screen size of that
feature is:

$$\mu_1^{\frac{1}{1}} (D_c) = K \frac{\mu_2^{\frac{1}{2}} (L)}{\mu_1^{\frac{1}{1}} (L)}$$

where $\mu_1^{\frac{1}{1}} (D_c)$ = mean screen size, K = shape factor, and $\mu_n^{1} (L)$=
n^{th} moment of the random intercept values. Other relationships
(see below) relate measured values to a specific surface area of
the feature of interest, the particle density per unit volume
of specimen, particle compositions, etc.

Applications in Mineral Technology

Mineralogical information obtained by slow manual methods of examination is already widely used in the mineral industry for process design and for the control of plants and processes. More

information would often be welcome but is difficult to produce in the short time usually available. The only practical solution to this problem is to automate the data collection procedures. This can be done for simple measurements on simple materials by equipment that is widely used in metallurgical and medical fields. However, many mineralogical materials are complex and difficult to measure and only now is suitable measuring equipment becoming available. Consequently, few details are yet available of the use of automatic mineralogical measurements in mineral processing.

Determination of Mineral Proportions. This is one of the simplest tasks for any automatic system. A television-type automatic image analyser has been used in a large Chilean copper mine to determine the chalcocite: chalcopyrite ratio in rock specimens obtained during the mine development programme [10]. The results are used to arrange the underground loading schedules so as to provide, as far as possible, a pre-determined ratio of these minerals in the mill feed. The Bureau de Recherches Geologique et Minieres (B.R.G.M.) laboratories in Orleans, France use a similar instrument to make routine determinations of mineral proportions in large numbers of specimens produced during test work in its Mineral Processing Section [11]. Similarly, large numbers of geological specimens are routinely measured by the Institute of Geological Sciences (I.G.S.) in London [12] to determine mineral proportions. The Mineral Sciences Laboratories of the Canada Centre for Mineral and Energy Technology (CANMET) Ottawa, also use a television-type image analyser to determine mineral proportions in materials sent for beneficiation tests [6]: for example, the proportions of hematite lamellae in ilmenite grains was measured to determine the maximum attainable titanium content of ilmenite concentrates.

Mineral proportions have also been determined by linear analysis at the Royal School of Mines, London [13] using a modified electron probe X-ray microanalyser. Much of the work carried out on this equipment has been concerned with the design of the system itself and with the development of suitable mathematical transformation equations. However, the system has also provided routine data for the mineral industry on the mineral proportions in complex specimens produced during mineral process design experiments [14] (e.g., Table 4). Many of these minerals were optically similar sulphides and sulph-arsenides that could not be distinguished automatically by optically-based, area-measuring devices. In addition, the particle sizes and the mineral proportions were often very small (Table 5). Similarly, the selected size fractions of a tin ore were measured to determine the proportions of cassiterite, mixed sulphides, and mixed silicates (Table 5).

Determination of Grain Size Distribution. The apparent size distributions of irregularly-shaped mineral grains that exist as (unliberated) components of bulk specimens can be determined readily with automatic area-measuring devices. The T.V.-type instruments measure either the sectioned areas of such grains or the lengths of selected intercepts across them - usually the longest intercepts along the direction of the raster. The transformation of these values into equivalent three dimensio-

TABLE 4

Linear Image Analysis of a Cobalt-bearing Concentrate

Random intercept length (L) µm	Minerals					
	Pyrite	Bornite	Chalcopyrite	Carrollite	Chalcocite	Mixed Silicates
2-4	96	15	15	20	14	81
4-6	139	19	21	28	10	88
6-10	553	42	44	99	48	268
10-16	416	35	46	63	29	279
16-25	528	27	42	58	41	262
25-40	398	22	53	50	27	225
40-63	232	8	29	31	14	178
63-100	119	8	22	24	12	107
100-160	58	2	13	6	4	36
160-250	16	1	5	1	6	10
250-400	-	-	0	-	-	2
400-630	-	-	1	-	-	-
Total (N)	2555	179	291	380	205	1536
Sum (L) µm	63287	3480	9505	8669	5583	42083
Mean (L) µm	24.8	19.4	32.7	22.8	27.2	27.4
% of mineral in specimen (by volume)	14.5	0.4	1.0	1.0	0.6	9.1
% of mineral in the concentrate* (by volume)	54.4	1.5	3.8	3.8	2.3	34.2
Specific gravity of mineral	5.0	5.4	4.2	4.8	5.6	2.7
% of mineral in the concentrate (by weight)	64.8	1.9	3.8	4.4	3.1	22.0
Total traverse length µm	915000	915000	915000	915000	915000	465000

*The specimen consisted of 73.4% epoxy resin matrix and 26.6% mineral grains by volume.

TABLE 5

Linear Analysis of a Cassiterite-rich, Cyclosizer Fraction
(20-26 μm Nominal Cassiterite Sphere)

Random intercept lengths (L) μm	Cassiterite grains	Sulphide grains	Silicate grains
2-4	4	53	113
4-6	12	74	125
6-10	21	140	207
10-16	32	197	252
16-25	38	278	371
25-40	26	466	731
40-63	1	225	649
63-100	-	56	209
100-160	-	3	44
160-250	-	-	2
Total (N)	134	1492	2703
Sum (L) μm	2180	39,383	89,101
Mean (L) μm	16.3	26.4	33.0
Percent of total specimen (by volume)	0.48	8.75	19.80
Percent of total mineral (by volume)	2	30	68
Specific gravity (approximate)	6.9	4.8	2.8
Percent (by weight)	4	41	55

Each traverse was 415,000 μm long: the matrix accounted for 70% (by volume) of the specimen.

nal grain sizes is imperfectly understood at present and it is common practice to use the untransformed values to compare results of tests on similar materials. Linear measuring instruments measure random intercept lengths and it is sometimes possible to convert these values into equivalent screen (or other) sizes that can be more readily understood by the mineral engineer [7]. Figure 4 compares the values obtained first, by screening, and then, by measuring random sections through the same particles. As expected, the largest values in linear analyses are (except for spherical particles) always larger than those obtained by screening. However, random intercept values that approach zero length are always found in any measuring sequence-irrespective of the true particle size - and, for particles of simple shape and small size range, the most commonly occurring chord length (i.e., the modal chord length) is approximately the same as the mean screen size.

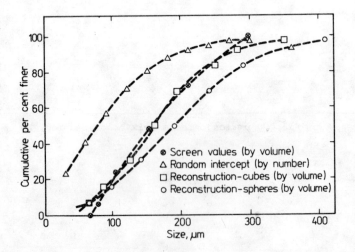

Fig. 4. Stereological transformation of size data obtained from random intercepts on liberated galena.

Determination of Particle Shape. The shape of a particle can be uniquely defined by the size distribution of random intercepts through it. The average shape of a number of similarly shaped particles can be established by measuring the random intercept length distribution through a uniformly-sized population of those particles. Suitable "monosize" particles are obtained by screening through a pair of closely-sized micro-mesh sieves e.g., 95 µm and 100 µm apertures.

Particle shape determinations have been carried out in this way on Norwegian ilmenite concentrates and on zircon particles from an Australian beach sand [15]. The results provide shape parameters for use in determining size distributions and they can also be used to predict the performance of screening equipment.

Determination of Particle Composition. Many attempts have been made to determine various liberation parameters by image analyses. For example, Cyclosizer fractions of a ground cassiterite ore were examined to follow the increase in liberation of the cassiterite with reduction of particle size (see Table 6). In any mono-sized fraction grains of the full, three dimensional, particle size must be liberated and grains smaller than full size must be part of composite particles. Uncorrected 1-D and 2-D measurements on such a specimen must, inevitably, suggest that some small unliberated grains exist (see section on grain sizing), even if all the grains are, in fact, liberated. Consequently, the real, three dimensional size of the grains must be established before this approach can provide unambiguous information regarding mineral liberation. This can

553

TABLE 6

Measurements of Cassiterite Grains in Cyclosizer Fractions

Random intercept lengths (L) μm	Number of intercepts (N) Nominal size of cassiterite spheres in fraction μm				
	+6-9	+9-14	+14-20	+20-26	+26-46
2	50	27	46	32	61
2-4	28	12	10	4	25
4-6	31	13	16	12	27
6-10	124	32	30	21	47
10-16	121	70	46	32	64
16-25	12	29	43	38	108
25-40	1	-	12	26	198
40-63	-	-	-	1	117
63-100	-	-	-	-	13
100-160	-	-	-	-	2
Total (N)	317	156	157	134	601
Sum (L) μm	2837	1722	2100	2180	16576
Mean (L) μm	8.9	11.0	13.4	16.3	27.6
Percent cassiterite (by volume)	0.63	0.38	0.47	0.48	3.68
Mean intercept length maximum expected cassiterite spherical diameter	0.99	0.79	0.67	0.63	(0.60)

The total traverse length was 450,000 μm for each specimen. Intercepts smaller than 2 μm have been ignored in calculations of total N, mean L, and volumetric proportion of cassiterite.

easily be done if the shape of the cassiterite grains is known. Unfortunately, the shapes of unliberated grains are often extremely variable and, in any case, are difficult to measure. Consequently, this method does not provide accurate information on particle liberation. However, even without shape factors, it is still possible to follow the trend of a liberation process using uncorrected "size" data [15]. Thus, the ratio of mean cassiterite intercept length to the maximum spherical diameter of cassiterite in the size fraction increases as the liberation of the mineral approaches 100% (Table 6). (In this instance, the mean intercept length is used because the modal intercept length is not accurately known).

Empirical relationships of this kind are useful for comparing results from a series of size ranges of a single material but they do not provide accurate values for the amount of liberation achieved nor do they give much information regarding either the nature or the composition of the unliberated particles.

However, it is now sometimes possible to transform linear measurements on composite particles into distributions of particle compositions. Thus, values of $\dfrac{L_{An}}{L_{An} + L_{Bn}}$, where L_{An} is the length of the linear intercept on mineral A in particle n, and L_{Bn} is the intercept length on all other minerals in that particle, can be measured readily during a linear traverse: these values can be stereologically transformed into 3-D (i.e., volumetric) particle compositions [16, 17]. Figure 5 shows the raw data and the transformed results obtained when measuring particles of an iron ore [2, 9]. This approach can, in theory, also be applied to area measurements but, there are, as yet, no suit-

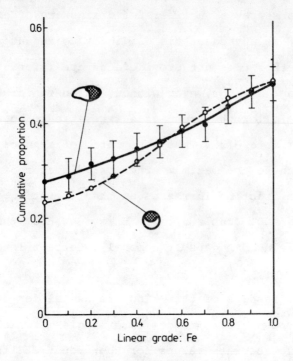

Fig. 5. Linear grade distribution functions from the sphere/
paraboloid model and from measurements of the iron
oxide/silicate particles.

able transformation data available. Barbery et al. [17] use a
different method for assessing particle composition. They estimate the size distributions of the mineral phases and of the
particles by a linear method that is independent of shape - provided the particles are convex and that any inclusions that they
contain are also convex. The method, unfortunately, requires the
accurate determination of high moments of intercept lengths and
this may limit its application.

The errors introduced into determinations of particle compositions by uncorrected area measurements are much smaller than

the errors introduced by uncorrected linear measurements [2] and, for this reason, many authors prefer to use uncorrected area measurements (rather than linear values) when studying liberation. However, it must be emphasized that direct area measurements can still introduce very large errors (Fig. 6) and that, whenever possible, it is best to use transformed, three dimensional, values.

A major research project is being set up at an Australian University [18] that will use an automatic image analyser to study liberation of minerals by the various methods that are available.

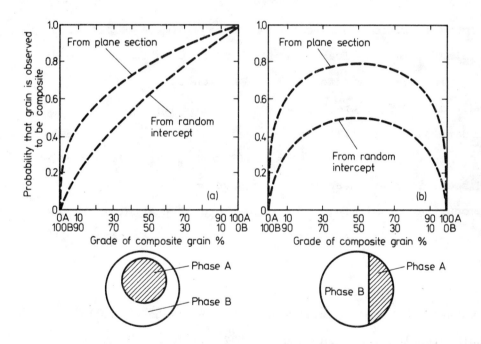

Fig. 6. Errors introduced by determining degree of liberation of spherical particles from examination of plane sections: (a) where grains are spheres and phase A occurs completely surrounded by phase B; (b) where grains are spheres and interface between phases A and B is a plane.

Miscellaneous Measurements. Determinations of specific surface areas of selected components, the number of features per
unit volume of specimen, etc. by linear measurements have been
reported by equipment manufacturers but are only rarely recorded in the technical literature of the mineral industry [8].

The application of sorting as a method of pre-concentration
depends on the spatial distribution of the minerals in a rock
and the facility with which that rock breaks to produce fragments of significantly different mineralogy. Image analysis results have been used to quantify rock textures [19] and the results have been used to indicate the fragment size at which
sorting is likely to be most effective.

Image analysis has also been used to estimate comminution
efficiency [20]; a clear relationship has been found between
the geometrical characteristics of broken fragments and the
conditions used to break them in a wide range of crushers,
grinders and ball-mills.

Automatic measurements of specific volume, specific surface
and specific total mean curvative have been carried out [21] on
the cupriferous minerals of a copper ore. The intergrowth characteristics of broken mineral particles have been studied by
manual, optical methods but there are no records that similar
data have been collected by automatic methods; for example, the
structure of broken particles has been assessed using an intergrowth - or locking - index where [22, 23]

$$\frac{S_v(A.B)}{S_v(A)} \quad \text{is the locking index}$$

$S_v(A.B)$ is the specific surface area of mineral A in contact with B (where B is the matrix)

$S_v(A)$ is the total specific surface of mineral A.

CONCLUSIONS

The great potential value of large amounts of swiftly-produced and accurate mineralogical data is not being fully realized by the Mineral Industry. As yet, only isolated attempts are being made to use the new generation of automatic and semi-automatic equipment to provide the mineralogical information needed for process design and plant control purposes. However, the measuring equipment is becoming more sophisticated, easier to use, and cheaper to buy, and it is confidently predicted that its use in the mineral industry will rapidly expand in the near future.

APPENDIX

To estimate the number of particles that must be measured to delineate an unknown probability density function with known precision [21].

In a histogram of f vs. x let:

f_i^1 =   number of values in the ith interval (to date).

n^1 =   total number of values (to date).

P_i =   probability that a value will fall into the ith interval.

h =   interval of the histogram

ϕ_i^1 = ordinates of the probability density function (to date).

$\hat{x}^1$ =   largest value (to date).

$\bar{x}^1$ =   mean of measured values (to date).

559

$\hat{f}^1$ = number of values in the largest category (to date).

e_u = error on the mean value - relative

e^1 = ordinate error (to date) - relative

(1) To establish the minimum number of measurements needed to determine the ordinates of the distribution function.

The best estimate of $\phi_i^1 = \dfrac{f_i^1}{n^1 h}$ and the relative error of ϕ_i^1 to $r\delta$ confidence limits =

$$e^1 = \frac{r}{\sqrt{n^1}} \quad \text{where r is usually 2.}$$

Thus, $n^1 > \dfrac{r^2}{(e^1)^2}$

If $r = 2$ and $e^1 = 5\%$

Then $n^1 > \dfrac{4}{25 \times 10^{-4}} = 1600$

(2) To establish the number of values needed to determine the mean value of the probability function to a stated precision.

$$n > \frac{\hat{x}^1 \hat{f}^1}{\bar{x}^1 e_\mu}$$

Thus, if $\hat{f}^1 = 1$; $\dfrac{\hat{x}^1}{\bar{x}^1} = 5$; and $e_\mu u = 1\%$

Then, $n > \dfrac{5 \times 1}{10^{-2}} = 500$

(3) To determine the probability that there are values greater than the largest value found to date.

$$p \left(\hat{x} > \hat{x}^1 \right) \qquad \frac{\hat{x}_i^1 \quad \hat{f}_i^1}{\bar{x}^1 \quad n^1}$$

Thus, if $n = 1600$, $\hat{f}_i = 1$ and $\dfrac{\hat{x}^1}{\bar{x}^1} = 5$

then, $p \left(\hat{x} > \hat{x}^1 \right) \leq \dfrac{5 \times 1}{1600} = \dfrac{1}{320}$

i.e., in the next 1000 measurements only 3 values greater than
$\hat{x}^1$ would be expected.

REFERENCES

1. Holmes A. Petrographic Methods and Calculations. Thomas
   Murby and Co., London, 1930, 17.

2. Stewart P. S. B. and Jones M. P. Determining the amounts and
   compositions of composite (middling) particles. 12th International Mineral Processing Congress, Sao Paulo, Brazil, 1977,
   Meeting B. Paper 4, (in press).

3. Timcak G., Jones M. P. and Rybar P. Effect of modelling conditions on the character of the size distribution of quasi
   random circle sections. Colloquium on the Application of
   Stereology and Computing, Vysoke Tatry, 1976, 107-124.

4. Petruk W. Bull C.I.M., 146-153 (1976).

5. Jones M. P. Automatic Image Analysis. Chap. 4. In: Physical
   Methods of Determinative Mineralogy, (ed. J. Zussman), Academic Press, London, 1977, 167-200.

6. Petruk W. Trans. Inst. Min. Metall., C272-277 (1978).

7. Barbery G. Powder Technol., 9, 231-240 (1974).

8. Jones M. P. and Barbery G. The size distributions and shapes of minerals in multi-phase materials: practical determination and use in mineral process design and control. Proc. 11th Intern. Min. Proc. Congr., Cagliari, 1975, 977-997.

9. Jones M. P. and Horton R. Recent developments in the stereological assessment of composite (middling) particles by linear measurements. Xlth. Commonwealth Min. and Metall. Congr. Hong Kong, 1978, Paper 52.

10. Araya R. Personal Communication, 1974.

11. Gateau C. and Prevosteau J. M. Size distribution analysis in situ on individual or interconnected phases by image analysis. Proc. 4th Congr. on Stereology, 1975, N.B.S. Spec. Pub. 431, 1976, 309-313.

12. Dearnley P. Personal Communication, 1975.

13. Jones M. P. and Shaw J. L. Automatic measurement and stereological assessment of mineral data for use in mineral technology. Proc. Xth Intern. Mineral Processing Congr. London. (ed. M. J. Jones), Inst. Min. Met. London 1973, 737-756.

14. Jones M. P. Private reports to mining companies, 1970-78.

15. Simovic M. Stereological determination of the size distribution of minerals. Imperial College, London, Mineral Technology Research Report, 46, 1973.

16. Horton R. Determination of the volumetric composition of idealised composite mineral particles by random intercepts. Ph.D. Thesis, University of London, 1978, 300.

17. Barbery G. et al. Étude theorètique et simulation de la reconstruction de la composition volumètrique de populations de particules composites à partir de mèsures realisées sur des sections. 2nd European Symposium on Quantitative Analytical Microstructures, Caen, 1977.

18. Partidge A. C. Personal Communication, 1979.

19. Doerr R. M. Microscopy, radial distribution analysis and sortability. Proc. 4th International Congr. for Stereology, 1975. N.B.S. Spec. Pub. 431, 1976, 305-308.

20. Cauwe Ph. Use of mathematical morphology to estimate comminution efficiency. Proc. 4th International Congr. for Stereology, 1975. N.B.S. Spec. Pub. 431, 1976, 299-303.

21. Bodziny J. and Kraj W. Stereological analysis as one of methods in modern granulometry. To be presented at 13th Inter. Min. Proc.-Congr. Warsaw. June 1979.

22. Amstutz G. C. and Giger H. Journ. Microscopy, 95, 145-164 (1972).

23. Steiner H. J. Liberation kinetics in grinding operations. Proc. 11th Int. Mineral Proc. Congr., Cagliari, 1975, 26.

24. Beaven C. H. J. How many measurements? To be presented at Powder Europa, Wiesbaden, Jan 1980.

ADDITIONAL REFERENCES

King R. P. Powder Technol., 21, 147-150 (1978).

Caye R., Pierrot J. M., Prevosteau J. M. and Ragot J. P. Bull. Soc. Fr. Min. Crist., 93, 571 (1970).

Fisher C.   Microscope, 19, 1 (1971).

Gateau C. and Prevosteau J. M. Éxploitation d'un analyseur d'images à l'étude de la structure des pores d'un matériau. Compt. Rend. Congres Rilem/IUPAC. Prague. 1973, IV, (c), 1974, 517.

Foster R. H. and Evans J. S. Microscope, 22, 323-339 (1974).

Beddow J. K., Vetter A. F. and Sisson K. Powder Metallurgy International, 8, 69-76 (1976).

King R. P. Journ. Sth. African Inst. Min. Metall., 170-172 (1975).

Grant G. et al. Multicompositional particle characterization using the S.E.M. microprobe. Scanning Electron Microscopy, 1976. Part III, Proc. Workshop on Techniques for Particulate Matter Studies in S.E.M. 1976, 401-408.

Bodziony J. Bull. Acad. Pol. Sci., XIII, 513-517 (1965).

Bodziony J. Bull. Acad. Pol. Sci., XIII, 519-522 (1965).

Kraj W. Bull. Acad. Pol. Sci., XV, 419-425 (1967).

Schaap W. An illustrated liberation-flotation recovery model
for a disseminated mineral in low-grade ore. To be published.

ABSTRACT

The paper provides a brief review of the traditional physical and optical methods of obtaining the mineralogical data
required for process design and plant control purposes. These
methods are shown to be generally too slow, and often too inac-
curate for the needs of the modern mineral industry. The physical methods of measurement cannot readily be improved but new,
and largely automatic, methods have been developed that can
largely replace manual, optically-based, measurements. These
new methods, called image analysing methods, are described and
sufficient information is provided to allow the mineral engineer to select the most appropriate type of measuring equipment
for his purposes. The special sampling and specimen preparation
requirements of the new equipment are briefly discussed and the
errors introduced during the measuring procedures are described.

The relationships between the features measured on thin or
polished sections and the three-dimensional features that they
represent in the bulk material are discussed in detail and appropriate stereological transformation formulae are provided.

Examples are given of the use of automatic methods of mineralogical analysis by the mineral industry. These include the
measurement of mineral proportions, grain size distributions,
particle shapes, particle compositions and rock textures for
mineral process design purposes.

RÉSUMÉ

Le travail passe en revue les méthodes traditionnelles-phy-
siques et optiques utilisées pour obtenir des données de la
minéralogie pour la mise au point et pour le contrôle des
processus. On a montré que ces méthodes sont trop lentes et
souvent pas assez précises pour les besoins de l'industrie
moderne. On ne peut pas améliorer facilement les méthodes
physiques de mesure - mais les méthodes nouvelles, automatiques dans leur majorité, peuvent remplacer les mesures optiques actuelles. Ces nouvelles méthodes appelées méthodes

d'analyse de l'image ont été décrites; le travail fournit suffi-
samment d'informations pour que les ingénieurs-minerallurgistes
puissent choisir le mieux possible le type de l'équipement de
mesure. On a brièvement discuté les conditions spéciales de
prélèvement et de préparation d'échantillons pour le nouvel
équipement et on a décrit les fantes faites pendant la mesure.

On a discuté la relation entre les grandeurs mesurées sur
des morceaux de roche fins ou polis et un système tridimension-
nel que ces mesures devraient caractériser. On a donné les
équations adéquates permettant la transformation stéréologique.
On a cité des exemples d'emploi, dans l'industrie, de ces
méthodes automatiques de mesures minéralogiques. Ces mesures
servent à trouver les proportions qualitatives entre les minéraux, à déterminer la distribution de la taille des grains des
minéraux, la forme des grains, la composition granulométrique
des groupements ainsi qu'à établir la structure de la roche.

ZUSAMMENFASSUNG

Der Beitrag gibt eine Übersicht der konventionellen physikalischen und optischen Verfahren zur Ermittlung von Daten hinsichtlich der Mineralogie, die für die Prozeßprojektierung und
Kontrolle der Anlagen notwendig sind. Es wird gezeit, daß diese
Methoden zu langsam und für die Zwecke der modernen Mineralindustrie häufig zu ungenau sind.

Es ist nicht leich die physikalischen Meßmethoden zu ver-
bessern. Aber die neu entwickelten Methoden, die in der
Mehrzahl automatische Methoden sind, können die bisher angewandten optischen Messungen ersetzen.

Diese neuen Methoden, genannt Spiegelmethoden, werden im
Beitrag beschrieben und es werden genügend viele Informationen
angegeben, damit den Aufbereiter-Ingenieuren die Wahl des geeig-
netesten Typs eines Meßgerätes gegeben werden kann.

Die besonderen Anforderungen hinsichtlich der Entnahme und
Vorbereitung der Proben für die neuen Meßgeräte werden kurz
diskutiert. Anbei werden die bei der Messung entstohenden
Fehler beschrieben.

Besprochen wird die Abhängigkeit zwischen den gemessenen
Größen auf dünnen und polierten Anschliffen und dem dreidimen-
sionalem System, das durch diese Messungen gekennzeichnet wird.
Es werden entsprechende Gleichungen angeführt, die eine steoro-
logische Transformation ermöglichen.
Beispiele der Anwendung von automatischen Meßmethoden in der
Mineralindustrie werden im Beitrag angeführt. Die Messungen
beziehen sich auf die Bestimmung der quantitativen Verhältnisse
zwischen den Mineralien, der Korngrößenverteilung einzelner
Mineralien, der Kornform, der Kornzusammensetzung von Verwach-
sungen, sowie auf die Ermittlung der Gesteintextur.

РЕЗЮМЕ

Произведен обзор традиционных физических и оптических методов, применяемых для получения минералогических данных, необ-
ходимых для проектирования и контроля процессов. Показано,что
эти методы являются слишком медленными, а часто очень неточны-
ми и не отвечающими требованиям современной промышленности.
Методы физических измерений нелегко усовершенствовать, однако
новоразрабатываемые методы, в большинстве случаев автоматичес-
кие, могут заменить применяемые до настоящего времени оптичес-
кие измерения. Описаны новые методы, называемые зеркальными,
и подано достаточное количество информации, которая даст возможность инженеру-обогатителю выбрать наиболее нужный тип изме-
рительного устройства. Коротко оговорены специальные требования
к пробоотбору и приготовлению образцов для новых устройств, описаны также погрешности измерений.

Обсуждена взаимосвязь между величинами, измеряемыми на тонких и отнолированных образцах, и изомерной системой, которую
эти измерения должны характеризовать.

Представлены соответствующие уравнения, позволяющие проводить
стеорологическое трансформирование. Приведены примеры производ-
ственного применения автоматических методов минералогических
измерений. Эти измерения включают установление количественных
пропорций между минералами, определение распределения величины
зерна отдельных минералов, формы зерна, состава сростов зерна,
а также определение текстуры породы.

LIBERATION ANALYSIS BY MEANS OF IMAGE ANALYSERS: THEORY AND APPLICATIONS

G. Barbery, G. Huyet and C. Gateau

Service Géologique National, Bureau de Recherches Géologiques et Minieres, Orléans, France

1. INTRODUCTION

The need for quantitative information on the distribution of particle composition and texture is obvious to all mineral technologists who are either working on the practical problems of the separation of minerals by physico-chemical process or in the field of modelling mineral processes.

The type of geometrical structures to be quantified is given as a reminder in Fig. 1.

In the face of such a problem, mineral technologists have been trying, ever since Gaudin [1, 2], to provide methods that will enable them to quantify the information to be obtained.

For a given population of solid particles, the interest lies in a number of minerals, usually fairly small, say up to five, which may be valuable, or on the contrary, harmful for the process to which this population is to be submitted. It would thus be appropriate to know:

568

- the proportion of each mineral of interest which is "free", and its variation with particle size, and then, for particles which are composite:
- the proportion of the external surface of the particles which is occupied by the minerals, and its variation with particle size,
- the volume distribution of each mineral of interest in composite particles, in each particle size range,
- the area of contact between various minerals, as a function of particle size.

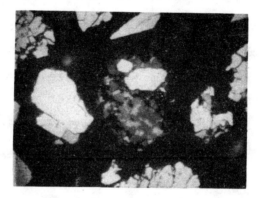

Fig. 1. Typical section through a population of particles containing mostly unliberated materials.

This is rather a lot of information, but it can be fairly stated that most mineral technologists would agree that if a fast, cheap, reliable and convenient method of obtaining it were available, they would feel much better about process design, process modelling and simulation.

Physical methods involving mainly separations by heavy luquids - up to a density of 4.5 - have been used for many years in order to get some of this information, and new deve-

lopments are available on laboratory scale [3] to extend this
limit to over 10 by use of mgnetohydrostatic separators or fer-
rofluids. Magnetic separation has also been used [4, 5]. These
methods can only provide reliable information for particle composition in the case where only two minerals are present in the
material, and preferably where there is a combination of a low
density and a high density mineral.

Since most of the problems that are encountered in mineral
technology occur on a scale which is measurable in µm (say between 1 and a few hundred µm), and since an intimate appraisal
of the nature of the mineral associations within particles is
required in order to obtain this information, it is quite natural that instrumental techniques involving optical or electronic microscopy of sectioned particles have been considered
the most promising technique ever since Gaudin.

Various difficulties are encountered in the process of obtaining this information and are of two types, conceptual and
instrumental.

1.1. Conceptual Difficulties

The main problem lies in the fact that in carrying out an
analysis of cross-sections of particles the raw data which is
obtained from the instrument, however perfect it might be, is
not directly applicable to three dimensional physical reality.
As a very quick example, Fig. 2 shows how simple composite
particles can be observed as "free" particles.

One should also assess the problem of transforming data
obtained in two or one dimensions, which corresponds either to

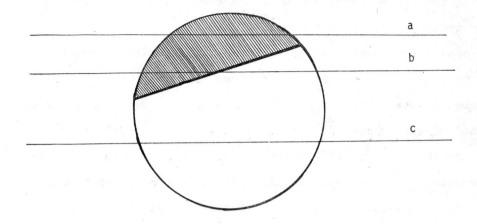

Fig. 2. Examples of ways of either sectioning a composite
        sphere by planes (a and c give apparently free
        sections), or drawing test lines on plane section b;
        lines a and c are apparently free.

the analysis of whole sections or the analysis of the sections
by test lines which are drawn on it, into information in three
dimensions. This field of applied mathematics is known as stereology, and, unfortunately, very few mathematicians are interested in the subject.

The fundamental relationships that can be used are the following, $[6, 7]$:

$$V_v = A_a = L_1 = P_p \tag{1}$$

$$S_v = 2 P_1 \tag{2}$$

$$S_v = \frac{4}{\pi} L_a \tag{3}$$

All these relationships are derived theoretically without having to make any hypothesis of the shape, size distribution or convexity of the various phases present.

These relationships are simple and quite powerful and, they may be used to provide some of the required information. If it is assumed that a monosized fraction - according to a convenient method, for instance, the fraction between two closely sized screens in a laboratory sieving operation, or the fraction corresponding to close sedimentation diameters - has been prepared, it is possible to obtain the following information by mounting at random the size fraction in a matrix, making a polished section and analysing it:

- volumetric proportion of the minerals of interest, with respect to overall particles:

$$V_{vm} = \frac{A_m}{A_p} = \frac{L_m}{L_p} \tag{4}$$

- specific surface area of particles:

$$S_v = \frac{2\ P_{1p}}{L_p} \tag{5}$$

or, if particles are convex:

$$\frac{4}{L_p} \tag{6}$$

or

$$S_{vp} = \frac{4}{\pi}\frac{L_{ap}}{A_p} \tag{7}$$

572

- proportion of the overall external surface area of particles occupied by a given mineral:

$$\frac{S_m}{S_{vp}} = \frac{P_{m/o}}{P_{1p}} \tag{8}$$

where m/o stands for the number of points on test-lines representing contact between mineral and the outside of particle, or

$$\frac{S_m}{S_{vp}} = \frac{L_{m/o}}{L_{ap}} \tag{9}$$

- and surface area of contact between various solid phases per unit volume of particles:

$$S_{vm_1m_2} = 2 \frac{P_{m_1m_2}}{L_p} \tag{10}$$

or

$$S_{vm_1m_2} = \frac{4}{\pi} \frac{L_{m_1m_2}}{A_p} \tag{11}$$

The operation, carried out on sequential size fractions, also provides relevant information on variation with particle size.

Any other relationship that can be used necessarily involves a hypothesis to be made concerning convexity or shape or particle size distribution. The most useful assumption in our opinion, which usually does not involve too much loss of generality, concerns the convexity of particles.

Let N_v convex particles be placed at random in a unit volume. One may define the average quantities as:

$$\overline{V} = \frac{V_v}{N_v} \quad \text{average volume of particles} \tag{12}$$

$$\overline{S} = \frac{S_v}{N_v} \quad \text{average surface area of particles} \tag{13}$$

For each particle, one can define an average "thickness" by:

$$I = \frac{1}{2} \iint_s \left(\frac{1}{R_1} + \frac{1}{R_2} \right) ds \tag{14}$$

where R_1 and R_2 are the main radii of curvature at a point on the surface of the particle with the integration being carried out over the whole particle

$$\overline{I} = \frac{\sum^{N_v} I_i}{N_v} \tag{15}$$

The remarkable properties of convex bodies enable one to derive the following relationships:

$$\frac{\overline{S}}{\overline{I}} = \frac{2}{\pi} \overline{B} \tag{16}$$

$$\frac{\overline{V}}{\overline{I}} = \frac{\overline{A}}{2\pi} \tag{17}$$

$$\frac{\overline{V}}{\overline{S}} = \frac{\overline{L}}{4} \tag{18}$$

$$\frac{\overline{V}^2}{\overline{S}} = \frac{\pi}{12} \overline{L}^4 \tag{19}$$

574

and
$$\frac{\overline{v^2}}{\overline{v}} = \frac{\pi}{3}\frac{\overline{L^4}}{\overline{L}} \quad \text{which is "Crofton's} \qquad (20)$$
$$\text{second theorem"}$$

In the derivation of a mathematical method to discover the volumetric composite particle composition from a section analysis, a limiting hypothesis must be made, as will be seen in the second part of this paper.

1.2. Instrumental Difficulties

The other group of problems encountered are instrumental. Instruments used in the measurements are essentially required:
- to be able to differentiate between various minerals,
- to be able to differentiate between all minerals and the mounting medium,
- and to be able to measure length or area with required precision and sensitivity.

Two types of instruments can be used for this purpose:
- optical instruments such as image analyzers with an optical microscope,

and
- instruments which use non optical signals such as electrons, X rays, ect..., which can, however, be transformed into pictures to be processed by image analyzers.

Jones and co-workers [8, 9, 10, 11] have been using a computer controlled electron microprobe; Lynch and co-workers in Australia [12, 13], are developing the use of the scanning electron microscope, whereas the present authors [14, 15], as well as other workers such as Petruk [16] in Canada, have been using optical image analyzers.

Problems do occur in all cases. In our organization in the case of the electron probe or the scanning electron microscope fitted with X ray analysis which is also being developed for this particular use at the present time [17], the main difficulty seems to lie in the speed of data collection (and the cost of analysis), as well as in the number of signals that are analyzed at the same time, since the discrimination between all minerals and the mounting medium is required in one stage. The use of multichannel energy dispersive X ray analyzers will provide a practical solution to this last problem [17].

For optical instruments, which will be presented in more detail, the problem lies in specimen preparation (especially in the type of finish of polishing obtainable, and optical differentiation between low reflectivity minerals and mounting media. This will be discussed in the third part of the paper.

2. THEORY OF THE METHOD

As has already been stated in 1.1., in order to progress further on the reconstruction of particle composition from one or two dimensional measurement, a limiting hypothesis must be made. Various approaches involving shape and size limitation may be followed here.

Jones and co-workers [10, 11] have been using the following two limiting assumptions:
- particles have the same volume,
- composite particle have a homogeneous shape, which means that
  composite particles can be assimilated to regular, well defined geometrical structures, such as spheres cut by a plane, a

cube cut by a plane or a sphere inside a sphere, for which abaca are being calculated. This also seems to imply that all particles have the same shape.

The results of their work have not been published yet in their entirety.

Another approach has been developed by the authors, which seems to be less limitative, at the cost, of course, of a lower degree of precision, as is usual in the application of stereology.

Particles are assumed to have the same volume, to be convex, and the only further assumption which is made is that phases inside particles are convex.

The resulting mathematical theory has been derived and will not be developed extensively here, since it has already been published [18]. It can be stated briefly as follows:

Let the population of particles having the same volume V_p consisting of N_p particles, of which $N_p = N_b + N_w + N_m$, where b stands for the mineral of interest free, w the rest (all other minerals present) free and m composite particles, be put in a volume (in a mounting matrix) V. The total volume of particles is $N_p V_p$. Let the total length of test lines L_t be drawn and μ'_{1_p} be colled the moment of order 1 from the origin for the distribution of intercepts over the particles:

$$\frac{N_p V_p}{V} = \frac{\mu'_{1_p}}{L_t} \tag{21}$$

$$V = \frac{N_p V_p L_t}{\mu'_{1_p}} \tag{22}$$

$$V_p = \frac{\pi}{3} \frac{\mu'_{4_p}}{\mu'_{1_p}} \tag{23}$$

$$E(V_b) = V \frac{\mu'_{1_b}}{L_t} \frac{1}{N_b + N_m} = \frac{N_p}{N_b + N_m} V_p \frac{\mu'_{1_b}}{\mu'_{1_p}} \tag{24}$$

$$E(V_b^2) = E(V_b) \frac{\pi}{3} \frac{\mu'_{4_b}}{\mu'_{1_b}} \text{ etc...} \tag{25}$$

The idea is to obtain N_b, N_w and N_m, as well as the distribution of volumes in m from these relationships by an optimization method. The optimization is carried out in the plane N_b, N_w. For each point, N_m is determined which also determines $E(V_b)$, $E(V_b^2)$, etc... Since all particles with the same volume, V_b and V_w can be further split into what belongs to a free particle, and what belongs to a composite particle. For example,

$$(N_b + N_m) E(V_b) = N_b V_p + N_m E(V_{bm}) \tag{26}$$

$$(N_b + N_m) E(V_b^2) = N_b V_p^2 + N_m E(V_{bm}^2) \tag{27}$$

and thus $E(V_{bm})$ and $E(V^2_{bm})$, for each point in the N_b, N_w plane. The two volume distributions V_{bm} and V_{wm} must be complementary, that is for each V_{bm} there must be a $V_{wm} = V_p - V_{bm}$. The optimisation is thus carried out by minimizing the sum of squares between the two distributions V_{bm} and $V_p - V_{wm}$. An incomplete Beta function is used in this optimisation. It has been thoroughly checked on a computer simulation of instrument operation, procedures and measurements. An example is given in Fig. 3.

578

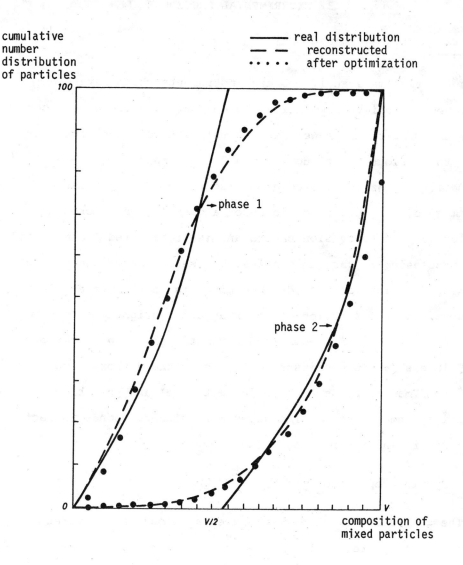

cumulative number distribution of particles

—— real distribution
— — reconstructed
· · · · · after optimization

100

phase 1

phase 2→

0

V/2

V

composition of mixed particles

Fig. 3. Results of computer simulation of the operation sequence: random sectioning of unimodal spherical binary particles, test lines applications and reconstruction according to the theory [18].

3. EXPERIMENTAL PROCEDURE

3.1. Principle

Automatic image analyzers are instruments which have been designed to achieve a quantitative characterization of the geometrical properties as well as the relative relationships between the various constituents of a 2-D document.

Optical signals are used as the source of data processing. An image of a sample observed under a conventional microscope is formed in a television camera and is transferred for analysis and processing to various modules. The selection of the various domains (sections of well-defined minerals in the present case) is obtained as a function of their apparent brightness (see Fig. 4). The image is decomposed automatically to a number of grey levels (64 in the instrument used by the authors, Quantimet 720 from Imanco) between the brightest level and pure black. In practice, the selection of a given mineral corresponds in fact to a discrimination between these grey levels.

3.2. Sample Preparation

The sample are originally prepared as close size a screen fraction. They are mounted at random in a matrix, then a polished section is made. The requirements of the mounting medium to be used are varied, and sometimes contradictory.
- Its viscosity must be low enough to avoid segregation of particles according to their specific gravity during curing.
- Its brightness must be very different from all the minerals contained in the sample.

(a)

(b)

Fig. 4. Detection of various minerals according to grey
level. (a) normal image, (b) image after electronic
enhancement. grey – sphalerite, white – pyrite

- It 'should polish to a fine finish compatible with the performance of the instrument.
- It should be strong enough to prevent particles dismounting during the polishing step.

Various methods have been tested, from wood alloy to teflon, from various cements to mineral fillers in resins. A large number from various manufactures have been used. Over one hundred various materials have been submitted to conventional mounting and polishing. Very few have been found to be acceptable. The following general method has been retained: - 1 cm^3 of powder to be analyzed is mixed with 2 cm^3 of Araldite AY103 (containing 10% by weight of HY951 hardener). This is poured into a cylinder 25 mm in diameter and 5 mm height, then put aside to set for 4 h under partial vacuum at $60^{\circ}C$. Polishing is carried out on a Stuers DP10 machine using 3 μm, then 1 μm and then 0.5 μm diamond powder. The last finish is carried out on a Stuers DP cloth type MOL using a Buehler chrome oxide (1-5 μm) polishing compound. Measurements are carried out within a few days of polishing to prevent undue oxidation of minerals.

The main problems lie in the low brightness range involved. Most resins that have been evaluated have reflectivity characteristics similar to silicate or carbonate minerals. As was stated in 1.2., a requirement of the system is to be able to differentiate between all minerals and the mounting medium at the same time (i.e., define particle outline). The resin which has been selected does not allow the use of an automatic discrimination at this stage, so the measurements require the use of an electronic pen to define particle outlines, thus reducing the speed and precision of the overall process.

3.3. Operation of the Instrument

Image analyzers usually have a powerful logic which enables the operator to carry out various types of measurements 14, 15 The present application restricts the use of the whole range of

the instrument to one-dimensional information, where the basic
design has been devised for 2-D analysis. The requirements of
the mathematical analysis as summarized in 2. are essentially
the moments of order 1 and 4 for intercept lengths over grains
containing only the mineral of interest, and over the particles.
In applications involving more than one mineral of interest, the
operations can be repeated or information gathered at the same
time, depending on the optical characteristics of the minerals.
The theory which has been developed also involves a hypothesis
to be made on particle convexity and on mineral grain convexity
inside particles. The second hypothesis is much more restrictive
as will be clear from Fig. 1.

In order to carry out measurements that are more in accordance with the theoretical model, intercepts are modified by assuming that a line drawn on the polished section cuts a particle
according to the following scheme: -

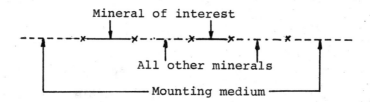

The transformation is carried out at particle level, in order to
artificially unify all intercept lengths pertaining to one phase.

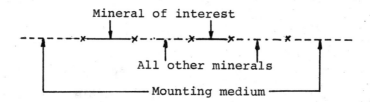

Obviously parameters which can be derived without this assumption (see 1.1.) are measured on the unmodified image.

The operation is carried out line by line, through a special electronic device which cuts the image into a series of test lines which are regularly spaced, as represented on Fig. 5. The sequence of operations is indicated in Fig. 6.

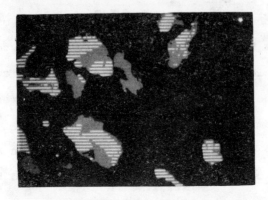

Fig. 5. Visualization on the image analyzer television screen of the test lines drawn on the section. Same sample as in Fig. 4.

3.4. Data Processing

The system is controlled by a computer (Hewlett Packard) which also carries out preliminary processing. An example of a computer print-out is given on Table 1.

- The total number of intercepts (traversée) is the number of times a particle section has effectively been cut by the test lines.

- Assay (teneur) is a percentage by volume.

- Moments of order n are the sum of intercept lengths (expressed in µm) raised to the power n.

- Intercept length size distribution (by number).

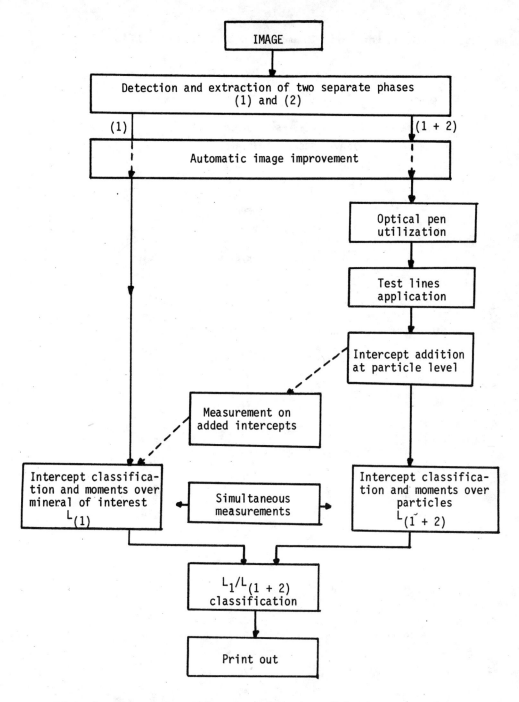

Fig. 6. Principles of measurements on the Image Analyzer for composite particle characterization.

Table 1

Calculator Print Out. Example on a Complex Sulfide Ore

```
*** ECHANTILLON 42 ***

. NOMBRE DE PARTICULES ANALYSEES      372.0

. NOMBRE TOTAL DE TRAVERSEES :       1318.0

. TENEUR   BLENDE                      5.8 %

MOMENTS :
---------
                     BLENDE        GANGUE        GRAIN

ORDRE  1.0          1.051E+03     1.702E+04     1.807E+04
ORDRE  2.0          1.592E+04     2.989E+05     3.211E+05
ORDRE  3.0          3.331E+05     6.266E+06     6.812E+06
ORDRE  4.0          8.776E+06     1.487E+08     1.642E+08


GRANULOMETRIE EN NOMBRE DE TRAVERSEES :
---------------------------------------:
     MICRONS         BLENDE        GANGUE        GRAIN

        0.0          100.0         100.0         100.0
        1.0            8.1          97.1         100.0
        1.9            7.7          95.8         100.0
        2.9            7.4          93.2          98.4
        3.8            6.8          89.9          95.3
        5.8            5.8          81.3          86.5
        7.7            4.4          71.7          76.4
        9.6            3.5          63.2          67.2
       11.5            2.7          53.3          56.8
       14.4            1.9          39.4          41.9
       19.2            0.8          21.3          22.9
       24.0            0.4           9.7          10.5
       28.8            0.2           3.1           3.4
       35.5            0.1           0.8           0.9
       48.0            0.0           0.0           0.0
       59.5            0.0           0.0           0.0
       72.0            0.0           0.0           0.0
       96.0            0.0           0.0           0.0
      120.0            0.0           0.0           0.0


     MIXITE          NOMBRE              MESURE
     ---------       TRAVERSEES      BLENDE        GRAIN

        0.00         100.0           100.0         100.0
        0.05           8.3           100.0           8.3
        0.10           8.2           100.0           8.2
        0.20           7.7            99.0           7.7
        0.30           7.2            96.9           7.2
        0.40           6.6            91.9           6.3
        0.50           6.1            88.0           5.8
        0.60           6.0            87.1           5.7
        0.70           5.6            84.0           5.4
        0.80           4.9            76.6           4.8
        0.90           3.5            57.8           3.5
        0.95           2.9            49.6           3.0
```

- Middling distribution, which is a classification of intercepts
  (by number) as a function of the ratio of intercepts over the
  mineral phase of interest and over the whole particle outline.
  Columns 3 and 4 represent distributions by measure and represent the percentage of each phase (the mineral studied and the
  rest) in each middling class.

4. APPLICATIONS

4.1. Test of the Method

A polished section carefully prepared by Stewart [9] was
studied, in order to test the method. Sample FB3F from Stewart's
paper was used, and all details on sample preparation, mineralogy
and composite grain characteristics, can be found in [9]. It consists of particles of quartz-iron oxides (hematite and magnetite),
- 495 + 417 µm in size and between 3.57 and 3.68 in specific gravity. Results of the method are summarized in Fig. 7, from which
it is possible to clearly visualize the conceptual difficulties
described in 1.1. In this particular case the transformation used
gives a uniform composition of composite, at a volumetric fraction of 0.466 in iron oxides. The difference between the sample
composition as predicted by Stewart and the present result is
difficult to explain, since the volume fraction of iron oxides
is measured in the present case without any assumption, using (1)
for area and linear measurements. All results provide a figure
between 0.45 and 0.50, very different from Stewart's 0.37. Jones,
in a later paper [11] and using the same material seems to imply
that some small experimental errors might have occurred in the
preparation of this particular sample.

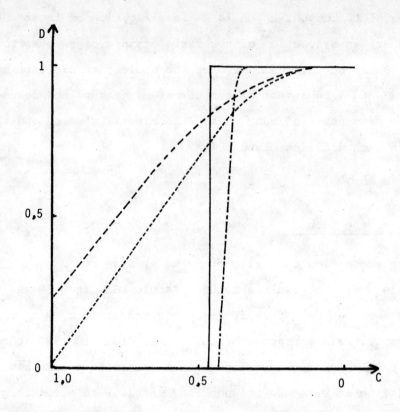

D   Cumulative distribution of iron oxides in particles having an iron oxide composition greater than C

C   Fraction in iron oxides measured (length, area or volume), or calculated (volume)

– – –   Intercept length measurement

– – – – –   Section area measurement

–.–.–.   Volumetric distribution based on specific gravity (after Stewart)

———   Calculated volumetric distribution from intercept length measurement (present method)

Fig. 7. Results of the analysis of Stewart's FB3F sample.

4.2. Grinding of Complex Sulfide Ores

A study of the effect of grinding parameters on the liberation characteristics of the various minerals contained in complex sulfide ores is in progress. Samples from the Bodennec
(Britany, France) ore body as well as from Huelva (Spain) are
being studied in pilot plant ball mill-classifier grinding circuits. The optical (mineral phases discrimination) difficulties
are particularly important here, and in addition to the fineness of the materials - size fractions as low as 10-15 μm are

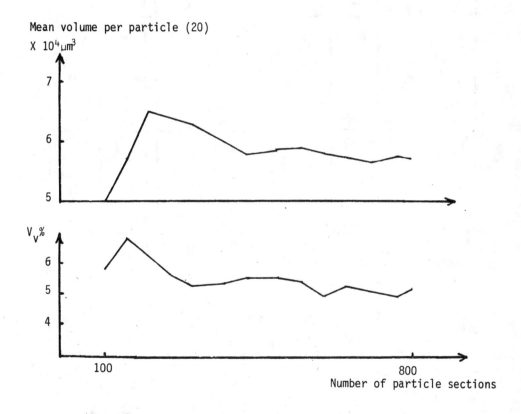

Fig. 8. Variation in sphalerite volumetric composition and
mean particle volume with number of particle sections
examined.

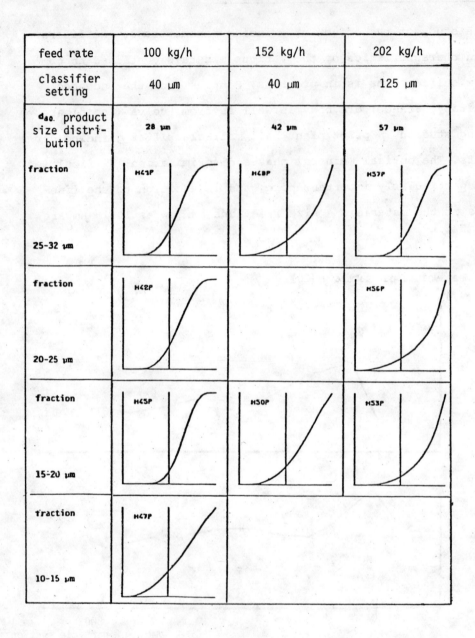

feed rate	100 kg/h	152 kg/h	202 kg/h
classifier setting	40 μm	40 μm	125 μm
d_{80} product size distribution	28 μm	42 μm	57 μm
fraction 25-32 μm	H42P	H48P	H57P
fraction 20-25 μm	H42P		H56P
fraction 15-20 μm	H45P	H50P	H53P
fraction 10-15 μm	H47P		

Fig. 9. Complex sulfide ore from Huelva (Spain). Pyrite volumetric composition of composite particles.

examined - have required a special study of the efficiency of data collection. Figure 8 shows the variation in apparent mineral volumetric composition and volume, according to (20). These variations allow the total number of particles section to be established. Some preliminary results are also given on pyrite liberation characteristics in Fig. 9.

5. CONCLUSIONS

The method which has been developed allows the composition of middling particles in the 1-1000 µm range to be determined. The number of assumptions which are made is limited, and the precision of the results seems adequate for most applications. The conceptual difficulties have been resolved, but, on a theoretical level problems still occur in the application of statistical theory to the measurements to establish confidence limits. Practical problems are also encountered when a mineral is present on fine inclusions. Instrumentally, the speed of data collection is limited at the present time practical difficulties presented by the optical characteristics of resin in particle-mounting, which necessitate the use of a light pen on the image analyzer. Further development on resin optical performance is required.

ACKNOWLEDGEMENTS

The authors wish to acknowledge the financial assistance of the Délégation Générale a la Recherche Scientifique et Technique, contracts 75.7.1552 and 76.7.0377.

REFERENCES

1. Gaudin A. M. Trans. AIME, 73, 253-310 (1926).

2. Gaudin A. M. Principles of Mineral Dressing. Wiley and Sons, New York, 1939.

3. Parsonage P. Trans. IMM, 86, B43-46 (1977).

4. Wiegel R. L. Trans. AIME, 258, 247-256 (1975).

5. Wiegel R. L. Trans. AIME, 260, 147-152 (1976).

6. Barbery G. and Prevosteau J. M. La mineralogie quantitative. Annales des Mines, 1976.

7. Underwood E. E. Quantitative Stereology. Addison-Wesley, Reading, Mass., 1970.

8. Jones M. P. and Barbery G. The size distribution and shapes of minerals in multiphase materials: practical determination and use in mineral process design and control. Proceedings of XIth International Mineral Processing Congress. Universita di Cagliari, Cagliari, 1975, 977-998.

9. Stewart P. S. B. and Jones M. P. Determining the amounts and compositions of composite (middling) particles. Paper 4, meeting 8, of the XIIth International Mineral Processing Congress, Sao Paolo, Brasil, 1977.

10. Jones M. P. et al. The assessment of composite particles from linear measurements. In: Sonderbaüde der Praktischen Metallographie. 8 Quantitative Analysis of Microstructures. 1978, Dr. Riederer-Verlag Gmgh, Stuttgart, pp. 182-191.

11. Jones M. P. and Hornton R. Recent developments in the stereological assessment of composite (middling) particles by linear measurement. 11th Commonwealth Mining and Metallurgical Congress, Hong-Kong, 1978, paper 52.

12. Thorne G. C. et al. Modelling of Industrial Flotation Circuits. In: Flotation - A. M. Gaudin Memorial Volume. (Ed. Fuerstenau M. C.), AIME New-York, 1976, pp. 725-752.

13. Grant G. et al. Multicompositional particle characterization using SEM-microprobe. In: Scanning Electron Microscopy, 1976, part III, pp. 401-408, ITT Research Institute, Chicago 1976.

14. Gateau C. and Prevosteau J. M. Examples of the applications of new possibilities for automatic image analysis. 1. Morphological analysis through simultaneous processing of several geometric characteristics. See [10], pp. 273-279.

15. Gateau C. and Prevosteau J. M. 2. Quantitative textural analysis with multiple image source. See [10], pp. 280-287.

16. Petruk W. CIM Bulletin, 69, 146-153 (1976).

17. Jeanrot P. J. Microscopie et de Spectroscopie Electronique, 3, 157-169 (1978).

18. Barbery G. et al. Etude théorique de la reconstruction volumétrique de populations de particules composites à partir de mesures réalisées sur des sections. See [10], pp. 212-223.

LIST OF SYMBOLS

A_a	area fraction of a feature of interest on a section
A_m	area fraction of a mineral of interest on a section
A_p	area fraction of particles on a section
$\bar{A}$	mean section area of particles
$\bar{B}$	average perimeter of particle sections
$E_{(x)}$	mathematical expectation of variable x
I	"thickness" of a convex particle
$\bar{I}$	mean "thickness" of a population of particles
L_a	perimeter per unit area of a feature on a section
L_1	length fraction of a feature of interest on a test line
L_m	length fraction of a mineral of interest on a test line
L_p	length fraction of particles on a test line
L_t	total length of test lines
L_{ap}	perimeter per unit area of particles section
$L_{m/o}$	length of contact between mineral of interest and mounting medium on a section
$L_{m_1 m_2}$	length of contact between two minerals on a section
$\bar{L}$	mean intercept length
$\bar{L}^4$	mean of the fourth moment of intercept length distribution

N_b number of free particles b

N_m number of composite particles

N_p total number of particles

N_v number of particles per unit volume

N_w number of free particles not containing b

P_l points per unit length crossing a surface of contact on test line

P_p point fraction in a feature of interest on a section

P_{lp} points per unit length crossing the interface particle/medium

$P_{m/o}$ points per unit length crossing the interface between a mineral of interest and mounting medium

$P_{m_1 m_2}$ points per unit length crossing the interface between two minerals

R_1, R_2 mean radii of curvature

S_v surface area per unit volume of a feature of interest

S_{vp} surface area per unit volume of particles

S_m available surface area of mineral per unit volume of particles

$S_{vm_1 m_2}$ surface area of contact between two minerals per unit volume of particles

$\bar{S}$ average surface area of particles

V total volume particles + mounting medium

V_b volume of a b domain

V_p volume of each particle in a monodisperse population

V_v volume fraction of a feature of interest

V_w volume of a w domain

V_{bm} volume of a b domain in a composite particle

V_{vm} volume fraction of mineral m

V_{wm} volume of a domain in a composite particle

$\bar{V}$ average volume of particles

$\bar{V}^2$ mean of the square of volumes of particles

μ'_n moment of order n from the origin

ABSTRACT

In mineral processing, the objective of most processes is the separation of minerals in mixtures in which they are originally associated with composite particles. Feed preparation processes as, for instance, grinding which takes place before beneficiation or separation processes, do not usually break particles at the boundary between mineral phases. They produce composite ("middling") as well as liberated particles. It is therefore necessary, in a particulate system, to determine the proportion of particles which are liberated as well as, ideally, the size distribution of minerals which remain associated in composite particles.

Up to now, there has been a lack of experimental techniques to completely characterize composite particulate systems. Heavy liquid separation which is commonly used to obtain information of this type can only be applied   to simple binary cases where one mineral has a low density.

The technique which is proposed in this paper involves the measurement of parameters on polished sections of particles mounted in a matrix, and the use of mathematical transformations to reconstruct in three dimensions the information obtained from these measurements.

For this purpose, a method of determining the components size distribution in mixed particles and the proportion of liberated particles in a population of composite and liberated particles, has been devised. The model taken for this analysis is as follows.

The particles are cut by a random plane (practically the polished section) and then the sections are scanned by test lines. The method involves the measurement of intercept length distributions on these test lines and a mathematical procedure.

To check the validity of the method, the principles of measurement have first been simulated on a computer.

Practical measurements have been made by means of image analyzers on polished sections prepared from various ores. Applications are presented for the grinding of complex sulfide ores.

RÉSUMÉ

En minéralurgie, l'objectif de la plupart des opérations est
de réaliser la séparation des minéraux à partir de mélanges dans
lesquels ils sont au départ engagés sous forme de grains mixtes.
Les procédés de préparation, le broyage par exemple, qui se
trouvent en amont des processus de séparation ou d'enrichissement,
ne provoquent pas la rupture des particules aux joints de grains.
Ils produisent des particules composites(mixtes) et des particules libérées. Il est donc nécessaire, dans un système de particules, de déterminer la proportion de particules qui sont libe-
rées et la distribution granulométrique des minéraux qui sont
restés associés dans les particules mixtes.

Jusqu' à prèsent, on manquait de techniques expérimentales
pour caractériser complètement les systèmes de particules mixtes.
Les séparations par liquides denses qui sont habituellement
employées pour obtenir ce type d'information ne peuvent etre
appliquées qu' à des cas simples de type binaire où un des minéraux a une densité peu élevée.

La technique qui est proposée dans la communication comporte
la mesure des paramètres sur des sections polies des particules
montées dans une matrice et l'utilisation de transformations
mathématiques pour reconstruire à trois dimensions l'information
obtenue à partir de ces mesures.

Dans ce but, on a mis au point une methode pour déterminer,
dans une population de particules composites et de particules
libérées, la distribution granulométrique des constituants des
particules mixtes et la proportion de particules libérées. Le
modèle qui a été retenu pour cette analyse est le suivant:

les particules sont coupées par un plan au hasard (en pratique, la section polie) et les sections sont balayées par des
lignes de tests. La méthode comporte la mesure des distributions
des longueurs d'intercept sur ces lignes de test et une procedure
mathematique.

Pour vérifier la validité de cette méthode, on a d'abord
simulé les principes de la mesure sur ordinateur.

En pratique, des mesures ont été effectuées au moven d'un
analyseur d'images, sur des sections polies de différents minerais. On présente des applications pour le broyage de minerais
sulfurés complexes.

ZUSAMMENFASSUNG

Das Ziel der Erzaufbereitung ist meistenfalls die Trennung
von Mineralen, die als Gemisch in der Form zusammengesetzter
Mineralteilchen auftreten. Prozesse, die der Anreicherung bzw.
der Trennung vorangehen und der vorbereitung des Aufgabegutg
dienen, z.B. das Brechen der Minerale, führen gewöhnlich nicht
zur Trennung der Mineralteilchen längs der Grenzphasen zwischen
den einzelnen Mineralen. Es entsteht ein kombiniertes Kornge-
füge und es bilden sich auch freigelöste Teilchen. Es ist deshalb zweckmässig, in einem System von Mineralteilchen das
Mengenverhältnis freigelöster Teilchen, und auch - in idealem
Fall - die Korngrössenverteilung dieser Minerale, die weiterhin
in Gestalt zusammengesetzter Teilchen auftreten zu ermitteln.
Bisher gibt es keine experimentellen Verfahren zur qualita-
tiven Bestimmung zusammengesetzter Mineralgefüge. Die Trennung
mit Hilfe schwerer Flüssigkeiten, die gewöhnlich hierzu verwen-
det wird, um Informationen dieser Art zu halten, kann lediglich
im Falle einfacher binärer Gefüge zur Anwendung gelangen, in
denen eines der beiden Minerale eine geringe Dichte aufweist.
Das hier vorgeschlagene Verfahren beruht auf Parametermes-
sungen polierter Schnittflächen der in einer Matrix erfassten
Korn-teilchen, sowie auf mathematischen Transformationen zur
dreidimensionaler Rekonstruierung der mittels dieser Messungen
erhaltenen Informationen.
Deshalb wurde ein Verfahren entwickelt, das in einer Menge
zusammengesetzter und losgelöster Mineralteilchen die Grössen-
verteilung der Komponenten in zusammengesetzten Teilchen, wie
auch das Mengenverhältnis losgelöster Teilchen zu ermitteln
hilft. Das zu einer solchen Analyse verwendete Modell gestaltet
sich folgendermassen:

Die Mineralproben werden in zufälligen Ebenen getrennt
(praktisch genommen in ihrer polierten Schnittebene) worauf die
Schnittflächen eingehend untersucht werden. Dieses Verfahren
schliesst Messungen und mathematische Berechnungen ein.

Um die Anwendbarkeit dieses Verfahrens nachzuprüfen, wurden
dessen Messgrundlagen zuerst in einem Digitalrechner simuliert.
Praktische Messungen wurden mittels eines Bildanalysators an
den polierten Schnittflächen verschiedener Erze durchgeführt.

Der Anwendungsbereich des Brechens komplexer sulfidischer
Erze wird eingehend erörtert.

РЕЗЮМЕ

При обогащении полезных ископаемых целью большинства процессов является выделение минералов из смешанных зерен. Процессы выделения например измельчение, которое находится во главе процессов разделения или не вызывает разрыва частиц на границе зерен Они вызывают образование смеси сростков и раскрытых частиц. Поэтому следует определить долю раскрытых частиц в смеси и грануломенгрический состав минералов, которые остаются в виде сростков.

До настоящего времени не были известны экспериментальные методы, позволяющие дать полную характеристику смешанных систем. Разделение в тяжёлых суспензиях, обычно применяемое для получения такого рода информаций, можно использовать только при простых двойных системах, в которых один из минералов обладает низкой полностью.

Метод, предположенный в настоящем докладе, заключается в измерении параметров на шлифах частиц, вмонтированных в основы, а также в применении математических преобразований с целью представления измерений полученных информаций в изометрии. Для этой цели был разработан метод определения гранулометрического состава компонентов сростков и доли раскрытых частиц в смешанной системе раскрытых частиц и сростков.

Для анализа принята следующая модель: частицы рассекаются по любой плоскости (в практике это шлифуемое сечение), а затем исследуются при помощи контрольных линий. Метод заключается в измерении длины пересечений контрольных линий и в математической процедуре.

Для проверки метода принципы измерения предварительно имитировались на ЭВМ.

Практические измерения были произведены при помощи анализаторов изображения на шлифах, приготовленных из различных минералов. Приведены примеры для измельчения комплексных сульфидных руд.

STEREOLOGICAL ANALYSIS AS A METHOD IN MODERN GRANULOMETRY

J. Bodziony and W. Kraj

Strata Mechanics Research Institute, Polish Academy of Sciences, Kraków, Poland

INTRODUCTION

Traditional granulometry has developed methods for determining the geometrical characteristics of grains in loose materials, i.e., the products of the crushing of rocks. Modern granulometry has recently become more and more interested in grained materials, i.e., solid bodies consisting of grains of one or more components. An example of such materials are rocks composed of crystals of one or more minerals.

Though from geometrical point of view a single crystal may be regarded as a convex body, sets of crystals of one mineral surrounded in the rock by crystals of other minerals may frequently present a great number of spatial configurations. Our notions of the spatial structure of a rock are usually based on the observation of the mosaic visible on flat sections made from rock samples. By analogy we might say that the task of reconstructing spatial structure from the mosaic visible on a flat section is similar to the task of reconstructing a flat mosaic on the basis of the knowledge of the chords along a secant lying on a plane.

An attempt at a qualitative characterization of particular structural elements may have at least two aims: (a) to supplement the qualitative mineralogical description of the rock with a quantitative one and (b) to determine the effect of the geometrical structure of the rock on its mechanical properties, i.e., on the behaviour of the rock during crushing and the liberation of the grains of a particular mineral.

A quantitative characterization of the particular elements of the spatial structure of a grained material and a geometrical characterization of the individual grains and their collectivity, i.e., a loose material, are the subject of the stereological analysis. In the first case the analysis is based on measurements or calculations made on plane sections of the samples. In the other case it is based on the measurements of the elements of projections of individual grains on a plane, i.e., their shadows. Stereological analysis may also be characterized as a method of three-dimensional interpretation of flat images, i.e., cross-sections and shadows.

Numerical Characteristics of Rock Structure

To characterize a single grain as a geometrical body we assume its basic functionals: volume V, surface F and the total mean curvature M. Considering the lack of acquaintance with the last quantity we quote its definition [1, 17]. If the grain constitutes a body confined by a smooth surface F of C_2 class, then

$$M = \frac{1}{2} \int_F \left[\frac{1}{R_1} + \frac{1}{R_2} \right] dF, \qquad (1)$$

where R_1, R_2 are the radii of the main curvatures at a point of
the surface F. If the grain is a convex polyhedron, then

$$M = \frac{1}{2} \sum_i l_i \, \varkappa_i, \qquad (2)$$

where l_i - is the length of the i-th edge, and $\varkappa_i$, $0 < \varkappa_i < \pi$
is the angle formed by the versors of the sides intersecting
along the i-th edge. A grain confined by a smooth surface may
be regarded as the limit of a sequence of polyhedrons circum-
scribed on it. It has been geometrically proved that a sequence
of values of mean total curvatures corresponding to a sequence
of polyhedrons and calculated by means of formula (2) tends to
the value given in formula (1). The total mean curvature of the
sphere $M = 4\pi R$ (R - sphere radius), total mean curvature of a
rectangular parallelepiped $M = \pi (l_1 + l_2 + l_3)$ (l_i - edge
length). Formula (1) is valid for concave bodies. Formula (2)
can be generalized for concave polyhedrons. Note that the quantities [V, F, M] have the dimensions $[1^3, 1^2, 1^1]$, respectively.

Let us consider a piece of rock in which we can distinguish
a single mineral. The remaining minerals are regarded as matrix.
The grains G_i (i = 1,...,N) of this mineral are sets of crystals
confined by the contact surface of the matrix. Let us denote by
V_R the volume of the piece of rock, and by N - the number of
grains located in it. To each grain G_i we assign three numbers
$[V_i, F_i, M_i]$. As the quantities characterizing the grains of the
distinguished mineral we assume the set of indices $[\bar{V}, \bar{F}, \bar{M}, \bar{N}]$,

whose names and definitions are given in Table 1, column 1 and 2, respectively as quantities characterizing the grains of the distinguished mineral. As follows from the definitions these are the mean value per volume unit of the rock. Let us assume that the piece of rock has been cut through by r planes located uniformly in space. On the obtained plane sections with areas f_j (j = 1,...,r) the grains are visible as plane figures. Let us denote the area and the perimeter of the i-th grain on the j-th section by f_{ij} and l_{ij} respectively. The total number of grains visible on the j-th section will be denoted by m_j. On summing the above quantities over all the sections we obtain $\sum f_{ij}$, $\sum l_{ij}$, $\sum m$, $\sum f_j$. These sum totals enable as to calculate the values of the estimators $\bar{V}_1$, $\bar{F}_1$, $\bar{M}_1$ of the unknown accurate values $\bar{V}$, $\bar{F}$, $\bar{M}$ according to the formulae in column 3, Table 1.

The measurements and calculations of the elements of the mosaic visible on the plane sections may be also carried out along the lines with the length s_j, situated at random or at regular intervals on those sections. Let us denote the length of the chord formed by the j-th line with the i-th grain by s_{ij} and the number of chords on the j-th line by n_j. After summing these values on all lines we obtain $\sum s_{ij}$, $\sum n_j$, $\sum s_j$, which on the basis of formulae given in column 4, Table 1, provide the values of the estimators $\bar{V}_2$, $\bar{F}_2$ of the unknown quantities $\bar{V}$, $\bar{F}$.

Points may be projected at random or situated in a systematic way on the plane sections of a rock sample. Let us denote the total number of projected points by z_R, and the number of points which have fallen on the grains by z_g. In column 1, Table 1, the estimator $\bar{V}_3$ of the specific volume $\bar{V}$ has been given.

TABLE 1

List of Estimators of Specific Volume, Specific Surface
and Specific Total Mean Curvature

| Magnitude | Definition | Estimators obtained from the | | |
| | | Plane | Linear Analysis | Point |
1	2	3	4	5
Specific volume $\bar{V}$	$\dfrac{\sum V_i}{V_R}\left[\dfrac{1^3}{1^3}\right]$	$\bar{V}_1 = \dfrac{\sum f_{ij}}{\sum f_j}\left[\dfrac{1^2}{1^2}\right]$	$\bar{V}_2 = \dfrac{\sum s_{ij}}{s_j}\left[\dfrac{1^1}{1^1}\right]$	$\bar{V}_3 = \dfrac{z_G}{z_R}\left[\dfrac{1^0}{1^0}\right]$
Specific surface $\bar{F}$	$\dfrac{\sum F_i}{V_R}\left[\dfrac{1^2}{1^3}\right]$	$\bar{F}_1 = \dfrac{4}{\pi}\dfrac{\sum l_{ij}}{\sum f_j}\left[\dfrac{1^1}{1^2}\right]$	$\bar{F}_2 = 4\dfrac{\sum n_j}{\sum s_j}\left[\dfrac{1^0}{1^1}\right]$	
Specific total mean curvature $\bar{M}$	$\dfrac{\sum M_i}{V_R}\left[\dfrac{1^1}{1^3}\right]$	$\bar{M}_1 = 2\pi\dfrac{\sum m_j}{\sum f_j}\left[\dfrac{1^0}{1^2}\right]$		
Specific number $\bar{N}$	$\dfrac{N}{V_R}\left[\dfrac{1^0}{1^3}\right]$			

Table 1 contains a list of the estimators obtained from plane, linear and point analyses carried out on plane sections. The estimators should be regarded as random variables, the values of which tend asymptotically to the unknown $[\bar{V}, \bar{F}, \bar{M}]$ with increasing representativeness of the measured population.

The problems connected with: (a) methods of deriving the estimators of indices referring to a unit volume of rock, (b) the validity range of the formulae, (c) definite methods of carrying out measurements and calculations on the cross-sections by means of various instruments, (d) discussion of errors - have been widely discussed in literature. We shall mention here some original studies concerning the methods of deriving the estimators. Thus, estimator $\bar{V}_1$ has been supplied by Delesse [14] and estimator $\bar{V}_2$ by Rosiwal [24]. Estimators $\bar{F}_1$ and $\bar{F}_2$ have been given by Saltykow [25]. Smith and Guttman [26] and by Hennig [18] Finally, estimator $\bar{M}_1$ has been given in study [2] as well as by Cahn [11], De Hoff [13] and Giger [16]. The formulae for the estimators - except $\bar{M}_1$ - are valid for arbitrary grain shapes. The extension of the validity of the estimator $\bar{M}_1$ on concave grains makes it necessary to provide an interpretation of the notion of $\bar{M}$ for this class of bodies.

Up to now no method for determining the estimator for $\bar{N}$ with equally general assumption has been given. Saltykow [25] has provided a method for determining the specific number of spheres. De Hoff [12] has derived a set of formulae for determining the specific number of grains geometrically similar to each other, when simultaneously postulating the nature of their size distribution. Study [19] has given the so-called method of coupled sections for determining the specific number of convex grains while simultaneously postulating the type of their random distribution in the rock, and this has been developed in [8] and [5].

A method for determining $\bar{N}$ would enable a wider application of the characteristics usually referred to a single grain. We are concerned here with the quantities:

$$\bar{\bar{V}} = \frac{\sum V_i}{N} = \frac{\bar{V}}{\bar{N}} \; ; \quad \bar{\bar{F}} = \frac{\sum F_i}{N} = \frac{\bar{F}}{\bar{N}} \; ; \quad \bar{\bar{M}} = \frac{\sum M_i}{N} = \frac{\bar{M}}{\bar{N}} \tag{3}$$

The set $[\bar{\bar{V}}, \bar{\bar{F}}, \bar{\bar{M}}]$ characterizes the average size of a grain of a particular mineral in the rock and corresponds to the set $[V, F, M]$, which characterizes the size of a single grain.

Stereological Analysis of Copper Ore

A mining deposit is not a homogeneous formation but is characterized by a variety of structural and physical properties. The values $\bar{V}, \bar{F}, \bar{M}, \bar{N}$ defined in the preceding chapter are determined from measurements on thin sections or polished sections of samples taken from the deposit. The natural variability of the deposit is the reason for the fluctuation of the measured quantities which is caused by the random choice of the place from which the sample has been taken. The values $\bar{V}, \bar{F}, \bar{M}, \bar{N}$ obtained from measurements are random variables. In stereological analysis we usually give some numerical characteristics of these random variables (mean value, variance). A full probabilistic characteristics of a random variable is given by the distribution function or the distribution density. A knowledge

606

of the distribution function or density makes it possible to determine all the moments, as well as the probability of the assumption by the random variable of a value from an arbitrary given interval.

To illustrate the application of the stereological analysis we shall present here the results of measurements of the specific volume $\bar{V}$, of the specific surface $\bar{F}$ and of the specific total mean curvature $\bar{M}$ of a set of cupriferous minerals found in the copper ore from the mine "Rudna".

Nine samples were taken from a piece of ore weighing ca. 30 kg. From each sample there were prepared three rectangular, polished sections 24 x 36 mm in size which were cut out in three directions perpendicular to each other. The grains of cupriferous minerals were visible on the sections as bright, metallic figures. Because of the sharp contrast between those minerals and the sandstone matrix it was possible to use an automatic device - a Quantimet 720 for the measurements. On each of the 27 microsections measurements were made on 12 separate fields of 2.2 x 1.5 mm in size at regular intervals on the sections. Due to the fact that the distance between the measured fields was considerably greater than the size of the figures, the measurements of the particular fields could be regarded as randomly independent. In each measured field the specific volume, specific surface and the specific total mean curvature were determined. Use was made of the estimators $\bar{V}_1$, $\bar{F}_1$ and $\bar{F}_2$ (the specific surface was determined by two methods) and of $\bar{M}_1$, which have been given in Table 1.

It should be noted here that the estimator $\bar{M}_1$ for the total mean curvature is valid only for convex bodies. The grains of cupriferous minerals in the examined ore are not all convex bodies, nevertheless this estimator was used in the present study for determining the specific total mean curvature.

Each set of results from the 324 measurements which was the realization of the random variables $\bar{V}_1$, $\bar{F}_1$, $\bar{F}_2$ and $\bar{M}_1$ was subjected to statistical elaboration. The frequency distributions and the empirical distribution functions of those variables were determined. The empirical distributions of all four variables were approximated with the continuous probability distribution "gamma" (Γ) [23]. The density of this distribution is defined by the formula:

$$g(x) = \begin{cases} 0 & \text{for } x \leqslant 0 \\ \dfrac{b^a}{\Gamma(a)}\, x^{a-1}\, e^{-bx} & \text{for } x > 0 \end{cases}$$

and the distribution function by the formula:

$$G(x) = \begin{cases} 0 & \text{for } x \leqslant 0 \\ \dfrac{b^a}{\Gamma(a)} \displaystyle\int_0^x s^{a-1}\, e^{-bs}\, ds & \text{for } x > 0 \end{cases}$$

The constants a and b are parameters of the distribution Γ. For these parameters the expected value m and the variance σ^2 are expressed by the formula:

$$m = \frac{a}{b} \qquad \sigma^2 = \frac{a}{b^2} \tag{4}$$

When approximating the empirical distributions using the distribution Γ, the first two moments of the theoretical distribution

608

(m and σ^2) were required to be equal to those of the empirical distribution. This enabled a and b to be determined.

In Figs. 1, 2, 3, 4 the distributions $\bar{V}_1$, $\bar{F}_1$, $\bar{F}_2$ and $\bar{M}_1$ obtained from measurements and approximated by the distribution have been shown.

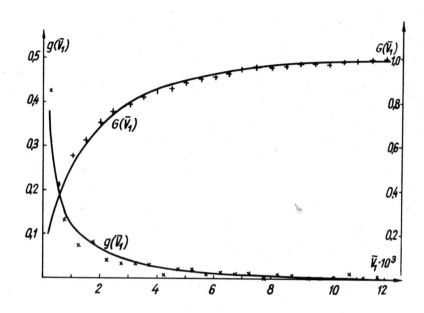

Fig. 1. Distribution of the specific volume $\bar{V}_1$. x - empirical values of probability, + - values of the empirical distribution function.

The assumption that the variables $\bar{V}_1$, $\bar{F}_1$, $\bar{F}_2$ and $\bar{M}_1$ have the probability distribution Γ was verified by means of two tests of goodness of fit: the χ^2 test and the Kolmogorov's test. On the significance level $\alpha = 0.05$ none of the tests gave reason for rejecting this assumption. The detailed results can be found in [10].

609

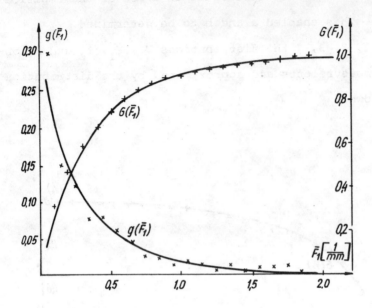

Fig. 2. Distribution of the specific surface F_1. x - empirical values of probability, + - values of the empirical distribution function.

As we have already mentioned the measurement results in the particular fields can be regarded as randomly independent. Thus the arithmetic means from all realizations are assumed to be the estimators of the average random variables $\bar{V}_1$, $\bar{F}_1$, $\bar{F}_2$, $\bar{M}_1$ and are denoted by $\bar{V}_{1s}$, $\bar{F}_{1s}$, $\bar{F}_{2s}$, $\bar{M}_{1s}$, respectively. The question arises as to the accuracy with which the arithmetic means approach the real average values. The repetition of the measurements on another sample taken from the same ore and the determination of the arithmetic means will in general give results different from those obtained by us. With this in mind we may regard the arithmetic means $\bar{V}_{1s}$, $\bar{F}_{1s}$, $\bar{F}_{2s}$, $\bar{M}_{1s}$ as random variables and determine their distribution of probability.

610

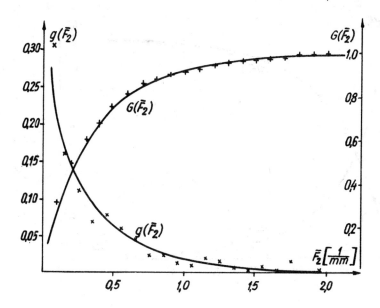

Fig. 3. Distribution of the specific surface $\bar{F}_2$. x - empirical values of probability, + - values of empi-
rical distribution function.

It is easy to prove that the arithmetic mean of n independent
random variables, each of which has the same probability distribution "gamma", also has the distribution "gamma". The parameter
a_1 and b_1 of the arithmetic mean distribution are expressed by
means of the parameters a and b of the distribution of a particular variable with the following formulae:

$$a_1 = na, \qquad b_1 = nb$$

According to (4), for the first two moments m_1 and σ_1^2 of the
arithmetic mean distribution we have:

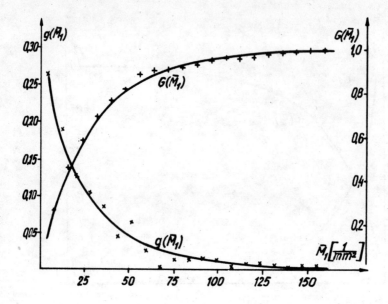

Fig. 4. Distribution of the mean specific curvature $\overline{M}_1$.
x - empirical values of probability, + - values of
the empirical distribution function.

$$m_1 = \frac{a_1}{b_1} = \frac{na}{nb} = \frac{a}{b} = m,$$

$$\sigma_1^2 = \frac{a_1}{b_1^2} = \frac{na}{n^2 b^2} = \frac{a}{nb} = \frac{\sigma^2}{n}$$

i.e., the arithmetic mean has the same mean value as a single variable, and its variance is n times smaller.

In Fig. 5 the distribution function and the probability density of the arithmetic means $\overline{V}_{1s}$ has been shown for purposes of illustration. The obtained distribution enables one to determine the probability that the arithmetic means fall within an arbitrarily chosen interval.

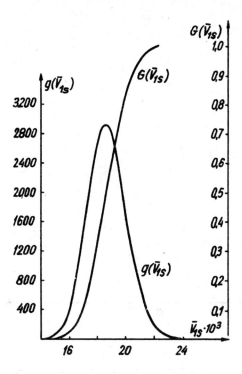

Fig. 5. Distribution of the arithmetic mean of the specific
   volume $\bar{V}_{1s}$.

It should be noted that the three numerical characteristics
$\bar{V}$, $\bar{F}$, $\bar{M}$ of the geometrical structure of a rock are not, in general, randomly independent quantities. For a structure composed
of similar bodies there exists a close functional relation between these quantities. The conditions under which a deposit is
formed favour the formation of crystals and complexes of similar shape. Hence the three quantities mentioned are usually statistically correlated.

In Fig. 6 the correlation of the variables $\bar{V}_1$, $\bar{F}_1$ obtained
from measurements made on sections of copper ore has been shown
in double logarithmic system.

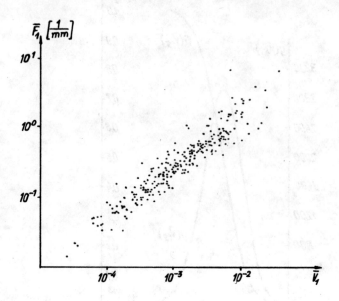

Fig. 6. Correlation between the variables $\bar{F}_1$ and $\bar{V}_1$.

Determination of the Surface and the Total Mean Curvature of
a Single Grain Using the Projection Method

The surface area F and the total curvature M of convex grains
can be determined from the measurements of perpendicular projections of the grains. A theoretical basis for this procedure
is provided by Cauchy's projection formulae [17]:

$$F = \frac{1}{\pi} \int \sigma (n) \; dn \qquad (5)$$

$$M = \frac{1}{2} \int b (n) \; dn \qquad (6)$$

$\sigma(n)$ here denotes the area of a perpendicular projection of a
grain on a plane normal to the direction n and b(n) the length

of a perpendicular projection of a grain on a straight line with the direction n, i.e., Feret's diameter of this grain in the direction n. The integration domain in both integrals is the full solid angle equal to 4 π stereoradians.

In practical application the determination of the surface area or the total mean curvature is based on the replacement of the integrals by approximate sums and on the measurement of projections in a few directions located randomly or uniformly in space.

The accuracy of the result obtained in this way depends on the number of projection directions and on the grain shape. Thus, for a sphere a single measurement suffices to accurately determine the value of the surface or of the total mean curvature. The flatter or longer the grain, the greater the dispersion of a single measurement of a projection in a randomly chosen direction.

We may consider theoretically the most disadvantageous extreme case where the grain degenerates with measurement of the shadow area into a plane fragment, and with the measurement of the total mean curvature into a segment. In both these cases the measured values of a single projection have a uniform probability distribution [6], [7], [4].

With a multiple projection we may distinguish the cases where the projection directions are randomly independent and where they are coupled. In the first case the arithmetic mean from the perpendicular measurements is assumed to be the magnitude of the area or the total mean curvature

$$F = \frac{4}{k} \sum_{i}^{k} \sigma(n_i) \qquad (7)$$

$$M = \frac{2\pi}{k} \sum_{1}^{k} b(n_i) \qquad (8)$$

where k is the number of measurements, $\sigma(n_i)$ - the area of the projection in the direction n_i, $b(n_i)$ - the length of the projection on a straight line with direction n_i. When projecting in independent directions the obtained values have a variance which is inversely proportional to the number of projection directions.

The measurements in coupled directions are more advantageous. With the right choice of directions, when they are uniformly located in space, the magnitude of the area or of the total mean curvature (also measured according to formulae (7), (8)), has a considerably smaller variance than when projecting in an equal number of independent directions.

Figure 7 shows the distribution functions of the magnitude of an area of a normal projection of a plane fragment when projecting in one direction (curve 1) and when projecting in k = 3, 4, 6 coupled directions, which form normals to a cube, octa- and dodecahedrons (curves 2, 3, 4). The independent variable s is here the ratio of the projection area σ to the area of the projected fragment of a plane σ_o, $(s = \frac{\sigma}{\sigma_o})$.

As has been pointed out in [9], these results can be used to obtain the distribution of the magnitude of an area, determined with a single projection, for a cube, octa- and dodecahedron.

616

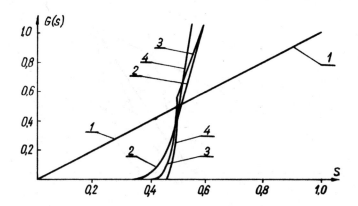

Fig. 7. The distribution function of the projection area of
a plane fragment when projecting in one direction
and in 3, 4 and 6 coupled directions.

Between the variable s and the surface area F of these regular
polyhedrons the relation

$$F = 4 \, k \, \sigma_o \, s$$

exists where σ_o is the area of a single side and k = 3, 4, 6,
respectively.

Figure 8 shows the distribution of lengths of a perpendicular projection of a segment with the length 2 (curve 1) and
that of a tetrahedron, cube, octa- and dodecahedron, in a randomly chosen direction (curves 2, 3, 4, 5). These polyhedrons
are inscribed in a sphere with radius 1.

617

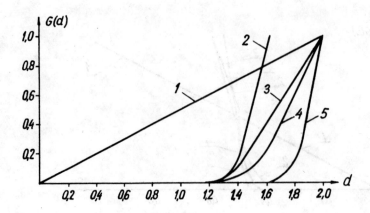

Fig. 8. The distribution function of the projection length
of a segment, a tetrahedron, a cube, an octohedron
and dodecahedron with a single projection on a
straight line.

Equivalence of Feret's Diameter and the Total Mean Curvature of a Convex Grain

Feret [15] has defined grain size as the mean distance of
tangents of a constant direction, drawn to the opposite sides
of the grain contour (with a sufficient number of grains of approximately the same size). Thus Feret has not provided a direct
definition for the size of a single grain, but has defined it
as the mean value of a collection of grains which are "approximately the same size". Grain size according to Feret, traditio-
nally called Feret's diameter, has been widely discussed in
literature. This notion is generally understood as the mean distance of the tangents drawn on a plane in a fixed direction to

618

the c itours of an orthogonal projection of the grains onto this plane on which, and this is important, these grains are lying. Considering the fact that the grains on the plane usually lie in their most stable positions, the average is taken only within a narrow range of the likely orientations of the grains with respect to this plane. Strictly speaking, while correctly formulating the definition of grain size, Feret failed to point out the method for realizing all possible spatial orientations of the grains in relation to the chosen direction.

Feret's diameter should be understood as the mean value of the distance between the planes supporting the grain taken from all possible orientations of the grain within the full solid angle equal to 4π stereoradians. Then we have

$$D_{Fe} = \frac{1}{4\pi} \int b(n)\,dn \tag{9}$$

where $b(n)$ is the width of the grain in the direction n, i.e., the length of an orthogonal projection of the grain on a straight line with direction n. It will be noted that the relation

$$D_{Fe} = \frac{1}{2\pi} M \tag{10}$$

which expresses the proportionality of the mean total curvature of the grain and Feret's diameter follows directly from the above formula and from formula (6). In terms of formula (10) we may speak of the equivalence of these two notions for every convex grain.

It is possible to prove [3] that Feret's mean diameter $\bar{\bar{D}}_{Fe}$ and $\bar{M}$ of the same collection of grains fulfil the relation

$$\bar{\bar{D}}_{Fe} = \frac{1}{2\pi} \frac{\bar{M}}{\bar{N}} = \frac{1}{2\pi} \bar{\bar{M}}.$$ (11)

It follows from this formula that the determination of $\bar{\bar{D}}_{Fe}$ may be based on the analysis of plane sections and may become independent of the analysis of projections on a plane.

A Natural Characteristics of the Size and Shape of a Grain

The quantities which in stereological analysis characterize the size of a single grain are the values of its functionals

$$[V, F, M] \qquad \text{or} \qquad [V, F \ D_{Fe}]$$ (12)

It should be stressed, however, that the assignment of a set of numbers (12) to a grain is not in one-to-one correspondence. To each grain we can assign precisely three numbers (12), whereas one or more grains of different shape may correspond to the definite three numbers, and it may also happen that no single convex grain corresponds to the selected three numbers. The unique characterization of a solid body through a set of numbers requires the determination of an at least countable set of numbers. An attempt of this kind was undertaken by Meloy [22].

Consequently, the use of its functionals is a natural approach to the numerical characterization of the shape of a grain [12]. This tendency is illustrated by the development of some concepts in the literature, e.g., by McAdams [20], [21]. For this purpose we shall make use of Blaschke's coefficient and diagram [17] [4].

620

Blaschke has derived a pair of coefficients

$$x = \frac{CF}{M^2} \; ; \qquad y = \frac{3C^2v}{M^3} \qquad\qquad (13)$$

where $C_\checkmark = 4\pi$ is Gauss's total curvature of a solid body. The coefficients (x, y) satisfy the inequalities $0 \leqslant x \leqslant 1$, $0 \leqslant y \leqslant x^2$. To a collection of geometrically similar grains there corresponds one pair of numbers (x, y).

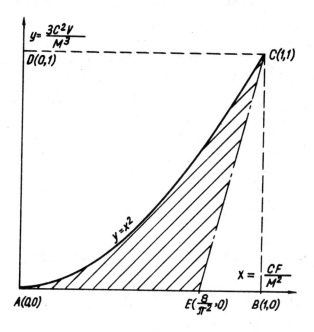

Fig. 9. Blaschke's diagram.

Figure 9 shows Blaschke's diagram and illustrates the variation area (x, y) for convex grains. We shall give an interpretation of the boundary of this area. A segment which is a degenerated convex body corresponds to the point A $(0, 0)$. To the curve AC with the equation $y = x^2$ there correspond extreme solid bodies which, with given F, M, have the greatest possible volume V. A sphere corresponds to the point C (1, 1). To the curve CE (with a hitherto unknown equation) there correspond extreme bodies which, with given F, M, have the smallest possible volume V. Plane convex figures (V = 0) which are degenerated bodies correspond to the segment AE. A circle corresponds to the point E $\left(\dfrac{8}{\pi^2}, 0\right)$.

A set of Blaschke's coefficients may be proposed as a set of coefficients of convex grain shape. However, in this case the correspondence is not one-to-one either.

The determination of the magnitude and shape of a grain on the basis of its main functionals is characterized by a logical bond with the quantities determined in stereological analysis of sections and projections.

REFERENCES

1. Blaschke W. Vorlesungen über Integralgeometrie. VEB Deutscher Verlag der Wissenschaften, Berlin, 1955.

2. Bodziony J. Bull. Acad. Polon. Sci. Ser. sci. techn., XIII, 469-475 (1965).

3. Bodziony J. Ibidem, XIII, 519-522 (1965).

4. Bodziony J. Unpublished paper.

5. Bodziony J., Górski J. and Kraj W. Bull. Acad. Polon. Sci. Ser. sci. techn., XIX, 153-160 (1971).

6. Bodziony J., Górski J. and Kraj W. Ibidem, XXIV, 175-183 (1976).

7. Bodziony J., Górski J. and Kraj W. Application of conjugate shadows to the determination of the surface area of convex bodies. Colloquium of the Appl. of Stereology, Wysoke Tatry, 1976, 1-17.

8. Bodziony J. and Kraj W. Bull. Acad. Polon. Sci., Ser. sci. techn., XVIII, 345-348 (1970).

9. Bodziony J. and Kraj W. Cauchy's projection formula as a basis for the method of determining surface area of convex bodies. Third Particle Size Analysis Conference. University of Salford, 1977, 70-81.

10. Bodziony J., Kraj W., Pindel Z., Ratajczak T. and Wilczyński J. Analiza stereologiczna minerałów miedzionośnych białego spągowca. Arch. Górn. (in press).

11. Cahn J. W. Trans. Met. Soc. AIME, 239, 610-616 (1967).

12. De Hoff R. T. Trans. Met. Soc. AIME, 233, 25-29 (1965).

13. De Hoff R. T. Trans. Met. Soc. AIME, 239, 617-621 (1967).

14. Dellesse A. Ann. mines, 13, 544-545 (1948).

15. Feret L. R. La grosseur des grains des matieres pulverulentes. Assoc. Internat. pour l'Essai des Mat. Zurich, 1931, 2, D, 428-436.

16. Giger H. Ermittlung der mittleren Masszahlen von Partikeln eines Körpersystems durch Messungen auf dem Rand eines Schmittbereiches. ZAMP, 1967, 18, 883-888.

17. Hadwiger H. Altes und Neues über konvexe Körper. Birkhäuser Verlag, Basel und Stuttgart, 1955.

18. Hennig A. Körper. Mikrosk., 11, 1-20 (1956).

19. Kraj W. Bull. Acad. Polon. Sci., Ser. sci. techn., XV, 419-425 (1967).

20. McAdams H. T. Trans. ASME, 85 B, 4, 388-394 (1963).

21. McAdams H. T. Powder Technology, 2, 5, 260-268 (1969).

22. Meloy T. P. Powder Technology, 16, 233-253 (1977).

23. Nieć M., Niedzielski B. and Blajda R. Zmienność i prawidłowość mineralizacji złoża rud cynku kopalni Bolesław. Mat. IV Kraj. Zjazdu Górn. Rud, 1976, Bolesław.

24. Rosiwal A. Geologischen Reichsanstalt, 5-6, 143-175 (1898).

25. Saltykov S. A. Stereometričeskaja metalografija. Moskva, 1970.

26. Smith C. S., Guttman L. Trans. AIME, 197, 81-86 (1953).

ABSTRACT

The paper points out the usefulness of stereological analysis, both in determining the geometrical characteristics of the structure of a rock (regarded as a ground material formed from crystals of one or more minerals) subjected to crushing, and also in determining the geometrical characteristics of grains as a product of crushing. Sets of characteristics referring on the average to a unit volume of a rock are given, as well as the results of their determination, taking as an example a set of cupriferous minerals of copper ore. The mathematical basis for determining the total mean curvature and the surface area of single grains based on the measurements made on projections have been presented. The equivalence of the total mean curvature of a grain and its Feret's diameter has been noted. The paper proposes to characterize the size and the shape of grains on the basis of the functionals of convex bodies as the principal quantities occurring in stereological analysis.

RESUME

Le travail met en evidence l'utilité d'analyses stéréologiques, à la fois en déterminant les caractéristiques géométriques de la structure d'une roche (regardée comme une matière granulée formée de cristaux d'un minéral ou de plusieurs) soumise au concassage et aussi en déterminant les caractéristiques géométriques des grains comme un produit du concassage. On a donné des séries des caractéristiques se référant à la moyenne d'une unité de volume d'une roche ainsi que les résultats de leur détermination, prenant comme exemple une série de minéraux cuprifères de minerai de cuivre. On y a présenté les bases mathématiques pour la détermination de la courbure totale moyenne et l'aire de la surface de simples grains en se basant sur les mesures effectuées sur les projections. L'équivalence de la courbure totale moyenne d'un grain et de son diamètre de Feret a été notée. Le rapport propose de caractériser la taille et la forme des grains, sur la base des fonctionnels de corps convexes, comme des quantités principales existant en analyse stéréologique.

ZUSAMMENFASSUNG

In der vorliegenden Arbeit wird auf die Zweckmässigkeit
stereologischer Analysen, sowohl bei der Bestimmung der geometrischen Struktur-Kennzeichen von Gestein (welches als körni-
ges Material angesehen wird, das aus Kristallen eines bzw.
mehrerer Minerale besteht und zerkleinert werden soll), wie
auch bei der Ermittlung der geometrischen Merkmale der Körner
als Produkt des Zerkleinerungsprozesses hingewiesen. Es werden
Reihen von Kennzeichen angeführt, die sich auf die durchschnit-
tliche Volumeneinheit des Gesteins beziehen, sowie Ergebnisse
von Untersuchungen an einer Reihe kupferhaltiger Minerale des
Kupfererzes gegeben. Es wird die mathematische Grundlage der
Bestimmung der gesamten mittleren Krümmung und der Oberfläche
der einzelnen Körner auf der Basis von Messungen, die an
Projektionen durchgeführt worden sind, dargestellt. Es wird
auf die Äquivalenz der gesamten mittleren Krümmung der Körnchen und deren Querschnitte hingewiesen. Abschliessend wird
vorgeschlagen, die Grösse und Gestalt der Körner anhand der
funktionalen konvexen Körper als grundlegende Grössen zu kennzeichen, die in einer solchen stereologischen Analyse auftreten.

626

РЕЗЮМЕ

Доказана пригодность стереологического анализа при определении геометрических параметров структуры породы (считаемой зернистым материалом, образованным из кристаллов одного или нескольких минералов), подверженной раздроблению, а также при определении геометрических параметров зерен, образованных в результате раздробления. Приведены характеристики, относящиеся к среднеудельному объему породы, а также результаты их определений на примере состава меденосных минералов медной руды.

Представлены математические основы определения полной средней кривизны и поверхности отдельных зерен на основе измерений, сделанных на проекциях. Подчеркнута эквивалентность полной средней кривизны зерна и его диаметра Ферета.

В докладе предлагается определение размеров и формы зерен на основе функционалов выпуклых тел как основных величин в стереологическом анализе.

EFFECT OF MECHANICAL STRESS ON STRUCTURE ALTERATIONS OF MINERALS

S. I. Denev and R. V. Stoitsova

Department of Mineral Processing, Higher Institute of Mining and Geology, Sofia, Bulgaria

INTRODUCTION

It is common knowledge that energy is still a most important consideration in communition processes. This may be attributed to the imperfection of modern comminution methods. As some authors emphasize [9, 10] , the reason for the increased consumption of energy may also be attributed to the current irrational organization of ore communition directed toward the liberation of minerals. As has been mentioned by V. I. Revnivtsev [10] and other authors [3, 6, 7, 8] the creation of new surface areas is less important than the degree of liberation of valuable minerals. Further, in order to make the characteristic of the grinding product more complete, the following factors must be taken into account: mineral grain and locked particle size, their character and that of the surface of the free grains and locked particles, and finally, the particle size distribution of the grinding product.

The "selectivity of mineral liberation" is a well known term. Every author [6, 7, 9] suggests a different definition for this. It seems to us that from the point of view of the rational organization of the grinding process for mineral liberation, the notion "selectivity of grinding" or "selectivity of mineral liberation" calls for refinement. It is also obvious that the selectivity of mineral liberation on grinding is associated with the energy consumed during grinding.

Different grinding methods give different liberation results [4, 6, 7, 8]. These differences are related to changes which take place in the structure of the ores and each specific mineral while undergoing various processing methods. Detailed studies of changes in mineral structure resulting from different size-reduction processes have assumed new importance. This primarily concerns studies of the character of the bond between various minerals and the changes occurring in those interactions when the minerals are subjected to various external forces. The purpose of this paper is to investigate the above-mentioned problems.

Different ores and minerals with both coarse and fine inclusions consisting of two or more minerals were investigated. The influence of various methods on mineral liberation was studied. The following methods were considered: common grinding in a ball mill, a rod mill and in a vibrating mill and impact grinding in a Snyder's device. The role of temperature and some surface-active agents was also investigated. The results from granulometric and mineralogical analyses were evaluated.

In our investigations we attempted to explain some basic grinding phenomena, such as the character of changes in minerals, particularly at the boundaries of grains in the interlocked particles subjected to different actions, the energy of mechanical actions during cracking and the selectivity of mineral liberation.

1. The Character of Mineral Changes

As was mentioned previously, various real ores were tested. Among the minerals they contained were quartz, galena, sphalerite, pyrite, chalcopyrite, magnetite, calcite and other minerals of minor importance. The above ores were tested in the following types of processes, independently or in combination: impact, compression, extension (extrusion), abrasion, sudden temperature and pressure changes and under the influence of surface-active agents.

1.1. Experimental Methods and Evaluation of Structural Defects

The great variety of minerals and mineral grain boundaries in the investigated ores made it possible to carry out more detailed studies of the microstructural defects in certain minerals and along grain boundaries as well as in the products of ore grinding. To evaluate certain structural features of the ores and the processing products with different physical properties, a methodology with a wide choice of optical and electron microscopy methods was worked out. Subsequent observation of the same samples of polished fractions containing various minerals before and after being subjected to different loading conditions made it possible to observe crack propagation in the grains or along the boundaries between them.

The microscopic studies were carried out by means of a multi-purpose "Zeis-N-2" research microscope and "EM 30/E Phillips" and "JEM-100C Jeol" electron microscopes.

Experimental methods consisted of: (a) the application of optical microscopy in transmitted and reflected light; (b) the observation of fracturing along destruction planes in reflected light; (c) the method of "etching pits" [1, 2]; (d) the chemical decoration method [5]; (e) electron-microscopic methods.

1.2. Results

Photography was widely used in all the tests. The valuable information thus obtained makes possible a proper analysis of the nature of changes taking place in the mineral structure as a result of applied load. To make the comparison more convenient, we decided to consider the changes in individual minerals as well as in mixed grains.

Galena. This is a mineral with a wide range of structural features. In the ores investigated it was found in the form of both coarse and fine grain disseminations in quartz, carbonates or with other sulphides. The boundaries of the intergrowths of these disseminations with other minerals were found to be smooth or uneven with mutual intergrowths. Grain locking can be so close that it is difficult to obtain full liberation of minerals under any loading conditions. Such mixed grains of galena with quartz and sphalerite pass into the grinding products as a result of fracturing that takes place in galena or in quartz (see Fig. 1).

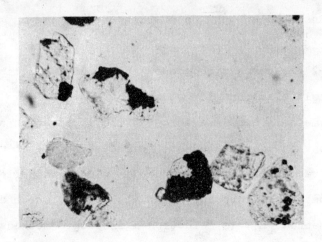

Fig. 1. Locked particles of galena with quartz and sphalerite at the uneven boundaries between the grains.
250 x magnification.

Cleavage along the smooth boundaries of galena with other
minerals was successful during thermal treatment of the ore
and in the case of sudden changes of pressure (i.e., in a
Snyder process). In this case a concentration of the dislocation centres is observed along the boundaries and in the bulk
of the galena itself (see Fig. 2).

Coarse mixed grains of galena subjected to sudden changes
of pressure were characterized by higher activity and heterogeneity of the liberated surfaces. This was established by a
comparison of their crystallization ability in solutions of
hydrochloric and nitric acids. Figures 3, 4 and 5 show the
surface of galena subjected to a different number of pressure
impulses with subsequent treatment in acids. As can be seen,
after three consecutive pressure impulses of 50 atm followed
by solution in acids (Fig. 4), it is possible to observe some

632

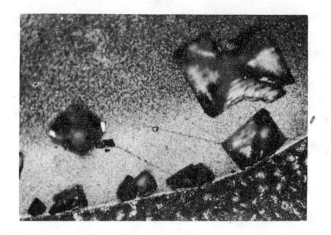

Fig. 2. Concentration of dislocation centres along the
smooth boundary between the galena and quartz
grains after heating and sudden cooling of the
ore lumps.
650 x magnification.

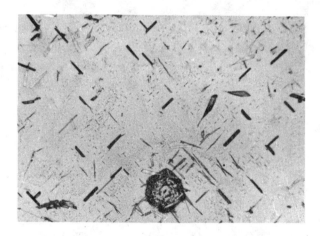

Fig. 3. Surface of coarse-galena grain after one pressure
impulse of 50 atm.
400 x magnification.

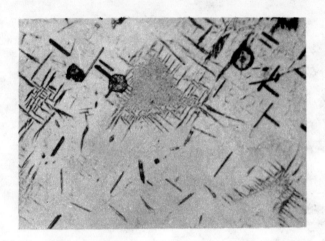

Fig. 4. Surface of the coarse-galena grain after three
successive pressure impulses of 50 atm each.
400 x magnification.

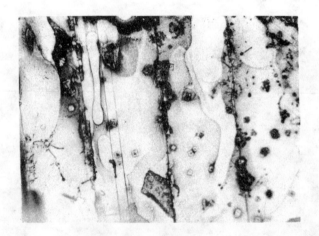

Fig. 5. Accumulation of dislocations and formation of
microcracks in the galena after three successive
pressure impulses.

dislocation centres of varying diameters and depth. Alongside
huge clusters of dislocation pits some microcracks can also be
seen (Fig. 5).

Sphalerite. In the tested ores, sphalerite grains are
usually characterized by complicated boundaries with galena and
quartz. The final products of comminution in ball and autogeneous mills (on an industrial scale) contain a lot of galena-
sphalerite or sphalerite-quartz mixed grains (Fig. 1).

In the tests with sudden changes of pressure and temperature,
the microstructural alterations are usually observed in the
sphalerite phase. These disturbances have a different orientation. The formation of single simple, and occasionally complex
microcracks can be observed with the application of internal
reflection. Single and complicated dislocation centres have

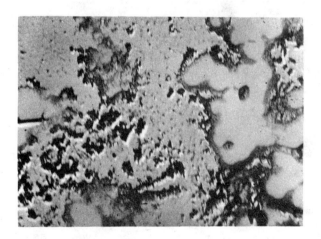

Fig. 6. Micromorphology of a detached sphalerite surface
after three successive pressure impulses and
addition of oleic acid.
3000 x magnification.

very different forms as can be seen on the surface. The number
of these centres increases after three consecutive impulses of
sudden changes in pressure and temperature (Fig. 6).

Disseminated Chalco-pyrite-pyritic Ore with Insertions of Gold Nuggets

The main ore minerals are chalcopyrite and pyrite disseminated in quartz in the form of insertions from 2-3 mm to a fraction of a µm in size. Pyrite is characterized by the automor-
phic form of individual crystals, disseminated separately in
quartz or in the form of polycrystal aggregates. Uneven boundaries between the quartz and chalcopyrite, grains are typical.
Microinsertions of various forms are often found in chalcopyrite.

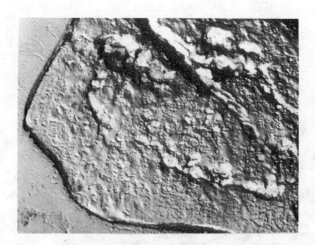

Fig. 7. Pyrite in quartz after four successive pressure
impulses of 50 atm with the addition of oleic acid
at the moment of pressure increase.
4500 x magnification.

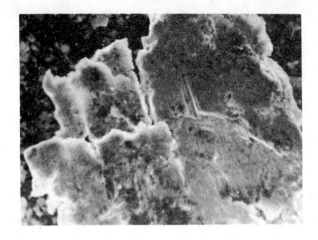

Fig. 8. Morphology of the gold grain liberated by grinding
after one pressure impulse of 50 atm.
250 x magnification.

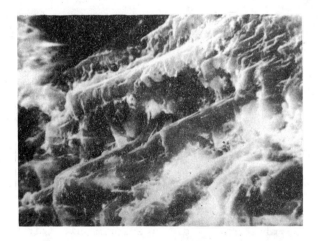

Fig. 9. Chalcopyrite surface after autogenous ore grining
in the presence of oleic acid. The smoothing of
sharp edges which is visible is typical of autogenous grinding.

Pressure impulses of 50-60 atm greatly influence pyrite, often resulting in the formation of single or grouped dislocation "pits", which cause the formation of microcracks (Fig. 7).

No changes in the quartz-chalcopyrite particles were observed.

Some changes of chalcopyrite were found after dry grinding of the ore when a small quantity of oleic acid was added to the mill. The raw ore contains a considerable amount of chalcopyrite of various shades. The colouring is due to the presence on the surface of chalcopyrite of chemical compounds which differ in composition and structure. These compounds exert a negative effect on the flotation of chalcopyrite. Dry autogeneous grinding in the presence of oleic acid resulted in chalcopyrite grains, free of surface impurities (Fig. 9).

Magnetite-Pyrrhotite Ore. This is a complex fine-disseminated ore with a carbonate gangue and certain quartz and arsenopyrite content. Pressure impulses of 30 and 60 atm exerted a positive influence on the grinding product. It was found that the impulse action in the presence of the surface-active agents resulted in a sudden decrease in the number of mixed magnetic grains where the particle-size distribution was constant. At the same time, with a grain size of 40-20 μm the number of magnetic and arsenopyrite grains of an ideomorphic form in a -40+20 μm size fraction increases. It is obvious that in the process of grinding such an ore, liberation takes place by cleavage along the boundaries between the grains of these two minerals.

Fig. 10. Micromorphology of the surface of magnetite assaying pyrite after three successive pressure impulses. 450 x magnification.

The electron microscope observations of the iron ore lumps with a high content of arsenopyrite before and after subject-ing them to impulses of pressure of 60 atm revealed a higher concentration of dislocated pits near the disseminations in magnetite and pyrrhotite (Fig. 10).

When the iron ore with quartz is subjected to pressure impulses, microcracks are formed alongside the grain boundaries around the magnetite disseminations (Fig. 11). This causes a more complete liberation of magnetite in the form of free grains and eliminates the overgrinding of quartz.

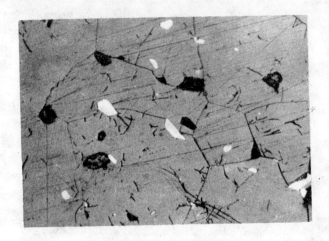

Fig. 11. Microcracks in quartz and around magnetite grains
after two successive pressure impulses.
450 x magnification.

Calcite. Even after one pressure impulse of 30 atm in
Snyder's apparatus some changes in the reflection ability of
calcite and visible deep oriented light effects in the crystals
took place. This fact is connected with disturbances in the
structure of calcite and the formation of microcracks which
are single at the very beginning and then grow more complicated and branched (Fig. 12).

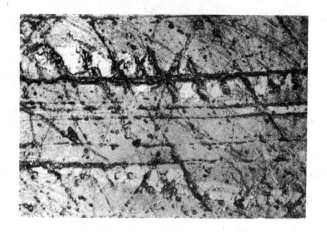

Fig. 12. Calcite surface after two pressure impulses and
subsequent treatment with hydrochloric acid.

1.3. Conclusions

Summarizing the results of the research on the process of
destruction by application of pressure and temperature impulse
changes, the following conclusions can be drawn: the impulse
treatment of ores with pressure of 30-60 atm results in an increase in grinding selectivity. Fracture occurs at the mineral
grain boundaries. The concentration of the macro- and micro-
defects formed depends to a great extent on the combination of
minerals in the ore. For example, in the sphalerite-galena-
quartz aggregates the maximum concentration of defects was
observed in the galena. In sphalerite-galena-calcite aggregates the maximum number of micro-defects occurs in the calcite,
then in the galena and sphalerite. In quartz-magnetite fine-disseminated ores many more defects were found in the quartz.

This results in the complete liberation of the magnetite grains without their additional overgrinding. In the pyrite-quartz aggregates an active fracturing of pyrite occurs. In the ores containing magnetite and sulphide iron minerals, a concentration of micro-defects is observed around arsenopyrite and magnetite. Fracturing occurs in pyrrhotite. With a sudden change of temperature in the range of 160-20°C the concentration of defects occurs alongside the mineral grain boundaries; this favours more selective liberation.

2. Energy of Breakage after Pretreatment

Former publications [10, 11] show that a certain amount of energy is needed to break a given lump of ore. Bond [11] defines that level as the sum of energy stored in the lumps before and during fracturing. It is obvious that this level will be reached gradually, at every stage of action to which   an ore lump is subjected. It will depend on the initial state of that lump, on its structure (macro- and micro-), as well as on the amount and nature of structural defects. The more defects occur during the initial destruction, the less is the amount of energy needed for the subsequent grinding to gain complete liberation of the mineral components. Thus, if the process of ore crushing is properly organized to get the desired liberation of minerals and if it is performed in stages as Revnivtsev recommends [10] , then in the general case according to Bond, we should get a decrease in the level of energy. However, this will only happen where the liberation stage of minerals mainly occurs by fracturing ore lumps along the contact grain boundaries. Then there is no overgrinding, and it is worth mentioning that liberation selectivity will be greater [12].

To be able to confirm these assumptions we carried out two experiments involving the crushing of a coarse-disseminated lead-zinc ore. In our first experiment (No. 17) the sample of ore containing 1- to 10 mm material was crushed in a vibro-mill for 5 min   (the mill was equipped with a roller of 1.2 kg). In the second experiment (No. 27) the same sample was heated to 160°C, then was quickly cooled with water to 20°C with subsequent grinding in the same mill for 4 min (the roller in the mill was of the same size but 0.250 kg in weight). The results of the experiments are presented in Table 1.

It is worth mentioning that the particle size distribution of the grinding products of these experiments was different (see Table 2). As can be seen from Tables 1 and 2, in spite of the fact that in test No. 27 the product was much coarser, liberation in that product was better than in test No. 17. An exception is observed only in the sphalerite-galena and galena-quartz mixed grains in the size fraction of - 1+ 0.5 mm.

The results obtained and presented in the tables also confirm a much lower level of energy when the ore is pretreated by changing the temperature.

TABLE 1

Particle-size Distribution in the Grinding Products, %

Particle size mm	-1+0.5 Test		0.5-0.3 Test		0.3-0.2 Test		0.2-0.12 Test		0.12-0.08 Test	
Grain type	No. 27	No. 17	No. 27	No. 17	No. 27	No. 17	No. 27	No. 17	No. 27	No. 17
Quartz	48	61	54	52	46	68	63	50	50	50
Ore-bearing	52	39	46	48	54	32	37	50	50	50
Total	100	100	100	100	100	100	100	100	100	100
Sphalerite	31	35	60	43	50	43	61	66	67	66
Galena	9	3	18	9	25	25	15	18	21	20
Pyrite	13	6	5	10	4	11	12	5	6	6
Sphalerite-galena	3	no	2	2	6	1	3	2	4	3
Pyrite-quartz	3	3	2	2	no	no	3	no	no	no
Sphalerite-quartz	23	50	10	24	8	19	4	6	1	4
Galena-quartz	13	3	3	10	7	10	2	3	1	1
Total	100	100	100	100	100	100	100	100	100	100

TABLE 2

| Particle size | Yield of size fractions, % | |
mm	Test No. 27	Test No. 17
+0.08	81.5	69.9
0.08-0.04	7.0	11.0
-0.04	11.5	19.1
Total	100.0	100.0

3. Liberation Selectivity

The problem of the selectivity of mineral liberation has been studied by many authors [3, 4, 6, 7, 9, 10, 12]. The term "selective liberation" of minerals generally means the liberation of the grains of each individual mineral contained in a given ore by means of crushing or grinding, with no reduction in the original mineral grain size and with no locked particles.

Various parameters and methods have been suggested to characterize liberation selectivity. Usually, these parameters are relative, as for example: "degree of liberation" [6]; "degree of selectivity of liberation" (expressed in %) [9]; "ratio of the primary number of grains to the total number of particles" (expressed in %) [12] and many others. All these definitions of liberation selectivity consider only one side of the problem, namely complete liberation of the mineral grains. Some suggested Equations [6] take into account the degree of grinding given by particle size before and after grinding.

It seems to us that the energy of liberation is another important parameter. It is obvious that the lower this energy level is at a given absolute liberation of mineral grains, the higher the liberation selectivity.

The process of liberation in the course of crushing is a thermodynamic one. The imperfection of the fracturing involves a much greater amount of energy than the free surface energy. However, it appears that the specific free surface energy of the minerals in the raw ore and in the grinding products can be successfully used for describing the process of mineral liberation.

If the total free surface energy of the boundaries between minerals disseminated in a given ore lump is denoted by E_o, the total free surface energy of mineral boundaries in the locked particles obtained after grinding denoted by E_2 and the total free surface energy of liberated mineral grains by E_1, then neglecting the free surface energy of the initial surface of the lump, we obtain:

$$E_1 = K(E_o - E_2) \qquad (1)$$

Coefficient "K" in Eq. (1) will in practice always be greater than one, because the newly formed surface of the liberated grains in the grinding product will always be greater than the difference between the surface of the contacts in the initial lump and the contact surface in the locked particles. Only in the ideal case where the free grains are not overground will coefficient "K" be equal to one, if no locked particles are formed. To find the physical meaning of coefficient "K", let us rearrange Eq. (1):

$$K = \frac{E_1}{E_o - E_2} \qquad (2)$$

As can be seen, "K" represents the ratio of the energies. And so, to define the theoretical limit of the changes in "K", let us analyze the right part of the Eq. (2): $K = 0$ when $E_1 = 0$. This case in only theoretically possible, when the breaking of the lump has not yet started. In practice, at an even lower degree of comminution there would also be free grains. Now, let us assume that free grains exist, but the surface energy of the boundaries in locked particles E_2 is equal to the initial surface energy of these contacts E_o, because there is no grain liberation. The level of energy in the process of crushing will be higher than the initial level. The denominator will then be equal to 0 and "K" will approach infinity. This means that the surface energy is being released, but that mineral liberation has not yet occurred. In this case, selectivity will be equal to 0. Denoting the selectivity factor by K_1, its value can be found from the following equation:

$$K_1 = \frac{1}{K} \qquad (3)$$

In practice, in the course of grinding the value of E_1 will increase steadily whereas E_2 decreases. For a given ore the value E_o is constant. At $E_1 = $ const. the lower the value of E_2, the lower value of "K" and the higher the selectivity (and the selectivity factor K_1). This depends on the crushing conditions. Changing the rate of crushing so that the E_1 value remained relatively low and E_2 decreased, would show that "K_1" increased. If grinding conditions are such that E_1 reaches a very high value, then despite the fact that E_2 is low, "K" will also be high, but the selectivity of liberation will be low. In such a case it is   possible to speak about complete liberation, but not proper selectivity.

The probable limit of "K_1" will be equal to 1. This will occur where $E_1 = E_0$ and $E_2 = 0$. This case is hardly probable because a reduction in the number of locked particles will result in a quick rise in E_1.*

To define a relative level of energy in the course of grinding, it is possible to include in E_2 the whole surface of the intergrowths. It is easily shown that in practice E_2 will always be less than E_0, and E_1 will always be greater than the difference (E_0-E_2) in the case of a certain acceptable degree of liberation.

CONCLUSIONS

The investigations once again confirmed the possibility of substantial structural changes in ores at the pretreatment stage before grinding. These changes depend on the ore (on the character of the mineral boundaries and the number of structural defects) and on loading conditions and methods. The application of a whole complex of various effects and the action

---

* It is certainly possible to assume that "K" will be equal to 1 even at a low value of $E_1 = (E_0-E_2)$. But this could only happen at the very beginning of the liberation process, when nearly all the grains are in the form of intergrowths and if is not really possible to consider grinding as mineral liberation process.

of surface active agents make it possible to create such conditions that on the one hand, the selectivity of mineral liberation increases and on the other, at a given selectivity, the total consumption of energy decreases. The specific surface energy of each individual mineral can be used for the simultaneous estimation of liberation selectivity and energy consumption. For the majority of the main ore-bearing minerals the value of the specific surface energy can be found in the literature, can be determined experimentally or can be calculated theoretically.

REFERENCES

1. Grigorev D. P. Ontogenesis of Minerals, Lvov University, 1961, 126.

2. Grigorev D. P. Ontogenesis of Minerals, Publishing House "Nauka", Moscow, 1975.

3. Denev S. I. Investigations into the improvement of minerals liberation in processing of finely disseminated iron ores. Varna, 1973, 306-324.

4. Denev S. I. et al. Minerals liberation in various comminution processes. Praga, 1970.

5. Distler G. I. et al. Decoration of solid surfaces. Publishing House "Nauka", Moscow, 1976.

6. Karmazin V. I., Denisenko A. I. and Sergo E. E. Autogenous grinding of ores. Publishing House "Nedra", Moscow, 1968.

7. Karmazin V. V. et al. Study of some trends in selective grinding and their application to processing of fine-disseminated iron ores. Proceedings Eleventh International Mineral Processing Congress, Special Volume. Cagliari, Italy 1975, 11-33.

8. Maluk O. P. et al. Features of iron ore minerals liberation during grinding and liberation improvement. Varna, 1978, 298-305.

9. Revnivtsev V. I. et al. Selective mineral liberation. San Paolo, 1977.

10. Revnivtsev V. I. Rational organization of the mineral liberation processes based on contemporary physics of solids. "Mekhanobr", 140, Leningrad 1975, 153-168.

11. Bond F. C. Grinding Principles. Proceedings of European Symposium on Grinding. Moscow, 1966, 195-205.

12. Blekhman I. I. and Finkelstein G. A. On the minerals liberation at minimum overgrinding. "Mekhanobr", 140, Leningrad 1975, 149-153.

ABSTRACT

An analysis has been made of the necessity of alteration of
mineral structure in order to reduce ore strength before grinding. Investigations into reducing strength by impulses of
abrupt pressure and temperature change in the presence of surface active agents have been carried out and the results obtained are given. It was found that there are some differences
in the behaviour of main ore minerals such as pyrite, galena,
chalcopyrite, sphalerite, quartz, magnetite and calcite. These
differences are determined by defects in the mineral structure,
by the character of the interfaces between mineral grains and
the nature of the action on the ores.

The possibility of increased selectivity of liberation of
minerals with simultaneous decrease of energy consumption for
grinding is shown.

A method for estimation of the selectivity of liberation
and energy consumption based on specific surface energy of the
minerals is suggested.

Methods of mineralogical investigations of alterations in
mineral structure based on the means of the optical and electron
microscopy are described.

RÉSUMÉ

Une analyse a été effectuée sur la nécessité de l'altération
de la structure de minéraux dans le but de réduire la robustesse
du minerai avant le broyage. Des études sur la réduction de la
force par impulsions du changement soudain de la pression et de
la température en présence d'agents tensioactifs ont été effectuées, et les résultats obtenus sont présentés. On a trouvé qu'
il y avait quelques différences dans le comportement de minéraux
issus des minerais basiques comme la pyrite, la galène, la chalcopyrite, la sphalérite, le quartz, la magnétite, le calcite.
Ces différences sont déterminées par des défauts dans la structure du minéral, par la nature des interfaces entre les minéraux et le mode d'action sur les minerais.

On montre la possibilité d'améliorer la sélectivité de la
libération des minéraux avec un décroissement de la consommation
d'énergie pour le broyage.

La méthode d'estimation de la sélectivité de la libération
et de la consommation d'énergie sur la base de l'énergie relative de la surface des minéraux est suggérée.

Les méthodes d'études minéralogiques de l'altération des
structures minérales basées sur la microscopie optique et
électronique, sont décrites.

ZUSAMMENFASSUNG

Es wurde die Notwendigkeit der Veränderung der Struktur von
Mineralen untersucht, um den Widerstand von Erzen gegen das
Brechen zu vermindern. Es ist die Möglichkeit, diesen Wider-
stand durch plötzliche Druck- und Temperaturschwankungen in
Gegenwart kapillaraktiver Mittel herabzusetzen, untersucht
worden. Die erhaltenen Ergebnisse werden erörtert. Im Verhalten
der wichtigsten Erzminerale, wie Pyrit, Bleiglanz (Galenit),
Chalkopyrit, Zinblende (Sphalerit), Quartz, Magnetit und Kalk-
spat (Kalzit) wurden Untersuchiede festgestellt, die durch
Störungen in der Struktur der Minerale, den Charakter der
Grenzphasen zwischen den einzelnen Mineralen und die Art ihrer
Einwirkung auf das Erz bedingt sind.

Es wird auf die Möglichkeit hingewiesen, die Selektivität
der Freisetzung der Minerale bei gleichzeitiger Reduktion des
Energieverbrauchs beim Brechen des Erzes zu erhöhen.

Vorgeschlagen wird eine Methode zur Bewertung der Selektivität des Freisetzens von Mineralen und in Anlehnung an die
relative Oberflächenenergie der Minerale des Energieverbrauchs,
für den Trennvorgang.

Es werden Verfahren zur mineralogischen Untersuchung von
Veränderungen in der Struktur von Mineralen mittels optischer
und elektronischer Mikroskopie dargestellt.

РЕЗЮМЕ

Дан анализ необходимости изменения структуры минералов с целью разупрочнения руд перед измельчением. Предлагаются результаты исследований по разупрочнению путем импульсов резкого изменения давления и температуры в присутствии поверхностно – активных веществ. Установлены различия в проведении основных рудосоставляющих минералов: пирит, галенит, халькопирит, сфалерит, кварц, магнетит, кальцит. Эти различия обуславливаются дефектами структуры минералов, характером конкретных поверхностей между ними и видом воздействия на руды.

Показана возможность повышения селективности раскрытия при одновременном уменьшении расхода энергии на измельчение.

Предложен метод оценки селективности раскрытия и расхода энергии на базе удельной поверхностной энергии минералов.

Описана методика минералогических исследований изменений в структуре минералов, основанная на возможностях оптической и электронной микроскопии.

DETERMINATION OF IRREVERSIBLY ACCUMULATED ENERGY IN GRINDING

K. Tkačova, F. Sekula, I. Hocmanova and V. Krupa

Mining Institute of the Slovak Academy of Sciences, Kosice, Czechoslovakia

INTRODUCTION

The solution of the relationship between the energy supplied to the grinding system and the quantitatively defined extent of disintegration is the basic assumption enabling one to evaluate the efficiency of the grinding process and to determine the criteria for its optimization.

The growth of knowledge about the disintegration mechanism has led to the application of new experimental procedures for the energetic balance determination of the grinding process. These procedures are based on the fundamental expression for the transformation of the grinding work W [1]

$$W = \Delta U_m + \Delta U_i - (-Q) \qquad (1)$$

ΔU_m is the increase in the internal energy of the disintegrated material subsystem

ΔU_i is the increase in the internal energy of the indentor subsystem

Q is the released heat.

The experimental investigation of the mechanical work transformation in the disintegration process may take one of two directions:

(1) determination of the total increase in the internal energy of the disintegrated material and the mechanical indentor subsystems ($\Delta U_m + \Delta U_i$) in the grinding process, or

(2) determination of the internal energy increase in the disintegrated material subsystem ΔU_m after termination of the process.

The aim of this work is to provide information about the methods based on the principles mentioned and to discuss the results obtained when investigating the grinding work transformation regularities by these methods.

EXPERIMENTAL

Quantitative Determination of the Total Increase in the Internal Energy of the Disintegrated Material and Mechanical Indentor Subsystems in the Grinding Process

A total increase in the internal energy of the disintegrated material and mechanical indentor subsystems was determined with laboratory-constructed equipment enabling one to measure the energy supplied to system W and the released heat Q.

The calorimetric mill described in Fig. 1 consists of an adiabatic automatically controlled calorimeter with a vessel (12) containing a grinding dish (10) and indentors (13). The calori-

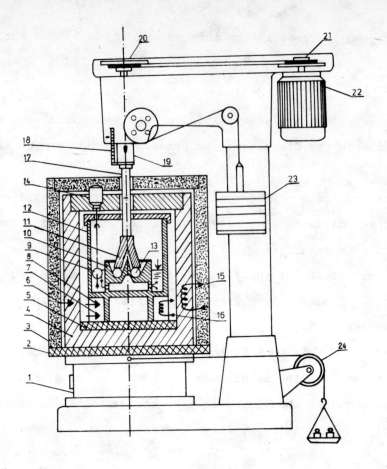

Fig. 1. Schematic diagram of the calorimetric mill. 1 - dyna-
mometric head, 2, 5 - thermoinsulating inset,
3 - thermoinsulating jacket, 4 - calorimeter jacket,
6, 7 - controlling thermocouples, 8 - indication diodes, 9 - thermohomogenization pump, 10 - grinding
dish, 11 - carrier and pressure element, 12 - calorimetric vessel, 13 - grinding balls, 14 - engine of
the thermohomogenization pump, 15 - heating body of
the jacket, 16 - heating body of the calorimetric
vessel, 17 - thermally insulated carrier rod, 18 -
mill balls height indication, 19 - spindle with soc-
ket, 20 - belt drive, 21 - driving pulley, 22 - driving engine of the spindle, 23 - draw rod with weight,
24 - roller with cable for twisting moment calibration.

meter is stabilized on a higher temperature level than that of the surroundings. The zero temperature boundary line between the grinding dish and the calorimetric jacket is automatically controlled. The heating current of the jacket is controlled by tyristors governed by amplified thermovoltage of the differentially connected thermocouples (6, 7) in the calorimetric vessel and in the jacket. The released heat is indicated by semiconductor detectors (8). Diodes are connected in a Wheatston bridge the output of which is led to the registrator through an amplifier. The calorimeter is fixed on a tensodynamometric head (1) for measurement of thrust and twisting moment.

The grinding of synthetic periclase and the natural carbonates calcite and magnesite was investigated. Data given in Table 1 characterize the properties of the mill feed. The theoretical values of the lattice energy [2] for the minerals studied are also listed in this Table.

TABLE 1

Characteristics of the Feed and the Theoretical Values of Lattice Energy of the Minerals Studied

Mineral	Lattice energy E $[kJ\ mol^{-1}]$	Mean grain size D_m $[\mu m]$	Impurities $[\%]$
Periclase	3 914	505	2.85
Magnesite	3 090	454	7.55
Calcite	2 713	390	4.02

The grinding regime was chosen to ensure approximately the same mechanical power input for all minerals compared. Grinding conditions are summarized in Table 2. The last column of Table 2 shows time intervals at which the irreversibly accumulated energy $W - Q = \Delta U_m + \Delta U_i$ values were recorded.

TABLE 2

Grinding Conditions

Mineral	Thrust	Total grinding time	Time interval
	N	s	s
Periclase	1,250 ÷ 1,700	750	150
Magnesite	760 ÷ 1,300	750	150
Calcite	560 ÷ 900	420	60 and 90

In Figs. 2 A and B, the irreversibly accumulated energy $W - Q$ is plotted against the supplied grinding work W and grinding time $\mathcal{T}$. For the grinding work dependence of $W - Q$ a hyperbolic tangent function is obtained (see Fig. 2 A):

$$W - Q = K \, t \, h \, \frac{W}{T} \qquad (2)$$

K is the limiting value of the internal energy increase in the ground material and mechanical indentor subsystems; T is a constant characterizing the active grinding zone. Constants K and T are marked in the schematic diagram in Fig. 3 A.

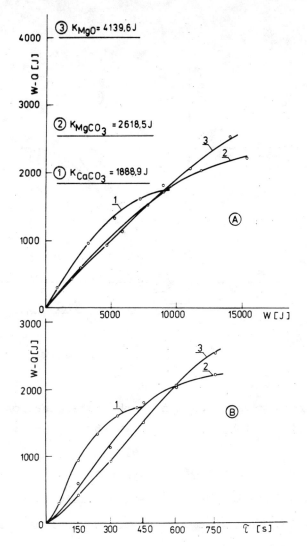

Fig. 2. Experimentally determined internal energy increase of the disintegrated material and mechanical indentors subsystems W - Q in relation to grinding work (A) and grinding time (B). 1 - calcite; 2 - magnesite; 3 - periclase.

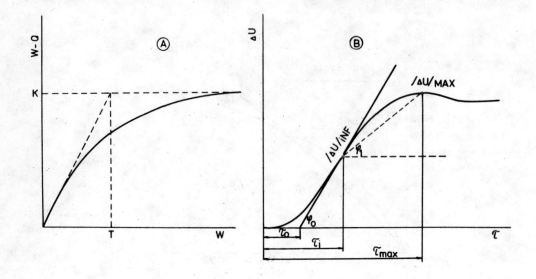

Fig. 3. Schematic representation of the determination of the
quantities of Eq. (2) - (A) and Eq. (6) - (B).

The first-order derivative of the hyperbolic tangent function
(2) gives the relationship for the energy efficiency of grinding.
From this, the grinding resistance ϱ has been defined as the
reciprocal value of the efficiency

$$\varrho = \frac{1}{\eta_o} c\, h^2\, \frac{W}{T} \qquad (3)$$

η_o is the initial grinding efficiency.

In Table 3 the constants of Eqs. (2) and (3) are given for
the materials investigated.

TABLE 3

The Constants of Eqs. (2) and (3)

Mineral	K $[J\ g^{-1}]$	T $[J\ g^{-1}]$	η_o $[\%]$
Periclase	4 139.6	20,000	20.70
Magnesite	2 618.5	11,500	22.70
Calcite	1 889.9	5800	32.58

Determination of the Internal Energy Increase in the Disintegrated Material Subsystem and Investigation of the Mechanism of Irreversible Energy Accumulation

The investigation of the accumulation of irreversible energy in the disintegration products is based on a thermodynamic model of the solid phase active state [2] which defines the activated solid material as a thermodynamically and structurally unstable arrangement of the elements of which the lattice is built.

Using the terminology of classical thermodynamics, the energetic content of the solid phase may be characterized by the internal energy U at a constant volume or enthalpy H at constant pressure. In the case of solid materials at atmospheric pressure internal energy and enthalpy may be considered equivalent since the influence of external pressure can be neglected [3]. The internal energy or enthalpy of solid material includes binding and oscillation energy. This has a free and bound form

$$U = F + T\ S \qquad or \qquad H = G + T\ S \qquad (4)$$

F - free energy, G - Gibbs energy, T S - enthropic factor representing the bound energy of the system.

Huttig [4] has defined the active state of the solid phase or activity A_T as the differences between the Gibbs energy of the activated form G_T^* and stable form G_T of a given material at temperature T

$$A_T = \Delta G_T = G_T^* - G_T \qquad\qquad (5)$$

The quantitative determination of the internal energy increase in the solid phase is possible on the basis of relations (4) and (5) from the difference between the enthalpic effects of dissolution of the activated disintegration products ΔH_T^* and of the stable form of crystalline material ΔH_T. Studying the changes in the specific surface and the crystalline phase content in the disintegration process, qualitative information can be gained about the distribution of irreversibly accumulated energy in the disintegration products.

For the investigation of the mechanism of irreversible energy accumulation, the products of the vibrational grinding of periclase, magnesite and calcite were chosen. The characteristics of the feed are listed in Table 1. The material was ground in a laboratory vibrational mill at a relative acceleration of $b/g = 7$. Grinding time ranged from 0.5 to 16 or 32 h in geometrical sequence, the degree of mill charging $\Upsilon = 75\%$ and feed weight $M = 100$ g.

The internal energy increase of the grinding products ΔU_m was determined by measuring the heat released at dissolution of 20 mg of magnesite and calcite in 5 M HCl and 10 mg of periclase in 2.5 M HCl. The dissolution of magnesite in the calorimeter would not be complete therefore dissolution heat has only been

662

calculated for the amount analytically determined to be actually dissolved. An adiabatic microcalorimeter made in our Institute [5] was used to indicate the heat released in the dissolution process. The sensitivity of the calorimetric measurements was 5×10^{-2} J; reproducibility R ranged from 3-5%, depending on grain size.

The specific surface was determined by the BET method with benzene as adsorbate. The sensitivity of this measurement was 10^{-2} m^2 g^{-1} and the reproducibility R ranged from 2-5%.

The crystalline phase content x_1 was found by X-ray measurements using a modified additional reference component method. The conditions of the X-ray measurements have been described elsewhere [6]. The diffraction lines measured are given in Table 4.

TABLE 4

Survey of Selected Diffraction Lines
and Relative Reproducibility R Values

Mineral	Diffraction line	d/n $[nm]$	R $[\%]$
Periclase	200	21.06	2.03
Magnesite	104	27.42	5.42
Calcite	104	30.35	2.68

The experimental results for the vibrational grinding products are shown in Figs. 4 and 5[*].

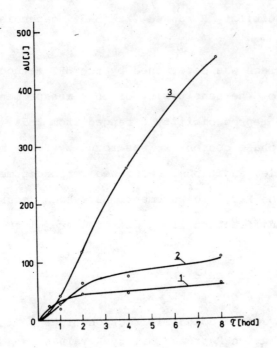

Fig. 4. Changes in internal energy increase ΔU_m with time of vibrational grinding τ up to 8 h. 1 - calcite; 2 - magnesite; 3 - periclase.

---

[*] The calorimetric mill grinding products obtained at the highest grinding times given in Table 2 were also analysed by this procedure. The internal energy increase values ΔU_m are compared with the values W-Q in Table 7.

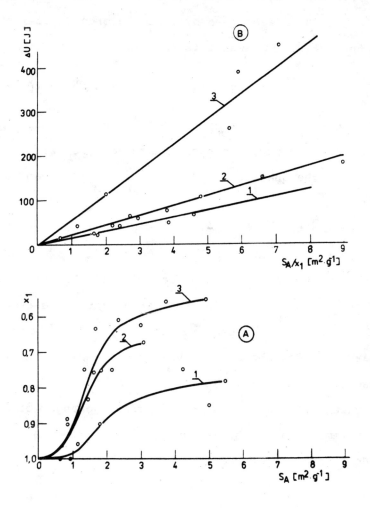

Fig. 5 A - Relation between the specific surface changes and crystalline phase content for products of long-term vibration grinding. 1 - periclase; 2 - calcite; 3 - magnesite.

B - Internal energy increase ΔU_m as a function of specific surface and crystalline phase content changes for products of long-term vibration grinding. 1 - calcite; 2 - magnesite; 3 - periclase.

The dependence of the internal energy increase on the grinding time τ may be described by a second-order differential Eq. [7], the solution of which is as follows:

$$(\Delta U_m)_i \; (\tau) = K \left\{ 1 - \left[\cos \vartheta \tau + \left(-\frac{\lambda}{\vartheta} \right) \sin \vartheta \tau \right] e^{\lambda \tau} \right\}$$ (6)

ϑ, λ are constants of the differential equation solution.

The internal energy increase changes of ΔU_m with time are described by the quantities presented in the diagram in Fig. 3 B.

They are:

τ_o - starting time, τ_{INF} - τ_{MAX} - time range where the internal energy increase ΔU_m is linear up to the value $(\Delta U_m)_{INF}$. The rate of internal energy increase in this region is $v_I = tg \, \varphi_o$. The quantity $v_{II} = tg \, \varphi_1$ determines the rate of decrease after the inflection point has been reached. τ_{MAX} denotes the time necessary to reach the maximum values of the internal energy increase $(\Delta U_m)_{MAX}$.

The values of quantities characterizing changes of ΔU_m with grinding time obtained by computing the experimental data on an IBM/370-145 are summarized in Table 5.

TABLE 5

Quantities Characterizing Changes of ΔU_m with Grinding Time

Mineral	$\tau_o 3.6 \times 10^3$ $[s]$	$(\Delta U_m)_{INF}$ $[J \, g^{-1}]$	$(\Delta U_m)_{MAX}$	$v_I \times 10^{-4}$ $[J \, g^{-1} s^{-1}]$	$v_{II} \times 10^{-4}$
Periclase	0.902	175.88	426.18	15.30	8.18
Magnesite	0.629	40.68	152.39	4.23	0.39
Calcite	0.167	13.80	51.70	5.43	0.51

From the quantities in Table 5 the value $(\Delta U_m)_{MAX}$ may be compared with the value K calculated according to (2) from the experimental data obtained with the calorimetric mill.

To explain the mechanism of the internal energy increase of the disintegration products. We studied the relation between the internal energy increase ΔU_m as a thermodynamic quantity on one hand and the specific surface S_A and crystalline phase content x_1 as surface and bulk characteristics on the other. Using nmerical methods, the linear relationship

$$\Delta U_m = k \frac{S_A}{x_1} \qquad (7)$$

was obtained. The value of slope k for each mineral were compared with the theoretical values of lattice energy E and the specific surface energy determined from the work necessary for splitting according to [2].

TABLE 6

Value of Constant k from Relationship (7) and the Ratio of k to the Compared Quantities σ and E

Mineral	k $[J\ m^{-2}]$	σ $[J\ m^{-2}]$	k/E x 10^{-3} [%]	σ/E x 10^{-3} [%]
Periclase	55.74	1.20	57	1.23
Magnesite	21.64	–	59	–
Calcite	14.96	0.23	55	0.85

DISCUSSION AND CONCLUSION

Investigation of the grinding work transformation by measuring the supplied work and the heat released gives information about the accumulation of irreversible energy in the grinding process. A total increase in the internal energy of the disintegrated material and the mechanical indentor subsystems $W - Q = \Delta U_m + \Delta U_i$ shows limiting value of several kJ per gram of disintegrated material. In accordance with this, the initial efficiency of grinding η_o ranges from 20-30%.

The internal energy increase values of the disintegrated material subsystem ΔU_m determined from the difference between the enthalpic effects of dissolution of activated disintegration products $\Delta H^{\ddagger}$ and the stable form of crystalline material ΔH, are lower. These differences are shown in Table 7, where the internal energy increase and immediate efficiencies determined by both methods for calorimetric mill grinding products obtained at longest times are compared.

TABLE 7

Values of Internal Energy Increase and Efficiencies
Determined by both Compared Methods for Calorimetric
Mill Products at Longest Grinding Time

Mineral	W $[J\ g^{-1}]$	$W-Q$ $[J\ g^{-1}]$	$\eta = \dfrac{W-Q}{W}$ $[\%]$	ΔU_m $[J\ g^{-1}]$	$\eta = \dfrac{U_m}{W}$ $[\%]$
Periclase	14 131	2 551.8	18.06	973.64	6.90
Magnesite	15 268	2 235.5	14.64	608.96	3.99
Calcite	9 004	1 723.4	19.14	39.84	0.44

The differences in the determined values are of a methodological nature and the reasons for them may be summarized as follows:

(1) Irreversible energy determined with equipment allowing the measurement of supplied work and released heat W-Q represents the total increase in internal energy of the disintegrated material and mechanical indentor subsystem.

(2) Total internal energy increase $\Delta U_m + \Delta U_i$ is determined directly in the grinding process.

(3) The internal energy increase of disintegrated products ΔU_m is determined after the grinding process is completed. Although determination closely follows the grinding process, some inactivation of the material may be assumed as a result of sorption processes causing saturation of residual bonds in the surface and of deformation relaxation in the bulk.

The determination of the internal energy increase in two different systems, in the calorimetric mill and vibrational mill by different experimental methods showed a similar kinetic course of internal energy accumulation for the disintegrated material system (compare Figs. 2 B and 4). The kinetics of the internal energy accumulation changes with an increasing amount of grinding work with a prolonged grinding time. The accumulated energy is limited by the boundary values K or $(\Delta U_m)_{MAX}$. The difference between the type of grinding system and the determination methods is expressed in the different absolute values of the internal energy increase. They differ in order and in the actual grinding time needed to reach the limiting value.

With a given method of internal energy increase determination, change in energy increase with time and its limiting value depends on the following factors:

(1) The properties of the initial material;

(2) The changing strength of the material due to a decrease in the number of a priori discontinuities and of plastic strengthening at a prolonged grinding time;

(3) Increasing agglomeration with increasing grinding work. This process is expressed in the reversible component as agglomeration heat.

The time dependence of the internal energy increase in contrast to the energy dependence shows a rise section τ_o (compare the diagrams in Figs. 3A and 3B). This rise can be explained by the somewhat lower intensity of grinding work transmission in this time region.

The energetic analysis of the grinding in the calorimetric mill and the kinetic analysis of the internal energy increase in the vibrational grinding products has shown some correlation between the limiting value of the accumulation capacity of the material and the lattice energy. The energy accumulation capacity of the material $(\Delta U_m)_{MAX}$ or K increases with an increase in lattice energy, similarly to the linear relationship (7)

$$k = U_m \frac{x_1}{S_A} .$$

A comparison of the value in Table 6 shows that the ratio k/E is constant for all minerals. For all compared minerals, k reaches approximately 50% of the theoretical lattice energy value. It has already been proved in our laboratory that for a given type of grinding equipment and for the same intensity of grinding work transmission, k is a material constant [6, 8].

670

The interpretation of the slope k as a material constant presumes the elucidation of all factors determining its magnitude. When dissolution of a solid phase takes place as a result of a chemical reaction between the solid and a liquid medium, the heat of dissolution can be divided into three main components:

$$\Delta H = \Delta H_C + \Delta H_R + \Delta H_S \tag{8}$$

ΔH_C is the heat of transformation of the dissolved substance from solid to liquid state. This quantity equals the work done against the cohesion forces of the solid phase

ΔH_R is the thermal effect of chemical reaction

ΔH_S is the heat of solvation

The dissolution of carbonates and periclase in hydrochloric acid is a exothermic reaction. Similarly, heats of solvation have a negative sign and together with the reaction heat, supply the energy necessary for distraction of the solid lattice.

The difference between the enthalpic effect of the dissolution of activated disintegration products ΔH^* and the stable form of crystalline material ΔH with complete dissolution of material is given by the difference of heats needed for transformation of building elements of lattice from solid to liquid state.

$$\Delta U_m = \Delta H^* - \Delta H = \Delta H_C - \Delta H_C^* \tag{9}$$

$$\Delta H_C^* < \Delta H_C \qquad \Delta U_m > 0 \tag{10}$$

The internal energy increase ΔU_m is the higher, the higher the ΔH_C value in the intact material and the more remarkable is a decrease in this value in the disintegration products as a result of destruction processes represented by the specific surface increase and by the crystalline phase content decrease.

In Fig. 5A it can be seen that the irreversibly accumulated energy distribution for both these processes depends on the crystallochemical properties of the minerals. From Fig. 5B it follows that with an equal degree of solid phase destruction characterized by the ratio S_A/x_1, the internal energy of the disintegration products increases with increasing lattice energy, thus determining the magnitude of the cohesion energy ΔH_C in an intact material.

REFERENCES

1. Sekula F., Dunay G., Merva M. and Krúpa V. Folia Montana (Suppl.) 48 (1976) (In Slovak).

2. Mayer K. Physikalisch-chemische Kristallographie. VEB Deutscher Verlag fur Grundstoffindustrie, Leipzig, 1968, 1st ed.

3. Dekker A. J. Solid State Physics. Akademia nakl. ČSAV, Praha 1966, translated from English into Czech.

4. Heinicke G. and Sigrist K. Zeitschrift für Chemie 11, 226 (1971).

5. Merva M. and Kupka J. Elektrotechnický časopis, 24, 108-112 (1973).

6. Tkáčová K. Silikáty 20, 321 (1976).

7. Tsien H. S. Engineering Cybernetics. Mc Graw-Hill Book Company, Inc., New York, 1954.

8. Tkáčova K. Folia Montana (Suppl.) 70 (1976).

ABSTRACT

The regularities of grinding work transformation with the disintegration of periclase, magnesite and calcite have been investigated.

The total increase of internal energy in the disintegrated material and mechanical indentors subsystems ($\Delta U_m + \Delta U_i$) in the grinding process was determined from the difference between supplied work W and released heat Q in a calorimetric mill. The increase of internal energy of the disintegrated material subsystem ΔU_m after grinding process termination was determined from the difference between dissolution heats of activated products of desintegration and the stable form of a crystalline material.

The energetic analysis of the grinding process in a calorimetric mill and a kinetic analysis of the internal energy increase in the products of vibrational grinding allowed the derivation of relationships describing the internal energy increase dependence on grinding work and grinding time. The limiting values of these relationships characterize the energetic accumulation capacity of the material.

The investigation of the mechanism of grinding work transformation in the grinding products has shown that internal energy increases linearly with increasing specific surface and decreasing crystalline phase content.

The constants of the relationships obtained in a numerical treatment of experimental results change in accordance with the theoretical value of the lattice energy of the investigated minerals.

RÉSUMÉ

Les régularités de transformation du travail de broyage pour la désintégration de la périclase, de la magnésite et de la calcite ont été examinées.

L'accroissement total de l'énergie interne de la matière désintégrée et des systèmes inférieurs de pénétrateurs mécaniques d'essai de dureté ($\Delta U_m + \Delta U_i$) dans le procédé de broyage fut déterminé par la différence du travail fourni W, et de la chaleur Q libérée dans un moulin calorimétrique. L'accroissement de l'énergie interne du sous-système de la matière désintegrée ΔU_m à la fin du procédé de broyage fut déterminée à partir de la différence des chaleurs de dissolution des produits activés de la désintégration et de la forme stable de la matière cristalline.

L'analyse énergétique du procédé de broyage dans un moulin calorimétrique et l'analyse cinétique de l'accroissement d'énergie interne dans les produits du broyage vibrationnel ont rendu possible la dérivation des relations décrivant la dépendance de l'accroissement de l'énergie interne par rapport au travail de broyage et au le temps de broyage. Les valeurs limites de ces relations caractérisent la capacité d'accumulation énergétique de la matière.

L'examen du mécanisme de transformation du travail de broyage dans les produits de broyage a montré que l'énergie interne croît linéairement avec la surface spécifique croissante et le volume décroissant de la phase cristalline.

Les constantes des relations obtenues par les traitements numériques des résultats expérimentaux changent en accord avec la valeur théorique de l'énergie de réseau des minéraux examinés.

ZUSAMMENFASSUNG

Es wurden Gesetzmässigkeiten der Transformation der Mahlarbeit bei der Zerkleinerung von Periklas, Magnesit und Kalcit untersucht.

Der gesamte Zuwachs an der inneren Energie von Subsystemen des zerkleinerten Materials und der mechanischen Indentore ($\Delta U_m + \Delta U_i$) im Mahlprozess wurde aus der Differenz der zugeführten Arbeit W und der in der kalorimetrischen Mühle freigegeben Wärme Q festgestellt. Der Zuwachs an innere Energie von Subsystem des zerkleinerten Materials ΔU_m wurde aus der Differenz zwischen der Lösungswärme der aktivierten Mahlprodukte und der Lösungswärme des Materials im stabilen Zustand bestimmt.

Eine energetische Analyse des Mahlverlaufs in der kalorimetrischen Mühle und eine kinetische Analyse des Zuwachses an
der inneren Energie in den Mahlprodukten der Vibrationsmahlung
hat die Ableitung der funktionellen Zusammenhänge die, die
Abhängigkeit des Zuwachses der inneren Energie des Systems von
der Mahlarbeit, bzw. der Mahldauer zu beschreiben ermöglicht.
Die Grenzwerte der erwähnten Beziehungen kann man als energetische Akkumulationskapazität des Materials bezeichnen.

Die Erforschung des Mechanismus der Transformation der Mahlarbeit in den Mahlprodukten zeigte, dass die innere Energie mit
der zunehmenden spezifischen Oberfläche und den abnehmenden
Kristallinität zunimmt.

Die Konstanten der bei der numerischen Bearbeitung experimenteller Ergebnisse erhaltenen Gleichungen ändern sich in
Übereinstimmung mit dem theoretischen Wert der Gitterenergie
der untersuchten Minerale.

РЕЗЮМЕ

Изучены закономерности трансформации работы измельчения
для разрушения периклаза, магнезита и кальцита. Сумарное возрастание внутренней энергии субсистем разрушаемого материала
и механических инденторов $\Delta U_m + \Delta U_I$ в процессе измельчения
определялось как разница приведенной работы W и возвращенного
тепла Q в калориметрической мельнице. Возрастание внутренней
энергии субсистемы разрушаемого материала U_m после окончания
измельчения определялось как разница тепла растворения акти-
вированных продуктов измельчения и стабильной формы кристал-
лического материала.

Энергетический анализ хода измельчения в калориметрической мельнице и кинетический анализ возрастания внутренней
энергии в продуктах вибрационного измельчения позволяет вы-
вести уравнения, которые описывают зависимость возрастания
внутренней энергии системы от работы измельчения или от времени измельчения. Предельные величины этих уравнений характе-
ризуют емкость накопления энергии в материале.

Исследование механизма трансформации работы измельчения в
продуктах разрушения показало, что внутренняя энергия возрас-
тает прямолинейно с возрастающей удельной поверхностью и умень-
шающимся количеством кристаллической фазы.

Константы уравнений, полученные при вычислительной обра-
ботке экспериментальных результатов, изменяются в зависимости от теоретического значения энергии решетки изучаемых минералов.

ANALYSIS OF BREAKAGE MECHANISMS IN AUTOGENOUS GRINDING

E. V. Manlapig, R. A. Seitz and D. J. Spottiswood

Department of Metallurgical Engineering, Michigan Technological University, Houghton, USA

INTRODUCTION

Autogenous grinding is widely used in the processing of low grade ores. Its use has undergone steady expansion during the past twenty-five years. During this period, the design, operation and control of autogenous grinding circuits has been largely a learning process based on trial-and-error methods. Pilot plant scale primary autogenous mills, such as the one used in work reported here (Fig. 1), have been involved in the study of autogenous grinding.

There are two approaches that are usually followed in the development of a mathematical model to simulate a process. The first is the empirical approach. The type of model developed provides no information basic to the process. The equations are developed from a large quantity of data containing the effects of some of the selected variables on process performance using regression techniques. As may be expected, the model

677

Fig. 1. Autogenous grinding test rig.

developed using this approach is applicable only to a narrow range of conditions. Furthermore, in the case of autogenous grinding, the model can usually describe just one type of mill and is not suitable for any other type of mill or the treating of different types of ore.

The second is the mechanistic approach. A mechanistic model is based on the mechanisms that govern the process. Compared to the empirical approach, the mechanistic model has a wider range of application. Because of the close relationship between the mathematical model and the actual events occurring in the process, the model developed for one mill may be applied within limits to another mill.

The mechanistic approach has been followed in this project. In this paper the results of the first part of the research project, the study of the different mechanisms of breakage occurring in the autogenous mill, are discussed. The contents of the autogenous mill may be considered to consist of coarse and fine ore particles. Therefore, this paper is divided into two parts - the analysis of breakage of the coarse and the fine particles.

Two procedures were followed to determine the breakage mechanisms of the coarse and the fines. Briefly, in the case of the coarse, a batch grinding procedure was followed whereby changes in the weight and volume dimensions of a number of tagged samples were analyzed with time. For the fines, continuous grinding tests were used; the procedure was based on the measure of the rate by which the quantity of an impulse tracer instantaneously injected into the mill decreased with time.

The factor that differentiates autogenous grinding from conventional grinding is that in autogenous grinding the ore is reduced to a fine product by the action of the ore itself. The "grinding media" consists of the pieces of rock that comprise the coarse size fractions of the mill feed. Due to the tumbling motion of the mill, these coarse pieces not only crush the fine particles that are trapped between them, but they get whittled away in size due to the rubbing action between themselves, and to a lesser extent between themselves and the mill wall.

In predicting the mill product it is important to know the manner in which the coarse particles decrease in size, as this is the key to understanding the variations in the size distribution of the mill content; this in turn affects the breakage of the fine particles.

In autogenous grinding it is essential that sufficient coarse material which can grind the fine sizes be maintained. If the ore breaks down easily, there would be few of these large particles and the mill would be filled with material too small to accomplish any breakage yet too large to be easily broken. Ideally the large particles must break slowly, and the type of breakage that accomplishes this is abrasion.

Abrasion is the mode of size reduction whereby small pieces of rocks are broken due to the constant rubbing of large ore pieces against each other, and against the mill wall. The abrasion mechanism acts upon rounded media producing particles that go directly to the pulp or product.

Closely related to the abrasion breakage mechanism is chipping. It is the rapid wearing away of corners and edges on the original feed or on the products of impact breakage of rounded media.

Experimental

Test Rig. This study was conducted in a 183 x 61 cm Hardinge Cascade mill. The mill was arranged such that it functioned as a batch mill.

Test Material. The material that was used for this study was taken from a magnetite-chalcopyrite ore.

Test Procedure. The mill was filled with test material of a predetermined size and mass distribution. A number of the coarse particles were selected, sized and tagged using a penetrating dye. The mill was then run and after 10 min the mill charge was inspected, the tagged particles removed and physical measurements taken. The tagged particles were then re-dyed and returned to the mill and the cycle repeated.

To maintain the conditions in the mill as constant as possible, the charge, less the tagged particles, was screened and weighed after every three cycles and the mass lost in each size was replenished.

ANALYSIS OF RESULTS

Shown in Fig. 2 is a log-linear plot showing the change in mass of a particle as it was ground. It may be noted that the initial rate of decrease in size of the sample was relatively

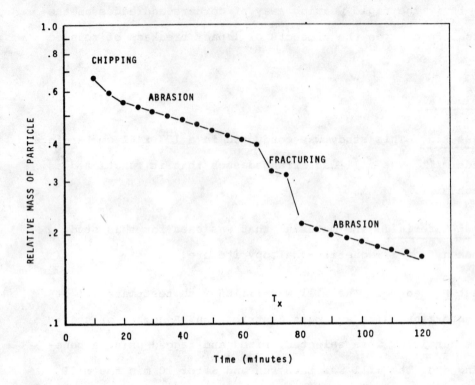

Fig. 2. Average relative mass of tagged particles as
a function of time.

rapid. This would be expected, as the dominant mechanism of
breakage was one of chipping of the edges and corners. The rate
of breakage was fast because the mechanism acted upon points
and edges - areas of high stress concentration - which broke
easily, and because the frequency of contact at these zones
was high.

As soon as these areas of weakness were worn away, the
effect of abrasion became dominant. During this stage of grinding, the rate of breakage was relatively slow. Digre [1] ex-

682

plained that during this stage of grinding individual grains
became torn away from the surface of the rounded rock due to
the frictional forces exceeding the strength of the matrix
cementing the grains.

The manner by which particles which have been broken by
abrasion from the parent rock are distributed in the finer sizes
was not analyzed in this study as it would have been extremely
difficult to locate these fine particles. It may be inferred,
though, that most of these fine particles report to the size
close to the product size, particularly those broken by true
abrasion. Wickham [2] and subsequently Stanley [3] proposed
that if the particles in a single size interval lose a proportion (y) of their mass as a result of an abrasion event, 0.354 y
(that is $(\frac{1}{\sqrt{2}})^3 y$) reports to the next smaller $\sqrt{2}$ size interval
while the remaining 0.646y is distributed among the finer sizes.

The dimensions of the parent rock as it was broken were also
determined. The lengths of the longest, intermediate and
shortest axial dimensions (S_L, S_M, and S_S respectively) were
determined and these are plotted in Fig. 3 on a logarithmic
scale. It may be seen that during the chipping breakage stage,
the length of the intermediate axial dimension S_M, was decreasing at a faster rate than the other dimensions S_L and S_S.
As soon as the chipping stage was over, the three axial dimensions decreased at almost equal rates.

At time T_X (Fig. 2), substantial changes in the mass of the
particles were observed. This may be attributed to breakage
along cracks in the rock probably brought about by high energy
collisions with other large particles in the mill or with the

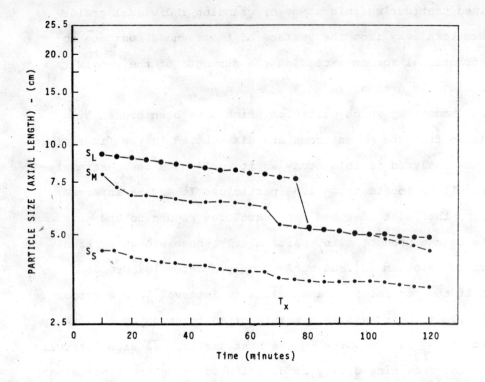

Fig. 3. Dimensions of tagged particle as a function of time.

mill liners. It could also be due to particle "fatique". This breakage is referred to as fracture breakage. Corresponding changes in the axial dimensions may be noted in Fig. 3.

Fracture breakage may also occur in rocks with well defined breakage planes which have been there even before the rocks enter the mill. Such fractures may be inherent, or introduced in the mining process, for example by blasting. It would be expected that breakage due to fracturing would occur during the first few minutes of residence of the rock in the mill if the fractures are already present. Ideally it is better if this type of fracture breakage does not occur to a large extent.

684

If it does, a build-up of small particles not capable of break-ing other rocks may develop.

The abrasion breakage becomes the dominant mode of comminu-tion again after the impact breakages at time T_x. It may be noted that the rate of breakage remained constant even after the fracture breakages. If may also be noted that the shortest dimension did not experience sharp changes in size during the fracture breakage period.

BREAKAGE OF FINE PARTICLES

Provided there is a sufficient quantity of coarse particles present in the mill, the fine particles can be ground by impact or attrition. The particle to be ground is caught between adja-cent coarse particles or between a coarse particle and the mill liner, and subsequently broken due to the forces acting on the fine particles. It has been proposed [1] that the rate of breakage due to attrition depends on the relative size between coarse and fine, the shape and degree of roundness of the par-ticles involved, and other parameters related to the mill.

In the study of the breakage mechanism of the coarse parti-cles, as described in the first part of this paper, the tests were conducted in a batch-operated autogenous mill. The change in size of tagged particles with time was studied, and in most cases it had been a relatively easy task to locate the tagged particles each time they had to be analyzed. However, it would not be simple to do the same in the case of fine particles, as it would be extremely difficult to locate and collect the tag-ged, fine particles in the mill. Therefore a different proce-

685

dure had to be developed. The study was conducted with the same
mill continuously operated in open circuit. The procedure was
based on the analysis of the rate by which the quantity of a
tracer (in this case, magnetite of a single size fraction),
instantaneously injected into the mill, decreased with time.

Experimental

Test Rig. This study was again conducted in a 183 x 61 cm
Hardinge Cascade mill with grate discharge and trommel screen.
Part of the trommel screen oversize was recirculated back to
the mill with conveyor belts, depending on the load in the mill.
The trommel undersize was discharged as tailings.

The grinding mill was equipped with load cells which provided
an indication of the mass of the material present in the mill.
The mill load reading, the power draw and the distribution of
the mill discharge were the measurements used to determine when
a steady state condition had been reached.

Test Materials. The feed to the mill consisted of rock
obtained from a local gravel quarry. The feed was sized, stored
separately and fed into the mill simulating a predetermined
feed size distribution.

The tracer used was magnetite (95% grade). The magnetite was
ground, screened and stored in single size fractions.

Test Procedure. The test mill was fed continuously 545
kilograms per hour of the test ore and sufficient water to maintain a trommel underflow density of 55%. When steady state was
reached, 3000 g of the tracer (magnetite of single size) was

introduced into the mill. Timed samples of the trommel undersize were then collected in buckets in regular intervals. The
magnetite was separated from the bulk of the sample using first
a drum magnetic separator, then cleaned in a Davis Magnetic
Tube. The final magnetic fraction was dried, screened, and
weighed.

ANALYSIS OF RESULTS

In this analysis, the results from a test using a tracer
consisting of -48 +65 mesh (-300 + 212 µm) magnetite are considered.

The magnetite tracer became thoroughly mixed with the other
material in the mill. Due to the action of the mill, the magnetite was ground. At the same time, some of the magnetite was
discharging from the mill. As a function of time, the amount of
-48 +65 mesh magnetite remaining in the mill was decreasing,
and the mass of -48 +65 mesh magnetite still remaining in the
mill (x_{65}) may be expressed as

$$\frac{dx_{65}}{dt} = - \begin{bmatrix} \text{rate of breakage} \\ \text{out of} \\ \text{-48 +65 mesh} \end{bmatrix} - \begin{bmatrix} \text{rate of discharge of} \\ \text{-48 +65 mesh} \\ \text{material from mill} \end{bmatrix} \quad (1)$$

Shown in Fig. 4 is a plot of the fraction of total magnetite,
broken and unbroken, remaining in the mill with time. This was
calculated from the original mass of impulse used, less the
cumulative mass of magnetite reporting to the product sample.
It can be seen in Fig. 4 that the transport mechanism through
the mill may be approximated as a lag followed by perfect
mixing. The rate constant of discharge, k_D, is 0.133 min^{-1}.

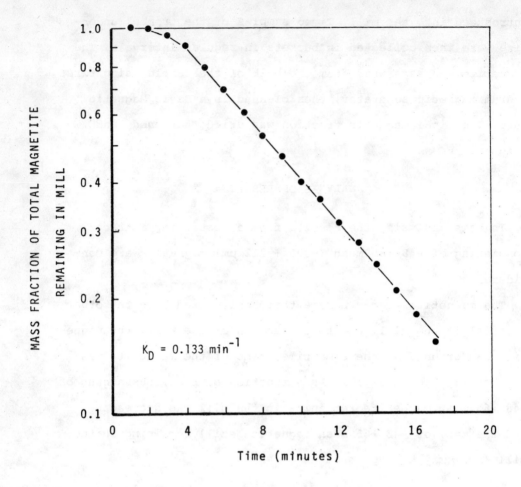

Fig. 4. Mass fraction remaining of total magnetite (broken
and unbroken) as a function of time following
introduction of −48 +65 mesh magnetite.

Within limits, it may be shown that in a perfect mixer, the
rate of discharge of each species present is related to the
rate of discharge of the entire contents. Consider that x_i is
the quantity of species i in the mill and $\sum x_i$ is the quantity
of all species, then

$$\frac{dx_i}{dt} = f(t) \; \frac{d \sum x_i}{dt} \qquad (2)$$

The discharge of all species follows the kinetic first order law as shown in Fig. 4, thus

$$\frac{d \sum x_i}{dt} = -k_D \sum x_i \qquad (3)$$

Substituting in Eq. (2) gives

$$\frac{dx_i}{dt} = -f(t) \, k_D \sum x_i \qquad (4)$$

However, $f(t)$ is equal to $\dfrac{x_i}{x_i}$, so Eq. (4) becomes

$$\frac{dx_i}{dt} = - \frac{x_i}{x_i} \, k_D \sum x_i \qquad (5)$$

that is,

$$\frac{dx_i}{dt} = -k_D \, x_i \qquad (6)$$

Therefore the rate of discharge constant k_D of the sum of the species is also the rate of discharge constant of each species.

From the fraction of $-48 +65$ mesh magnetite in each magnetite sample taken, the amount of $-48 +65$ mesh magnetite still remaining in the mill at different times - assuming perfect mixing in the mill - may be approximated. Shown in Fig. 5 is the plot of the mass of $-48 +65$ mesh magnetite in the mill expressed as a fraction of the original quantity introduced into the mill. It may be noted that the total rate of disappearance of the $-48 +65$ mesh magnetite (x_{65}) follows the first order law, that is

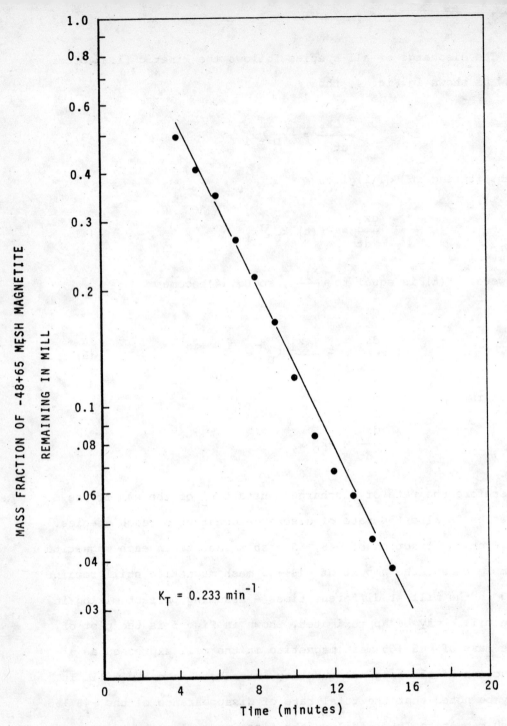

Fig. 5. Mass fraction remaining of unbroken (-48 +65 mesh)
magnetite as a function of time following introduction
of -48 +65 mesh magnetite.

$$\frac{dx_{65}}{dt} = -k_T \, x_{65} \qquad (7)$$

where $k_T = 0.233 \text{ min}^{-1}$. As this is a first order Equation and as the rate of discharge is also first order, it may be inferred that breakage is also first order. Therefore

$$\frac{dx_{65}}{dt} = -k_D \, x_{65} - k_B \, x_{65} \qquad (8)$$

and

$$k_T = k_D + k_B \qquad (9)$$

Thus the rate of breakage of the -48 +65 mesh fraction is 0.100 min^{-1}.

CONCLUSIONS

Experimental procedures have been developed to determine the breakage mechanisms for the different sizes of particle in an autogenous mill. It has been observed that abrasion and attrition are the two major mechanisms of breakage for the coarse and the fine particles respectively. It was also observed that these two modes of breakage follow the first order law. It has been recognized that in the case of the coarse sizes, two other modes of breakage - namely chipping and fracturing - must be considered.

ACKNOWLEDGMENTS

The authors wish to acknowledge the staff of the Institute of Mineral Research of Michigan Technological University for

their assistance and for providing the facilities for the study
of the breakage of fine particles. Their permission to publish
data on the breakage of coarse particles is also acknowledged.

REFERENCES

1. Digre M. Wet Autogenous Grinding in Tumbling Mills. <u>Acta
   Polytechnica Scandinavica</u>, Ch. 88, 1969.

2. Wickham P. Comminution of Pebbles and Fine Ores. M. Eng. Sc.
   Thesis, University of Queensland (unpublished) 1972.

3. Stanley G. G. Mechanisms in the Autogenous Mill and Their
   Mathematical Representation, J. Inst. S. Afr. I. M. M.,
   Nov. 1974, pp. 77-97.

ABSTRACT

The comminution of particles in an autogenous mill was
studied to determine the mechanisms of breakage in this type of
mill. Batch and continuous grinding experiments were conducted
in a pilot plant scale autogenous mill. Impact and abrasion
breakage were observed as the dominant mechanisms in the process. It is experimentally shown that abrasion breakage follows
a first order rate law. The paper also shows that impact breakage is first order. A comparison between the mechanisms of
breakage in the autogenous mill and conventional ball mill is
also presented.

RÉSUMÉ

On a étudié le broyage de grains dans un broyeur autogène
pour déterminer le mécanisme du processus. Les essais pério-
dique et continue à l'échell semi-technique a été menée dans
un broyeur autogène. L'observation montre qu'au cours du
processus examiné c'est le broyage par chocs et abrasion qui
domine. On a démontré expérimentalement que le broyage par
abrasion peut être décrit par l'équation du premier ordre.
Dans le travail on a montré que de pareiless relations sont
valables pour le broyage par chocs. On a comparé le mécanisme
du broyage dans un broyeur autogène et celui dans un broyeur
à boulets conventionnel.

ZUSAMMENFASSUNG

Es wird der Zerkleinerungsprozeß in einer autogenen Mühle
untersucht, um den Mechanismus dieses Vorganges zu bestimmen.
Periodische und kontinuierliche Mahlversuche wurden im halb-
technischen Maßstab durchgeführt.

Es konnte beobachtet werden, daß in dem untersuchten Prozeß
die Zerkleinerung durch Auschlag und Abreitung dominiert.

Es wurde experimentell nachgewiesen, daß die Zerkleinerung
durch Abreitung anhand einer Gleichung erster Ordnung umschrie-
ben werden kann.

Im Beitrag wird veranschaulicht, daß ähnliche Abhängigkeiten ebenfalls für die Zerkleinerung durch Auschlag gelten. Es wurde ein Vergleich des Zerkleinerungsmechanismus in einer autogenen Mühle und in den konventionellen Kugelmühlen dargestellt.

РЕЗЮМЕ

Исследовано раздробление частиц при самоизмельчении с целью определения механизма растрескивания. Произведены опыты по периодическому и непрерывному измельчению на опытном заводе. Наблюдалось появление трещин под влиянием удара и истирания как доминирующие механизмы процесса. Экспериментально установлено, что трещины под действием истирания образуются в соответствии с законом скорости первого порядка.

В докладе показано также, что растрескивание под действием удара, является также первого порядка. Произведено сравнение механизмов растрескивания в мельницах самоизмельчения и традиционных шаровых мельницах.

EFFECT OF CHEMICAL ADDITIVES ON WET GRINDING OF IRON ORE MINERALS

H. El-Shall, A. Gorken and P. Somasundaran

Henry Krumb School of Mines, Columbia University, New York, USA

INTRODUCTION

With the rapid depletion of high grade iron ore deposits, development of technology to treat vast reserves of complex low grade ores efficiently becomes imperative. A major problem in this regard is the fine liberation size which requires very fine grinding of the ore.

Grinding being the most energy intensive process in milling, it becomes an important task to increase the efficiency of it. Even though there have been scattered empirical attempts by researchers in this regard, physico-chemical aspects of this problem have not received much attention. A review of the past work had shown that the addition of chemicals can produce beneficial grinding effects [1]. There have been reports of successful use of grinding aids on a commercial scale in Germany and Yugoslavia for increasing the capacity of mills substantially [2]. It is to be noted, however, that there have also been reports suggesting the contrary [1]. The majority of the work that we reviewed was found to be in conflict with each other due to lack of proper control of all the relevant variables and possibly owing to experimental artifacts that can arise out of sieving of fines that have not been properly dispersed after contacting with surfactants. In addition, there can also be complications which arise from difficulties in controlling the chemical composition of the environment in the mill particularly during grinding of complex ores [3]. It is clear that much care is needed in controlling and monitoring all the relevant conditions of the grinding environment for a useful study of the effect of chemical additives in grinding.

In this study, effect of commonly used collectors and dispersants on grinding is studied under different physico-chemical conditions with the specific aim of deriving information that is required for the understanding of the mechanisms involved. Mechanisms that have been proposed in the past for the effect of additives on comminution processes include those based on adsorption-induced surface energy changes and adsorption-induced mobility of near-surface dislocations [4, 5]. In the case of grinding, chemical additives can affect grinding also by modifying the flow of pulp in the grinding mill, reagglomeration of the freshly produced fines, frothing characteristics of the pulp during grinding and possibly even interactions between balls and mineral particles.

Fluidity modifiers and dispersants have been reported to produce both increase and decrease in grinding efficiency [6, 7]. For example, Hartley et al. [7] have reported a marked decrease in grinding efficiency during grinding of molybdenum

696

ore upon using sodium tripolyphosphate. Since such chemicals are often added in the grinding mill, it is important to establish the conditions under which they can be helpful in grinding.

MATERIALS AND METHODS

Minerals

Minerals used in this study were quartz crystals of 99.9% purity (Hot Springs, Arkansas) purchased from Ward's Natural Science Establishment. Two different samples of hematite were used: hematite 1 (Itaberia ore) supplied by Bethlehem Steel Corporation and Hematite 2 supplied by Inland Steel Co.

Surfactants and Chemicals

Dodecylammonium chloride (DDACl) of practical grade purchased from Eastman Kodak, Dowfroth-250, sodium silicate certified reagent and oleic acid of technical grade purchased from Fisher Scientific Company and sodium tripolyphosphate (STPP) and sodium hexametaphosphate (SHMP) which were purchased from Pfaltz and Bauer, Inc. were used in this study. pH adjustments were made using reagent grade KOH, HNO_3 and NaOH, or HCl. Reagent grade KNO_3 and NaCl were used for adjusting the ionic strength. The ferric nitrate crystals used were purchased from Fisher Scientific Company. Ground products were always dispersed with the help of sodium silicate. Triple distilled water was used for the preparation of all solutions.

Experimental Procedure

Grinding Tests. Grinding of quartz in the presence of dode-cylamine was carried out in a (18.75 cm dia x 20 cm length) stainless steel ball mill with six lifters. 114 stainless steel balls, each of 2.5 cm, 1.88 cm and 1.25 cm diameters with a total weight of 11.9 kg were used as the ball charge. The load volume was 45% of that of the mill. All the experiments were done at a speed of 80 rpm (78% C.S.) and a pulp density of 68% solids by weight. The feed size was 4 x 8 mesh. For grinding of quartz or hematite in the presence of sodium silicate, STPP and SHMP the milling conditions were:

ball loading, J = 0.2 of the mill volume,

sixty-nine 2.6 cm diameter stainless steel balls,

mill speed, ϕ = 59% critical speed,

pulp density = as indicated,

slurry volume, u = 0.5 of the void volume between the balls,

feed size = 10 x 14 mesh.

All quartz grinding tests were done for 10 min.

Hematite was ground for 7.5 min in a steel ball mill of the same dimensions as the stainless steel one. Conditions used for studying hematite/oleate system were the same as those used in the case of grinding quartz in the presence of amine but the hematite feed size was 10 x 14 mesh.

The size distribution of the ground products was determined using the wet-dry sieving method where the -400 mesh size frac-tion was first separated using wet sieving and the +400 mesh size fraction was subsequently dried and sieved on a Ro-tap for 15 min.

Microscopic Studies. Various size fractions of the ground product were examined under a microscope and compared with totally dispersed standards both to assess the magnitude of the effects of experimental artifacts that are introduced in the past due to incomplete dispersion of the ground products and to ensure that such artifacts are totally eliminated in the present study. Also, in order to study the extent of dispersion during grinding, wet samples taken from the mill were microscopically examined.

Turbidity Tests. To determine the aggregation behaviour of mineral fines in the mill, 0.3 g samples of -400 mesh quartz were prepared in an agate mortar and were mixed with 50 cc. of a 10^{-4} mole/l ferric nitrate solution adjusted to the desired pH, ionic strength and surfactant concentration to simulate the grinding environment. Ferric nitrate was added to account for the iron that is released from the mill during grinding. The resultant suspension was tumbled for 10 min and the turbidity of a sample of it was determined using a Spectronic 20 Spectrophotometer at a wave length of 620 mm.

Flotation Tests. Denver (D2) laboratory flotation machine was used for conditioning at 1500 rpm and for the flotation at 1200 rpm. The pulp density in both cases was 30%. The flotation feed was -48 +400 mesh prepared by grinding -6 +14 mesh size fraction of the quartz in the stainless steel ball mill with 20% ball load, 68% critical speed and 65% pulp density. When the collector was added after grinding, the test procedure included grinding of quartz for 10 min in distilled water at natural pH, wet screening of the ground products to recover

the -48 +400 mesh size fraction for flotation, transferring this
size fraction to the flotation cell (water from screening step
was used for flotation), adjustement of pH and ionic strength
(I.S. = 3 x 10^{-2} M), and after the addition of the collector,
conditioning of the pulp at 1500 rpm for 10 min, measurement of
flotation pH, addition of a few drops of Dowfroth-250 and flotation till completion at 1200 rpm. Procedure in tests where collector was added in the mill on the other hand included addition
of water containing electrolyte and acid or an alkali to the
solid in the mill, grinding for 10 min, measurement of pH, wet
screening, transferring of the required size fraction with solution from screening step to flotation cell, readjustment of pH,
addition of a few drops of the frother and flotation till completion at 1200 rpm.

Electrophoretic Mobility Measurements. Electrophoretic mobility measurements were made with a Zeta-meter and samples of the
solution prepared for the turbidity tests were used for this
purpose.

RESULTS AND DISCUSSIONS

Effect of Preconditioning in Water

The effect obtained for preconditioning the hematite with
water is illustrated in Fig. 1 and 2. The results indicate
clearly that improved grinding can be obtained by contacting the
ore with water prior to grinding for a certain length of time.
The optimum time in our case was found to be around 15 min. It
is to be noted that the conditioning procedure was very simple
and did not require elaborate equipment. To determine whether

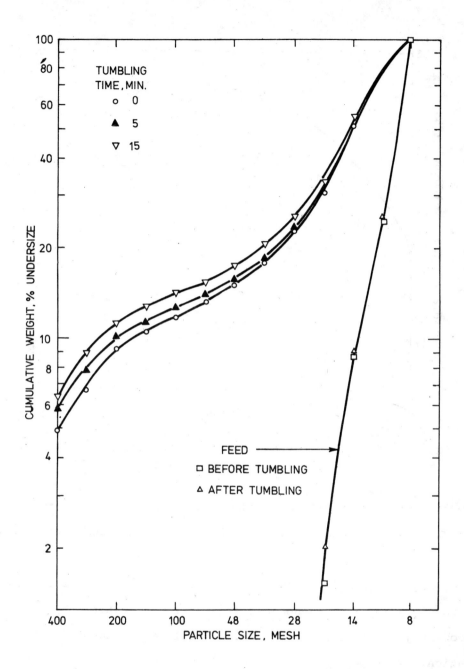

Fig. 1. Effect of tumbling the ore in water before grinding,
on the size distribution of hematite 1 (grinding
time = 0.5 min).

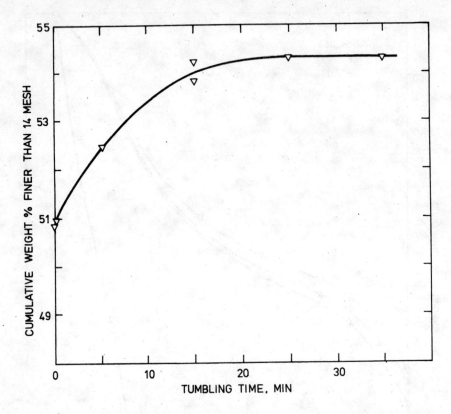

Fig. 2. Effect of tumbling time, in water before grinding,
on the grindability of hematite 1.

the conditioning itself had produced any grinding, the size distribution of the feed was redetermined after tumbling for 15 min.
Results given in Fig. 1 show that conditioning itself resulted
in negligible grinding. The effect observed in the present case
is possibly due to the enhanced penetration of water into the
porous regions of the ore particles facilitating their disintegration.

Effect of Collector Addition

The effects of addition of dodecylamine on the grinding of quartz and oleic acid on the grinding of hematite were studied at different pH levels. Typical results obtained for the size distribution of quartz ground in water and amine solutions and dispersed in different ways before sieving are given in Fig. 3. It can be seen that the size distributions obtained for the same product ground in 10^{-1} mole/l amine solution but dispersed in one case using 6.3 kg/t of sodium silicate and the other case using alcohol and acetone washes differ markedly from each other. Whereas beneficial effects are apparent when the products are washed with acetone and alcohol washes, in the absence of such washes significant reduction in grinding is indicated. A microscopic study of the ground product showed incomplete dispersion with sodium silicate to be the reason for the above observation.

For the case of ground product dispersed with the help of sodium silicate alone, significant coating of the coarser particles by the fines was observed while alcohol and acetone washes eliminated such coating completely (see Fig. 4). It is to be noted that sodium silicate is commonly used to obtain dispersion of the ground product. The results obtained here suggest the possibility that the data reported in literature for the effect of surfactants on grinding may be invalid since it appears that the ground products have seldom been examined under a microscope.

The effect of amine addition at concentrations lower than 10^{-1} mole/l and at other pH levels were next investigated.

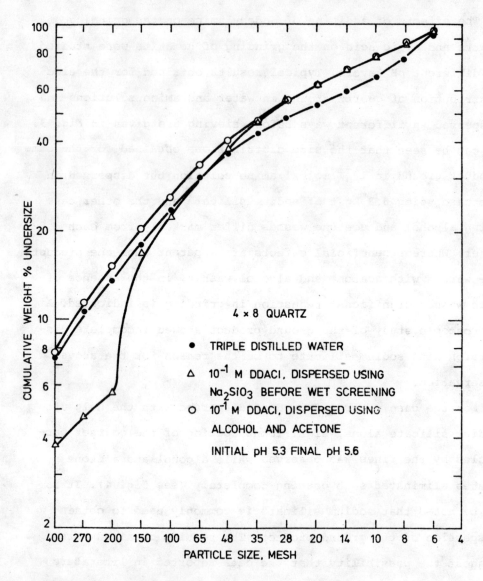

Fig. 3. Gaudin-Schuhmann size distribution of quartz ground
in 10^{-1} mole/l dodecylammonium chloride solution in
stainless steel ball mill at natural pH.

Fig. 4a. Photomicrograph of (-14+20 mesh) size fraction of
quartz ground in 10^{-1} mole/l amine in stainless
steel mill, dispersed using 6.3 kg/t sodium
silicate.

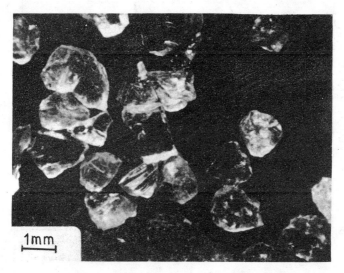

Fig. 4b. Photomicrograph of (-14+20 mesh) size fraction of
quartz ground in 10^{-1} mole/l amine in stainless
steel mill; dispersed using 6.3 kg/t sodium silicate and then washed with alcohol and acetone.

Results given in Fig. 5 confirm that amine addition can be beneficial under both alkaline and neutral pH conditions. Additions
of amine to acidic solutions were, however, found to produce a
definite retardation of the grinding. These results are comparable with those obtained for the flotation of quartz using amine.

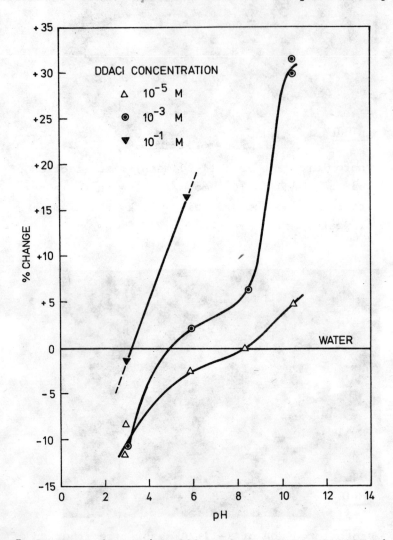

Fig. 5. Percent change in -200 mesh quartz produced owing to
the addition of dodecylammonium chloride at different
pH values.

Maximum flotation of quartz is obtained in this case around pH 10 to 11 [8]. This observation has been well correlated with the formation of a highly surface active amine-aminium complex in this pH range [9].

The study of the effect of oleic acid addition on the grinding of hematite also produced similar effects. A significant increase in grinding was obtained particularly around pH 8 (see Table 1); note that for oleic acid solutions this is the pH region where maximum amount of acid-soap complex is expected to form [8]. Clearly there appears to be a strong correlation between the effect of the surfactants on grinding and the formation of the highly surface active ionomolecular complexes in solution.

TABLE 1

Effect of Addition of Oleic Acid on the Rate of Grinding
of Hematite 2 at Different pH Values, Compared
to that Obtained in Water Alone

Concentration of oleic acid, (mole/l)	% change in amount of -400 mesh produced			
	pH 3.0	pH 6.6	pH 8.7	pH 11.0
0.0 (water)	-	-	-	-
3×10^{-7}	+1.0	-2.8	+9.0	-1.0
		$(-4.1)^{*}$	$(+10.0)^{*}$	
3×10^{-5}	+2.3	+7.8	+9.0	+4.5

*duplicate experiments.

The process of grinding can be influenced by long-chain surfactants such as the ones used here in a number of ways. In such

cases, flocculation of the mineral fines, enhanced coating of
the coarse particles by the ultrafines, frothing and the resultant increase in the overall viscosity, entrapment of fines in
the froth and, alterations in the nature of friction between
particles as well as between balls and particles are among factors that have to be taken into account. Several of these processes will in turn be governed by the alterations in experimentally accesible properties such as zeta-potential of the particles, surface tension of the solution etc. The extent of flocculation, on the other hand, can be followed by determining the
turbidity of the suspension under relevant conditions. The
results obtained for the transmission of the light through the
suspension and the electrophoretic mobilities of the particles
in water and 10^{-5} mole/l dodecylammonium chloride solutions,
both of them containing also 10^{-4} mole/l ferric nitrate, are
given in Figs. 6 and 7 respectively. Comparison of the results
obtained for flocculation (as indicated by the increased light
transmittance of the supernatant) with changes in grinding rates
at various pH values show excellent correlation between the two
properties. Higher the flocculation, lower is the grinding rate.
The decrease in grinding rate in the presence of this surfactant can thus be attributed, at least partly, to the flocculation of the ground product. Addition of amine in concentrations
greater than 10^{-5} mole/l had produced less flocculation as well
as more grinding. Flocculation itself is related to the electrophoretic mobilities given in Fig. 7 for the same system. Increased mobilities above about pH 7 is correlated with the reduced flocculation in this pH range. This is in agreement with
the data in literature for the aggregation of mineral fines in

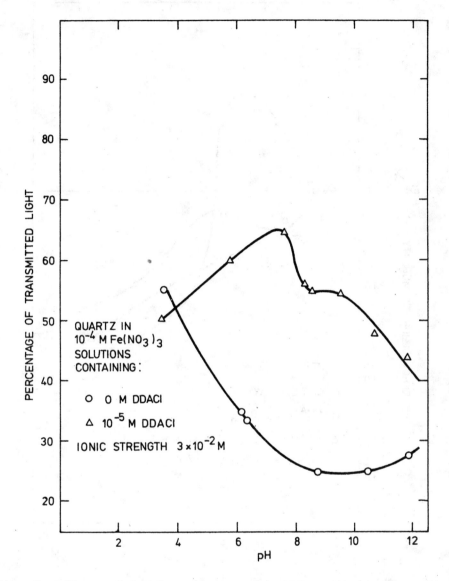

Fig. 6. Effect of dodecylammonium chloride additions on the turbidity of quartz slimes in 10^{-4} mole/l $Fe(NO_3)_3$ solutions as a function of pH.

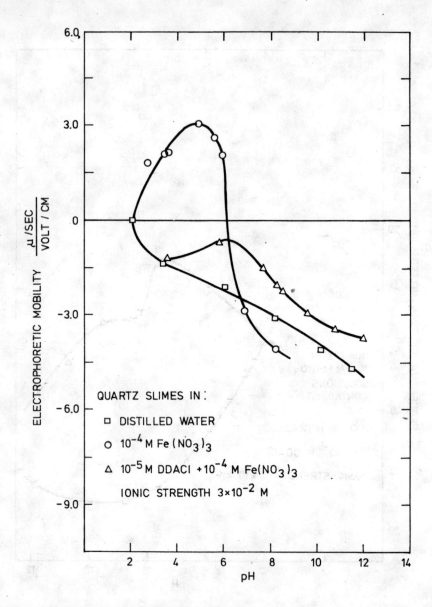

Fig. 7. Effect of Fe(NO$_3$)$_3$ and dodecylammonium chloride additions on electrophoretic mobility of quartz.

surfactant solution [10]. A flocculation model that is based upon the zeta-potential of the particles and resultant repulsion was successfully tested here. In addition to the above, the increased grinding in amine solutions under alkaline pH conditions can also be related as indicated earlier to the surface activity of the amine under these conditions as shown by both surface tension and flotation [8]. It might be noted at this point that the grinding of quartz in water alone does not correlate with the flocculation of its fines in solutions containing only the ferric nitrate. Increased grinding is obtained at lower pH values where flocculation increases (see Figs. 7 and 8). The flocculation results again correlate well with the electrophoretic mobility of quartz obtained in solutions containing only $Fe(NO_3)_3$ (see Figs. 6 and 7).

Effect of Addition of Surfactants on Subsequent Flotations

Flotation recoveries of quartz at two levels of amine additions are given in Figs. 9 and 10 as a function of pH for the cases where the collector was added before and after grinding. Flotation obtained was poorer when the collector was added in the grinding mill than when it was added after grinding at lower levels of addition (0.023 kg/t). At higher levels (0.15 kg/t) there was not noticeable difference between the results for the two cases. It is to be recalled that at the higher concentration of 10^{-3} mole/l (0.15 kg/t) the grinding efficiency had improved for this system. The observed effect at lower levels can be attributed to the removal of the adsorbed collector by the wash water used during the wet screening. It appears that at higher levels of collector addition, there is excess collector

711

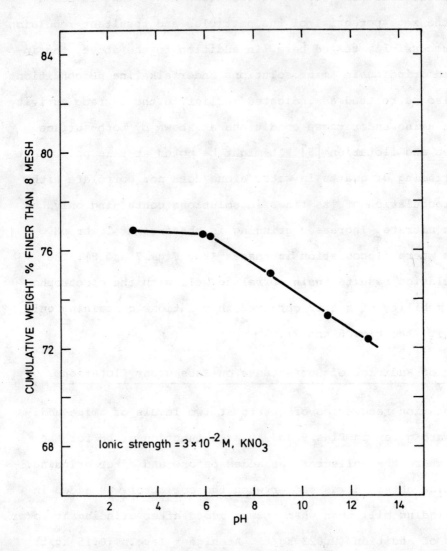

Fig. 8. Effect of pH on wet grinding of quartz in stainless
ball mill.

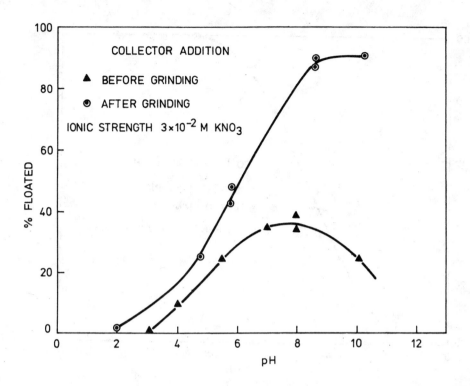

Fig. 9. Flotation of quartz using dodecylammonium chloride
(0.023 kg/t).

adsorbed so that even after washing sufficient amount remains
to produce flotation at least in the alkaline range. It is not
clear why there is no decrease in flotation due to such removal
in the acidic range where the flotation has remained incomplete
even when the collector was introduced after the grinding stage.

Effect of Addition of "Dispersants"

The results obtained for the effect of sodium silicate additions on wet grinding of quartz and hematite are given in Figs. 11
and 12 respectively. It is clear that the addition of silicate
does in general produce a decrease in grinding rate. This can

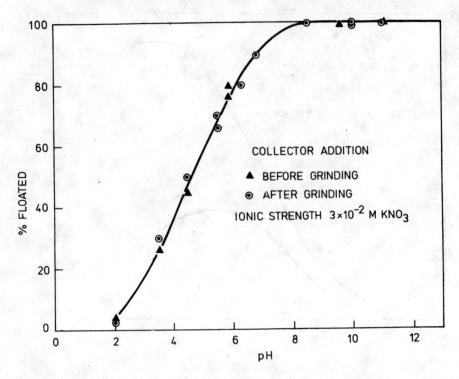

Fig. 10. Flotation of quartz using dodecylammonium
chloride (0.15 kg/t).

also be seen by examining the data for the effect of different
additions of sodium silicate (Table 2) and sodium trypolyphosphate (STPP) and sodium hexametaphosphate (SHMP) (Table 3) on
the rate of production of -400 mesh quartz. It can be seen that
the phosphates also cause a decrease in the grinding efficiency
at all levels.

Interestingly, such detrimental effect of the above dispersing agents is noticed only in the alkaline pH range (~pH 10.5)
with no effect at other pH conditions. Also, whereas STPP addition was found to produce a decrease in grinding rate in the

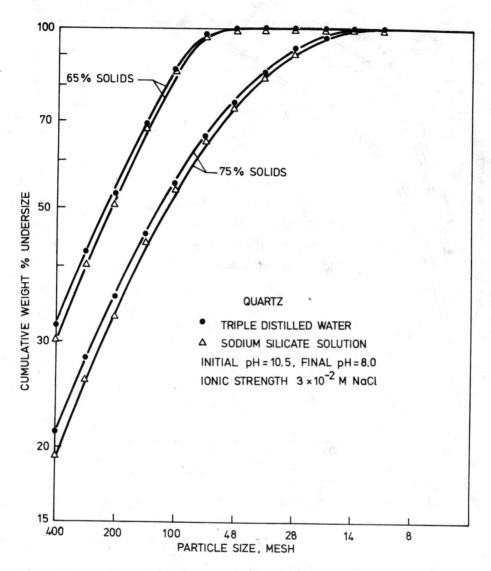

Fig. 11. Gaudin-Schuhmann size distribution of quartz ground
in water and in 0.23 kg/t sodium silicate solution
at two different pulp densities.

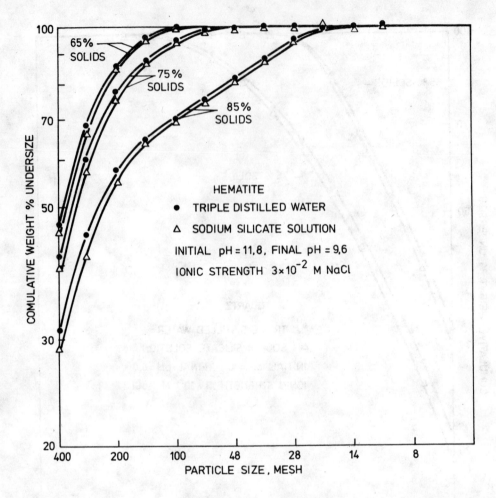

Fig. 12. Gaudin-Schuhmann size distribution of hematite 1
         ground in water and in 0.45 kg/t sodium silicate
         solution at three different pulp densities.

TABLE 2

Effect of Different Levels of Addition of Sodium Silicate on
the Rate of Production of Quartz Fines as Compared to
Corresponding Values Obtained in Water Alone

Levels of Addition kg/t	% change in amount of -400 mesh		Remarks
	65% solids	75% solids	
0.0 (water)	-	-	pH = 10.5; Ionic
0.05	-3.7	-3.5	strength = 3 x 10^{-2}M
0.11	**	-10.0 (-8.3)*	NaCl
0.23	-5.3	-9.6	* duplicate tests
0.45	**	-6.6 (-7.9)*	
1.36	-1.5	-5.2	** not conducted

TABLE 3

Effect of Different Additions of STPP and SHMP
on the Rate of Production of -400 mesh of Quartz
as Compared to that Obtained for Grinding
in Water Alone

Levels of Addition kg/t	% change in amount of -400 mesh		Remarks
	STPP	SHMP	
0.0 (water)	-	-	pH = 10.5; pulp
0.05	-5.1	-4.8	density = 75% solids;
0.23	-5.7 (-6.9)*	-7.0 (-5.9)*	Ionic strength =
1.36	-5.8	-5.9	3 x 10^{-2} M (NaCl).
			* Duplicate tests.

case of quartz, its addition resulted in an increase in the grinding of hematite at both 0.10 kg/t and 1.36 kg/t levels (see Table 4), but again only in the alkaline range.

TABLE 4

Effect of Different Levels of STPP on the Rate
of Production of -400 Mesh of Hematite 1,
as Compared to that Obtained for Grinding
in Water Alone

Levels of Addition kg/t	% Change in Amount of -400 mesh	Remarks
0.1	+4.9 (+5.4)[*]	pulp density = 65% solids;
0.23	+4.4 (+5.4)[*]	pH = 11.0; Ionic strength
0.45	+4.5	= 3 x 10^{-2} M (NaCl)
1.36	+4.6	[*]Duplicate tests

In order to ascertain the state of dispersion of the ground products in the presence of the above reagents, their samples were subjected to microscopic examination. These tests showed the presence of considerable flocculation inside the mill in the absence of sodium silicate and total dispersion in its presence. Typical microphotographs of the ground products obtained in water and in a sodium silicate solution are given in Fig. 13. It is likely that particles are possibly no longer coating the balls and the mill walls in the presence of sodium silicate and consequently escaping the ball impacts. Such a situation could indeed contribute towards a decrease in the grinding efficiency.

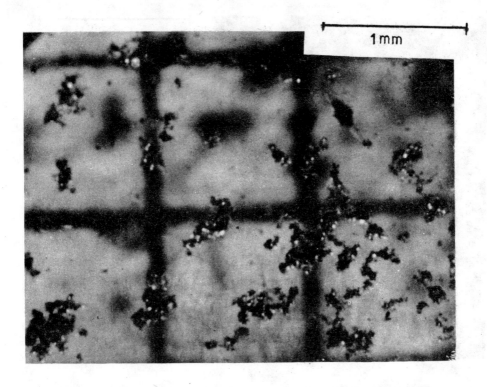

Fig. 13a.   Typical photomicrograph of hematite 1 ground
            in water (wet condition).

The effects observed here are of considerable theoretical
and practical importance since dispersants such as those discussed above are often added in processing circuits. Clearly
further studies to establish the behaviour of the dispersants
and flocculants in detail and to develop a full understanding
of the mechanisms involved should prove fruitful.

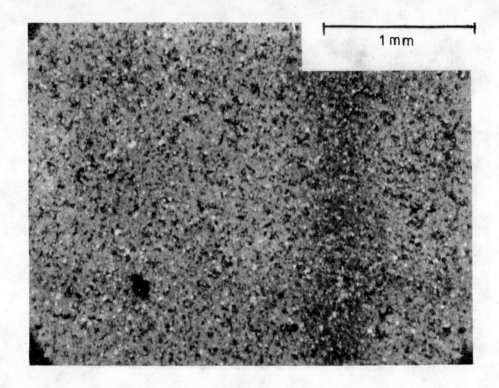

Fig. 13b. Typical photomicrograph of hematite 1 ground
in 0.45 kg/t sodium silicate solution.

SUMMARY AND CONCLUSIONS

(1) Effect of organic (dodecylammonium chloride and oleic acid)
and inorganic (sodium silicate, sodium trypolyphosphate and
sodium hexametaphosphate) additives on the wet grinding of
quartz and hematite under various pH conditions has been
investigated in this study.

(2) Grinding of quartz using amine could be improved under certain pH and amine levels. In the alkaline pH range, improved
grinding could be obtained at all amine levels; larger additions were, however, necessary to produce beneficial effects

720

under natural pH conditions. Interestingly, under acidic
conditions a decrease in grinding was observed at all amine
levels. These results correlate well with flotation and surface tension reductions that are obtained with amine solutions at different pH levels.

(3) Addition of oleic acid in amounts of 3×10^{-5} mole/l produced beneficial effects on hematite grinding under all pH
conditions.

(4) An attempt has been made to elucidate the mechanisms involved by studying flocculation and electrokinetic behaviour
of the mineral system under similar conditions.

(5) Most importantly, it was observed that microscopic examination of the ground product before size analysis is necessary
to ascertain absence of any aggregation. The common practice
of the use of sodium silicate was found to be insufficient
in the present study for proper dispersion of the ground
product even when it was added in excess amounts.

(6) Effect of amine addition before grinding on the flotation
recovery of quartz was also investigated. Poor flotation
was obtained when the collector was added in the grinding
mill at lower levels of addition (0.023 kg/t).

(7) A study of the effect of certain dispersants (as sodium
silicate, sodium hexametaphosphate and sodium tripolyphosphate) in the mill showed that the grinding of quartz
decreases significantly under the conditions tested.

(8) Detrimental effects were also observed upon the addition of
sodium silicate during grinding of hematite. On the other

hand, the use of sodium tripolyphosphate was found to improve the grinding rate of hematite under certain conditions.

(9) Microscopic examination of the samples from the mill indicated a correlation between the extent of dispersion of the mineral fines and the decrease in grinding possibly due to reduced coating of the balls and the mill walls by the fines.

ACKNOWLEDGMENTS

The authors acknowledge American Iron and Steel Institute for support of this research and Professor C. C. Harris for helpful discussions.

REFERENCES

1. Somasundaran P. and Lin I. J. I. and E. C. Process Design and Development, 11, 321-331 (1972).

2. Locher F. W. and Seebach H. M. I. and E. C. Process Design and Development, 11, 190-196 (1972).

3. Ryncarz A. and Laskowski J. Powder Tech., 18, 179-185 (1977).

4. Rehbinder P. A. On the Effect of Surface Energy Changes on Cohesion, Hardness, and Other Properties of Crystals, Proc. Sixth Phys. Congr., State Press, Moscow, 1928, p. 29.

5. Westwood A. R. C. Effects of Adsorption on Hardness and the Mobility of Near-Surface Dislocations in Nonmetals, Ch. in Advances in Materials Research, 2, Microplasticity, Interscience Publishers, New York, 1968, pp. 365-382.

6. Hanna K. M. and Gamal A. E. Powder Tech., 17, 19-25 (1977).

7. Hartley J. N., Prisbrey K. A. and Wick O. J. Energy Reduction in Ore Grinding, presented at the 83rd Annual Convention of the Northwest Mining Association, Spokane, Washington, 1977, 18.

8. Ananthapadmanabhan K., Somasundaran P. and Healy T. W. The Chemistry of Oleate and Amine Solutions in Relation to Flotation, paper presented at 107th Annual AIME Meeting, Denver, 78-B-67.

9. Somasundaran P. Intern. J. Miner. Processing, 3, 35-40 (1976).

10. Somasundaran P., Healy T. W. and Fuerstenau D. W. J. Colloid and Interface Science, 22, 599-605 (1966).

ABSTRACT

A study on the effect of both inorganic and organic additives on wet grinding of iron ore constituent minerals (quartz and hematite) has shown that improved grinding can be obtained but only under certain levels of the additive concentration and pH. Under other conditions, the chemicals additions can produce even deleterious effects. These effects are compared with those normally obtained for flotation.

Zeta potential and flocculation characteristics of the systems determined under conditions similar to that of grinding tests have been used to elucidate the mechanisms involved. It was found that the effect of the chemical additives can often be masked by their ability to flocculate the ground products. Microscopic examination of the ground products (dispersed and sieved) has clearly shown the possibility for the existence of major experimental artifacts due to incomplete dispersion in the past work.

Also, the interaction of such additives with the performance of subsequent flotation is also examined here.

RÉSUMÉ

Une étude sur l'effet des additifs minéraux et organiques sur le broyage humide des minéraux constitués de minerai de fer (Quartz et hématite) a montré qu'une amélioration du broyage peut être obtenue mais seulement sous certaines limites de concentration d'additifs et de pH. Sous d'autres conditions, les additions chimiques peuvent même produire des effets délétères. Ces effets sont comparables à ceux obtenus normalement par flottation.

Le potentiel Zeta et les caractéristiques de floculation des systèmes déterminés sous des conditions semblables à celles des essais de broyage sont utilisés pour élucider les mécanismes impliqués. On a trouvé que l'effet des additifs chimiques peut être souvent masqué par l'aptitude de ces derniers à floculer les produits du sol. Une étude microscopique des produits du sol (dispersés et passés au tamis) a clairement montré l'existence possible d'artifices majeurs expérimentaux causés par une dispersion incomplète dans le travail précédent.

De même, l'interaction de tels additifs avec l'accomplissement de la flottation consécutive est examinée ici.

ZUSAMMENFASSUNG

Die Untersuchung des Einflusses sowohl organischer als auch anorganischer Zusatzstoffe auf's feuchte Mahlen eisenerzhaltiger Minerale (Quarz, Eisenglanz) hat erwiesen, dass die Ergebnisse des Mahlens nur bei einem bestimmten Konzentrationswert der Zusatzstoffe (Additive) bei bestimmten pH-Werten verbessert werden können. Unter anderen Bedingungen kann der Zusatz chemischer Additive sogar nachteilige Auswirkungen haben. Diese Effekte werden mit denjenigen verglichen, die normalerweise bei der Flotation zu beobachten sind.

Das Zeta-Potential und die Flockungsmerkmale von Systemen, die unter ähnlichen Bedingungen wie die des Mahlens untersucht worden sind, haben dazu beigetragen, den hier einbezogenen Mechanismus zu erläutern. Es wurde festgestellt, dass der Einfluss chemischer Zusatzstoffe in vielen Fällen, dank ihrer Fähigkeit das mahlane Produkt zu flockulieren, maskiert werden kann. Mikroskopische Untersuchungen der Mahlprodukte (die dispergiert und gesiebt wurden) haben eindeutig erwiesen, dass ein Auftreten grösserer experimenteller Artefakte infolge der unvollständigen Dispersion in vorangegangenen Untersuchungen durchaus möglich ist.

Auch die Wechselwirkung zwischen solchen Zusatzstoffen und der darauf folgenden Flotation ist untersucht worden.

РЕЗЮМЕ

Исследование результатов влияния неорганических и органических добавок на мокрое измельчение минеральных компонентов железной руды (кварца и гематита) показало, что процесс измельчения можно улучшить, однако только при определенных значениях концентрации и pH. В других условиях химические добавки могут даже вызвать нежелательные последствия. Это влияние сравнивалось с эффектами, получаемыми обычно при флотации.

С целью объяснения механизма процесса использованы дзета-потенциал и параметры флокуляции систем, определённые в условиях, сходных с условиями, возникающими при исследуемом измельчении. Установлено, что влияние химических добавок может быть часто замаскировано благодаря их способности к флокуляции измельченных продуктов.

Микроскопические исследования измельченных продуктов (диспергированных и просеянных) выявили явную возможность появления ошибок в опытах вследствие неполной дисперсии в предыдущих работах. Исследовано также воздействие таких добавок на параметры последующей флотации.

DISCUSSION

PAPER 21

B. V. PILAT (Kazmekhanobr, USSR)

I would like to make one remark which is not connected with the report itself, but with the oral presentation where it was said that methods for determining the degree of mineral liberation have not been established so far.

Such a method has been developed in the course of our investigations and has proved successful in a number of cases. The essence of this method is to find the relationship between the fluorescence spectrum of elements for a given size fraction of the ore in relation to the spectrum of the same ore. The method can be applied to multicomponent ores. To accomplish the phenomena under observation other methods can be used, for example, nuclear magnetic resonance which specifies the surface mineral properties, thus using quantitative instead of qualitative criteria. All this allows the correlation of the degree of the intergrowth liberation with the degree of mineral overgrinding and the flotation to be carried out.

It seems to me that the authors of this very original paper could have got more complete information by applying these additional experimental methods.

H. KELLERWESSEL (KHD Humboldt-Wedag A.G., Köln, Federal Republic
of Germany)

Boundaries between grains in the interlocked particles are
seen in the polished sections of the specimen. Is it possible
to estimate the content of separate phases by means of this
technique? If so, this would be very important for the flotation process.

M. P. JONES*(Imperial College, London)

The work described in the paper is comparable to the work
being done by my co-workers at the Royal School of Mines, London.
Both schools now have a similar problem - the effects of the
various models that are used on the accuracy of the results.
The B.R.G.M. approach uses a shape-independent model but requires the calculation of the first and fourth moments of intercept length distributions and is only applicable to linear measurements. The R.S.M. approach uses a shape-dependent model, requires the calculation of the first and second moments of the
intercept ratio distributions, and can, in principle, be used
for both linear and area measurements.

Both methods work best on particles that are approaching the
liberated stage (i.e., particles that contain either one, and
or very few, interfaces).

I would be glad if the authors would expand on what they
have said regarding the use of multi-channel energy dispersion
of X-rays as a potential method for linear analysis. Our work

---

* Contributed remarks

728

suggests that this approach is of limited value because of the comparatively long time needed to analysis a single "point" on the linear traverse.

The test lines that they used on the Quantimet image analyser seem to cross each particle, on average, about four times. Are these lines randomly independent and does it matter whether they are or not?

The overall proportion of the iron-rich phase in Stewart's sample of iron ore can readily be obtained from the linear measurements. Since each particle is known to be composite, and within small limits are known to be of the same composition, then the overall proportion of iron-rich mineral is the same as the average particle composition.

PAPER 22

G. K. KRYLOV (State Science and Technology Council, U.S.S.R.)

I followed with great interest the papers on ore communition presented by my Colleagues from Bulgaria ([23] - Denev, Stoitsova), the U.S.A. (El - Shall, A. Gorken, P. Somasundaran; E. V. Manlapig, R. A. Seitz, D. J. Spottiswood, [25, 26]) and Czechoslovakia ([24] - K. Tkačova, F. Sekula, I. Hocmanova, V. Krupa). I was also interested by papers on the determination of the particle size of minerals presented by specialists from Poland ([22] - Bodziony and Kraj) and France ([21] - G. Barbery, G. Huyet, C. Gateau).

In spite of the fact that "communition of minerals" accounts for only 10% of the total number of papers presented at the plenary sessions of the Congress, the importance of these papers is very great for the processes of communition are not so easily modelled as other processes in the field of mineral processing. Their scientific development requires even greater effort and they require more than half of the capital costs and the same operation costs as flotation. More than 50% of the total energy consumption is in the flotation of non-ferrous metal ores and in the iron-ore industry expenses are even higher.

All the problems presented by Prof. Jones in his introductory lecture are of interest to me.

I fully agree with the suggestions presented in the paper by the Bulgarian specialists concerning the establishment of terminology used in communition. This term corresponds to the technological process in the cement industry and does not correspond at all to the process of the liberation of mineral grains from non-ferrous and other minerals.

I think it is time we reminded ourselves about an idea expressed more than half a century ago by Prof. Czeczott, who made a considerable contribution to the development of flotation and the training of specialists in Poland and the U.S.S.R.: "Don't crush too much!" (Don't crush anything that is not important). Unfortunately, this advice is not being given due consideration and in the process of flotation losses result far more from overgrinding than from poor liberation.

Taking into account the above-mentioned facts, I suggest that we pay more attention to the problem of mineral communition at the 14th Congress.

In the reports mentioned much attention was devoted to the problem of the expediency of the effect of surface-active agents and other agents in the improvement of mineral liberation. But the liberation of the mineral grains of non-ferrous metals and other mining resources is not an end in itself. As we know, reduction of losses of precious components is determined by many factors, among them physical and electrochemical processes on the surface of the minerals and in the pulp which are particularly intensive in the process of ore communition.

The redox potential kinetics in a communition cycle is sometimes 1-2 times higher than during flotation.

In this connection, I would like to put one question to my colleagues from the USA and Bulgaria about the influence of surface active substances on subsequent technological operations, and to my colleagues from Poland and France about the validity of the analysis of the particle size of mineral suspensions for industrial conditions.

PAPER 23

J. BODZIONY (Strata Mechanics Research Institute, Polish
    Academy of Sciences, Kraków, Poland)

Professor Denev describes one of the most important problems concerning the mechanism of comminution and liberation of minerals. I have in mind innergranular and intergranular fractures. Unfortunately Prof. Denev has not made any measurements of newly created surfaces. The paper by Mivic from Norway is closely connected with this work.

K. ŻMUDZIŃSKI (CUPRUM Research and Design Establishment, Wrocław, Poland)

(1) While testing the influence of mechanical action on selective grinding, only pressure changes were considered. Other actions occurring with different ways of ore crushing and grinding, e.g., abrasion, chipping, fracturing and impact, were not taken into account.

The results of these investigations would be very useful when choosing the proper comminution methods for ensuring maximum mineral liberation.

(2) We would welcome the authors' suggestions about the application of the results of the investigation in practice.

(3) Because the authors did not give a detailed description of experimental methods used it will not be possible for other people to apply these methods in their own studies.

D. OČEPEK (Yugoslav Committee for Mineral Processing, Ljubljana, Yugoslavia)

Attention has been drawn to microcracks which are the starting points for fracture propagation. This is, however, exclusively a question of revealing phases. Can one influence the number of microcracks?

Surface active agents have been mentioned. What is the role of these substances?

V. KHOROCHEV (Institute of Chemical Technology, USSR)

I have followed with great interest the paper presented by Dr. Spottiswood on the "Analysis of the breakage mechanisms in autogenous grinding".

Recently, autogenous grinding has found world-wide application in the practice of communition and is still in use. E.g., at present, "Kaskad" type mills with a drum diameter of 7-9 m are widely used. There evidence are studies concerning the design and operation of mills with a working volume of 380 m^3. Semiautogenous grinding is widely used with the addition of steel balls. But the mechanism of autogenous grinding has not been properly studied so far. In connection with this, the new observations and results obtained by the authors of the paper on a mill 1.83 m in diameter is of great importance.

In my contribution to the above paper I would like to find out at what rotation speed the published results were obtained? What is the authors' point of view on the three following questions:

(1) What is the validity of your method of breaking lumps in a 1.83 m mill for industrial "Kaskad" type mills 7-9 m in diameter?

(2) Would you indicate the optimum parameters of autogenous grinding obtained in your investigations? Namely, what is the most appropriate mill drum diameter, rotation speed, particle-size distribution of mill feed and solid-liquid ratio in the mill? What would you think about a change in the mecha-

nism of fracturing ore lupms in a "Kaskad" mill by an addition
of 8% by volume steel balls?

S. DENEV (Higher Institute of Mining and Geology, Sofia,
    Bulgaria)

(1) Have the authors measure the temperature and viscosity
of the pulp from the autogenous mill?

(2) Did you optimise pulp viscosity in the mill, and if so,
what was the optimal density?

J. TĘSIOROWSKI (Wrocław Technical University, Wrocław, Poland)

The nature of an autogenous process consists in self-commi-
nution of both coarse and fine material in the chamber of the
mill. Both groups of particles decrease in size during the process. But in this situation the ground material may appear in
a whole mass and, as far as I am aware it sometimes appears as
a dimension of material, let's say a neutral fraction, which
can neither belong to coarse nor to fine particles. It stopped
being a grinding body at a certain point in the process, and
has not yet become ground material. The size of this neutral
fraction depends on many factors, e.g., the construction of the
mill. This phenomenon can considerably delay the whole comminution process. I would like to ask Dr. Spottiswood give us his
view on this problem.

734

K. ŻMUDZIŃSKI (CUPRUM Research and Design Establishment,
Wrocław, Poland)

(1) Could you give us the size of the "coarse" particles
subjected to grinding?

(2) It is not quite clear whether the results illustrated
in Fig. 2 refer to one marked particle or to the average weight
of all the marked particles introduced into the mill.

V. I. REVNIVTSEV (Mekhanobr Institute, USSR)

This paper was of very great interest to us because we have
been carrying out analogous investigations in the "Mekhanobr"
Institute and have drawn the same conclusions about the dominating role of abrasive action in the mechanism of communition
during autogenous grinding (Dr. V. P. Yashin).

However, we are of the opinion that our American colleagues
have not sufficiently appreciated the contribution of the impact
load during communition, probably because of the small diameter
of the mill used.

To examine this, our Institute carried out the investigations in a slightly different way.

For many ores, varying both in their granulometric composition and in strength, industrial and pilot plant investigations
on autogenous grinding were carried out, taking into account
the criteria of similarity (the pilot plant investigations were
carried out in a mill of 2.1 m in diameter; industrial scale
devices were 5.7 and 9 m in diameter). A comparison of the
results obtained on both scales revealed that in the case of

fractured ores the investigations carried out in a small mill
were not adequate. In this connection a special programme of
additional impact tests was developed which made it possible to
imitate the impact breakage of ore in the mills under comparison. As a result, the usual calculation of expected output of
the autogenous industrial mill, (Q_2) based on the results of
the pilot plant investigations (Q_1) was carried out according
to the following equation:

$$Q_2 = Q_1 \left(\frac{D_2}{D_1}\right)^n \left(\frac{L_2}{L_1}\right)^m$$

(where D and L are diameter and length respectively, of the
mills compared). The improved formula derived in the Mekhanobr
Institute yielded:

$$Q_2 = Q_1 \left(\frac{D_2}{D_1}\right)^n \left(\frac{L_2}{L_1}\right)^m K_j$$

where K_j is the correction coefficient for ore resistance to
impact breakage.

In this connection, I would like to ask the following
questions:

(1) What is the trend of your further investigations and
how are you going to accomplish closed-circuit grinding?

(2) In the introductory part of your report you inform us
about your mechanical approach in the development of a mathematical model of the process and the resulting model for a particular mill could be utilized for the description of the process
in other mills but with certain limitations. What are these
limitations? In which way could the obtained relationships be

736

applied to the description of the process in mills of 7 and 10.5 m in diameter?

The paper gives very limited information about the tracing of certain lumps. What is your method of tracing of separate lumps ground in an autogenous mill?

M. Z. DOGAN (Middle East Technical University, Ankara, Turkey)

It was interesting to hear a paper on autogenous grinding which is still popular in the field of comminution.

The paper introduced by Dr. Spottiswood and his associates attempts to confirm the views put forward by Prof. Digre that abrasion and attribution are the two major mechanisms of breakage for coarse and the fine particles, respectively. In addition, two other modes of breakage, namely, chipping and fracturing must also be taken into consideration in the case of coarse sizes.

In our opinion, impact breakage cannot be overlooked in this system, as large diameter primary autogenous mills up to 32 feet exist to-day. Recently completed MSC research work at our university has indicated that autogenously ground Turkish ores have high compressive strength and high vickers hardness values in relation to impact and abrasion breakage mechanisms respectively.

B. PARKER (Billiton International Metals, The Netherlands)

(1) There is an increase in the importance of the role of autogenous milling in that the natural characteristics of the ore are utilised. This generally provides an effective means of energy conservation.

(2) Specification of a milling system remains a problem especially as the grinding circuit as a unit process is capital-intensive.

(3) Coarse breakage testing. What is the % loading of material in the test mill?

(4) Fracture breakage. Have the authors changed the mill design or operation parameters in an attempt to induce or delay the onset of fracture breakage?

(5) Can the authors foresee a test procedure to provide results for mill design specific to the grinding requirements of a particular ore?

PAPER 26

D. W. FUERSTENAU (University of California, Berkeley, USA)

If your hypothesis that the amine causes the formation of flocs, and that the flocs can then be ground, I would anticipate that the surface area of the product would have been increased. Thus, it would have been interesting to have measured specific surface areas of the product. The same increase in the production of colloidal-sized particles would account for the reduction in flotation rate when comminution was carried out in the presence of amine.

G. RINELLI (Laboratorio per il Trattamento dei Minerali, C.N.R., Roma, Italy)

I wish to congratulate the authors for the accuracy of the experiments they have carried out on a subject where many

contradictory results have been obtained in the past. I completely agree with the authors that the lack of proper control
is the main reason for these contradictions.

I would like to ask the authors if they have controlled the
reproducibility of the size distribution obtained with the wet-
dry sieving method they have used, and if the differences
observed under different grinding conditions, which sometimes
are rather slight, are beyond the limits of the errors of the
method.

H. J. SCHULZE (Forschungsinstitut fur Aufbereitung, Akademie
            der Wissenschaften, Freiberg, German Democratic
            Republic)

We have carried out similar investigations on the wet grinding of quartz [1]. In our opinion the transfer of energy from
particle to particle, and hence the effect of grinding, is
greater when there are only very thin layers or unstable liquid
films between them. In fact, we have observed that the percentage of coarse particles decreases with a growth of the ionic
strength of electrolytes (HCl), i.e., when the range of the
electrostatic repulsive forces decreases. In $AlCl_3$ solutions
the effect of disintegration is greatest when the ZPC of the
quartz surface has been reached. In the case of dodecylamine
adsorption on the quartz surface (pH 2-3) we had expected, on
the basis of our investigations into the stability of thin
films [2], that the breakage would be also good, as no stable
layers can exist. On the other hand, grindability is the

poorer, the higher the amine concentration. We suppose that regular dissipation of energy is taking place in the adsorption layer, which reduces the effect of disintegration. An aggregation of particles, however, cannot be precluded.

You have, however, observed the improved effect of disintegration in the case of higher amine concentrations, even at pH = 2.

(1) How do you estimate the significance of energy dissipation in thin films or adsorption layers?

(2) In your opinion, is the inclination of quartz to aggregate at higher pH values and higher amine concentrations (Fig. 5) less than in the case of low pH values and low amine concentrations?

REFERENCES

1. Bernhardt C., Schulze H. J. and Ortelt M. Powder technology, (in press).
2. Schulze H. J. Coll. Polym. Sci., 256, 1037 (1978).

M. CARTA (Università di Cagliari, Cagliari, Italy)

Rebinder's effect has always fascinated researchers. It clearly explains the effect of chemical additives on comminution.

In our laboratories at the University of Cagliari we have worked out an experimental technique for the measurement of the cutting of pure minerals and rocks under entirely controlled conditions with and without the addition of surface active reagents. It has been shown that cutting increases by some 20-30%

after the addition of reagents. The results may be related to a certain degree to drilling and to a lesser degree to grinding.

K. ŻMUDZIŃSKI (CUPRUM Research and Design Establishment, Wrocław, Poland)

(1) In Fig. 1 grinding time is probably mistakenly given as 0.5 min. I think it should be 7.5 min, as mentioned in the description of the experimental procedure.

(2) Why did you use such a large quantity of Na_2SiO_3 (6.3 kg/t) for the dispersion of pulp after grinding? 1-2 kg/t Na_2SiO_3 is normaly used for this purpose (page 703).

(3) It is not quite clear whether the conclusions concerning grinding efficiency (page 458) are connected with the influence of flocculation on grinding results or on screen analysis.

(4) You state that Na_2SiO_3 and phosphates have a negative influence on quartz and hematite grinding. However, it would be advisable to check under a microscope whether the screen analysis was impaired by flocculation.

(5) If you found that Na_2SiO_3 had not fully dispersed the grinding product this may be a reason for screen analysis inaccuracies. It seems to me that you should use alcohol or acetan to get complete dispersion.

E. FORSSBERG (University of Lulea, Sweden)

Firstly, I would like to remark that Dow Z-200 is not a frother but rather a collector. I think there must be some misunderstanding in this case.

Secondly, I would like to ask about the interpretation of
the effect of additions of amine collectors before and after
grinding as shown in Fig. 9 and 10 according to page 699
the fraction minus 400 mesh is removed before the
flotation experiments. Therefore in my opinion it is likely
that the amount of flotation collector, i.e., amine, is not
enough when the addition is only 0.023 kg/t. Most of the amine
will be adsorbed on the fraction below 400 mesh and thus very
little collector will remain for the flotation of the coarse
fraction. In the case of a heavy addition of amine, 0.15 kg/t,
there will be a surplus of collector and also the coarse fraction used in the flotation experiment will be hydrophobic.
I therefore suggest that another interpretation of the influence of additions of amine before and after grinding might be
possible.

G. A. HARRIS (Dow Chemical, California, USA)

The authors refer to Z-200 frother. Z-200 is a collector
for sulphides. Did the authors possibly use the Dowfroth 200
frother?

H. SCHUBERT[*] (Bergakademie Freiberg, German Democratic Republic)

I would like to congratulate the authors of this excellent
contribution and to express my agreement with their opinion
concerning the effect of additives in the process of grinding.

------

* Contributed remarks

Some years ago we investigated the process of dry-grinding with additives [1] and found that these substances primarily influence the forces of reciprocal action between the particles and thus also the behaviour of the ground material. This consequently affects the transfer of forces or energy in the course of grinding. As far as dry-grinding is concerned, the most favourable conditions are naturally those when the adhesive attraction between the particles is small. This is to be ascribed to the presence of adsorption layers of surface active agents.

On the other hand, attention should be drawn to the effect of additives on the results of the analysis of particle size, which may differ from method to method [2].

In our opinion, there is therefore no so-called Rehbinder effect (reduction in strength resulting from adsorption) when a brittle material is being crushed. And it would be difficult to explain such an effect in virtue of the mechanism of disintegration of brittle materials [3].

REFERENCES

1. Graichen K. and Muller H. Beitrag zur Aufklarung der Wirkungsweise von Mahlhilfsmitteln Contribution to the Explanation of the Effect of Grinding Additives). Freiberger Forschungshefte, A550, 5-84 (1975).

2. Graichen K., Kulbe K. H. and Schubert H. Beeinflussung ausgewahlter Methoden der Korngrossenmesstechnik durch Tenside (The Influence of Tensides on Some Selected Methods of Grainsize Measuring Techniques); Freiberger Forschungshefte, A531, 33-40 (1975).

3. Schubert H. Aufbereitung fester mineralischer Rohstoffe (The Dressing of Solid Mineral Raw Materials), Leipzig, VEB Deutscher Verlag fur Grundstoffindustrie, Vol. 1, 3rd edition, 1975.

AUTHORS' REPLIES

J. BODZIONY and W. KRAJ

Dr. Krylov's question which refers directly to our paper was to what degree the method of stereological analysis presented in our paper may be applied to the granulometric analysis of suspensions of mineral grains under industrial conditions.

In our report we have presented some applications of the stereological analysis based on the measurements made (a) on flat cross-sections (i.e., on microsections or thin polished sections), (b) on the shadows of grains.

To carry out the measurements on cross-sections it is necessary to glue the samples of grains and to prepare a flat cross-section which must satisfy certain requirements. Considering the time necessary to prepare a polished section we may speak now only of "off line" applications. Stereological analysis may be carried out in a laboratory equipped with the instruments for preparing the cross-sections and for carrying out measurements on them. A wider application of stereological analysis based on the measurements of shadows requires the construction of appropriate apparatus and this has not been achieved so far.

744

St. DENEV

We offer the following replies to the questions raised by
Dr. Žmudziński:

(1) We have studied not only the effect of pressure changes
on the grinding results, but also ordinary ball and rod grinding, heating and abrupt cooling followed by grinding in a
vibrating mill, grinding in electrohydraulic mill and in an
impact mill. There is a method of grinding organization for
each type of ore, where maximum selectivity is obtained in the
liberation of minerals.

(2) At present, the method of grinding organization for a
individual type of ore could only be defined in advance (approximately) on the basis of mineralogical analysis results.

(3) The methods of investigation include a preliminary
mineralogical analysis of the substance for grinding, preparation for grinding (crushing, grain-size analysis), effect of
pressure and temperature on the ore and autogenous grinding.
This is again followed by mineralogical analysis, grain-size
analysis, calculation of grinding and liberation parameters.

In reply to Dr. Bodziony's question, we are not yet fully
acquainted with the work of Dr. Malvig from Norway. We used
only sieve analysis for determining the particle-size distribution of the ground product in our tests. The dimensions of
the inclusions in intergrowths in different fractions were
measured by microscope.

In reply to two questions from Professor Očepek we would like to point out that:

(1) In all cases of mechanical, thermal or other action upon the ore, it is the microfissures that are affected. Our purpose was to make microcracks occur mainly along the boundaries of intergrowth, which increases the selectivity of liberation.

(2) Special investigations on an agglomeration of particles in the presence of surface active agents were not carried out in our tests.

Turning to Dr. Krylov's contribution we would like to explain that when surface active agents are used in the grinding process, it is of course necessary to account for their influence on the subsequent processes of ore concentration. We selected those surface active agents which do not have a negative effect on the subsequent processes.

D. J. SPOTTISWOOD

Mr. Parker raises a number of questions, and I will respond to them briefly. Firstly, he makes the point that autogenous grinding provides an effective means of energy conservation. While this may be true for some ores, it is not generally true. If fact, the opposite is generally true when direct energy consumption is considered. The situation is less clear when the energy requirements of producing grinding media is taken into account. However, the justification for going to autogenous grinding is not the saving of energy.

For both the batch and continuous autogenous grinding tests reported, the mill was approximately 35% loaded. The mill charge in the batch tests was made up to the size distribution previously found on reaching steady state in the continuous grinding of that ore.

The question regarding fracture breakage is an interesting one. The authors have not changed either mill design or operating parameters to affect the onset of fracture breakage. However, it is interesting to consider how this might be done. If the impact forces on the media forming particles are minimized by using a smaller diameter mill, then fracture breakage would be expected to be delayed.

When autogenous grinding is considered for an ore, it is common practice for the mill manufacturer to test the ore in some way for "media competency". Such a test is really to see if fracture breakage is significant. If the ore is deemed "competent", further investigation of autogenous grinding as a grinding option is undertaken. If the ore is deemed not "competent", primary autogenous grinding is not considered further. (Semi-autogenous grinding is not considered here). No attempt is made to make the ore "competent" or to delay the onset of fracture breakage. However, ore that is not "competent" in a large diameter-to-length mill design might well prove to be "competent" in a small diameter-to-length mill design of another manufacturer. Thus the tests in use by the various mill manufacturers for determining media "competency" already provide us with the tools to determine the best design for a particular ore.

Prof. Dogan rightly points out that impact breakage is important in large diameter autogenous mills. In this paper there is no intent or attempt to make any distinction between attrition breakage and impact breakage.

Prof. Dogan also refers to completed work relating compressive strength to the impact breakage mechanisms and Vickers hardness to the abrasion breakage mechanisms. It will be most interesting to see this work reported.

In reply to Professor Denev, the temperature in the mill was not measured. The tests were carried out over a relatively short period of time and so the temperature of the feed water was constant. Also, the pulp density in the mill was not determined. Water was added at a rate to give a trommel undersize pulp density of 55%. The effect of pulp density on the performance of the mill was not investigated.

As Dr. Tesiorawski points out, there is an intermediate size fraction in the autogenous mill load that belongs to neither the "coarse" nor the "fine" fraction. This intermediate fraction has not yet been studied in the present project. However, the work of Stanley [1] clearly showed that in both pilot scale and industrial scale autogenous mills there was an intermediate size fraction at which the rate of breakage was greatly reduced. This is shown in Fig. 1.

The effect of this low rate of breakage of an intermediate fraction is to cause a build-up in particles in this size range. If this fraction is large, as it is in some mills, it may be treated by either (1) crushing the material in this size fraction of the mill product and recycling it to the mill, or (2)

748

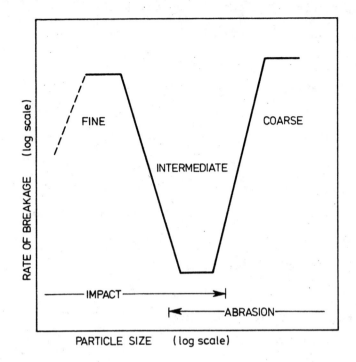

Fig. 1. Effect of particle size on the rate breakage
        (after Stanley [1]).

adding steel balls to the mill. In both cases the rate of
breakage of this size fraction is increased.

The amount of material in this size fraction may vary. For
instance, when the ore being mined provides a smaller amount
of material forming competent media, there is frequently a
build-up of this intermediate size fraction. If this change is
expected to be of only short duration, then the excess material
can be stockpiled for future reclaiming. But if the change is
expected to be permanent, then a circuit or operating change is
required.

Dr. Khorochev raises the complex question of scale-up of autogenous mills. Extensive work in rod and ball mills, and the work of Stanley [1] in autogenous mills, has indicated that the mechanism of breakage of a particular size fraction is the same in a small mill as in a large mill. Thus the breakage can be expected to follow a first order rate law in a large autogenous mill. That is not to say, however, that the rate constant in the breakage equation will remain the same. It is the relationship between the rate constant in the pilot scale mill and the corresponding rate constant in a full sized mill that has not been determined. And of course it must be kept in mind that there is no single rate constant, but a range of rate constant dependent on the operating conditions of the mill. This is an area that will require very extensive work if such a scale-up model is to be developed.

If a small amount of steel balls are added to an autogenous mill (as of course is the case in semi-autogenous grinding) then it is expected that the mechanism of breakage of the ore will remain the same but with an increase in the rate of breakage of the fine and intermediate sized particles. The coarse particles would continue to break primarily by the abrasion mechanism. Fine particles would continue to break primarily by the impact breakage mechanism; the rate of breakage would be higher, and the range of particles undergoing impact breakage would extend to larger sizes.

The size of the particles considered as "coarse" particles is shown in Fig. 3 of the paper. The tagged particles had a largest dimension of approximately 10 cm and a smallest dimension of approximately 5 cm. In Fig. 2 of the paper, the results shown are averages for all marked particles. Dr. Żmu-dziński's question on this has resulted in the correcting of the Figure to so indicate.

Professor Revnivtsev's comments are most welcome. It is en-couraging to hear that similar results have been obtained at the Mekhanobr Institute on the mechanisms of breakage in auto-genous grinding and the type of equation which describes these mechanisms. The work on scale-up and the work relating grinding test results and impact and loading tests on individual par-ticles would appear to be of great value. It would be most interesting to see this work reported in detail. It would also be useful to have more information on the classification of ores based on mineralogy and granular structure as related to their breakage in autogenous grinding mills.

P. SOMASUNDARAN

Dr. Schulze has brought out the important question of the role of liquid films between particles in determining energy dissipation during transfer of force and therefore grinding efficiency. Indeed, the energy dissipation in the film, which in turn should be determined among other things by the visco-sity of the thin liquid film, should be a governing factor in the overall mechanism. However, sufficient substantiated infor-mation is not yet available on the role of properties of such films or adsorbed layers in determining the efficiency of force transmission or grinding. In addition to the point raised here, we believe that a related factor to be considered is the role

751

of such properties in controlling the fluidity of the pulp and thereby the overall grinding process. Results shown in Fig. 5 indicated a lower additive effect in the acidic pH range and this is attributed to the floc formation in the presence of amine in this range. We actually expect increased flocculation in the alkaline pH range, but we also obtain increased grinding in this pH range due to the predominating beneficial role of the highly surface active ionomolecular amine-aminium complex (Ref. 9).

In answer to Dr. Krylov, we feel that the effect of additives on downstream operations is an important problem that should receive attention. We have observed during our tests that the addition of surfactants as grinding aids can affect subsequent filtration badly. In addition, we have also studied the role of point of addition of surfactants, i.e., grinding mill or conditioner, and the results obtained have been discussed in the text of our paper. Apart from the above, we have not yet studied the effect of additives on other downstream operations.

We agree with Prof. Fuerstenau that specific surface area is a good criterion to determine the degree of fineness of the ground product and we have measured surface area of products also. Detailed analysis of our surface area results will be given elsewhere. But in brief, surface area results suggest that amine addition is beneficial for grinding under all conditions. For example, addition of 10^{-3} M/1 amine produced an increase in surface area of ground product from 0.3690 m^2/g to 1.9590 m^2/g at pH 10.5 and from 0.414 and 0.447 m^2/g (duplicates) to 1.337 and 1.264 m^2/g at pH 3.0. It might be noted that surface area results indicated beneficial effects under all pH conditions whereas size analysis suggested such an effect only under alkaline conditions. It is not, however, clear why the formation of flocs itself should lead to an increase in net grinding and net surface area. In fact, as a limiting case one could conceive of a steady state when a mechanical equilibrium between flocculation of ground product and their regrinding would be achieved with no net grinding. The possibility of any effect due to excessive removal of amine by fines has been considered elsewhere.

In answer to Prof. Forssberg and Dr. Harris, as frother, we did use Dowfroth-250 and not Z-200 as indicated in the text. Regarding the alternative exaplanation for the effect of amine, it is indeed likely that a good portion of the amine will be adsorbed on the fines. However, there is no reason as to why the adsorption density on the coarse should be less than that on the fines, at least in the size range under consideration. Therefore we believe that at a concentration of 0.023 kg/t enough amine could have adsorbed on the +400 mesh fraction and caused its flotation only if the amine was not washed out. Nevertheless, we agree that the effect of adsorption by fines can be significant and that this could be partly responsible for such effects.

We offer the following answers to the comments of Dr. Zmudziński.

(1) The grinding time of 0.5 min after tumbling that we have given in Fig. 1 is correct.

(2) 1 to 2 kg/t Na_2SiO_3 is usually adequate for dispersing mineral suspensions, but only when they have not been contacted with surfactant solutions of high concentrations. When we observed that surfactant contacted mineral pulps did not disperse with 1 to 2 kg/t of Na_2SiO_3, larger amounts were used. Mineral pulps contacted with 10^{-1} mole/l amine could not be dispersed even with 6.3 kg/t Na_2SiO_3, the highest dosage used. This led us to use alcohol and acetone washes in addition to sodium silicate.

(3) We believe that flocculation of the mineral matter inside the mill is a contributing factor to the observed detrimental effects.

(4 and 5) We carefully examined the ground products under a microscope after each test. In the case of tests in the presence of sodium silicate and phosphates, the ground products were fully dispersed and therefore there was no need for alcohol and acetone washes.

Dr. Rinelli has touched upon one of the most important problems that one has to be concerned about while studying the effect of chemical additives on grinding. The effects of chemicals on actual size reduction itself can be small and, in addition, chemicals can produce artifacts if the ground product is not fully dispersed before size analysis. In such a case, the grinding effect might be totally masked or false conclusions might even be drawn. In fact, I believe that the conflicting nature of past reports might be partly due to such artifacts. In our work, we have examined samples of all the ground products under a microscope to guarantee their full dispersion prior to size analysis. In addition, several duplicate tests have been conducted to verify the observed effects. For example, the effect due to tumbling can be seen by comparing results of two tests (53.8% and 54.2%) with those of control tests (50.9% and 50.8%). Yet another example is the effect of amine (-11.4% to +31.8%) illustrated in Fig. 5 which also gives results for duplicates at pH 10.5 (-30.2% and +31.8%) and pH 3.0 (-8.6% and -11.4%). It should be noted that the duplicate tests in Fig. 5 were performed by two independent workers. The effect of amine is clearly significant.

We are pleased to see the overwhelming interest shown by our colleagues in this important problem and we thank all of the above contributors for their comments. We are also grateful to Prof. Schubert and Prof. Carta for their valuable remarks.

Session 4

Hydrometallurgy

Chairmen: A. Pomianowski
J. Wójtowicz

ELECTROOXIDATION OF CHALCOPYRITE IN ACID CHLORIDE MEDIUM; KINETICS, STOICHIOMETRY AND REACTION MECHANISM

M. Ammou-Chokroum, P. K. Sen and F. Fouques

Centre de Recherches sur la Valorisation des Minerais, École Nationale Supérieure de Géologie Appliquée, Nancy, France

INTRODUCTION

Complex Sulphide Minerals and Hydrometallurgy

It is known that useful minerals present in certain types of complex sulphide ores of copper, lead and zinc are difficult to beneficiate in a selective way by means of the conventional methods of flotation, because of their fine granulometry and intimate association with pyritic gangue, which constitutes the bulk of the ore. Because of the difficulties encountered in applying to these minerals the usual treatment procedures for sulphide minerals, consisting of selective flotation and the pyrometallurgical treatment of concentrates, the hydrometallurgical method as applied to bulk concentrates or run of mine ores may be considered to be applicable [1, 2]. From this point of view, reactor leaching of valuable minerals ought to be simultaneously total, rapid and selective in relation to the pyrite present. While recalling the numerous previous investigations conducted

759

on the chemical dissolution of selected industrial concentrates, it seems that controlled oxidation in acidic chloride medium can be considered as favourable. However, it appears that no usual chemical oxidizing agent, like gaseous Cl_2 and O_2 or the cations Fe^{3+} and Cu^{2+}, can achieve the aims of selectivity and rapidity, and thereby satisfy fully the imperative conditions for leaching sulphide minerals. In view of the intrinsic limitations of the oxydoreduction reactions, it is necessary to envisage other methods for the oxidation of these minerals. It is for this reason that one can think of conveniently utilizing the semiconducting properties of the principal sulphides [3] for oxidizing these minerals by electric current, i.e., removing the electrons through the intermediate action of a generator [4].

Electrooxidation at an Imposed Potential

This approach should not be confused with the electrochemical generation of a chemical oxidizing agent in the pulp, the latter having been carried out by gaseous Cl_2 in a chloride medium [5] and misnamed electrodissolution. By electrooxidation the direct participation of the solid in an electrolyzing circuit is meant. For this purpose, the solid, necessarily powdered and conditioned in an agitated pulp in the case of composite materials, exchanges electrons with a chemically inert current carrying lead; the moving particles are oxidized in a very short time, as soon as they come in contact with the anode which acts as an obstacle immersed in the pulp.

Contrary to the usual industrial practice of electrodeposition of metals, electrooxidation ought to be carried out at an

imposed potential and not at a fixed current intensity [6]. As
the solid is subjected to a constant current electrooxidation
procedure, it becomes passivated because of the formation of
oxidation products in course of the reaction. Its potential increases during its dissolution, beyond a certain degree of advancement, its potential assumes the value at which the attacking solution is electrolyzed. This parasite reaction presents
a two-fold inconvenience: on the one hand, it causes a decrease
of the energy efficiency of the operation and diminishes the
fraction of the current employed for the solubilization of the
solid; on the other, it generates in a chloride pulp gaseous
Cl_2, which totally oxidizes the materials and thus alters the
selectivity of dissolution. It is for this reason that the
electrooxidation of complex sulphide minerals can only be effected potentiostatically. This operating procedure has another
advantage - it enables selective dissolution of certain phases
in relation to others. Indeed, every sulphide mineral has a
domain of electrooxidizability which is particular to this mineral in a given range of potential and varies with the physico-
chemical conditions of the medium. It follows that when a mixed
material is subjected to electrodissolution while operating at
a potential in the domain of electrooxidizability of a single
phase, the latter is dissolved to the exclusion of others.

With a view to defining the conditions of application of the
principle of electrodissolution to complex sulphide minerals at
an imposed potential, it is necessary to know with a great deal
of precision the electroreactivity of the different species of
sulphide constituents as a function of potential and physico-

chemical variables of the electrolyte. It is in this perspective that the investigations as reported in this article were carried out on the mineral chalcopyrite

Oxidation of Chalcopyrite by Chemical Methods

The oxidation of chalcopyrite by ferric ions [7, 8] takes place according to an overall favourable stoichiometry, since the sulphide ions of the crystal are essentially oxidized to elemental sulphur:

$$CuFeS_2 + 4\ Fe^{3+} = Cu^{2+} + 5\ Fe^{2+} + 2\ S\downarrow \qquad (1)$$

However, metal recoveries obtained with flotation concentrates under ordinary temperature and pressure conditions are mediocre. It is for this reason that a study of the reactivity of this mineral has been the object of a large number of investigations [9]. With a view to explaining the sluggish chemical nature of the mineral chalcopyrite, two principal theories have been proposed.

(1) Elemental sulphur: according to this theory, which is the oldest and most commonly agreed upon [10, 11, 12, 13, 14], the chemical rate of reaction is limited by the diffusion of oxidants through the sulphur layer.

(2) Intermediate sulphide: according to this reaction mechanism, developed by A. R. Burkin and his collaborators [16, 17, 18, 19], the reaction is slackened because of the transport of matter across a compact layer composed of a sulphide, which grows at the chalcopyrite surface through a mechanism of the solid state diffusion of the cations at different rates.

During some recent studies [20, 21], one of us has retained
this hypothesis because of the following facts:

(1) The general shape of the experimental curves of dissolution of copper as a function of time (Fig. 1) shows that two
kinetic regimes contribute to the total reaction. After an initially high rate of dissolution, the chalcopyrite shows a decrease in reactivity according to a parabolic law; it thus attains a slow and a constant rate, leading to steady state conditions. The phenomena can be treated according to a paralinear
law [22].

(2) The kinetic analysis of the experimental results, and
notably, the high values of activation energies for the different stages of the reaction enable us to attribute the control
of these reactions, not to oxidant diffusion in the liquid
phase, but to a chemical process and/or solid state diffusion.

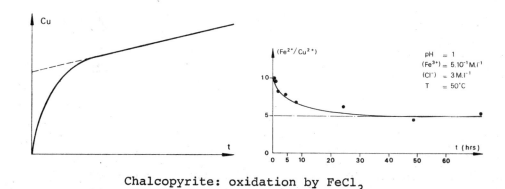

Chalcopyrite: oxidation by $FeCl_3$

Fig. 1. General shape of   Fig. 2. Evolution of the iron
        kinetic curves.   (bivalent)-copper dis-
                                          solved ratio (cumula-
                                          tive values) as a func-
                                          tion of time.

(3) The initial phase of the reaction is different not only because of its higher rate of dissolution, but also because it has a particular stoichiometry. With a view to establishing the stoichiometry of the reactions it is usual to measure the evolution of Cu^{2+} and Fe^{2+} in the leach solution. Contrary to the simplified reaction (1), the ratio Fe^{2+}/Cu^{2+} is very much greater than 5 during the initial phase of reaction [12, 13, 14]. It subsequently decreases quite rapidly attaining a value of approximately 5 (Fig. 2). In addition the copper and the iron released by the chalcopyrite do not appear in the solution at identical rates. This phenomenon, already observed by other workers [23, 14, 18] utilizing dissolved oxygen instead of Fe^{3+} as an oxidizing agent, is equally verified during the electrochemical oxidation of a chalcopyrite pulp (Fig. 3); during the

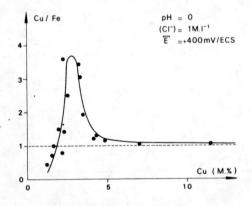

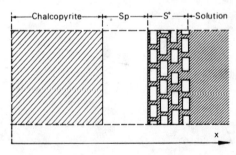

Fig. 3. Chalcopyrite: Electrochemical oxidation.
Evolution of Cu/Fe ratio
(instantaneous values)
with the progress of
the reaction.

Fig. 4. Chalcopyrite: oxidation
by $FeCl_3$. Paralinear
model: schematic sec-
tion through reaction
zone.

first few instants of the reaction, the iron is solubilized more rapidly than the copper. In accordance with the high value of activation energy (ΔE), this phenomenon may be attributed to the solid state diffusion of the two cations at different rates.

It is for these reasons that we have admitted that the solubilization of copper reflects a chemical transformation of the sulphide subjected to oxidation. From this point of view, the "passivation" of the chalcopyrite results in a superficial transformation of the mineral in a passivating sulphide, S_p, less reactive than the original sulphide (Fig. 4).

Subsequent investigations conducted by us on this mineral and in particular the research undertaken in connection with electro-dissolution have led us to re-examine this reaction scheme.

Experimental Conditions

The electrooxidation of chalcopyrite was conducted in an acidic chloride medium in the absence of ferric ions, i.e., in an inert electrolyte from the point of view of oxydo-reduction. The reaction conditions whose influence have been studied are as follows:

- temperature: ambient to $75^\circ C$, at ordinary pressures under N_2 with a view to limit oxidation by atmospheric oxygen;

- electrolytic solution: the pH of the solutions varies between 0 and 2 and is fixed by HCl. The total chloride ion concentration (between 1 and 5 M) is adjusted by the addition of NaCl. Although the experimental solutions are not dilute, the concentration and activity of ions are taken to be the same.

Two samples of chalcopyrite were used. One of these was syn-
thesized [24] at a high temperature as powder; it was used
either in pulps or in the making of electrodes with graphite
paste [25] . The other is a natural polycrystalline sample, used
as massive electrodes of known surface area.

The basic electrochemical set-up is the classical three
electrode system [26] . The electrode potential of the chalcopyrite electrode (T: working electrode) is determined by a comparison of its value with that of a calomel reference electrode
(KCl saturated, at $25^{\circ}C$ = E.C.S. = +245 mV/N.H.E.). In the text
below the numerical values of the potentials are reported in the
S.C.E. scale. An electrolytic current pases between T and a
third electrode, which is the counter electrode (C.E.).

Three types of measurements are thus feasible.

Potentiometry: when there is no applied potential at the
chalcopyrite electrode there is no net current in the circuit
and "T" assumes a certain potential (E_r), termed the "rest potential". In chloride solutions without oxidants, E_r is called
the "drift potential" (E_a). Its subsequent variations as a function of time is only a qualitative measure of the evolution of
the mineral-solution interface; its physical significance can
be complex and not immediately accessible. When E_r assumes a
fixed and reproductible value which corresponds to a well-defined equilibrium involving non-negligible interfacial concentrations of electroactive species, this potential is termed "mixed
potential".

When a constant or variable potential is applied at a chalcopyrite electrode, the current which traverses the interface

766

measures the rate of the electronic exchanges taking place at the sulphide surface, and this characterizes its proper electrochemical reactivity. Two types of measurements may be conducted.

Electrodissolution at Imposed Potential. The electrooxidation of chalcopyrite at a constant potential was conducted according to two procedures, each one presenting its own sphere of interest.

When the chalcopyrite is conditioned as a massive electrode of known reaction surface area, the variation of electrolytic current characterizes the evolution of the specific oxidation rate of the mineral as a function of time and potential applied, i.e., as a function of electrical forces acting at the mineral-solution interface. As the anodic current (I_A) is expressed in terms of the surface area of the electrode, the resulting current density (i_A) measures the quantity of electrons exchanged per unit time and surface. The specific reaction rate for electrochemical oxidation is thus obtained. Besides, in this experimental set up, the electrons are exchanged with the electric circuit through the intermediate rear face of the sample, i.e., with an interface which stays unchanged as the electrochemical reaction progresses, thus the real kinetic parameters for the oxidizability of the chalcopyrite-electrolyte solution are measured. This, however, is not the case with the second type of experimental set up for electrodissolution at imposed potential.

When utilizing an agitated pulp of chalcopyrite the exchange of electrons between the grains of chalcopyrite and the current carrying leads, in conformity with the objective of practical application, takes place through the intermediate surface of the mineral. The composition and resistance of the latter vary as a function of the degree of attack. In addition, since the hydrodynamic conditions and the frequency of shocks are not easily controlled in such a reactor, this set-up has been utilized for determining the stoichiometry of the reactions and not the kinetics proper.

Polarization Curves. These E-I curves are established by linearly increasing the potential applied to a chalcopyrite electrode and thereby registering the variations in corresponding current intensities. In an acidic chloride medium, the elementary anodic curves thus registered are tangential to the axis of potentials and significant anodic currents start to pass through the interface at the minimum anodic potential, E_A. In the case of a solid which is passivable, these curves characterize its overall electrochemical behaviour and allow the appreciation of the influence of reaction variables on the kinetics of oxidation.

ELECTROCHEMICAL REACTION KINETICS

The study of the oxidation of chalcopyrite by ferric ions shows the important influence of temperature and oxidant concentration on the overall rate of the reaction. However, the reason for this influence is indeterminate as every variable can act on one and/or other systems, the mineral chalcopyrite on the one hand, and the ferric ions on the other hand. The results obtained in chemical kinetics therefore directly lend themselves neither for the prediction of the electrochemical behaviour of chalcopyrite, nor, more particularly, for the quantifying of the influence of operating parameters on the kinetics of its electro-oxidation. Two types of experiments have been conducted: the tracing of polarization curves and electrodissolution at an imposed potential.

Polarization Curves

Materials and Methods. The experimental set-up utilizing the system of three electrodes previously presented is shown schematically in Fig. 5. The working electrode is composed of a sulphide disc rotating around its vertical axis at a controlled speed. This rotating disc electrode system is achieved by filling up a cylindrical cavity carved out at the extreme end of the turning electrode with a mixture of graphite paste and pulverized chalcopyrite. As the active surface of the sulphide is

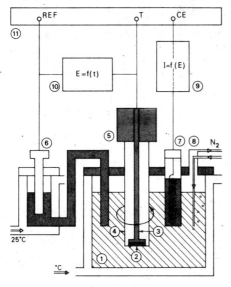

1. Thermostated reactor
   Rotating electrode:
2. Sulphide disc
3. Current leads
4. Insulating cover
5. Motor
6. Reference electrode
   (S.C.E. at 25°C)
7. Platinum counter electrode
8. Nitrogen circuit
9. Recorder for E/I curves
10. Potentiometric recorder
11. Potentiostat and pilot

Fig. 5. Electrochemical kinetics: schematic experimental set up.

indeterminate, it is not possible to calculate the current density. For this reason, the experimental results are presented as potential-current intensity diagrams. This manner of presentation does not present any major inconvenience since the intensity of current defining the curves depends strongly on the potential sweep rate because of the changing nature of the interface. Moreover, as the experimental method of the fabrication of the electrodes is standardized, it is possible to compare the recorded curves.

The following experimental procedure was adopted. Before recording the curves the working electrode, whose speed of rotation is fixed at 700 r.p.m., is immersed in the chloride solution for 45 min. During this time the change in rest potential (E_a) is recorded as a function of time. For recording the E-I curves, a potential increasing linearly at a rate of 75 mV/min is applied at the electrode, which attains a quasistationary value of E_a after 45 min. The intensity is recorded on a linear scale. The upper limit of the anodic sweep was fixed at +800 mV, this being limited by the electroactivity field of the solvent.

Results. In the general case, the elementary anodic curve of chalcopyrite in an acidic chloride solution (Fig. 6) shows schematically two peaks of oxidation which are situated at approximately +400 mV (A) and +500 mV (B). Subsequently, a horizontal portion of the current intensity is observed, followed by a rapid increase of current corresponding essentially to the electrolysis of the solvent. This elementary curve is thus characterized by important variations of current, defining the presence of two peaks of current intensity; these correspond to

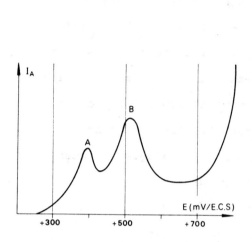

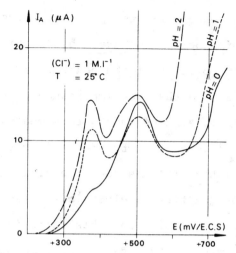

Fig. 6. Chalcopyrite: electrochemical kinetics.
General shape of ele-
mentary anodic curve.

Fig. 7. Chalcopyrite: elementary anodic curve.
Influence of pH.

different reactions which take place successively on the electrode. The origin of peak A will be discussed later; peak B corresponds to the principal electrochemical reaction. The decrease
of current intensity which determines this peak is due to a decrease in the active surface of the electrode.

Influence of Variables

Influence of pH. Figure 7 shows that peak B is not significantly influenced by pH. Moreover, in accordance with the evolution of the electroactivity domain of the electrolyte, the
electrolysis of the solvent is displaced towards negative potentials as the pH increases.

Influence of Chloride Ion Concentration. Like pH, this variable does not have a notable effect on the elementary anodic curve, except for the place of solvent electrolysis (Fig. 8).

Influence of Temperature. If this factor has little influence on the position of the peaks in the potential scale, it is seen from Fig. 9 that the importance of peak B increases rapidly with temperature. Even though tnis measurement is approximate due to lack of control of the reacting surface, the activation energy determined for this reaction from an Arrhenius diagram by means of the quantity of electricity associated with peak B, is approximately 10 kcal/mole. This value is too high for reaction B to be controlled by a diffusion process in the liquid.

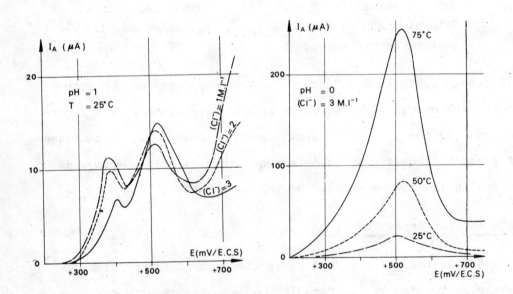

Chalcopyrite: elementary anodic curve

Fig. 8. Influence of chloride   Fig. 9. Influence of tempera-
         ion concentration.   ture.

Reaction B thus presents all the characteristics of chemical oxidation of chalcopyrite by ferric ions, i.e.
- strong dependence on temperature, and conversely, insensitivity to the chemical variables (Cl^-) and pH,
- decrease of rate and passivation of the interface as the reaction progresses.

The following measurements permit the description of the electrochemical properties of the reaction interface after oxidation.

Behaviour of an Electrode after Oxidation

Elementary Anodic Return Curve. If, after having traced the "first" elementary anodic curve (while increasing the potential till the superior limit), the direction of sweep is inversed the "return" curve is recorded as represented in Fig. 10. It may be noted that the "first" and "return" curves are not the same. The current intensities involved during the decrease of potential values are quite inferior to those recorded during the "first" curve.

After anodic passivation the electrode does not recover its active state when its potential is decreased; as peak B is not associated with a reversible electrode reaction, the solid is passivated. The following measurements lead to a slight modification of this last proposition.

Evolution of E_a after Anodic Passivation. If the imposed potential on the electrode is cut off after it has attained the superior limit of the "first" anodic curve, the rest potential presents the following evolution - after a rapid decrease during

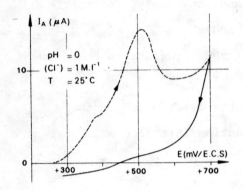
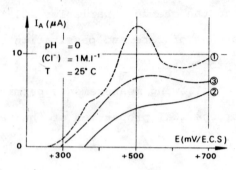

Chalcopyrite: elementary anodic curve

Fig. 10. Return curve.   Fig. 11. Evolution after varying

immersion times.

the first ten minutes, E_a tends to regain a value near to that

attained by the electrode after 45 min of immersion.

The passage of a certain quantity of electricity has thus

modified the interface. However, the evolution of E_a shows

equally that the passivated interface changes as a function of

time, by simple immersion in acid, to regain approximately the

same characteristics it had before passivation. The passivation

of the solid is thus not totally irreversible. This is confirmed

by the following measurements.

Successive Elementary Anodic Curves. The elementary anodic

curves illustrated in Fig. 11 have been traced successively with

the same electrode; curves (2) and (3) have been recorded with

an electrode previously passivated by the "first" anodic sweep

(curve 1), following varying immersion times in acid, i.e. 6 min and 140 min. It may be stated that an increase in the time of immersion augments the current intensities involved during the subsequent anodic sweep, without attaining the value obtained during the "first" sweep.

In accordance with the evolution of E_a, the passivated interface in contact with the acidic solution regains an electroactive state after a certain time interval. Only the formation of new electroactive interfacial species during its contact with the acidic solution can be invoked to explain this spontaneous reactivation of the electrode.

Electrodissolution at Imposed Potential

Materials and Methods. The experimental set-up utilized for these measurements at fixed potential is identical to the preceding one. In this case, however, the graphite paste is replaced by a turning disc of massive chalcopyrite covered in resin. The face exposed to the solution was carefully polished by a diamond paste (till ¼ μm); the geometric surface of the mineral interface, approximately 4 cm^2, was taken to be its real surface because of the high quality of the polishing operation, and the results are expressed as current density.

After 30 min immersion, the working potential is suddenly applied to the electrode, thereby marking the onset of the recording of the current as a function of time. The influence of temperature and the chemical variables were studied at +500 mV because this is the maximum value of the potential at which selective electrodissolution of the chalcopyrite can be effected in the presence of pyrite.

Results. When a constant potential is applied to the electrode, it is observed that the oxidation current does not maintain a fixed value. After a rapid decrease during the first few instants of electrodissolution, the current intensity approaches a constant value. This evolution pattern of the anodic intensity I_A leads to the following three remarks.

(1) There is no univocal relationship between E and I_A as in the case of a regime of pure activation: the rate of the electrooxidation reaction is not directly determined by the potential applied to the electrode.

(2) The recordings of i_A = f(t) are the homologues of the kinetic curves of the dissolution of copper through the chemical oxidation of chalcopyrite, which were modelled according to a paralinear law. During the first phase of the reaction, the graphical representation of i_A = f($\sqrt{t}$) is a straight line (Fig. 14 B): the parabolic decay of the reaction rate for this step suggests the development of an inhibitive layer of increasing thickness. After this phase of reactivity decrease, the system follows a stationary regime.

(3) As the initial phase involves only slight progress of the reaction, it is this stationary regime which ought to be retained for measuring the kinetics of the electrodissolution of the mineral.

The influence of the operating variables is as described below.

Influence of pH and Chloride Ion Concentration. Figures 12 and 13 show that pH and Cl^- have a relatively negligible influence on the kinetics of the reaction. If the rate of the initial

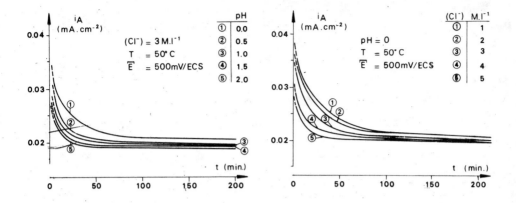

Chalcopyrite: kinetics of potentiostatic electrooxidation

Fig. 12. Influence of pH.   Fig. 13. Influence of chloride
                                              ion concentration.

phase decreases a little when the pH and Cl⁻ concentration increase, the rates attained during the stationary regime are for
all purposes equal, whatever the chemical conditions.

Influence of Temperature. Contrary to the preceding variable,
an increase in temperature has a very marked effect on the initial and final rates (Fig. 14A). Moreover, it may be stated
that the higher the temperature, the greater the time necessary
for attaining the stationary state: its installation involves
an increasing quantity of matter with increasing temperature.
At +500 mV, the reaction rates attained during the stationary
regime lead to an activation energy of 10 kcal/mole.

Influence of Potential. As can be expected, the kinetics of
dissolution depends strongly on the potential (Fig. 15A). However, it is seen from Fig. 15B that if the initial rate as a

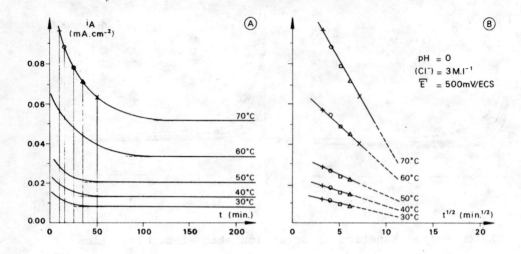

Fig. 14. Chalcopyrite: kinetics of potentiostatic electrooxidation. Influence of temperature.

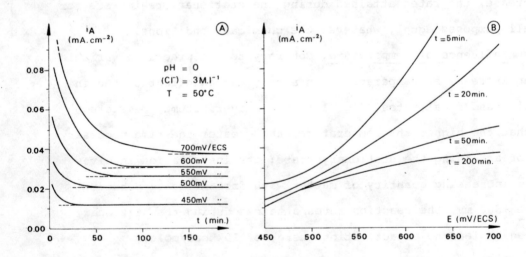

Fig. 15. Chalcopyrite: kinetics of potentiostatic electrooxidation. Influence of potential.

function of potential follows an exponential law typical of electrochemical reactions, the kinetic regime undergoes a change as the reaction progresses. The law of evolution of stationary current values as a function of E shows that, contrary to the initial reaction, the rate of the final reaction is relatively little influenced by an increase in the applied potential. The greater the decrease of the electrical efficiency of dissolution with an increase of E, the less important this influence is. During the stationary regime, the kinetics of electrodissolution is therefore not controlled by an electrochemical reaction.

Conclusions

The study of the kinetics of electrooxidation permits one to draw the following conclusions:

(1) Contrary to pH and the concentrations of chloride ions of the lixiviating solutions, the temperature and the working potential allow effective manipulation of the kinetics of chalcopyrite dissolution.

(2) The rate of the reaction decreases more or less rapidly, according to the working temperature and potential, thereby reaching a stationary value.

(3) The kinetics of oxidation during the stationary state (which is a measure of the practical rate of electrooxidation of the mineral) is little influenced by the working potential, contrary to electrochemical reactions. This characteristic shows that the reaction involved is not a simple electrooxidation of the chalcopyrite; one cannot rule out that the kinetics of the stationary regime is influenced by chemical processes.

(4) One can reasonably correlate the evolution of the anodic current intensity with the interfacial transformations of chalcopyrite. If the progressive slowing down of dissolution is attributed to a porous layer of sulphur with gradually increasing thickness, this phenomenon itself is not sufficient to explain the stationary regime. The layer of sulphur which is insoluble in the reaction medium continues, in effect, to build up in thickness as the reaction progresses. If the sulphur formed had directly influenced the kinetics of the reaction, the latter would have shown a progressive decrease in rate. This was not experimentally verified.

(5) This "passivated" reaction interface with which the porous sulphur layer is associated presents some remarkable properties

- It is reactivated by the sole process of acidic immersion
- If the decrease in current reflects a diminution of its reactivity, the installation of a stationary regime shows, however, that this residual electroactivity is maintained regularly. According to the paralinear model [27] , this phenomenon has been attributed to a rehomogenization of the solid composition by a process of solid state diffusion, the Sp layer being the location of a concentration gradient during electrooxidation. However, one cannot exclude the possibility of a chemical reaction imposing its rate on the stationary state; it generates a species regularly at the interface which is ultimately oxidized by electrochemical means. A more precise interpretation than these observations is proposed in the following paragraphs using information furnished by a study of the stoichiometry of the reactions.

780

The study of the stoichiometry of the electrooxidation of chalcopyrite as a function of the operating variables holds a scientific as well as a technical interest. From the point of view of the identification of the reaction mechanism, it is known that the solubilization of cations at different rates has been frequently observed during the initial phase. This remarkable phenomenon is at the base of the kinetic models which attribute the decrease of reactivity of the mineral to its superficial transformation to a less reactive sulphide. As regards the applicability of electrooxidation to minerals, the cost of energy is determined essentially by the distribution of the sulphide ions of the crystal between elementary sulphur and sulphate anions. In conformity with the following two extreme reactions,

$$CuFeS_2 = Cu^{2+} + Fe^{2+} + 2 S^\circ + 4\bar{e} \qquad (2)$$

$$CuFeS_2 + 8H_2O = Cu^{2+} + Fe^{2+} + 2SO_4^{2-} = + 16H^+ + 17\bar{e} \qquad (3)$$

One of the advantages of the production of elemental sulphur is that it consumes four times less electrical energy than that of sulphate anions.

Methods and Materials

The experimental set-up employed for this study with apparatus developed by Coole [28], is represented schematically in Fig. 16. The chalcopyrite particles, fluidized by mechanical agitation of the pulp, dissolve electrically at an imposed potential in an intermittent manner during their brief contact

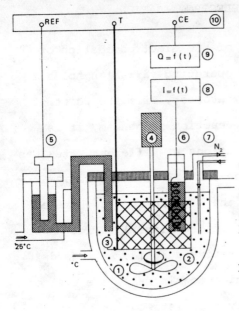

1. Thermostated reactor
2. Sulphide pulp
3. Platinum grid
4. Mechanical agitation
5. Reference electrode (SCE at $25^{\circ}C$)
6. Counter electrode
7. Nitrogen circuit
8. Current recorder
9. Coulometer
10. Potentiostat

Fig. 16. Scheme of experimental set up for electrodissolution in pulp.

with a rigid electrode formed by a platinum cylindrical grid with a large surface area. The quantities of Cu^{2+}, Fe^{2+}, Fe^{3+} and SO_4^{2-} solubilized are determined by the analysis of solution samples as a function of the stage of the reaction, the latter being measured by a coulometer. It must be stated that the ratio Fe^{2+}/Fe^{3+}, determined simply by the imposed potential at the platinum grid is not of any particular interest, except for establishing the charge balance of the reactions. Indeed, the proportion of elementary sulphur formed at different stages of the reaction is calculated by charge and material balances, assuming that the electrical efficiency is 100%. At the end of the experiment, the elemental sulphur in the solid residue is analysed by volatalization in a vacuum at $120^{\circ}C$; this was done as a control measure. The results are reported as the quantity of solid oxidized in moles-percentage.

Remarks

(1) As in the case of the electrooxidation of a rotating disc, the oxidation current of the pulp at first decreases rapidly to attain a stationary regime, during which the current decreases linearly at a very slow rate with a decrease in the quantity of solid. Curiously, it is observed that this stationary regime commences at a value of current which is lower for higher values of working potentials. For this reason the standard potential adopted for these experiments was fixed at +400 mV. This phenomenon, attributed initially to the acceleration of the reaction by the reduction of ferric ions in the chalcopyrite structure at low potential values, results more simply from the adherence of the particles on the current carrying electrode. The adherence of the grains (whose superficial properties are modified by oxidation) becomes more pronounced when the initial reaction takes place at higher potentials, i.e., more rapidly.

(2) With a view to taking samples from the solution, the applied potential and agitation are interrupted to permit decantation of the particles. After the necessary 4 to 5 min sampling operation, agitation is again established and the potential then reapplied. When electrodissolution commences, the current intensity is greater than before the sampling. After a decrease, which takes place at a smaller scale according to the same law as the initial phase of dissolution, the current value rejoins the stationary regime in continuation of the preceding value. The mineral grains are thus reactivated by simple immersion in the acidic solution, like the electrodes utilized for tracing the E-I curves.

(3) Where the reaction is considerably advanced, the residual solid has a characteristic greyish blue colour. However, X-ray analysis of this solid does not reveal phases other than elemental sulphur and chalcopyrite. The detection limit under identical conditions is approximately 3%.

Results

Solubilization of Cations. The diagrams presented in Fig. 17A correlate the solubilization of copper to that of total iron $(Fe^{2+} + Fe^{3+})$. The ratio Cu/Fe (Fig. 17A) is constant, being approximately unity during the whole reaction, irrespective of operating conditions. As a first approach, the two cations are solubilized according to the composition of the mineral. However, a more precise examination (Fig. 17B) of the stoichiometry for initial stages of advancement reveals the anomaly

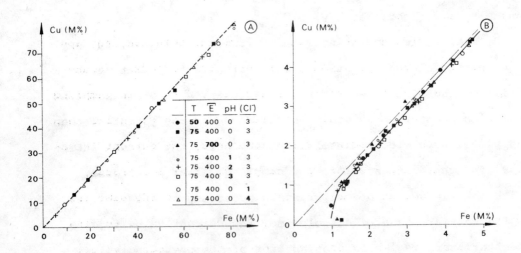

Fig. 17. Chalcopyrite: stoichiometry of potentiostatic electrooxidation. Solubilization of cations.

previously noted (Fig. 3): the solubilization of copper is initially less important than that of iron. As the reaction progresses, the ratio Cu/Fe tends to reach a value near unity (marked on the diagram by a dotted line).

Oxidation of Sulphide Ions. In accordance with Fig. 18, the distribution of sulphide ions of the crystal between elemental sulphur and sulphate ions is constant for the greater part of the reaction under the given reaction conditions. For smaller degrees of advancement, however, the percentage of elemental sulphur formed undergoes a little variation, the importance and the nature of which depends on the operating conditions.

The temperature (Fig. 18A) and the concentration of chloride ions (Fig. 18B) do not practically influence the $S^o/S^o + SO_4^{2-}$ ratio: 99.7%, i.e., the quasi-totality of the sulphide ions, are oxidized as elemental sulphur. The pH and especially the potential, influence the stoichiometry in a more perceptible way. When the pH (Fig. 18D) increases, the percentage of sulphate ion produced tends to increase slightly: from 0.3 at pH = 0, this percentage attains a value of 1.2% at pH = 3. The potential (Fig. 18C) has a still more marked effect: from 99.7% at +400 mV, the percentage of sulphur formed decreases to 97.6% at +700 mV.

Conclusions

(1) The quasi-totality of the sulphide ions being oxidized to elemental sulphur, the reaction takes place according to a favourable stoichiometry.

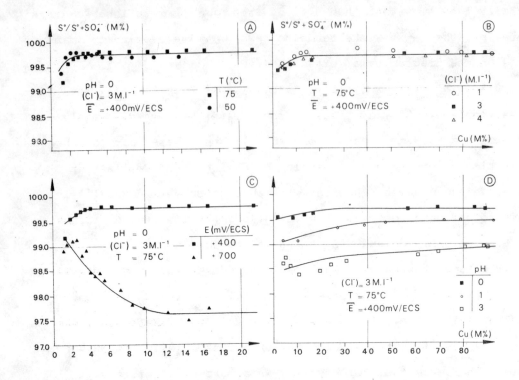

Fig. 18. Chalcopyrite: stoichiometry of potentiostatic
electrooxidation. Oxidation of sulphide ions.
Influence of temperature (A), chloride ion concentration (B), potential (C) and pH (D).

(2) The reaction conditions examined have no effect on the
solubilization of the two cations and only slightly influence
the oxidation of the sulphide ions. However, in accordance with
the following equations (relative to pH = 0 and at two potentials at which the iron is totally in bivalent and trivalent
states respectively),

+ 400 mV : $CuFeS_2 + 0.024\ H_2O =$

$Cu^{2+} + Fe^{2+} + 1.994\ S^o + 0.006\ SO_4^{2-} + 0.048\ H^+ + 4.036\ e$ (4)

786

+ 700 mV : $CuFeS_2$ + 0.192 H_2O =

Cu^{2+} + F^{3+} + 1.952 S^o + 0.048 SO_4^{2-} + 0.384 H^+ + 5.288 e   (5)

the increase of the electrical energy consumption between +400 mV
and + 700 mV is 31%. To discourage the production of sulphate ion
and the oxidation of iron especially, the energy balance for the
reaction is optimized by operating at an acidic pH and lower
potential.

(3) Whether the oxidation of chalcopyrite is effected chemically or electrochemically, the percentage of sulphate ·ion produced is identical. The formation of these anions which does not
require the presence of an oxidizing agent in solution cannot
thus result from the secondary oxidation of elemental sulphur;
these are formed by a direct oxidation of the sulphide phase, and
are produced along with the elemental sulphur.

(4) The initial phase is marked by a special and changing
kinetics; the stoichiometry of this step presents the same characteristics. One is naturally led to consider the initial kinetics and the stoichiometry as two aspects of the same phenomenon. The superficial transformations of chalcopyrite in acidic
medium allow one to explain these aspects as discussed below.

ACIDIC REACTION OF CHALCOPYRITE

The electrochemical measurements show that the period immediately following the immersion of a chalcopyrite electrode in
acidic solution is marked by a rapid transformation of the interface.

The rest potential of an electrode changes a lot during the 30 min following its immersion. The kinetics and magnitude of this evolution which is reproductible depends especially on the pH and the temperature. This phenomenon is particularly important at pH = 0, for which the curve $\bar{E}_a$ = f(t) shows, after a rapid increase of potential, a maximum value followed by a progressive decrease towards a quasi-stationary potential (Fig. 19). The evolution of E_a is moreover correlated with an important variation of peak A, situated at +400 mV on the polarization curves (Fig. 6). When the duration of prior immersion increases, peak A has a tendency to disappear. Like the evolu-

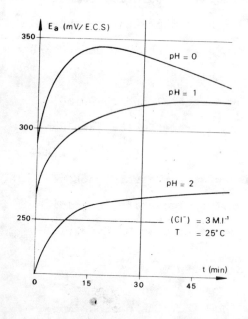

Fig. 19. Chalcopyrite: influence of pH on the evolution of the rest potential (E_a) in an aerated acidic chloride solution.

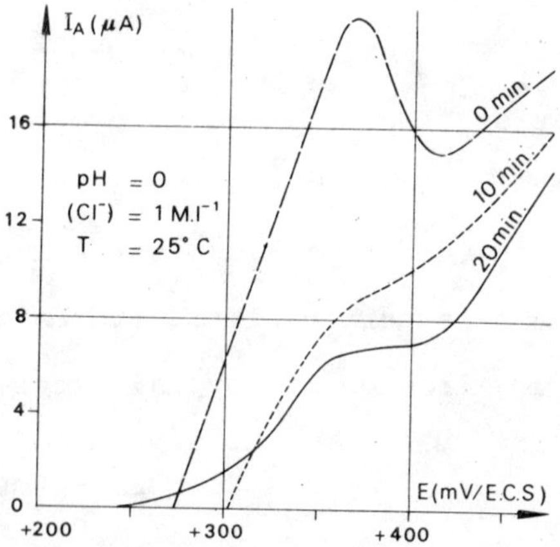

Fig. 20. Chalcopyrite: elementary anodic curve. Evolution of peak A at pH = 0 as a function of immersion time prior to recording of curve.

788

tion of E_a, this variation depends strongly on the pH. At pH = 0, the anodic peak A decreases rapidly along with the increase in duration of prior immersion (Fig. 20). The tracing of the E-I curve immediately following the immersion shows a peak A with a very important current intensity, resembling a "mixed" curve. When the duration of immersion increases, the curves resemble more an elementary curve tangential to the potential axis. The peak A practically disappears at the end of 45 min of immersion. On the contrary, at pH = 1 and 2, peak A, even though less apparent as compared to its initial importance, subsists after 45 min of immersion (Fig. 7).

In conformity with the "mixed" aspect of the E-I curves traced immediately after the immersion of the electrode, and with the reproducibility of the evolution of E_a, E_r is initially a mixed potential. This potential is determined by an equilibrium involving electroactive interfacial species present in non-negligible concentrations. During the first few instants following the immersion of the electrode these species are abundant at the interface and give rise to an important oxidation current. The decrease of the electrochemical peak A as a function of time reflects an impoverishment of these electroactive species by oxidation. These are thus oxidizable not only electrochemically but also through chemical means. The role of the oxidizing agent in solution is played by dissolved oxygen whose reduction reaction, $O_2 + 4 H^+ + 4 e = 2 H_2O$, is favoured when the pH decreases in conformity with experimental observations. Also, as the oxidation reaction progresses the initial "mixed" potential of the electrode becomes a "drift" potential. This

789

evolution of E_a, also observed by Baur et al. [14] in acidic sulphate solution, is associated with an important and rapid solubilization of copper during the first 10 min. The origin of these phenomena, which lead to a modification of the reaction interface, cannot be attributed to the dissolution of superficial soluble compounds like iron or copper sulphate observable through ESCA analysis [29]. These compounds are formed by atmospheric oxidation of chalcopyrite in moist air. Their dissolution takes place in effect by simple dissociation without electronic exchange, whereas reaction "A" is associated to an electrochemical peak. One is apt to believe that during the first few minutes which follow the immersion of the mineral the surface is the location of a reaction producing electroactive species associated with peak A.

With a view to gaining more precise information on the nature of these phenomena, the kinetics and the stoichiometry of this reaction have been studied utilizing chemical methods [30].

Experimental Procedure

The pulp, diluted largely with respect to the solid (500 ml + 2 g of pulverized chalcopyrite) is kept in a closed reactor under N_2 to limit the oxidation reaction by dissolved oxygen in the acidic solution. The dissolution curves for copper and iron were established through analysis of liquid samples taken at known intervals of time; the elemental sulphur is determined at the end of the experiment using the solid residue.

Results

Observations. The comparison of kinetic curves of copper and iron from the same experiment allow three reaction steps to be distinguished (Fig. 23).

Step I. The first phase, which lasts only a few minutes, is characterized by the following experiment facts:

(1) Quasi-instantaneous solubilization of copper and iron in relatively large quantities; a small quantity of sulphate ions are simultaneously detected in the solution which are attributed to the dissolution of surface compounds formed by atmospheric oxidation.

(2) The solubilization of iron, present exclusively in the bivalent state, is superior to roughly double that of copper.

(3) The importance of the reaction increases slightly with temperature and more markedly with a decrease in pH (Fig. 21-22).

(4) The pH of the attacking solution measured in a dense pulp increases rapidly: the reactions consume H^+ ions.

(5) Not only is there production of elemental sulphur, but there is also a small quantity of H_2S detected easily in dense pulps. An acid-base reaction therefore takes place simultaneously with the oxidation reaction.

(6) Compared to the initial chalcopyrite, after the reaction the solid presents a surface enriched strongly in copper, as determined by ESCA analysis (on a reaction layer of 30 Å approximately). This copper is associated with a new sulphide structure.

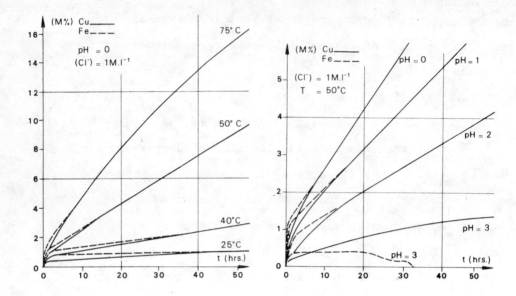

Chalcopyrite: acidic chloride medium

Fig. 21. Influence of tempera-   Fig. 22. Influence of pH on the
ture on the kinetics   kinetics of solubiliza-
of solubilization of   tion of Cu^{2+} and Fe^{2+}.
Cu^{2+} and Fe^{2+}.

Step II. The second phase of the reaction has the following
characteristics:

(1) The copper dissolves at a higher rate than that of iron.
However, in conformity with the parabolic nature of its kinetic
curve, the copper solubilization decreases as the reaction progresses.

(2) The rate of solubilization of cations increase as the
temperature and concentration of H^+ ions increase.

(3) If elemental sulphur is produced during this step as
during the previous one, H_2S is no longer detectable.

(4) At the end of this step, the total quantity of copper solubilized attains a value similar to that of iron. The progress of the corresponding reaction is therefore determined by the relative rates of solubilization of these two cations. The higher the temperature and the more acidic the solution, the more quickly the second phase of the reaction is terminated. The quantity of solid involved in this reaction increases according to the same law.

(5) The surface of the particles, even towards the end of this stage, as examined by ESCA, shows the same enrichment in elemental sulphur and copper sulphide as observed at the end of the first step.

Step III. During this final phase of the reaction which lasts till the complete solubilization of the solid.

(1) Fe^{2+} and Cu^{2+} dissolve at the same rate; the reaction reaches a stationary state.

(2) Cu^{2+}, like Fe^{2+} is solubilized according to a linear law; the slight decrease, observed for advancements of reaction greater than 10%, results from the decrease in grain diameter.

(3) The kinetics of solubilization of cations increase markedly with temperature (ΔE = 17 kcal/mole) and less markedly with an increase in H^+ concentration.

(4) The surface of the grains is enriched in copper sulphide as in the preceding case.

Discussion and Interpretation

Step I. It appears that the experimental facts on the whole may be accounted for by admitting that the mineral-solution interface is the location of several simultaneous reactions.

(1) Solubilization of the products of atmospheric oxidation which contributes in a less important way to the overall reaction.

(2) An extremely rapid acid-base reaction of the chalcopyrite which involves a readjustment of the degree of oxidation of the cations solubilized, as brought out by the following reactions:

$$Cu^+ Fe^{3+} S_2 = + 4 H^+ = Cu^+ + Fe^{3+} + 2 H_2S \uparrow \qquad (6)$$

$$Cu^+ + Fe^{3+} \qquad\qquad = Cu^{2+} + Fe^{2+} \qquad\qquad (7)$$

(3) Contrary to Fe^{2+}, a part of the Cu^{2+} is precipitated by H_2S through a secondary reaction taking place on the surface of chalcopyrite:

$$Cu^{2+} + H_2S \qquad\qquad = CuS \downarrow + 2 H^+ \qquad\qquad (8)$$

The overall equation for the double reaction of "acid-precipitation" resulting from the two preceding reactions is therefore:

$$CuFeS_2 + 2 H^+ \qquad\qquad = CuS \downarrow + Fe^{2+} + H_2S \uparrow \qquad (9)$$

(4) Oxidation of $CuFeS_2$ and a fraction of CuS by the residual dissolved oxygen:

$$CuFeS_2 + O_2 + 4 H^+ = Cu^{2+} + Fe^{2+} + S° \downarrow + 2 H_2O \qquad (10)$$

$$CuS + 1/2\ O_2 + 2 H^+ = Cu^{2+} + S° \downarrow + H_2O \qquad\qquad (11)$$

Thus, contrary to what is generally found, at low temperature the chalcopyrite exhibits an acid-base type of reaction. However, it is well established that this reaction takes place at a high temperature and in a slightly oxidizing atmosphere [31] . CuS, well spread on the surface of chalcopyrite or present pseudo-morphologically on the grains, has been observed by several authors [32, 13] . More recently, Harvey and Dudas [33] recommend utilization of this reaction for activating chalcopyrite concentrates, by totally transforming these into covellite while eliminating the iron by dissolution.

In terms of the first step, the chalcopyrite surface is thus covered by elemental sulphur and CuS, which then constitute the solid-solution interface.

Step II and III. During these two steps, the kinetics of the reactions are slower than those during step I. Iron, produced exclusively as ferrous ions, dissolves at a linear rate. The copper dissolution follows a changing kinetic law.

In accordance with the fact of the joining together of the kinetic curves of Fe^{2+} and Cu^{2+} during step II, the oxidation of the solid effectively reduces the relative proportion of CuS; however, contrary to what follows from the lack of evolution of H_2S, CuS, which is responsible for the superficial enrichment of the solid surface in copper, continues to be generated during steps II and III.

The continuation of this reaction is demonstrated by the following experiment. Following the evolution of cation solubilization of a very thick pulp of chalcopyrite maintained in a closed air-tight reactor, copper and iron solubilizations at

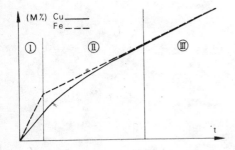

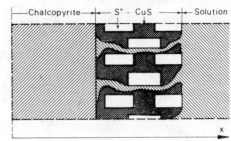

Fig. 23. Chalcopyrite: acidic
chloride medium.
General shape of
kinetic curves for
the dissolution of
Cu^{2+} and Fe^{2+}.

Fig. 24. Chalcopyrite: chemical
oxidation. Schematic
section through
reaction zone.

different rates is observed at the beginning of the reaction,
which is in accordance with the preceding results. However, some
hours later, the copper dissolved earlier disappears from the
solution and the rate of iron solubilization decreases corres-
pondingly. In addition, the atmosphere of the reactor is charged
by H_2S. An identical observation has been made by Atwood and
Curtis [34] while studying the lixiviation of concentrates by
Cu^{2+}.

These results show that not only the acidic reaction continues beyond the step I, but also that the precipitation of CuS
produces a slowing down of the Fe^{2+} solubilization rate.

This last proposition has been verified by dissolving powdered chalcopyrite in an acidic solution containing traces of
Cu^{2+} (to limit the oxidation by Cu^{2+}). The quantity of CuS pre-

cipitated at the interface ought to be more important with an increase of the initial concentration of Cu^{2+}. It is observed that as the initial concentration of Cu^{2+} increases, the linear rate of dissolution of iron in effect decreases. The same pheno- menon has been observed by Baur et al. [14]. These authors also point to "the similarity between the shapes of the covellite and chalcopyrite (kinetic) curves". Thus, the quantity of CuS precipitated at the interface determines the rate of solubiliza- tion of Fe^{2+}.

If the sudden decrease in the reaction rate after Step I is correlated to the formation of a layer of sulphur, the increase in its thickness as the reaction progresses does not contribute to the rate decrease. The porous layer of elemental sulphur does not therefore directly influence the kinetics. Besides, the diffusion of dissolved oxygen in the solution between the pores of sulphur cannot be the rate-determining step since the activation energy of the reaction is high.

If one takes into account the preceding observations, it may be admitted that the precipitation of CuS blocking the pores of the sulphur layer effectively isolates the surface of the chalco- pyrite and cuts off access of the oxidant to the surface. Dur- ing steps II and III, the chalcopyrite is thus only dissolved by the acidic reaction. Moreover, this reaction, whose rate is measured by the solubilization of Fe^{2+}, can continue only with the elimination of CuS. Because of the persistence of CuS at the solid-solution interface, the acidic reaction of chalcopy- rite is necessarily more rapid than the dissolution of CuS by oxidation. This latter reaction controls the overall rate of the reactions. In addition, when steady state is attained the quantity of CuS decreases in comparison with the quantity present during the initial phase, being limited by the volume of pores formed by elemental sulphur. This fact explains the reduction of the difference between Fe^{2+} and Cu^{2+} solubilized.

Conclusion

The progress of the reaction can be described in the following manner.

During the initial phase of the reaction, several reactions take place simultaneously at the chalcopyrite surface: an acidic reaction which is extremely rapid and oxidation reactions of chalcopyrite and of the newly formed CuS. The latter covers the interface and gives rise to a porous sulphur layer whose thickness increases as the reaction progresses. The sulphur pores constitute a particular reaction zone, where the movement of the electrolyte is restricted and in which a strong concentration gradient exists. Whereas the reaction products are concentrated here, the chalcopyrite surface becomes isolated from the oxidant. Thus, the sulphur layer, which does not constitute an inhibiting barrier at the interface in the usual sense, plays only an indirect role in the reactions. During the stationary state following the initial phase, the surface of the chalcopyrite is in essence attacked by the acidic reaction since the oxidant cannot reach the surface. The reaction products at the same cime continue to accumulate within the sulphur network. As Fe^{2+} is liberated in the solution, Cu^{2+} is precipitated by H_2S. This reaction regenerates the acidity of the medium, transport the copper to an external region of the solid where it forms CuS, and blocks the pores of the sulphur network. The CuS precipitation leads to a decrease of the acidic reaction rate, and limits the reaction area to the small section of pores.

The next step is simply the oxidation of interstitial CuS at the solid solution interface; this reaction controls the overall reaction rate. As the external interface is regularly replenished by CuS as a result of the acidic reaction, the overall reaction rate is not influenced by an increase of thickness of the sulphur layer and is linear.

Thus, during steady-state conditions two different reactions take place at the reaction front (Fig. 24): the acidic reaction at the chalcopyrite - solution interface, and the chemical oxidation of CuS at the solid-solution interface. The elemental sulphur is thus formed exclusively by the oxidation of CuS which plays the role of an intermediate compound between whole of H_2O and S°. After the initial phase, the stoichiometry of oxidation of sulphide ions is thus attributed not to the reaction of chalcopyrite but to CuS oxidation. Also, the measured activating energy (17 kcal/mole) corresponds to the oxidation of CuS alone.

This reaction mechanism and in particular the double reaction of acid-precipitation allows interpretation of several experimental facts. The evolution of the chalcopyrite surface at the beginning of the reaction results from its covering by a relatively important quantity of CuS and subsequently from the dissolution of CuS. This evolution of the surface explains the variation of the rest potential and of the peak A of the E-I curves. That is why the peak A is attributed not to the electro-

chemical oxidation of Fe^{2+}, as postulated earlier [27], but to
the oxidation of CuS produced at the onset of the reaction. Its
evolution as a function of pH and duration of immersion conforms
to the decrease of the quantity of interfacial CuS.

To explain the stoichiometric anomalies of the initial phase
of oxidation and notably the differences of solubilization of
copper and iron, it is no longer necessary to invoke hypothetical mechanisms of solid-solution exchange or solid-state diffusion: the precipitation of CuS accounts well for these phenomena.
From the point of view of the reactivity of chalcopyrite, it may
be stated that only the solubilization of iron represents the
proper reactions of chalcopyrite because of the participation of
copper in secondary reactions.

GENERAL CONCLUSIONS

Reaction Mechanisms

The preceding results as a whole show that the phenomena associated with the oxidation of chalcopyrite, whether chemically
or electrochemically, result in the same type of evolution.
After an initially rapid phase, the reaction rate decreases and
reaches a steady state dissolution condition. One might think
that the preceding mechanism, proposed to account for the kinetics and stoichiometry of the reactions of chalcopyrite in an
acidic oxidizing medium, is equally applicable for describing
the mechanism of its electrodissolution. During this latter
reaction, the development of a porous layer of elemental sulphur
at the chalcopyrite surface creates a particular type of reaction zone which limits the influence of chemical parameters

800

relative to the solution. However, the effect of this porous protecting layer on the electrochemical mechanism differs slightly according to type of electrolysis considered.

While carrying out electrodissolution in a pulp, the potential of electrodissolution is applied through the current carrying lead at the external solid-solution interface alone.

During the initial phase of the reactions, the chalcopyrite is dissolved through acidic reaction and electrooxidation; the simultaneous precipitation of CuS modifies the Cu/Fe ratio.

As the reactions progress, the thickness of the sulphur isolates the surface of chalcopyrite, not only hydrodynamically from the solution, but also electrically from the current carrying lead. The chalcopyrite sulphur interface is attacked only by the acidic reaction, whereas the CuS precipitates within the reaction zone of sulphur. The reactivation of grains, through simple immersion in the acidic solution, and their bluish colour due to impregnation of sulphur by small quantities of CuS, show that the acidic reaction takes place simultaneously with electrooxidation. This latter reaction, occurring only at the external surface of the grains, involves CuS exclusively, as during chemical oxidation. The double acid-precipitation reaction thus assures the provision of the external surface of the grains with electrooxidizable CuS. Therefore, the stoichiometry of the oxidation of sulphide ions in the stationary regime is thus relative to the CuS alone. The evolution of the $S^{o}/S^{o} + SO_4$ ratio during the start of the reaction is attributable to the dissolution of products of atmospheric oxidation and to the decrease of the participation of chalcopyrite in the electrooxidation reaction.

When carrying out electrochemical oxidation of a massive electrode at an imposed potential, the electrical contact between the current carrying lead and the chalcopyrite is not modified by the reaction.

At the beginning of electrolysis, two types of reactions take place simultaneously at the solid-solution interface the double acid-precipitation reaction on the one hand and the electrochemical oxidation of chalcopyrite and CuS on the other. The anodic current then follows an exponential law as a function of potential as is typical of electrochemical reactions.

If the precipitation of CuS lends a certain conductivity to the layer of sulphur, its electrical resistance increases when its thickness grows. It is thus the siege of a potential gradient. As the working potential is relative to the external solid-solution interface only, the potential decreases progressively in the direction of the chalcopyrite surface. When the thickness of the S^o-CuS front increases, this internal interface is subjected to a more and more low potential. Beyond a certain reaction stage, increasing with the working potential, the sulphur layer attains such a thickness that the applied potential at the chalcopyrite surface is less than its minimum potential of electrooxidation. It follows that the chalcopyrite is only attacked by the acidic reaction and the kinetics follows a stationary regime. The electrodissolution then takes place only at interstitial CuS as before, and its overall reaction rate is determined by the rate of production of CuS in the electrooxidation zone. The kinetics is therefore controlled by the acidic reaction whose activation energy of 10 kcal/mole is comparable

to those for reactions of the same type. It is for this reason
that the rate of electrooxidation during the steady state regime
is, paradoxically, little influenced by the potential.

In accordance with this mechanism, the regular increase of
potential applied at chalcopyrite electrode during the registration of E-I curves causes an increasing thickness of solid to be
involved in the electrooxidation zone of the interfacial potential gradient. After the rapid solubilization of superficial CuS
leading to peak A, the electrodissolution associated with peak B
takes place according to the same mechanism as the reacting
phase leading to a stationary regime. This mechanism is also
responsible for the continuing low values of current intensity
noted after the decrease of current at peak B.

Applications to Beneficiation

The preceding results and the consideration of other impera-
tives of hydrometallurgical treatment allow one to rationally
choose the optimal operational conditions for electrooxidizing
potentiostatic treatment, as applied to complex sulphide minerals
with a view to extract the copper associated with chalcopyrite
in acidic chloride solutions.

The Working Potential. The electrooxidation can be carried
out at 450-500 mV; the rate of the stationary regime is maximum
with practically no further increase. The use of a higher potential would, moreover, present the following drawbacks:
- the percentage of sulphate anion and especially ferric ion produced would increase, thus decreasing the energy efficiency of
the operation.
- the rate of electrooxidation of pyrite would be non-negligible.

803

Electrolytic Solution

- The concentration of chloride ion has practically no influence
on the kinetics and stoichiometry of the reactions. However, it
would be interesting to operate on concentrated solutions, unless the subsequent treatment of leach solution presents difficulties. Under these conditions, not only the dissolving power
and the conductivity of the solution are increased, but the
solubilization of pyrite is decreased, since its domain of electrooxidation is displaced towards more positive potentials with
an increase of chloride ion concentration.

- While operating on weakly acidic solutions with pH values of
approximately 1, the kinetics of the reactions, little influenced by pH, are not decreased. Besides, the production of sulphate
ion, increasing with an increase of pH, is limited. The consumption of acid by impurities of the materials employed and the
production of H_2S are low.

Temperature. An increase of temperature enhances the kinetics
without changing the electrical efficiency and the selectivity
of the reactions. However, the interest presented by a process
at an elevated temperature depends strongly on the purity of the
materials being treated. Heating clearly contributes to higher
efficiency for selected or bulk concentrates rather than for run
of mine ores, where the phases subjected to electrooxidation
represent 2-4% of the total solid.

Because of the dependence of certain operating parameters on
the degree of purity of the material being treated, the final
choice of conditions for a given material will necessarily
result from a compromise which can only be gained through a
pilot plant study.

Besides, the present study deals with only electrochemical and chemical kinetics of the reactions. Before applying these fundamental results on an industrial scale, several theoretical and practical problems must be solved. The success of this method of treatment is indeed related to the development of:

- electrochemical industrial reactors, favouring the physical kinetics of the operations (transport of matter to the electrodes, heat and current transfer,...);
- materials of electrolysis (electrode, membrane,...) adapted not only to acidic chloride concentrated mediums, but also to the hydrodynamic conditions of thick pulps;
- potentiostatic generators of high power.

The interest aroused by this theoretical and technological research should nucleate their further development, since the sphere of their applicability goes beyond the mere treatment of complex sulphide minerals, as all powdered materials with conducting constituents (metallurgical wastes, blast furnace dusts, nickeliferrous laterites...) worth beneficiating may be treated.

ACKNOWLEDGEMENTS

This research was funded by the Délégation Générale à la Recherche Scientifique et Technique and the Centre National de la Recherche Scientifique.

REFERENCES

1. Woodcock J. T. Austr. Inst. Min. Met. Proc., 198, 47-84 (1961).
2. Wadsworth M. E. Minerals Sci. Engng., 4, 36-47 (1972).

3. Shuey R. T. Semiconducting Ore Minerals. Elsevier, Amsterdam, 1975.

4. Habashi F. Minerals Sci. Engng., 3, 3-12 (1971).

5. Schneiner B. J. and Lindstrom R. E. Extraction of molybdenum from ores by electrooxidation. USBM. TPR 47 (1972).

6. Kruesi P. R. Process for the recovery of metals from sulfide ores through electrolytic dissociation of sulfides. U.S. Patent No. 3, 673,061 (1972).

7. Haver E. P. and Wong M. M. Bur. of Mines, R.I. 7474; J. Metal. N.Y., 23, No.2, 25-29 (1971).

8. Dutrizac J. E. and MacDonald R. J. C. Min. Sci. Engng., 6, 59-100 (1974).

9. Subramanian K. N. and Jennings P. H. Can. Metall. Q., 11, 387-400 (1972).

10. Sullivan J. D. Trans. A.I.M.E., 106, 515-546 (1933).

11. Dutrizac J. E., MacDonald R. J. C. and Ingraham T. R. Trans. Met. Soc. A.I.M.E., 245, 955-959 (1969).

12. Conde J. Etude de la cinetique de dissolution de la chalcopyrite par les sels ferriques. Ph. D. Thesis. Nancy, 1974.

13. Jones D. L. The leaching of chalcopyrite. Ph. D. Thesis, U.B.C., Vancouver, 1974.

14. Baur J. P., Gibbs H. L. and Wadsworth M. E. The Metall. Soc. of A.I.M.E., pamphlet 72-B, 96, 62 (1972).

15. Peters E. The Physical Chemistry of Hydrometallurgy. Proceedings of Intern. Symp. on Hydrometallurgy. Chicago (Ed. D. J. I. Evans and R. S. Shoemaker). A.I.M.E., New York 1973

16. King J. A. Solid state changes in the leaching of copper sulphides. Ph. D. Thesis, University of London, 1966.

17. Burkin A. R. Min. Sci. Engng., 1, 4-14 (1969).

18. Ferreira R. C. H. Leaching of chalcopyrite. Ph. D. Thesis, University of London, 1972.

19. Ferreira R. C. H. and Burkin A. R. Leaching and reduction in hydrometallurgy. I.M.M., London, 1975.

20. Ammou-Chokroum M., Cambazoglu M. and Steinmetz D. Bull. Soc. Fr. Minéral. Cristallogr., 100, 149-161 (1977).

21. Ammou-Chokroum M., Cambazoglu M. and Steinmetz D. Bull. Soc. Fr. Minéral. Cristallogr., 100, 161-177 (1977).

22. Webb W. W., Morton J. T. and Wagner C. J. of Electroch. Soc., 103, 107-111 (1956).

23. Ichikuni M. Bull. Chem. Soc. Japan, 35, 1765-1768 (1962).

24. Dutrizac J. E. and MacDonald R. J. C. Mat. Res. Bull., 8, 961-972 (1973).

25. Adams R. N. Electrochemistry at Solids Electrodes. Marcel Dekker, 1969.

26. Ammou-Chokroum M. Bull. Soc. Fr. Minéral. Cristallogr., 98, 121-129 (1975).

27. Ammou-Chokroum M., Steinmetz D. and Malve A. Bull. Soc. Fr. Minéral. Cristallogr., 101, 1, 26-43 (1978).

28. Coole S. Electrochemical investigation of the dissolution of copper sulphide. Ph. D. Thesis, University of Columbia, 1972.

29. Brion D. (I.R.C.H.A.). Private communication (1977).

30. Ammou-Chokroum M. and Sen P. K. Réaction acide de la chalco-pyrite (to be published).

31. Warren I. H. Australian Journal of Applied Sciences, 9, 36-51 (1958).

32. Stanczyk M. H. and Rampacek C. Oxidation Leaching of Copper Sulfides in Acidic Pulps at Elevated Temperatures and Pressures. U.S. Bur. Mines Rep. Inv. 6193 (1963).

33. Harvey W. W. and Dudas F. O. Trans. SME/AIME, 262, 46-57 (1977).

34. Atwood G. E. and Curtis C. H. Hydrometallurgical process for the production of copper. U.S. Patent No. 3, 785-944 (1974).

ABSTRACT

The electrooxidation of chalcopyrite, carried out at an
imposed potential in an acid chloride medium, is studied with a
view to formulating new ways of beneficiating complex sulphide
minerals. The stoichiometry of the reaction is little influenced
by the reaction variables. However, the charge balances involved
in the operation depend essentially on the potential, which determines the degree of oxidation of the iron. The rate of electrooxidation at first decreases, and then stationary, which
depends particularly on the temperature. It appears that, as in
the case of chemical oxidation, electrochemical kinetics is controlled by the acidic reaction of chalcopyrite and the associated precipitation of CuS in the superficial layer of sulphur.

RÉSUMÉ

L'électrooxydation de la chalcopyrite, à potential imposé et
en milieu acide chloruré, est étudiée en vue de définir de nouvelles modalités de valorisation hydrométallurgiques des minerais sulfurés complexes. La stoechiométrie de la réaction est
peu influencée par les variables réactionnelles; cependant, le
bilan électrique de l'opération dépend essentiellement du potentiel, qui détermine le degré d'oxydation du fer. La vitesse
de l'électrooxydation décroît d'abord, puis suit un régime sta-
tionnaire, qui dépend surtour de la température. Il semble que,
comme lors d'une oxydation par voie chimique, la cinétique
électrochimique soit contrôlée par la réaction acide de la
chalcopyrite et la précipitation de CuS, dans la couche de
soufre superficielle, qui lui est associée.

ZUSAMMENFASSUNG

Es wird die Elektrooxydation von Kupferkies (Chalkopyrit) in
einem sauren Chloridmedium mit aufgezwungenem Potential erörtert,
mit dem Ziel, neue Verfahren zur Anreicherung komplexer sulfidischer Minerale zu finden. Die Stöchiometrie der Reaktion wird
nur wenig von den Reaktionsvariablen beeinflusst; die bei einer

808

solchen Operation auftretende Beschickungsbilanz ist jedoch in wesentlichen Masse vom Potential abhänging, welches den Oxydationsgrad des Eusens bestimmt. Die Geschwindigkeit der Elektrooxydation sinkt zunächst mal, worauf ein stationäres Regime einsetzt, das insbesondere von der Temperatur abhängig ist. Es konnte festgestellt werden, dass ebenso wie im Falle chemischer Oxydation, die elektrochemische Kinetik durch die saure Reaktion des Kupferkieses und durch die dabei auftretende Fällung von CuS aus der obersten Schwefelschicht beeinflusst wird.

РЕЗЮМЕ

Исследован электрохимический процесс окисления халькопирита при наложенном потенциале в подкисленном растворе хлоридов с целью разработки новых методов обогащения комплексных сульфидных минералов.

Переменность параметров реакции влияет в небольшой степени на стехеометрию реакции, тем не менее баланс зарядов, участвующих в операции, зависит прежде всего от потенциала, который определяет степень окисления железа.

Скорость электрохимического окисления первоначально уменьшается, а затем стабилизируется, что зависит прежде всего от температуры. Оказалось, что, как и при химическом окислении, кинетика электрохимической реакции регулируется кислой реакцией халькопирита и сопровождающим её выделением CuS в поверхностном слое серы.

ELECTROCHEMICAL LEACHING OF COPPER SULPHIDE ORES

R. Bertram, E. Hillrichs, N. Galitis, R. Müller and H. Greulich

Institut für Physikalische Chemie, Technische Universität, Braunschweig, BRD

There are several methods of winning valuable metals from ores, such as hydrometallurgical or bacterial leaching. Electrochemical methods of metal-winning from ores have recently gained much importance. This applies in particular to copper winning from sulphide minerals such as chalcocite (Cu_2S), covellite (CuS) and chalcopyrite ($CuFeS_2$) due to the accelerated solution of the metal components from semiconducting copper sulphides under the influence of an electric current. Copper may be deposited on the cathode with simultaneous anodic dissolution. Because of the formation of elementary sulphur or sulphate ions on the anode electrochemical methods have contributed to the development of suitable technologies.

Data presented in this paper result from the electrochemical investigations of solid electrodes and the simulation of reactor and suspension chambers.

The solubility of metal components have been studied in aqueous solutions as well as in fused salts.

810

Literature Review

First of all, we should mention several works dealing with the kinetics and reactions of the electrochemical dissolution of Cu_2S, CuS and $CuFeS_2$. Under apparently stable thermodynamic conditions chalcocite and covellite enter into reaction in the presence of sulphuric acid according to the following chemical equations.

$$Cu_2S \rightleftharpoons CuS + Cu^{2+} + 2e \qquad (1)$$

$$CuS \rightleftharpoons S + Cu^{2+} + 2e \qquad (2)$$

The reaction as described in Eq. (1) goes through some non-stoichiometric phases CuS ($1 \leqslant x \leqslant 2$) [1-6]. The kinetics of these electrochemical reactions is limited by the formation of surface coating and, at high potential, by the formation of sulphur.

High current efficiency has been obtained by Cole [3] in a simple suspension chamber and by Mackinnon [7] using bed electrode with electrolyte passing during the dissolution of copper sulphides.

Bertram and Illi [8], investigated the current-voltage characteristic of solid electrodes $CuFeS_2$. At higher potentials the sulphur surface layer on the electrode reduces the rate of dissolution.

For the reaction

$$CuFeS_2 \longrightarrow Cu^{2+} + Fe^{3+} + 2S + 5e \qquad (3)$$

one obtains 76% current efficiency. No limitation of current density that might result from the introduction of defect-electrons into the CuFeS$_2$ n-type semiconductor has been observed.

Many authors [9, 10, 11, 14] deal with relatively high current efficiency in the suspension chamber with loose material distribution.

REACTIONS ON COPPER SULPHIDE ANODES

The types and kinetics of basic reactions were investigated by cyclic voltammetry on solid electrodes. Potentiostatic investigations were carried out in the chamber with a 3-electrode system.

A polished face of cylindrical moulding made from copper sulphides placed in synthetic resin is a working electrode. The potential of anode is measured by a Luggin capillary using a 3.5 molar calomel electrode. The voltammograms presented here are for 1 m H$_2$SO$_4$ at 293 K. Copper sulphides Cu$_2$S and CuS were prepared from chemical elements. The chalcopyrite used in the investigation comes from the Mitterberg copper-mine near Mühlbach Hochkőnig (Salzburg, Austria).

From the current-voltage characteristic it is evident that this characteristic depends on given conditions. Current density measured on Cu$_2$S electrodes has, at higher potential, a clearly marked maximum (Fig. 1), Cu$_2$S surface is affected by CuS.

At these and other current maxima some new, as yet undescribed oxide surface coatings are formed. They considerably brake the process of dissolution. Comparably thin layers occur on CuS electrodes in the low potential range. At about 1.9 V Cu$_2$S and CuS electrodes dissolve with a further increase in

812

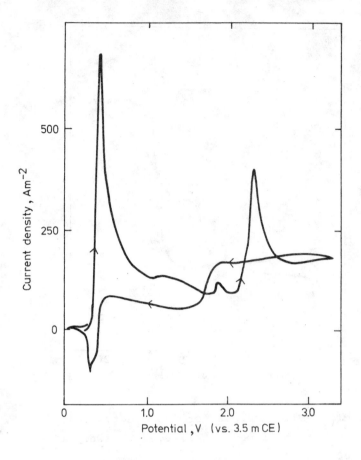

Fig. 1. Cyclic voltammograms for the Cu_2S electrode in 1 m H_2SO_4 (initial potential 0.15 V, sweep rate - 0.0004 $v \cdot s^{-1}$).

current (Fig. 2). The plastic sulphur layer formed during the reaction limits current density. Alterations of the surface of Cu_2S electrodes against the current-voltage characteristic in molar sulphuric acid solutions are shown in Fig. 3 as examined under a scanning microscope.

813

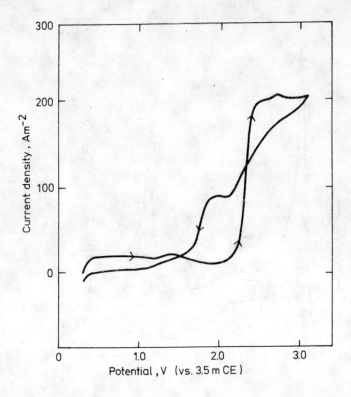

Fig. 2. Cyclic voltammograms for CuS electrode in 1 m
H$_2$SO$_4$ (initial potential: 0.32 V, sweep rate -
0.004 Vs^{-1}).

At low potentials the sulphur gets out to the surface
through the cracks formed. The thin surface layer hampers the
reaction and any greater topographical changes. At a minimum
potential of about 1.9 V the passive surface layers become
permeable. Increasingly rapid sulphur formation results in
greater changes in surface structure (Fig. 3c, d, e).

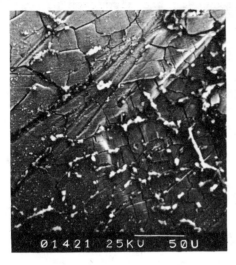
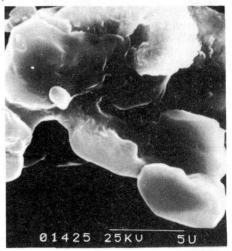

a - magnification 340 x

b - sulphur from picture a
5000 x

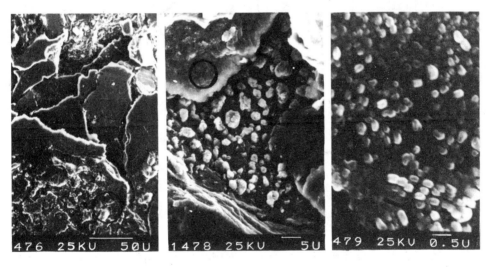

c - magnification
   300 x

d - fragment of c
   - 1200 x

e - fragment of d
   - 12 000 x

Fig. 3. Cu_2S electrode images obtained by scanning microscope, sweep rate 0.004 Vs^{-1}, increase of potential
from E_R = 0.15 V to 1.5 V (a, b) or 2.0 V (c, d, e).
Segments of pictures are marked with a small circle.

815

If chalcopyrite electrodes are polarized in the direction of the anode then the electrode dissolves at a high current density starting from 0.8 V according to reaction (3). Increasing coating of the surface with crystalline sulphur [11] (Fig. 4) limits solubility. From the cyclic voltammograms a conclusion can be drawn concerning the irreversible anodic oxidization of $CuFeS_2$.

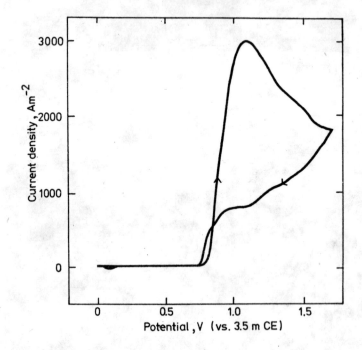

Fig. 4. Cyclic voltammograms for $CuFeS_2$ electrode in 1 m H_2SO_4 (initial potential 0.4 V, sweep rate – 0.004 Vs^{-1}).

REACTIONS OF CHALCOPYRITE SUSPENSION
AND BED ELECTRODE

In anodic leaching in the vibrational system and in bed reactors ground ores are used.

In the suspension chamber used (Fig. 5, cf. [12]) the macro-kinetic effects of electrochemical oxidation of chalcopyrite were investigated. In order to avoid the cathodic destruction of $CuFeS_2$ particles [13] the anodic chamber with a suspension of chalcopyrite in sulphuric acid is separated by an anion ex-change membrane from the cathodic chamber. A feeder electrode – a gold metal plate of 18 cm^2 is in contact with approx. 20 ml of electrolyte and up to 50 g of $CuFeS_2$.

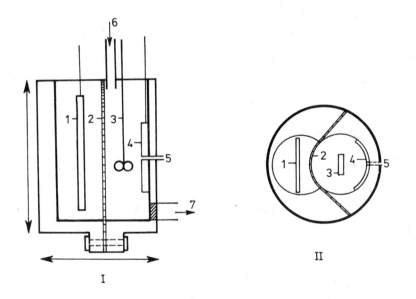

Fig. 5. Schematic diagram of suspension chamber.
I – end view, II – top view; 1 – platinum cathode,
2 – anion exchange membrane, 3 – mixer, 4 – gold
anode, 5 – Luggin capillary, 6 – electrolyte inlet,
7 – electrolyte outlet.

Original studies showed that at the appropriate rate of stirring (20-40 rps), current density and the amount of copper dissolved increase together with the concentration of solids. Current density is a function of Feeder electrode potential and it decreases slightly as the reaction continues (covering CuFeS$_2$ particles with sulphur). This assumption seems to be reasonable since the reaction is directly affected by the contact between ore particle and Feeder electrode.

In the investigations with bed reactors the technological aspects were looked at primarily [11]. The arrangement of electrodes in bed reactors allows one to perform experiments with a perpendicular parallel flow of current and electrolyte (Fig. 6).

About 10.31 of electrolyte flows through 80 g of ore per hour. 600 g of CuFeS$_2$ can be placed in the drum-attrition reactor. All tests were performed galvanostatically at 0.5 or 1 A.

Acid concentration level, coarser fractions and electrode material (gold is better than coal, titanium or lead) exert a favourable influence on the rate of copper dissolution.

A decrease in reaction rate following an increase in leaching time results mainly from the thicker sulphur coating on the surface of particles. The best current efficiency was observed with a parallel flow of current and electrolyte using an anode of gold and a bed containing ore particles of 1-2 mm in size.

Because of worse contact among copper grains the leaching in the drum-attrition reactor led to a decrease in the rate of dissolution.

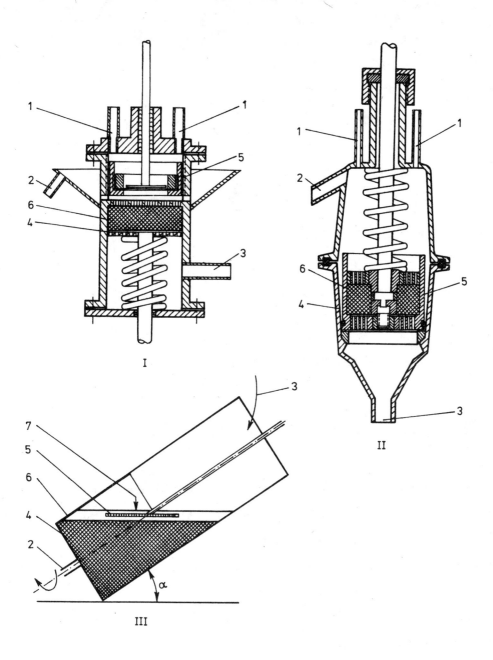

Fig. 6. I - Bed reactor (parallel flow of current and
electrolyte). II - Bed reactor (perpendicular flow
of current and electrolyte). III - Drum-attrition
reactor; 1 - gas off-take, 2 - electrolyte outlet,
3 - electrolyte inlet, 4 - Feeder anode, 5 -
cathode, 6 - ore bed, 7 - electrolyte level

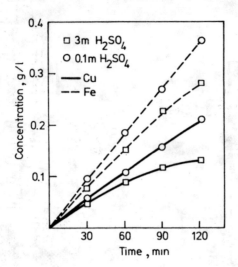

Fig. 7. Leaching vs. time in bed reactor with a flow of
current perpendicular to the flow of electrolyte
(particle-size is 1-2 mm, current 0.5 A).

ANODIC DISSOLUTION OF COPPER SULPHIDES
IN FUSED SALTS

Up to now electrolytical leaching of sulphide ores has
mainly been investigated using aqueous solutions. The good dissolving properties and high conductivity of some fused salts
allow them to be utilized in the leaching of $CuFeS_2$ and other
copper sulphides. Also, from the point of view of ecology,
fused salts seem promising since the leached sulphur is obtained in the form of an elementary substance.

As follows from our investigations, in the $ZnCl_2$-KCl system
chalcopyrite dissolves at low anodic overpotentials on the
formation of Cu^+, Fe^{2+} and elementary sulphur. The current-
voltage curve shown in Fig. 8, characterizes this process by a
maximum at about 1 V.

820

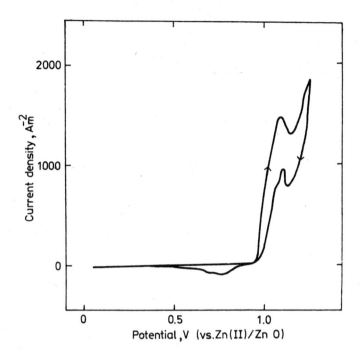

Fig. 8. Cyclic voltammograms for a $CuFeS_2$ electrode in
54 mol% $ZuCl_2$/46 mol% KCl fused at 573 K (initial
potential = 0.65 V; sweep rate = 0.005 Vs^{-1}).

Original studies showed that metal components dissolve
electrochemically in fused salts also and that there exists the
possibility of winning the metal on a cathode.

REFERENCES

1. Mathieu H. J. and Rickert H. Zeitschrift f. Phys. Chemie,
   Neue Folge, 79, 79 (1972).

2. Koch D. F. A. and McIntyre R. J. J. Electroanal. Chem.,
   71, 285 (1976).

3. Cole S. H. Ph. D. Thesis, University of Columbia, 1972.

4. Biegler T. and Swift D. A. Hydrometallurgy, 2, 335 (1976/77).

5. Hepel T. Pr. Nauk Inst. Chem. Nieorg. Metal. Pierwiastkow Rzadkich Politech. Wrocław, 29, 77 (1976).

6. Hepel. M. and Hepel T. J. Electroanal. Chem., 81, 161 (1977).

7. Mackinnon D. J. Hydrometallurgy, 1, 161 (1976), Hydrometallurgy, 2, 65 (1976).

8. Bertram R. and Illi H. Chem. Ing. Techn., 48, 141 (1977).

9. Sawamoto H. Mem. Fac. Eng. Nagoya Univ., Japan, 14, 197 (1962).

10. Oki T. and Ono S. Nippon Kogyo Kaishi, 83(10), 1159 (1967).

11. Bertram R., Celement M., Galitis N. and Illi H. Erzmetall, 30(11), 491 (1977).

12. Pickett D. J. Elsevier Sci. Publ. Comp., Amsterdam, 1977.

13. Biegler T. J. Electroanal. Chem., 85, 101 (1977).

14. Galitis N., Clement M. and Bertram R. Erzmetall, 2 (1979).

ABSTRACT

The anodic dissolution of different semiconducting copper
sulphides (chalcocite, covellite, chalcopyrite) was studied in
sulphuric acid electrolytes. The current-voltage characteristic
of solid electrodes was investigated by means of cyclic voltom-
metry. Variations of the voltammograms were interpreted as
being due to different processes and to permeation of the surface coatings. Electron micrography shows a change in surface
topography during anodic dissolution. A bed reactor was constructed to study the reaction of a $CuFeS_2$ suspension on a gold
anode. The anodic dissolution of chalcopyrite was investigated
using a fluidized-bed technique. Finally, the possibility of
the anodic dissolution of copper sulphides in fused salts is
discussed.

RÉSUMÉ

La dissolution anodique de différents sulfures de cuivre
semi conducteurs (Chalcocite, Covellite, Chalcopyrite) a été
étudiée dans des électrolytes d'acide sulfurique. La caractè-
ristique du courant-tension des électrodes solides a été examinée à l'aide de la méthode de voltamètre-cyclique. Les
variations des voltgrammes ont été interprètées comme provenant de différents procédés et de la diffusion des couches de
surface. Des photographies, faîtes par microscopie électronique,
montrent le changement de topographie de la surface pendant la
dissolution anodique. Nous présentons aussi une cellule de vase
qui a été réalisée pour étudier la réaction d'une boue agitée
de $CuFeS_2$ sur une anode d'or. La dissolution anodique de la
chalcopyrite a été examinée en utilisant la technique du lit
fluidisé. Finalement la possilité d'une dissolution anodique
des sulfures de cuivre dans des sels fondus sera discutée.

ZUSAMMENFASSUNG

Die anodische Auflösung von verschiedenen halbeitenden Kupfersulfiden (Chalkosin, Covellin, Chalcopyrit) wurde in schwefelsauren Elektrolyten untersucht. An festen Elektroden wurde die Strom-Spannungsabhängigkeit mit cyclischer Voltammetrie studiert. Aus der Struktur der Voltagramme muss auf verschiendene Teilprozesse und Deckschichtbildungen geschlossen werden. Elektronenmikroskopische Aufnahmen zeigen die Veränderungen der Oberflächenmorphologie während der anodischen Auflösung. Anschliessend wird eine Suspensionszelle vorgestellt, in der die Reaktionen von gerührten $CuFeS_2$ - Suspensionen an einer Gold-Anode untersucht werden. Deneben wird auch über Versuche mit Festbettelektroden aus Chalkopyrit berichtet. Auf die Möglichkeit der anodischen Auflösung von Kupfersulfiden in Salzschmelzen wird abschliessend hingewiesen.

РЕЗЮМЕ

-Исследовано анодное растворение различных полупроводниковых сульфидов (халькозина, ковеллита, халькопирита) в сернокислых электролитах. Изучены кривые зависимости силы тока от напряжения твёрдых электродов методом циклической вольтметрии. Характер вольтграмм указывает на происхождение разных процессов и образование поверхностных слоёв. Изображения, полученные методом электронной микроскопии, представляют изменение морфологии поверхности во время анодного растворения. Представлена также камера "во взвышенном состоянии", предназначенная для исследования реакций перемешиваемого $CuFeS_2$ на золотом аноде. Проведены также исследования с использованием твёрдых халькопиритных электродов. Кроме того, рассмотрена возможность анодного растворения сульфидов меди в расплавленных солех.

824

ACID HYDROMETALLURGICAL LEACHING OF COPPER AND OTHER METALS FROM COMPLEX POLISH SULPHIDE CONCENTRATES

F. Łętowski

Institute of Inorganic Chemistry and Metallurgy of Rare Elements, Wrocław Technical University, Wrocław, Poland

INTRODUCTION

Investigations into hydrometallurgical methods for the treatment of copper sulphide concentrates are being developed all over the world but pyrometallurgy, which for the time being has at its disposal more reliable technologies, is a permanent challenge to hydrometallurgy. There are only two examples of pure hydrometallurgical methods i.e., methods eliminating environmental pollution and using no pyrometallurgical processes, now in use in industrial-scale plants. These are Cymet [1] and Duval [2] processes based on leaching by acid solutions of ferric and cupric chlorides. The very effective Arbiter process [3] consisting of ammonia leaching employed by Anaconda Co has been in use for about one year.

Although the processing of copper concentrates in Poland is, for the time being, based on pyrometallurgical technologies, studies on hydrometallurgical methods [4] have been carried out by the Technical University in Wroclaw since 1972. They were performed to develop a complex nonpolluting treatment of domestic concentrates allowing the recovery of copper, silver, lead, and if possible, other components.

Since the main component of domestic concentrates is an easily leached chalcocite, it was rather pointless to base the technology on leaching by a more active leaching agent than $Fe_2(SO_4)_3$. In view of this, we based our technology on this conventional leaching agent which is one of the oldest. The adoption of $Fe_2(SO_4)_3$ proved to be justified since the process of spent leaching agent regeneration as well as that of obtaining pure copper directly from the leaching solution were easy to carry out.

The purpose of the present paper is to provide an outline of a complex method developed at Technical University in Wroclaw. In 1976 the method was tested in pilot plant continuous installation yielding about 500 kg concentrate per day. The installation was constructed in the Experimental Service of Technical University of Wroclaw "Hydromech" in Kowary. The experimental data given in the paper are the result of 3 weeks' balance testing simultaneously carried out in a laboratory installation (26 kg concentrate/day).

Two other process modification were proposed earlier. The first modification (Fig. 1 a) tested on a laboratory scale [5] consisted of the precipitation of copper from a leaching solution under hydrogen pressure [6] and the regeneration of the leaching agent by the oxidation of $FeSO_4$ under oxygen pressure. The second modification tested in pilot plant yielding about

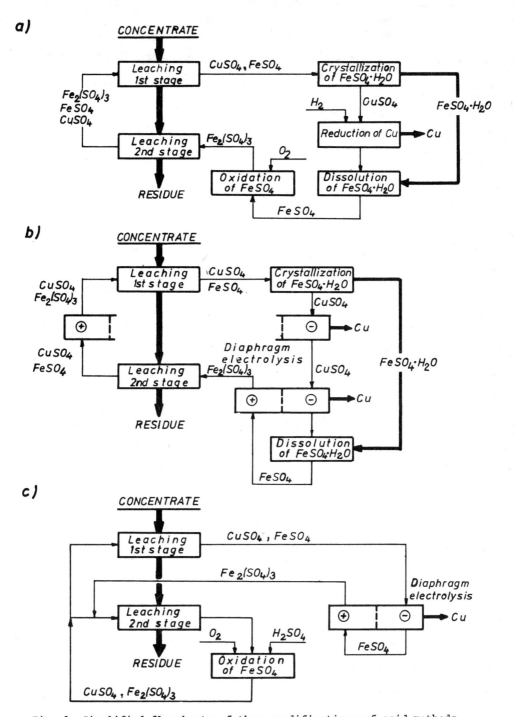

Fig. 1. Simplified flowsheets of three modifications of acid methods developed by the Technical University of Wrocław. Only the main solution components are indicated.

500 kg concentrate per day involved the electrowinning of copper in diaphragm electrolysers and the double-stage anodic recovery of the spent leaching agent [7] (Fig. 1 b). In both processes an excess of the spent leaching agent which prevented pure copper from being obtained was removed from the solution as crystalline $FeSO_4 \cdot H_2O$ by heating the solution to $170^\circ C$ [8]. The process under discussion, i.e., the 3rd modification displayed in Fig. 1 c in which copper is obtained in diaphragm electrolysers, eliminates the technically difficult process of the high temperature crystallization of $FeSO_4 \cdot H_2O$. Instead, the concentration of leaching agent is lowered to a permissible level and its deficit in the leaching process is made up by the additional oxidation of $FeSO_4$ under an increased oxygen pressure [9].

AN OUTLINE OF THE TECHNOLOGY

The flowsheet of the main process for the electrowinning of cathode copper is given in Fig. 2. It consists of two circulation system of solutions: an inner circuit including leaching, electrolysis and leaching agent regeneration, and an outer circuit which is used to remove impurities from the inner circuit, to wash the residue after leaching and to decompose the carbonates which occur in Polish concentrates.

Carbonate Neutralization. The consumption of sulphuric acid during the decomposition of the carbonate deposit deads mainly dolomite is an unfavourable factor, but it does not exceed 2 kg H_2SO_4 per kg of copper in concentrate.

Carbonate neutralization is a simple operation carried out at $60-80^\circ C$ at a high rate.

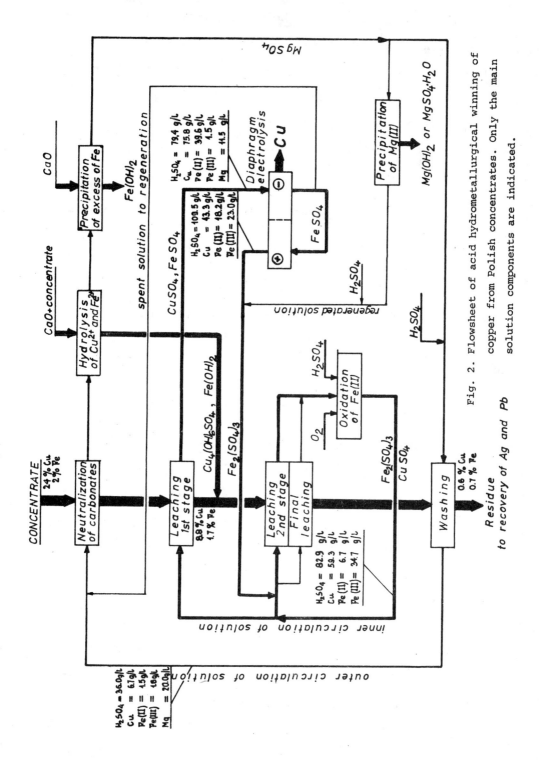

Fig. 2. Flowsheet of acid hydrometallurgical winning of copper from Polish concentrates. Only the main solution components are indicated.

The concentration of $MgSO_4$ in the outer circuit was regulated by precipitation of magnesium either in the form of $Mg(OH)_2$ (precipitation by means of lime) or in the form of monohydrate sulphate $MgSO_4 \cdot H_2O$ (by crystallization at $200-230^\circ C$).

The latter method enables one to obtain a final product ready for sale but it presents difficulties when employed in a continuous process.

Leaching. The first stage of leaching is crucial for the maximum utilization of leaching agent. In the solution directed to electrolysis the concentration of leaching agent should not exceed 3 g Fe(III)/l. The leaching time in the first stage was longer than that sufficient for the transition of chalcocite to a more difficult soluble covellite, and at $90-95^\circ C$ it did not exceed 1 h.

The second leaching stage is connected mainly with the further dissolution of covellite. At $90-95^\circ C$, after 4 h of leaching the copper content of the concentrate decreased to 2.2% Cu.

Although chalcocite constitutes the main component in Polish concentrates, some 1% to 10% of copper still occurs in the form of barely soluble chalcopyrite and bornite. Therefore the decrease in copper content in the solid phase to 0.6% Cu takes place just after next 6 h during the so-called "final leaching". After this operation, total recovery of copper from the concentrate increased to 97.5%.

The recovery of the copper remaining in solid residue in the form of chalcopyrite also turned out to be possible through the leaching of the residue by a sodium chloride concentrated solution carried out in order to recover silver and lead.

Electrolysis. Diaphragm electrolysis was carried out in segment-electrolysers, the construction of which enables size regulation of any cell. Anode and cathode compartments were separated by PVC diaphragms [8, 10]. Concentration of copper and sulphuric acid during the continuous process in cathode compartments differed from that in the solution directed to electrolysis (Fig.2) and was equal to 43.3 g/l Cu and 109.5 g/l H_2SO_4.

With a cathode current density of 250 A/m^2 the current efficiency of the cathodic process was 96%. The product was a compact cathode of 99.96% Cu containing 4-20 ppm Fe, 4-6 ppm Pb, 9-13 ppm Ag, 30-40 ppm S, and complying with other tests requirements characteristic for electrolytic copper.

In the anodic process a partial regeneration of the leaching agent (ferric sulphate) as well as sulphuric acid regeneration took place. The efficiency of the anodic oxidation of Fe(II) to Fe(III) was only 30-50%. The remaining 50-70% of electric energy was used up in the simultaneous process of H_2SO_4 regeneration.

Electrolysis was carried out at 45-55°C. Power consumption presented 1.76 kWh/kg Cu.

Because the efficiency of the anodic oxidation of ferrous sulphate was considerable lower than the cathodic efficiency of copper deposition, there occurred a deficit of oxidant - Fe(III) in the circulating solution. This deficit was made up for in the intensive oxidation process of ferrous sulphate under oxygen pressure. In fact this deficit was higher than that due to the difference in cathodic and anodic process efficiency as a consequence of the presence of some other components in the concentrate apart from copper sulphides reducing of ferric sulphate.

Oxidation. Within 20 min of the oxidation process under oxygen pressure $p_{O_2} = 520$ kPa and at 90-98°C it is easy to oxidize 85-90% of the ferrous sulphate. During this process the concentration of Fe(II) changed on the average from 27.4 to 6.7 g/l, and the concentration of Fe(III) increased respectively to 34.7 g/l. The oxidation rate was considerably influenced by the intensity of the gaseous and liquid phase agitation.

Lead and Silver Recovery. The solid residue after leaching by ferric sulphate still contains 1.38-2.50% Pb, 0.60-0.82% Cu, 0.033-0.046% Ag, 1.2-1.5% Fe, about 8% elemental sulphur, about 10% gypsum coming from dolomite decomposition and the remaining unreacted concentrate components including organic substances containing about 10% carbon and solid hydrocarbons.

Further processing of the residue aimed at silver and lead recovery and increasing the total copper recovery. The flowsheet of the process based on leaching by concentrated sodium chloride solution and then on selective cementation of silver and precipitation of lead carbonate is shown in Fig. 3.

Extraction of above 96% of the lead remaining in residue, mainly in the form of $PbSO_4$, is easy at 80-90°C after 20-30 min of leaching in 25% solution of NaCl. Under the same conditions not more than 50% of silver is subject to leaching [11]. Mild reduction conditions in the solution resulting from the presence of ferrous ions and the contact of the solution with the elements of apparatus made from metals allowing easy silver cementation, account for this low degree of silver leaching.

Therefore leaching was carried out under low oxygen pressure of about 208 kPa [12]. After 30 min of leaching at 115°C the

832

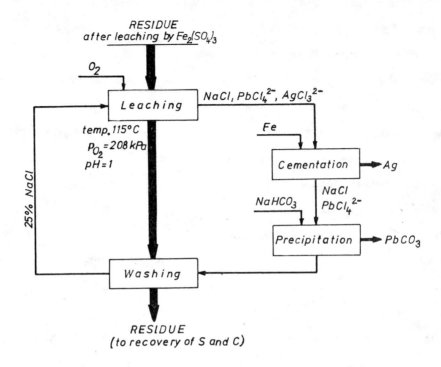

Fig. 3. Simplified flowsheet of silver and lead recovery from solid residue
after leaching the concentrate with ferric sulphate. Only the main
solution components are indicated.

recovery of silver was 85%, of copper, 70% and of lead, 97.4%.
The solution after leaching contained 0.1 g/l Ag, 0.2 g/l Cu,
3.67 g/l Pb and 0.7 g/l Fe(III) was subject to cementation on
iron. After this operation the concentration of silver and copper
decreased to 0.019 g/l Ag and 0.030 g/l Cu respectively. The next
operation consisted of $PbCO_3$ precipitation and the lead concentration in the solution after this process decreased by
0.12 g/l Pb.

Both the cementated silver and precipitated $PbCO_3$ carbonate
required a further relatively simple processing stage in order to
be purified as a final product ready for sale [12].

Sulphur and Carbon Utilization. Sulphur recovery is not only important from the economic point of view. Dry storage in the open of the waste after leaching would be a danger to the environment due to the slow oxidation of elemental sulphur. Therefore it should be stored in a limited air access area, e.g., under water, or the sulphur should be removed from the waste material.

Studies have been carried out on the known methods of sulphur extraction from the solid phase [13, 14]. The most interesting idea entails the use of the considerable flotability of sulphur and organic carbon. Their hydrophobic nature makes it possible to carry out effective flotation within the whole range of pH without using collectors [13]. After 15 min of flotation at about 65°C, the yield of sulphur and carbon from unwashed residue after leaching amounts to 95% for sulphur and 90% for organic carbon. This "secondary concentrate" contains about 20% sulphur and 19% carbon and its heating value is 1100 kcal/kg. After an additional reagent-free 2nd stage of flotation, the "secondary concentrate" contains 31.8% sulphur, 24.4% carbon and a adequately sufficiently higher heating value.

Such a concentration of sulphur, carbon and hydrocarbons affords possibilities for the burning of these components with a heat effect comparable to the heating value of peat or brown coal. Burning in an inconsiderable excess of oxygen, e.g., in fluidized-bed oven, affords possibilities for obtaining a considerable concentration of SO_2 in gases sufficient for practically full transformation into sulphuric acid. If the gases contain more than 7-10% SO_2, the production of sulphuric acid is stable and can be carried out with maximum environmental safety.

834

The waste after secondary flotation is barren and presents no danger to the natural environment.

Interesting results were obtained by introducing secondary flotation immediately after the leaching of copper by ferric sulphate. Apart from sulphur and carbon, silver and the rest of the copper were also concentrated by flotation. Lead occurred in the form of $PbSO_4$ and did not flotate and was concentrated in the secondary waste.

Some of the parameters of the proposed technology which were obtained during the balance test and in studies on waste utilization are presented in Table 1.

TABLE 1

Some Experimental Data on the Acid-Hydrometallurgical Winning of Copper from Polish Concentrates, Based on a 3 weeks' Balance Test Performed in Laboratory Installation Yielding about 26 kg Concentrate per Day, and also on Investigations of Waste Utilization

Specification	
(1) Total yield of copper from concentrate after chloride leaching	99.3%
(2) Yield of cathodic copper (99.96% Cu)	97.5%
(3) Yield of lead from concentrate	96.0%
(4) Yield of silver from concentrate	83.3%
(5) Content of copper in residue after ferric sulphate leaching	0.6% Cu
(6) Metal content in residue after chloride leaching	0.17% Cu
	0.065% Pb
	0.006% Ag
(7) Sulphur and organic carbon content in secondary concentrate after flotation of residue	20-32% S
	19-24% C
(8) Consumption of sulphuric acid (100% H_2SO_4)	2.0 kg/kg Cu
(9) Consumption of oxygen in $FeSO_4$ oxidation process	0.64 Nm^3O_2/kg Cu
(10) Consumption of power in diaphragm electrolysis	1.76 kWh/kg Cu

PHYSICO-CHEMICAL CHARACTERISTICS OF THE METHOD

The characteristic thermodynamics of copper sulphide leaching by ferric sulphate is so fundamental that there is no need to discuss it here [15-18]. Moreover, the kinetics of copper sulphide leaching by ferric sulphate has also been frequently described [15, 16, 19-22].

Among the many properties of sulphate ions which are essential in hydrometallurgy, their ability to form complexes with Fe^{3+} and Fe^{2+} cations is rarely discussed [19, 23, 24]. As evident from the equilibria calculated on the basis of the data above (Sapieszko et al. [25]) and which is shown in Fig. 4, the concentration of free Fe^{3+} ions does not exceed 3% of total concentration of Fe(III) in concentrated solutions of sulphates at $80^\circ C$ and when pH = 0. Under this conditions 65% of the total concentration of Fe(III) remains in the form of $FeSO_4^+$ complexes and 32% in the form of $FeHSO_4^+$ complexes.

Ferrous ions Fe^{2+} form considerably weaker complexes with sulphates. In the solution where pH = 0 and the temperature is $25^\circ C$, only 3% of iron(II) occurs in the form of complex ions of $FeHSO_4^+$, 6% in the form of neutral $FeSO_4$ molecules and 91% in the form of non-complexed Fe^{2+} ions (Fig. 5). The relatively inconsiderable "oxidizing activity" of ferric sulphate during leaching process is the result of the strong complexation of Fe^{3+} ions. This affords the possibility of using the solutions of high Fe(III) concentration. A sufficiently high concentration of $Fe(SO_4)_3$ is technologically desirable since it allows an easy increase of the copper concentration in the solution to the level required in electrolysis [8, 10, 26].

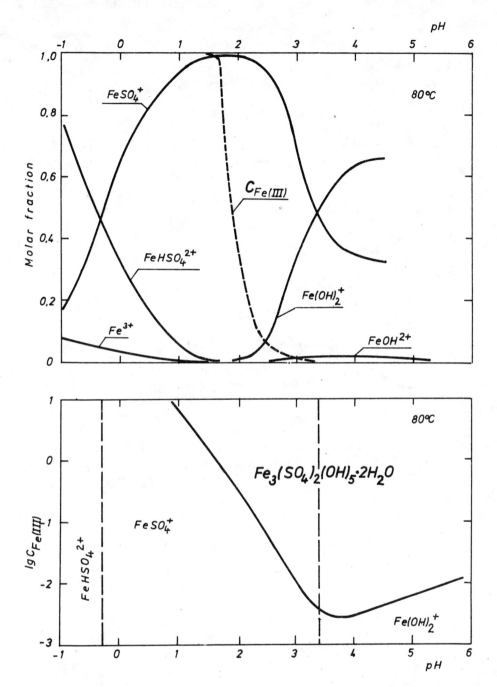

Fig. 4. Effect of pH on the molar contribution of iron(III) sulphate
complexes in ferric sulphate solution at 80°C; initial iron(III)
concentration $C_{Fe(III)}$ = 1 M, concentration of sulphates
$C_{SO_4^{2-}}$ = 3 M, and effect of pH on the solubility ranges of hydrogen
jarosite at 80°C, $C_{SO_4^{2-}}$ = 3 M [4].

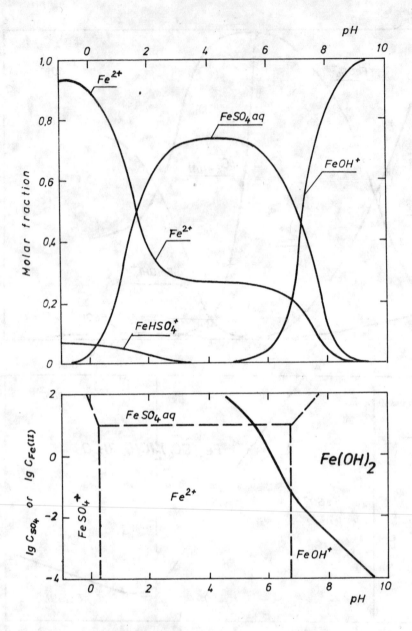

Fig. 5. Effect of pH on the molar contribution of iron(II) sulphate complexes at $25^\circ C$; initial iron(II) concentration $C_{Fe(II)} = 1$ M, $C_{SO_4^{2-}} = 3$ M, and effect of pH on solubility ranges of ferrous hydroxide and on relative predominance ranges of $FeHSO_4^+$, $FeSO_4 aq$, Fe^{2+} and $FeOH^+$ at $25^\circ C$ [4].

The influence of the proportion of $C_{Fe(II)}/C_{Fe(III)}$ concentrations on the redox potential

$$E_{Fe^{2+}/Fe^{3+}} = E^{o}_{Fe^{2+}/Fe^{3+}} - \frac{RT}{F} \ln\frac{[Fe^{2+}]}{[Fe^{3+}]}$$

where $E^{o}_{Fe^{2+}/Fe^{3+}}$ is a normal potential of electrochemical reaction $Fe^{2+} = Fe^{3+}+e^-$, and which at $25^{o}C$ is equal to 0.77 V, is shown in Fig. 6. The dependence calculated with regard to complex-formation with sulphates is represented by the solid line. For purposes of comparison, the dependence without complexation i.e., in the case where the $C_{Fe(II)}/C_{Fe(III)}$ quotient

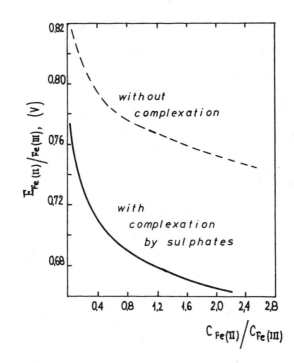

Fig. 6. Effect of the $C_{Fe(II)}/C_{Fe(III)}$ ratio on the redox potential $E_{Fe^{2+}/Fe^{3+}}$. Solid line - in the $FeSO_4$ and $Fe_2(SO_4)_3$ solution, $C_{Fe(II)} + C_{Fe(III)} = 0.54$ M, $C_{H_2SO_4} = 0.51$ M. Broken line - without complexation.

may be identified with the quotient of ferrous and ferric ions concentrations (activities) $[Fe^{2+}]/[Fe^{3+}]$ is denoted by the broken line.

It seems that up till now there has been little agreement as to the kinetics and mechanism involved in the oxidation of ferrous sulphate under oxygen pressure. This is due to the two possible process mechanisms which exist. One of these refers to oxidation with the simultaneous formation of solid hydrolysis products [27, 28], and the other refers to oxidation in acid solutions without hydrolysis [9, 29, 30].

In our case oxidation was carried out in acid solution under conditions which prevented the precipitation of the solid product of hydrolysis. The influence of temperature and oxygen pressure on the oxidation rate is shown in Fig. 7 [9, 13]. The changes in the concentration of Fe(II) and Fe(III) complexes during oxidation at 95°C and under oxygen pressure P_{O_2} = 527 kPa are shown in Fig. 8. They were calculated in accordance with equilibria shown in Fig. 4 and Fig. 5. The initial concentration of ferrous sulphate was equal to 0.54 M.

As a result of strong complexation, the concentration of Fe^{3+} ions during oxidation process is inconsiderable and is practically stable. Therefore the oxidation rate does not actually depend on an increase of the Fe(III) concentration. Moreover, the oxidation rate is proportional to the concentration of Fe^{2+} ions weakly complexed by the sulphates and decreases with a decrease in their concentration [9, 27-30].

In addition to complex-forming properties which have a considerable influence on the leaching process as well as on spent

840

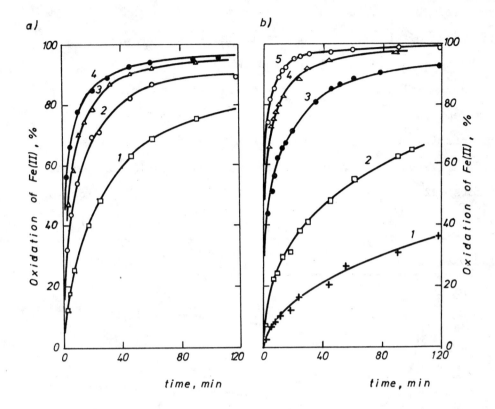

Fig. 7. Oxidation of FeSO$_4$ solution under oxygen pressure. Initial concentration of iron(II) C$_{Fe(II)}$ = 30 g/l, copper concentration
C$_{Cu}$ = 50 g/l, initial sulphuric acid concentration C$_{H_2SO_4}$ = 50 g/l.
(a) Effect of partial oxygen pressure on the Fe(II) oxidation rate
at 95°C: 1 - 137 kPa, 2 - 218 kPa, 3 - 520 kPa, 4 - 1060 kPa;
(b) Effect of temperature on the Fe(II) oxidation rate under
partial oxygen pressure p$_{O_2}$ = 520 kPa: 1 - 40°C, 2 - 65°C, 3 -
- 95°C, 5 - 135°C.

leaching agent regeneration, sulphates allow the precipitation

of the excess of leaching agent from the solution at elevated

temperatures, either in the form of basic sulphates Fe(III) -

jarosite salts, or in the form of monohydrate salt of Fe(II) -

FeSO$_4$ · H$_2$O. The winning of compact cathodes from sulphate solutions is also easier than from solutions containing e.g., mainly chlorides. Besides, owing to the presence of sulphates the concentration of Pb^{2+} and Ca^{2+} ions in the solutions during leaching by ferric sulphate is lowered, which is an advantage.

The general conclusion of the discussion is that sulphates in an exceptionally profitable way break the considerable "oxidation activity" of ferric ions. On the other hand, Beckstead et al. [19], Pawlek [31], Braitwaite and Wadsworth [24] and other authors 22 show that in spite of this, effective application

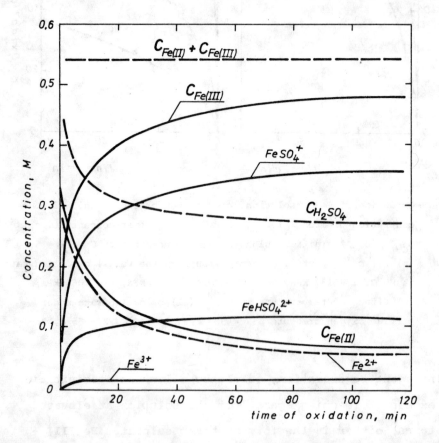

Fig. 8. Variations in the soluble components concentration during oxidation of ferrous sulphate under oxygen pressure p_{O_2} = 520 kPa and at $95^{\circ}C$ [4].

of ferric sulphate to the leaching of the least soluble sulphide
to be found in copper concentrate, i.e., chalcopyrite, is still
possible.

CONCLUSION

As yet, it is difficult to compare the cost of copper winning
from concentrate by this acid-hydrometallurgical method with the
cost of copper winning by pyrometallurgical methods. Such a comparison will become much more reliable when pilot plant industrial production is underway, the more so since data as to the place
and conditions of the concentration of metals accompanying
copper in Polish ores requires some additional investigations in
a long-term continuous process.

There is also the possibility of decreasing sulphuric acid
consumption during dolomite decomposition by the modification
of ore flotation. Such a modification would involve the direction to hydrometallurgical processing of the so-called "sandstone
concentrate fraction" obtained in domestic plants [32]. This
fraction contains less dolomite than the currently produced concentrate for pyrometallurgical plants. The question of concentrate separation into the fraction with higher sandstone content
and the fraction with higher dolomite content has not been taken
into account by industry mainly because there has been no need
for such a selection in pyrometallurgical processes.

Strong arguments for the proposed hydrometallurgical method
exist:

(1) The yield of copper from the concentrate is comparable or
    higher than that resulting from pyrometallurgical processes.

(2) The technology is complex; it allows lead and silver recovery, the utilization of sulphur and carbon with a desirable results as far as energy is concerned, permits the direction of gases rich in SO_2 to the production of sulphuric acid, and also allows one to obtain a magnesium sulphate by-product should it prove to be economically viable.

(3) This technology eliminates environmental pollution. In the proposed process, solutions recycle in a closed circuit and the only waste product is the remainder of ore material from which, apart from accompanying metals, sulphur and carbon can also be removed.

(4) The acid hydrometallurgical winning of copper developed by the Technical University of Wrocław is not applicable to concentrates alone.

ACKNOWLEDGMENTS

The author wishes to thank his co-workers, Z. Adamski, H. Bogdanowicz, J. Brzeźniakiewicz, T. Chmielewski, M. Czarnecki, J. Drzymała, L. Fereniec, A. Jędrczak, R. Kaczmarski, B. Kołodziej, S. Rumianowski, G. Sokalska, J. Wódka and J. Mordalski who all took part in the laboratory continuous balance tests as well as the studies on waste utilization.

844

REFERENCES

1. Allen E. S., Kruesi P. R., Hazen W. C. and Goems D. M. Cymet electrometallurgical process for the treating of base metals sulphide concentrates. The Metallurgical Society of AIME National Meeting, Dallas 1974, TMS Paper A 74-7 (1974).

2. Atwood G. E. and Curtis C. H. Hydrometallurgical process for the production of copper. Duval Co, Pat. USA 3785944 (15.01. 1974) and 3879272 (16.03.1975).

3. Kuhn M. C., Arbiter N. and Kling H. Can. Min. Metall. Bull., 67, 62-73, Feb. (1974).

4. Łetowski F. Hydrometallurgy of domestic copper raw materials. Pr. nauk. Inst. Chem. Nieorg. PWr, nr 45, Ser. Monografie, (1979) 3-168. Polish text.

5. Łętowski F. Winning of copper from concentrates by new hydrometallurgical methods. Pr. nauk Inst. Chem. Nieorg. PWr, nr 21, Ser. Konf.,(1974) 17-24. Polish text.

6. Łętowski F. and Rumianowski S. Rudy Metale, 22, 174-178 (1977). Polish text.

7. Łętowski F. A new hydrometallurgical process for electrolytic copper production. II International Symposium on Management of Copper Resources, Lublin 27-28.04.1977. Proc. Vol. II, Ref. M9, ZBiPM Cuprum, Wroclaw 1977.

8. Łętowski F., Kołodziej B., Czernecki M., Jędrczak A. and Adamski Z. Hydrometallurgy, 4, 169-184 (1979).

9. Klighoffer O., Chmielewski T. and Łętowski F. Rudy Metale, 21, 63-66 (1976). Polish text.

10. Kozłowska-Kołodziej B. Rudy Metale, 23, 392-395 (1978). Polish text.

11. Sokalska G., Doroszkiewicz E. and Letowski F. Rudy Metale, 22, 690-694 (1977). Polish text.

12. Sokalska G., Łętowski F. and Czernecki M. Part II. Rudy Metale 23, 438-440 (1978). Polish text.

13. Łętowski F., Sokalska G., Czernecki M., Drzymala J. and Mordalski J. Use of hydrometallurgical methods for extraction of copper, silver and other metals from flotation concentrates. Suppl. Raport nr 114, Inst. Chem. Nieorg. Politechnika Wrocławska, Wrocław 1977. Polish text.

14. Fereniec L. and Łętowski F. Rudy Metale 22, 541-544 (1977). Polish text.

15. Dutrizac J. E. and MacDonald R. J. C. Minerals Sci. Engng, 6, 59-100 (1974).

16. Burkin A. R. (Ed.) Leaching and reduction in hydrometallurgy. The Institution of Mining and Metallurgy, London 1975.

17. Tseft A. L. Gidrometallurgithetskie metody pererabotki polimetallithetskoqo syria (Rus.), Izd. Nauka, Alma Ata 1976.

18. Łętowski F. Principles of Hydrometallurgy, WNT, Warszawa,1975. Polish text.

19. Beckstead L. W., Munoz P. B., Sepulveda J. L., Herbst J. A., Miller J. D., Olson F. A. and Wadsworth M. E. Acid ferric sulfate leaching of attritor-ground chalcopyrite concentrates. In: Extractive Metallurgy of Copper. Vol. 2 (Eds. J. C. Yannopoulos and J. C. Agarwal), pp. 611-632, AIME, New York, 1976.

20. Jones D. L. and Peters E. The leaching of chalcopyrite with ferric sulphate and ferric chloride. In: Extractive Metallurgy of Copper. Vol. 2 (Eds. J. C. Yannopoulos and J. C. Agarwal) pp. 633-653, AIME, New York, 1976.

21. Roman R. J. and Benner B. R. Minerals Sci. Engng, 5, 3-24 (1973).

22. Habashi F. Chalcopyrite, Its Chemistry and Metallurgy, McGraw-Hill, New York,1978.

23. Bhappu R. B., Johnson P. H., Brierley J. A. and Reynolds D.H. Trans. Soc. Min. Engrs, AIME, 244,307-320 (1969).

24. Braithwaite J. W., Wadsworth M. E., Oxidation of chalcopyrite under simulated conditions of deep solution mining. In: Extractive Metallurgy of Copper. Vol. 2 (Eds. J.C. Yannopoulos and J.C. Agarwal) pp. 752-775, AIME, New York, 1976.

25. Sapieszko R. S., Patel R. C. and Matijević E. J. Phys. Chem., 81, 1061-1068 (1977).

26. Kaczmarski R. and Kołodziej B. Studies on electrolysis of solutions after the leaching of copper concentrates with ferric sulphate. Pr. nauk. Inst. Chem. Nieorg. PWr, nr 29, Ser. Konf., (1976) 29-39. Polish text.

27. Saprigin A. F. and Gusar L. S. Zhurn. Prikl. Khim., 47, 1690-1695 (1974).

28. Sysoeva V. V. and Rotinjan A. L. Zhurn. Prikl. Khim., 44, 254-260 (1971).

29. Huffman R. E. and Dawidson N. J. Am. Chem. Soc., 78, 4836-4842 (1956).

30. Mathews C. T. and Robins R. G. Proc. Aust. Inst. Min. Met., 242, 47-56 (1974).

31. Pawlek F. E. The influence of grain size and mineralogical composition on the leachability of copper concentrates. In: Extractive Metallurgy of Copper. Vol. 2 (Eds. J.C. Yannopoulos and J.C. Agarwal), pp. 690-705, AIME, New York 1976.

32. Żmudziński K. and Madej W. Trends in development of ore processing technology in LGOM (Lublin-Głogów Copper Basin). II International Symposium on Management of Copper Resources, Lublin 27-28.04.1977. Proc. Vol. II, Ref. Pl, ZBiPM Cuprum, Wrocław, 1977.

ABSTRACT

Development of the hydrometallurgical method of treatment of
Polish copper sulphide concentrates with application of ferric
sulphate solution recycled in a closed circuit is presented.
The most important features of the non-polluting complex process
based upon the leaching and electrolytic processes and the most
important results in our investigations are as follows:

- know-how of the diaphragm electrolysis for winning of copper
  cathode 99.96% Cu from leaching solution with simultaneous
  anodic recovery of the leaching agent which makes possible to
  close the main inner circuit of solution,

- introduction into the inner solution circuit of the additional
  regeneration process of the leaching agent under increased
  oxygen pressure to compensate the oxidizer deficiency,

- application of the second, so called outer solution circuit,
  to provide continuous bleed of impurities accumulated in the
  leaching solution,

- development of separate methods for the recovery of silver
  and lead.

In the present paper some results of continuous laboratory
tests and studies on the utilization of waste sulphur and carbon
are discussed.

RÉSUMÉ

On a presenté des études sur le développement du traitement
hydrométallurgique des concentrés de sulfure de cuivre polonais
par application d'une solution de sulfate ferrique recyclée dans
un circuit fermé. Les plus importantes caractéristiques du procédé non polluant basé sur le lessivage et sur l'électrolyse, de
même que les plus importants resultats des recherches sont les
suivants:
- savoir-faire d'électrolyse à diaphragme pour l'obtention de
  cathodes compactes de cuivre à 99.96% à partir de solutions
  issues d'un lessivage avec recupération anodique simultanée

848

de l'agent lessivant qui rend possible la fermeture du circuit
intérieur principal d'une solution,

- introduction dans le circuit intérieur de la solution d'une
  régénération additionelle de l'agent lessivant sous une pression élevée d'oxygène afin de compenser le déficit d'oxydant,

- application d'un second circuit extérieur de solution qui
  permet de faire sortir les impuretés accumulées dans la solution après le lessivage,

- développement de méthodes séparées pour la recupération de
  l'argent et du plomb.

Dans ce travail on a parlé de quelques résultats d'essais
continus effectués pendant 3 semaines dans une installation à
l'échelle du laboratoire ainsi que d'essais d'utilisation du
soufre et du carbone.

ZUSAMMENFASSUNG

Der vorliegende Bericht befasst sich mit Untersuchungen der
Entwicklung der hydrometallurgischen Aufbereitung polnischer
Kupfersulfidkonzentrate bei der Anwendung einer Ferrisulfat-
lösung mit Rezirkulation in geschlossenem Kreislauf. Die wichtigsten Merkmale des auf elektrolytischem Auslaugen beruhenden,
abfallosen, komplexes Prozesses sind die folgenden:

- Kenntnis der Membranelektrolyse zur Gewinnung einer Kupfer-
  kathode mit 99.96% Kupfergehalt aus einer Laugenlösung bei
  gleichzeitiger Rückgewinnung des laugenden Reagens worduch
  es möglich wird, den inneren Kreislauf der Lösung zu schli-
  essen;

- Enführung eines zusätzlichen Regenerationsprozesses des Aus-
  laugereagens unter erhöhtem Sauerstoffdruck in den inneren
  Kreislauf der Lösung, um den Mangel an Oxydationsmitteln
  auszugleichen;

- Einsatz eines zweiten, sog. äusseren Lösungskreislaufs, um
  ein kontinuierliches Ableiten der in der laugenden Lösung
  angesammelten Verunreinigungen zu gewährleisten;

- Entwicklung zusätzlicher Verfahren zur Gewinnung von Silber und Blei.

Der Bericht erörtert auch einige Ergebnisse kontinuierlicher 3-wöchiger Laborversuche und Untersuchungen über die Weiterverwertung des, bei diesem Prozess anfallenden Schwefels und Kohlenstoffs.

РЕЗЮМЕ

Представлены исследования по разработке гидрометаллургического метода переработки польских сульфидных концентратов меди с применением раствора сернокислого железа, в системе замкнутой циркуляции. Наиболее важными преимуществами комплексного процесса, незагрязняющего окружающей среды, основанного на процессах выщелачивания и электролиза, являются следующие:
-изученность диафрагменного электролиза для получения катодной меди чистотой 99,9% Cu из выщелачивающего раствора при одновременной регенерации анодного раствора, дающей возможность замкнуть главную внутреннюю систему циркуляции,
-введение во внутреннюю систему циркуляции дополнительного процесса регенерации выщелачивающего раствора при повышенном давлении кислорода с целью восполнения дефицита кислорода,
-применение второй, так называемой внешней циркуляции раствора, с целью обеспечения непрерывного отвода загрязнений, накопившихся в выщелачивающем растворе.

В настоящем докладе рассмотрены некоторые результаты непрерывных 3-недельных лабораторных опытов, а также исследования по утилизации отбросной серы и угля.

SILVER CATALYSIS IN FERRIC SULPHATE LEACHING OF CHALCOPYRITE

J. D. Miller and H. Q. Portillo

Department of Metallurgy and Metallurgical Engineering University of Utah, Salt Lake City, USA

INTRODUCTION

During the past decade considerable research effort has been directed toward the development of hydrometallurgical processes for the treatment of copper sulfide concentrates. In some instances this research effort has resulted in pilot and full-scale plant operations such as the Arbiter process [1] the CLEAR process [2] and the Cymet process [3]. An important aspect of hydrometallurgical process development is that all copper sulfide minerals should be amenable to the leach, including chalcopiryte the most resistant of all copper sulfides.

The acid ferric sulfate leaching system, which has been studied extensively and is adventagous in that no new components are introduced into the system, has not been developed commercially. Recently, however, a flowsheet and supporting data based on an acid ferric sulfate leach were presented at the Annual AIME Meeting [4]. One of the unique features of the flowsheet was attrition grinding of the chalcopyrite concentrate to an average particle size of one micron prior to leaching in order to achieve reasonable reaction rates (80% reaction in 3 h).

After review of the current level of understanding of the ferric sulfate leaching of chalcopiryte, the catalytic influence of soluble silver salts on the reaction will be considered. A paucity of information is available on the nature of the catalytic ferric sulfate leach and this investigation was designed to determine details of the reaction mechanism and to determine how it differs from the uncatalysed ferric sulfate leach.

Ferric Sulfate Leach

In sulfuric acid solutions of ferric sulfate, chalcopyrite dissolves according to the following reaction,

$$CuFeS_2 + 4Fe^{3+} \longrightarrow Cu^{2+} + 5Fe^{2+} + 2S^0 \qquad (1)$$

This reaction stoichiometry has been observed by a number of investigators [5, 6, 7, 8, 9]. Exceptions to this consensus are the early work of Sullivan [10] and the more recent results reported by Jones and Peters [11]. The topochemical nature of the leaching reaction is clearly illustrated in Fig. 1 which shows the cross section of a partially reacted chalcopiryte particle surrounded by a dense, tenacious sulfur layer.

852

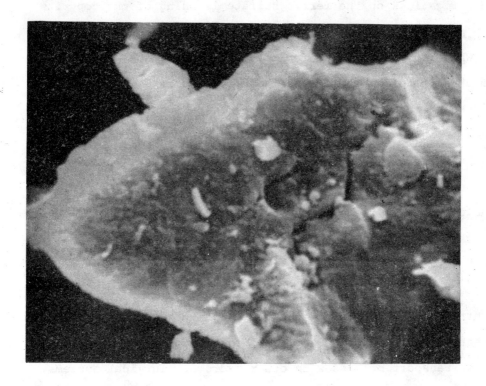

Fig. 1. SEM photograph of the cross section of a partially
leached chalcopyrite particle (10 µm) showing the
sulfur layer and topochemical nature of the
uncatalysed ferric sulfate leach.

The formation of an elemental sulfur layer on the chalcopyrite surface may significantly influence the reaction kinetics by establishing a diffusion barrier. The details of rate
control for this particular reaction have not been well
established. Some investigators [5, 11] attribute rate control to a surface reaction. Other investigators [6, 7, 8, 9,
12, 13] report that the reaction rate is limited by transport
in the chalcopyrite lattice or through the elemental sulfur
reaction product layer. A summary of the results of

investigations on the ferric sulfate leaching of chalcopyrite are presented in Table 1.

When the elemental sulfur reaction product does appear to form a diffusion barrier and the rate becomes limited by transport through this layer, rather slow reaction kinetics have been observed. Baur et. al., [12] using radiochemical techniques, suggested mass transport rate control for Transvaal chalcopyrite after approximately 5.3×10^{-6} g·cm^{-2} chalcopyrite had reacted at 85°C. This corresponds to a thickness of consumed chalcopyrite of 1.25×10^{-6} cm which is necessary to form the coherent diffusional-resistant layer of sulfur. Some question of this interpretation of rate control arises because of the large activation energies observed which normally are not observed for rate control by pore transport processes in other hydrometallurgical systems. Subsequently, these high activation energies were explained to be due to a surface diffusion process and/or the idea that the porosity and tortuosity in the sulfur layer are highly temperature dependent and change in such a way to give an apparent activation energy of 20 kcal/mole [8]. Another concern of the mass transport model is that the reaction kinetics are largely independent of both reactant (Fe^{3+}) and product (Fe^{2+}, Cu^{2+}) concentrations; results which are not consistent with the model. This anomalous situation was explained as either being due to complexation reactions which maintain a constant reactant activity or due to adsorption and surface saturation of reactant [8].

TABLE I. SUMMARY OF REACTION KINETICS FOR FERRIC SULFATE LEACHING OF CHALCOPYRITE

Investigators	System & Observations	Activation Energy kcal/mole	Suggested Rate Limiting Process
Dutrizac, et al. (1969)	Rotating disc technique. Natural (Temagami) and synthetic $CuFeS_2$. Rate independent of ferric concentration. Parabolic kinetics.	17.3 (50 to 99°C)	Transport control. Diffusion of ferrous ions through elemental sulfur.
Lowe (1970)	Continuous flow of solution through packed bed of particles (4x14 mesh). Rate independent of $Fe_2(SO_4)_3$ and H_2SO_4 concentrations.	17.8 (32 to 52°C)	Surface reaction controlled. Surface saturation followed by chemical reaction.
Baur, et al. (1974)	Suspended particles (5-40 microns) in stirred reactor. Transvaal $CuFeS_2$. Parabolic kinetics.	20.3 (27 to 91.5°C)	Transport control. Diffusion of ferric ions through elemental sulfur.
Jones and Peters (1976)	Stirred reactor, 90°C, massive ($\approx$1.0 cm cubes) and particulate (12 to 400 mesh) $CuFeS_2$ from Craigmont Mine B.C.: Some S^0 oxidized to SO_4. No particle size dependence below 48 mesh. Linear kinetics to 40% reacted.		Electrochemical surface reaction.
Beckstead, et al. (1976)	Stirred reactor, monosize $CuFe_2S$ particles and attritor ground particles prepared from Pima concentrate (1-40 microns). Rate independent of $Fe_2(SO_4)_3$, $FeSO_4$, $CuSO_4$ and H_2SO_4 concentrations. Well defined rate dependence on particle size. Parabolic kinetics.	20.0 (60 to 90°C)	Transport control. Diffusion of ferric ions through elemental sulfur.
Munoz, et al. (1978)	Stirred reactor, monosize $CuFeS_2$ particles (4, 12 and 47 microns) prepared from Pima concentrate. Rate independent of $Fe_2(SO_4)_3$ and H_2SO_4 concentrations. Parabolic reaction kinetics.	20.0 (60 to 90°C)	Transport controlled. Transfer of electrons through elemental sulfur reaction product. The rate constant for the leaching reaction and its temperature coefficient predicted from the electronic conductivity of elemental sulfur and its variation with temperature.

Most recently, these data have been reconsidered together with new experimental data and the results interpreted using Wagner's theory of oxidation [9].

$$J_i = - \frac{t_i \sigma}{z_i^2 e^2} \frac{d\mu_i}{dx} + z_i e \frac{d\phi}{dx} \tag{2}$$

Analysis of the data suggests that the rate limiting process may be the transport of electrons through the elemental sulfur layer as depicted schematically in Fig. 2.

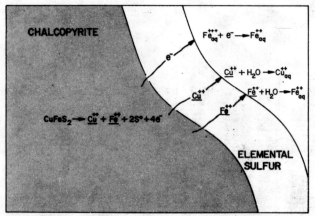

ACID FERRIC SULFATE LEACHING OF CHALCOPYRITE — RATE CONTROL BY ELECTRONIC TRANSPORT THROUGH ELEMENTAL SULFUR REACTION PRODUCT LAYER

Fig. 2. Schematic representation of the transport process in the ferric sulfate leaching of chalcopyrite. Note that the hydrated ferric ion does not advance through the sulfur product layer, but rather is discharged at the sulfur-solution interface.

Predicted reaction rates calculated from first principles using
the physico-chemical properties of the system (conductivity of
elemental sulfur, $t_e\sigma'$, and the free energy change for the reaction, ΔG) agree satisfactorily with experimentally determined
rates. See Fig. 3.

$$\frac{d\alpha}{dt} = (300) \; \frac{3t_e\sigma' \; \Delta G}{\rho \, d_o^2 e^2} \; \frac{(1 - \alpha)^{1/3}}{1 - (1 - \alpha)^{1/3}} \tag{3}$$

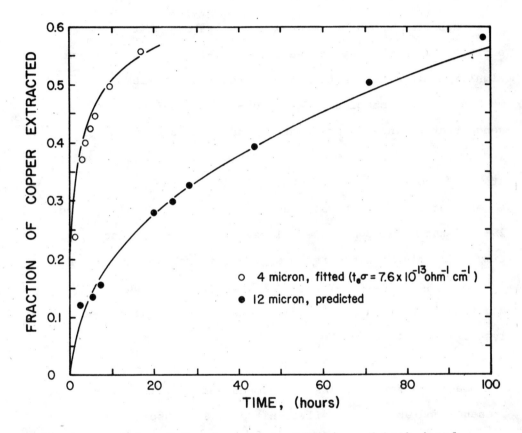

Fig. 3. Uncatalysed ferric sulfate leaching of both 4 and
12 μm monosize chalcopyrite particles at 90°C. Data
for the 4 μm response was fitted using the electrical conductivity of elemental sulfur as the only
adjustable parameter. With this value the leaching
response of the 12 μm material was predicted.

Further evidence [9] which supports this analysis includes
an experimental activation energy of 20 kcal/mole which is
approximately the same as the apparent activation energy for
the transfer of electrons through elemental sulfur
(23 kcal/mole), calculated from both conductivity and
electron mobility measurements reported in the literature.

Silver Catalysis

It has been shown by several investigators that the
addition of soluble silver salts to an acid oxidation leach
significantly enhances the rate of reaction. Pawlek [14]
worked with two samples of attritor-ground chalcopyrite
concentrate; minus 40 μm material and minus 3 μm material.
The leach was carried out under 2 atmospheres of O_2 pressure
at $110^{\circ}C$ and a concentration of 125 g/l solids. In the
absence of silver catalyst, the minus 40 μm material reacted
25% and the minus 3 μm material reacted 51% for a reaction
time of 30 min. In the presence of the silver catalyst
(0.75% of the concentrate weight) the coarse (minus 40 μm)
and fine (minus 3 μm) material reacted 30% and 95% respectively.

McElroy and Duncan [15] studied the bacterial leaching
(thiobacillus ferrooxidans) of ground chalcopyrite in the
presence and absence of silver nitrate. The suspension was
aereated for 50 to 60 h and lime was used to maintain the
pH at 2.0 since the bacterial action produces sulfuric acid.
For a silver addition of 500 g per metric ton (0.05%) copper
extractions of 60% to 100% were obtained. In the absence of

858

silver addition, copper extractions ranged from 20% to 60%.

Snell and Sze [16] developed a silver catalyzed acid ferric sulfate leach for copper sulfide concentrates. The particle' size distribution was 92% minus 200 mesh, the pulp density varied from 10% to 40%, the working temperature was 90°C to 120°C, ferric sulfate was added from 10% to 40% by weight, sulfuric acid was 5% by weight and the silver addition ranged from 50 to 500 ppm (0.004% to 0.04% of the concentrate weight). Under optimum conditions a recovery of 93% copper was obtained for a 3 h leach. All of the above mentioned researchers concluded that essentially complete silver recovery could be achieved from the sulfur residue for catalyst recycle.

Although it has been demonstrated that silver addition in acid ferric sulfate leaching of chalcopyrite and similar systems [14, 15, 16] accelerates greatly the rate of reaction, mechanistic details of the catalytic effect are not known. In view of this fact, the principal objectives of this research program are as follows:

(1) Examine the nature of the exchange reaction between Ag^+ and $CuFeS_2$ in the absence of oxidation

    - determine the stoichiometry of the reaction,

    - determine the kinetics of the exchange reaction as a function of concentration, particle size and temperature.

(2) Examine the catalytic role of Ag^+ in the acid ferric
sulfate leaching of chalcopyrite

    - determine the stoichiometry of the reaction,

    - identify important aspects of the reaction
kinetics such as concentration, particle size
and temperature,

    - characterize the reaction products (SEM, XRD).

EXPERIMENTAL TECHNIQUE

In order to study the nature of the exchange reaction
between Ag^+ and $CuFeS_2$ (in the absence of oxidant), and Ag^+
catalysis in the acid ferric sulfate leaching of $CuFeS_2$, two
different types of experiments were performed and will be
described subsequently. In both cases, experiments were
carried out under atmospheric pressure using a four-necked
unbaffled cylindrical reactor submerged in a constant temperature oil bath. The stirring speed was kept constant at
600 rpm, controlled with a Dyna-Mix variable speed stirrer.
A schematic diagram of the apparatus is shown in Fig. 4.

Materials. Reagent grade silver nitrate (99.9% purity),
ferric sulfate (21% Fe^{3+}), sulfuric acid (96.5 $\pm$ 1.5%) purity
and distilled deionized water were used in all experiments.
The chalcopyrite used in this research was obtained from
a Pima flotation concentrate. Chemical and mineralogical
analyses are shown in Table 2, which data were provided by
the U.S. Bureau of Mines, Salt Lake City Metallurgy Research
Center.

860

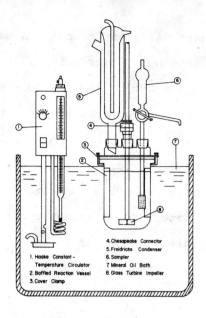

Fig. 4. Schematic diagram of leaching apparatus.

TABLE 2

Analysis of Pima Concentrate

Chemical Analysis		Mineralogical Analysis	
Element	%	Mineral	%
Cu	27.2	$CuFeS_2$	80
Fe	29.2	FeS_2	5
S	20.8	SiO_2	5
Sb	0.60	Al_2O_3	0.93
Zn	0.50	CaO	0.52
Mo	0.14	Talc and Chlorites	8
Pb	0.07		
As	0.02		

Sample Preparation. Three different monosize samples were prepared from the concentrate by wet screening (325 x 400 mesh) and sizing with a Warman Cyclosizer (Cyclone No. 5 and Cyclone No. 3). In preparing the monosize samples, break-up of any possible agglomerates was done by using an ultrasonic probe for 15 min before the final screening. In addition, gangue minerals were separated from the monosize chalcopyrite samples with a Carpco Laboratory Model Magnetic Separator. The products prepared in this fashion had an exceptionally high purity. Also a 2.5 x 5 μm monosize sample was prepared by the Donaldson Company with an Accucut Model B air classifier. Results of the chemical analyses for each monosize sample (characterized by the median size of their narrow size distribution) are shown in Table 3.

TABLE 3

Physical and Chemical Properties of
Monosize Chalcopyrite Samples

Size	Chemical Analysis		Specific Surface	Specific
μm	% Cu	% Fe	Area (m^2/g)	Gravity
4.8	26.5	29.5	0.480	3.75
13.5	30.5	28.5	0.195	3.92
28.0	31.5	30.5	0.092	3.92
51.2	33.5	30.5	0.031	3.92

Size Distribution Determinations

The particle size distribution for each sample was determined by the Microtrac Particle Size Analyser [17]. A representative sample was introduced into the sample basin (usually 0.5 to 2.0 g) which was automatically mixed with dilution water maintaining a representative particle size distribution. The suspension was then circulated to the sample cell for measurement. Basically, particles passing through the sample cell scatter some of the light from the helium-neon laser which is collected by a lens and projected through a filter/chopper, the fixed sector disk and the rotating "Compumask" optical filter. Light scattered by larger particles illuminates a small area surrounding the axis of the laser beam, whereas smaller particles illuminate a larger area, farther removed from the axis of the beam. The "Compumask" filter, with cutouts designed from computer analysis, selectively passes scattered light through a lens to the photodetector. The microprocessor correlates the angular position of the "Compumask" and the photodetector output, providing the digital display and the printer with the calculated amount of particles of a specified size. The Microtrac is suitable for measuring particle sizes ranging from 2 to 200 μm (in 13 channels). A major advantage of its use is the very rapid size analysis which can be performed on a variety of particulate samples. A set of determinations were made for each monosize sample. The size distributions are presented in Fig. 5. Hereafter, in view of the results

863

obtained, the monosize chalcopyrite samples will be characterized by their median particle size; 4.8, 13.5, 28, and
51.2 μm respectively.

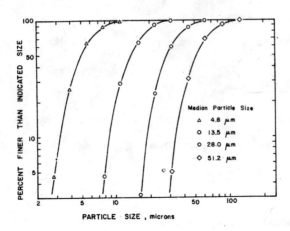

Fig. 5. Size distribution of monosize chalcopyrite
samples as determined by Microtrac analysis.

Surface Area Measurement

Determination of the surface area was carried out by
using the PERMARAN Specific Surface Area Meter. Basically the
PERMARAN measures the air permeability or flow resistance
of the sample. From flow resistance values, specific surface
areas can be estimated using the Carman-Kozeny equation.
A more detailed explanation of its easy operation and theoretical bckground can be found in the Permaran Manual [18]
and in instructions prepared at the University of Utah [19].
The specific surface areas for each of the monosize samples
are shown in Table 3. The correlation between the median

particle size and specific surface areas is presented in
Fig. 6.

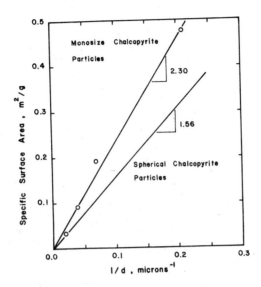

Fig. 6. A comparison of the specific surface area-
particle diameter relationship for the monosize
chalcopyrite samples with the idealized relationship for spherical chalcopyrite particles. The
slope representets the area shape factor divided
by the product of the volume shape factor and
the density $(C_2/C_3 \rho)$.

Specific Gravity Determination

The specific gravity of each of the monosize samples
was determined by using a Hubbard Specific Gravity Bottle
(Pycnometer) with acetone as the solvent. The results are
tabulated in Table 3.

Chemical and Mineralogical Analysis

Chemical analysis for the elements of interest was done using a PERKIN ELMER 305A Atomic Absorption Spectrophotometer according to the instructions provided in the operating manual. Ferrous ion concentration was determined by titration with a standard ceric sulfate solution using ferroin as an indicator [20].

The amount of elemental sulfur was determined by dissolving the sample in carbon disulfide at 40°C. Basically the apparatus consists of a heater, a reflux flask, an extraction tube (where the sample is placed in a pure cellulose thimble commonly used in extraction separations) and a condenser. After 4 to 5 h of extraction, the liquid phase, which contains soluble sulfur, is evaporated and the remaining residue is the soluble sulphur that was originally present in the sample.

X-ray analyses of feed material and reaction products were carried out using the powder method with a Norelco Diffractometer and CuKα radiation generated at 35 kV and 15 mA.

Surface morphology of the various products obtained before and after leaching were examined and analyzed using the HITACHI Series 500 scanning electron microscope with an X-ray elemental analysis attachment (KEVEX).

Exchange Reaction Experiments

The exchange reaction kinetics were determined by measuring the depletion of silver concentration with time.

Aware of the very fast reaction between Ag^+ and chalcopyrite, even at room temperature, a potentiometric method was selected for this purpose.

Equipment. The silver concentration was determined using an Orion Sulfide Ion Activity Electrode (Model 94-1600). In addition an Orion Double Junction Reference Electrode (Model 90-02), a PHM-62 Standard pH meter and a REC 61/REA 160 SERVOGRAPH curve recorder were used. The last two units are manufactured by RADIOMETER-COPENHAGEN. The reaction vessel, a cylindrical glass flask joined to a four-necked lid by a metallic clamp, was used for the experiments as shown in Fig. 4. The central neck of the lid was fitted with a Chesapeake connector and small glass rod agitator shaft equipped with a Teflon turbine impeller. Before starting the experiments a thermometer and a reflux condenser were connected to two of the necks. The fourth opening was used for purging with nitroges gas.

Procedure for Measurement of Silver Ion Concentration

Standard acid solutions of 10^{-2}, 10^{-3}, 10^{-4} and 10^{-5} M Ag^+ were prepared by diluting $AgNO_3$ in distilled deionized water to a total ionic strength of 0.76 M supported by sulfuric acid. Potentiometric measurements were carried out to construct the necessary calibration curves. Both electrodes were immersed in solutions of known concentration. To avoid the absorption of atmospheric oxygen during the measurement, nitrogen gas was bubbled through the test solutions kept at a constant volume of 100 ml. Magnetic stirring with a Teflon-coated iron bar was employed. A heater-stirrer was used in experiments where heating was necessary. Electrode potentials were attained rapidly and in every case the equilibrium potentials were read within 30 s after having placed the electrodes in the standard solutions. The reproducibility for different solutions of the same Ag^+ concentration was within $\pm$ 1 mV providing that the electrode surface was kept clean. It should be emphasized that anomalous results were obtained for experiments carried out above 50°C, probably due to contamination of the outer-chamber filling solution of the double junction reference electrode. However, the problem was solved by covering the outer-chamber filling hole and by changing the filling solutions after each experiment.

The exchange reaction kinetic experiments were done according to the following procedure:

(1) The leaching solution (990 ml) at a specified silver ion concentration and 0.25 M H_2SO_4 was prepared, poured into the reactor and stirred at 600 rpm until the desired temperature was reached.

(2) The reference and silver sulfide electrodes were placed in the reactor. When the system achieved an equilibrium potential, the graph paper in the strip chart recorder was advanced at the desired speed.

(3) The reaction was initiated when the specified mono-size sample was poured into the reactor, usually as a 10 ml suspension.

(4) The potential recorded by the strip chart as a function of time measured the kinetic response of the system.

Catalysed Ferric Sulfate Leaching Reaction

As stated previously, the second part of this investigation is related to the leaching of chalcopyrite in the presence of silver with ferric sulfate as the oxidizing agent.

Equipment. The experiment set-up employed in these experiments was already shown in Fig. 4. Again all leaching experiments were carried out in a total volume of 1 l. Temperature was always maintained constant $\pm$ 0.2°C. The same water, chemicals and solids already described were used in all the experiments.

Procedure. In almost all the leaching experiments a two-hour acid wash (0.25 M H_2SO_4) of the monosize samples was necessary since as much as 18% of the copper in the 4.8 µm sample is soluble. Acid soluble copper for each monosize sample is reported in Table 4 expressed as a percentage of the total copper in the sample.

The following procedure was used to follow the silver catalysed acid ferric sulfate leaching of chalcopyrite.

(1) A specified amount of ferric sulfate was dissolved with a minimum of the 0.25 M sulfuric acid solution. The ferric solution, was heated separately to the desired temperature before pouring into the reactor.

TABLE 4

Percent of Copper Released During Acid Washing of Monosize Chalcopyrite

Sample	% Copper
4.8 µm	18.0
13.5 µm	4.5
28.0 µm	2.0
51.2 µm	1.0

(2) The reactor was filled with the remaining amount of 0.25 M sulfuric acid solution and heated to the desired temperature at which time the monosize sample was introduced into the reactor

(3) After 2 h of washing a 3 ml sample was withdrawn just before introducing the silver solution (~2 ml) necessary to achieve the desired silver concentration.

(4) After the addition of the silver solution (30 s), the ferric solution (prepared in step 1) was poured into the reactor. This was the starting point (time "zero") for determination of the rate of reaction.

It should be pointed out that the sequence: solids, silver solution, and ferric solution was selected because it gave the most rapid kinetic response. All samples (3 ml) taken at timed intervals were cooled immediately in a container of ice. After cooling the samples were centrifuged and the aqueous phase diluted as necessary and analysed for copper and/or ferrous concentrations as described in previous sections. The extent of reaction was calculated in terms of the fraction of the copper extracted from the acid-washed sample. The final leach residue was washed twice with distilled deionized water, dried and saved for further characterization using the techniques and methods already described.

RESULTS AND DISCUSSION

The nature of silver catalysed, acid ferric sulfate leaching of chalcopyrite was studied by first evaluating the chalcopyrite exchange reaction with silver (in the absence of oxidant) followed by study of the actual silver catalysed ferric sulfate leach. As mentioned previously in the introduction, the uncatalysed ferric sulfate leaching of chalcopyrite has been extensively studied and most recently the reaction kinetics explained to be controlled by electronic transport in the elemental sulfur reaction product layer.

Silver Exchange Reaction

The reaction of silver ion with chalcopyrite in the absence of oxidant was examined both with respect to reaction stoichiometry   and with respect to initial reaction kinetics.

Stoichiometry. Preliminary observations of the reaction of silver ion with chalcopyrite were that a blue-black product rapidly formed at the chalcopyrite surface. Analysis of this reaction product by X-ray diffraction showed that the reaction product consisted of Ag_2S (argentite) and unreacted $CuFeS_2$ with all reported "d" spacings identified. One unidentified peak was consistently found at a 2θ value of 28.2-28.4°. This peak may represent some intermediate solid solution such as reported by Cabri et. al. [21] SEM examination of the reaction product showed that the coherent film consisted exlusively of silver and sulfur. The exchange reaction stoichiometry can then be written most simply as:

$$CuFeS_2 + 4Ag^+ \longrightarrow 2Ag_2S + Cu^{2+} + Fe^{2+} \qquad (5)$$

Solution analyses, however, show some deviation from the indicated stoichiometry. Rather than a 4/1 mole ratio of Ag^+/Cu^{2+} and Ag^+/Fe^{2+}, the solution analyses were 3/1 and 5/1 respectively. These results may reflect the fact that one XRD peak was not identified and consequently the reaction stoichiometry may be slightly different than indicated due to the presence of an unidentified minor solid phase. The results obtained seemed to be independent of acid strength (0.1 M to 1.0 M H_2SO_4) at a temperature of 90°C.

Initial Reaction Kinetics

The initial reaction kinetics were determined by following the depletion of silver ion with a specific ion electrode and were studied as a function of initial silver concentration, particle size and temperature. The potential difference between the silver electrode and the reference electrode is related to the silver ion concentration at constant ionic strength by the Nernst-type equation,

$$E_t = E^o + B \log (Ag^+)_t \qquad (6)$$

where:

E_t = potential at any time, t

E^o = standard cell potential

B = experimental constant, including log activity coefficient (59 mv per decade of concentration)

$(Ag^+)_t$ = silver concentration at time, t

For the case of first order reaction kinetics, the integrated rate expression has the following form:

$$\log \frac{(Ag^+)_t}{(Ag^+)_o} = - \frac{kA}{V} t \qquad (7)$$

where:

k = reaction velocity constant, cm/s

A = surface area, cm^2

V = solution volume, cm^3

t = reaction time, s.

Combination of Eqs. 6 and 7 results in the following equation

$$E_t - E_o = \frac{kAB}{V} t \qquad (8)$$

from which the reaction velocity constant can be determined from a plot of $E_t - E_o$ vs. t. Alternately, the potential values can be converted to silver ion concentration using the standard curve and the kinetics represented in the usual manner according to Eq. 7. Generally the initial kinetics

873

followed the first order relationship until the thickness of the Ag_2S film exceeded approximately $50A^{\circ}$.

Silver Concentration. As is evident from the integrated first order rate expression (Eq. 7), a plot of the kinetic data for the system should be independent of the initial silver concentration. Such was found to be the case for a wide range of concentrations (over 2 orders of magnitude) and for two different monosize samples (4.8 µm and 51.2 µm) at 25° as shown in Fig. 7. (See also Table 5).

Particle Size. The effect of particle size was also considered in the analysis of the initial reaction kinetics. Generally the reaction velocity constant would be expected to be largely independent of the particle size even for rate control by diffusion in the mass transfer boundary layer. As can be seen in Table 5, the reaction velocity constants for the 4.8 µm and 51.2 µm samples do not differ greatly, 2.67×10^{-2} cm/s and 1.28×10^{-2} cm/s respectively.

The initial high rate of this first order reaction would suggest that the rate may be limited by diffusion in the mass transfer boundary layer. To test this hypothesis, the experimental reaction velocity constants were compared to predicted mass transfer coefficients for stirred reactors estimated using Harriot's approach [22, 23] which is based on the Sherwood correlation [24]. The excellent agreement between experimental and prediced values is seen in Table 5.

TABLE 5

Reaction Velocity Constants Determined from Initial Rate Data for the
Silver Exchange Reaction with Monosize Chalcopyrite Particles at 25°C

Size (μ)	Weight Chalcopyrite (g)	Initial Silver Concentration (mol/l)	Experimental Reaction Velocity Constant (cm/s)	Predicted Mass Transfer Coefficient* (cm/s)
4.8 (0.480 m²/g)	2.0	1.35×10^{-4}	2.47×10^{-2}	2.63×10^{-2}
	2.0	1.45×10^{-4}	2.75×10^{-2}	
	2.0	1.00×10^{-4}	2.75×10^{-2}	
	4.0	1.00×10^{-4}	2.78×10^{-2}	
	1.0	2.50×10^{-5}	2.94×10^{-2}	
	2.0	2.70×10^{-5}	2.60×10^{-2}	
	2.0	2.40×10^{-5}	2.67×10^{-2}	
	2.0	2.70×10^{-5}	2.68×10^{-2}	
	4.0	3.20×10^{-5}	2.38×10^{-2}	
		Average	2.67×10^{-2}	2.63×10^{-2}
51.2 (0.031 m²/g)	2.0	1.23×10^{-4}	1.20×10^{-2}	1.25×10^{-2}
	2.0	1.25×10^{-5}	1.28×10^{-2}	
	10.0	1.75×10^{-5}	1.30×10^{-2}	
	2.0	1.35×10^{-6}	1.35×10^{-2}	
		Average	1.28×10^{-2}	1.25×10^{-2}

*The predicted mass transfer coefficients were obtained using Harriot's
approach [22, 23] for suspended particles in agitated vessels.

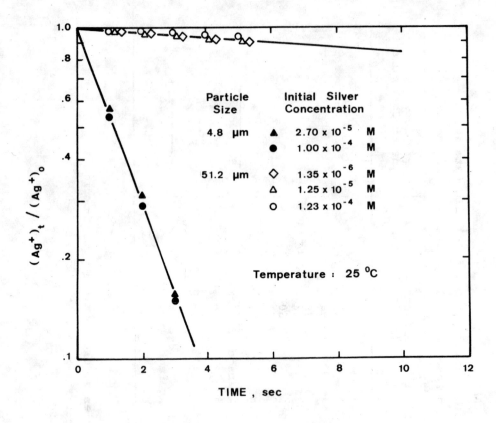

Fig. 7. First order rate plot of fraction of silver
reacted for two monosize chalcopyrite samples
at 0.25 M H_2SO_4, 0.2% solids, 600 rpm and
various initial silver concentrations.

Temperature. Finally, if the initial reaction kinetics
are controlled by a mass transfer process in the aqueous
phase, then the temperature coefficient for the rate phenomenon should typically correspond to an activation energy of
less than 5.0 kcal/mole. As shown in Fig. 8, the reaction

velocity constants increase with increasing temperature at two levels of silver addition for the 51.2 μm sample.

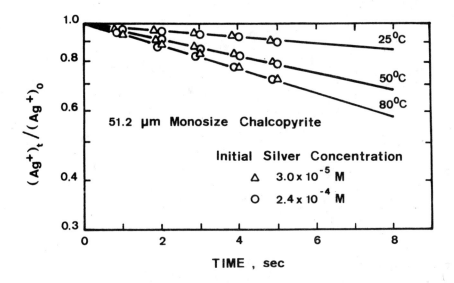

Fig. 8. First order rate plot of fraction of silver reacted for the 51.2 μm monosize chalcopyrite sample at 0.25 M H_2SO_4, 0.2% solids, 600 rpm, and selected temperatures for two different initial silver concentrations.

An Arrhenius plot of the data is presented in Fig. 9 and an apparent activation energy of 4.2 kcal/mole is observed for this rate process which supports the hypothesis of rate control by mass transfer in the aqueous phase. Similar results were obtained for the 4.8 μm sample and the apparent activation energy was found to be 3.1 kcal/mole.

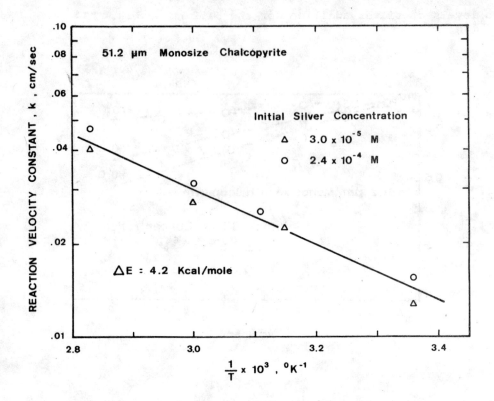

Fig. 9. Arrhenius plot of the reaction velocity constant
for the silver exchange reaction with the 51.2 μm
monosize chalcopyrite sample at two different
initial silver concentrations. Data taken from
Fig. 8.

Silver Catalysed Ferric Sulfate Leach

The stoichiometry of the silver catalysed ferric sulfate
leach of chalcopyrite was studied as well as important
features of the reaction kinetics.

Stoichiometry. The silver catalysed reaction appears to exhibit the same stoichiometry as the uncatalysed presented in Eq. 1. In the absence of chloride salts, elemental sulfur together with Ag_2S constituted the reaction product as determined by X-ray diffraction. Solution analyses for copper and ferrous revealed a Fe^{2+}/Cu^{2+} mole ratio of 5.08 (average of 18 values from 4 different experiments) at all stages of the reaction which closely corresponds to the 5/1 ratio specified by the stoichiometry of the suggested reaction in Eq. 1.

Reaction Kinetics. Analysis of the leaching reaction kinetics is complicated by the fact that the rate and extent of reaction, besides being dependent on normal kinetic parameters, is also dependent on chloride impurity levels in the reagent grade ferric sulfate as well as the experimental procedure used to initiate the reaction. This latter effect has been observed in the ammonia-oxygen-chalcopyrite system [25] and should always be carefully considered in heterogeneous reactions involving the formation of a reaction product layer.

Using the procedure described in the experimental technique section, in which reagent grade ferric sulfate was added as the last step to initiate the reaction, the products of the reaction were found to contain silver chloride as well as elemental sulfur and silver sulfide. The formation of the silver chloride resulted from small levels of chloride present in the reagent grade ferric sulfate (0.005%). In this regard, some kinetic experiments were run in which silver

879

chloride formation occurred whereas in other experiments, the chloride impurity was removed before the experiment began. Considerable difference is observed with respect to the leaching response of coarse particles in the presence and absence of chloride as shown in Fig. 10.

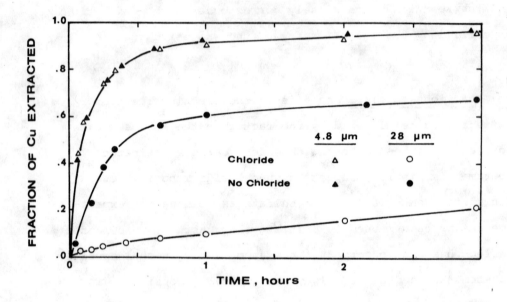

Fig. 10. The effect of chloride impurity on the rate and extent of the catalysed reaction for two different particle sizes at 0.25 M H_2SO_4, 1 M Fe^{3+}, 0.2% solids, 600 rpm and 90°C. (1.0 x 10^{-3}M Ag^+).

The formation of silver chloride significantly inhibits the reaction kinetics not only for the 28 μm sample, but also for the other monosize material with the exception of the 4.8 μm sample. In view of the experimental procedure which allows for Ag_2S to form first followed by addition of ferric, the silver chloride detected in the product layer must form by reaction with the chloride impurity. Under typical experimental conditions (10^{-3} M Ag^+ and 1 M Fe^{3+}), the silver chloride which forms amounts to as much as 37% of the total silver in the system and is sufficient to significantly inhibit the reaction of coarse particles. As a result of these simultaneous reactions a homogeneous mixture of Ag_2S, $AgCl$ and S^o forms on the unreacted chalcopyrite particle.

Not only can the reaction kinetics be complicated by the presence of the chloride impurity, but even in the absence of chloride, the leaching response is sensitive to the experimental procedure used for reaction initiation. Figure 11 contrasts the leaching response for different procedures in the absence of chloride. As might be expected when the chalcopyrite is allowed to react first with the ferric sulfate (open squares), the reaction kinetics are slow due to the formation of the elemental sulfur layer during the initial 5 min prior to the addition of silver. On the other hand, when the silver is added first (open circles) a much more rapid leaching response is observed. Note, however, if the silver sulfide-coated chalcopyrite particles are filtered and dried for 15 min at approximately 80^oC open to the atmosphere (closed circles) the reaction rate is severely limited. Finally, if the chalcopyrite is added to the leach solution containing both Ag^+ and Fe^{3+} (open triangles), an intermediate leaching response is observed.

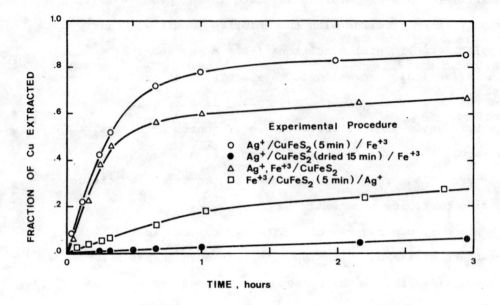

Fig. 11. The effect of experimental procedure for reaction initiation on the rate and extent of the catalysed reaction for 28 μm particles at 0.25 M H_2SO_4, 1 M Fe^{3+}, 0.2% solids, 600 rpm and 90°C. (1.0 x 10^{-3}M Ag^+).

These results, the possible formation of silver chloride and the variation with experimental procedure, are indicative of the complexities involved in the evaluation of the rate data for the leaching reaction. SEM examination of cross section through the reaction product indicated that the phases Ag_2S, S^o and sometimes AgCl (all identified by XRD) were well mixed under a variety of conditions with no evidence of distinct regions of one phase or another. However, due to the small amount of the silver compounds present, detection of a distinct region of predominance such as a layer next to the surface, would be difficult.

Initial Silver Concentration. The effect of the initial silver concentration on the rate and extent of reaction is shown in Fig. 12, for data collected in the presence of chloride (silver chloride found in the reaction product).

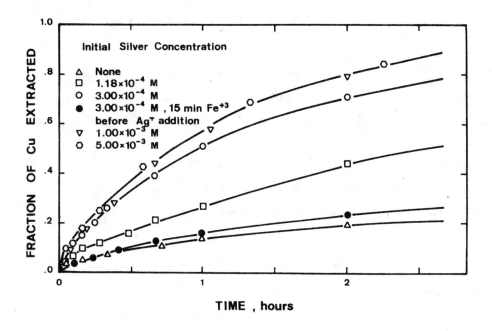

Fig. 12. The influence of the initial silver concentration on the rate and extent of the catalysed reaction for 4.8 μm particles at 0.25 M H_2SO_4, 0.1 M Fe^{3+}, 0.2% solids, 600 rpm and 90°C.

The rate increases with an increase in initial silver concentration up to 1×10^{-3} M. Further additions beyond this level do not enhance the rate of reaction and may even reduce the rate slightly. Detailed analysis of this particular set of rate data is complicated by the fact that the reactant, Fe^{3+}, concentration changes appreciably during the course of the reaction. Notice again that when the sequence of reagent addition is altered such that the ferric sulfate is introduced prior to silver addition (15 min lag time), the reaction does not experience the catalytic influence of the silver and the reaction proceeds as though it were uncatalysed. These results also reflect the insulating properties of the tenacious sulfur film and its resistance to mass transfer when it forms on the chalcopyrite surface.

Particle Size. One of the most diagnostic features in the analysis of kinetic data is the particle size dependence of the reaction rate. An inverse first order dependence on the initial particle size could be indicative of rate control by diffusion in the aqueous phase or by surface reaction. An inverse second order dependence on the initial particle size would suggest rate control by diffusion through a growing reaction product layer. Neither case is observed in the silver catalysed ferric sulfate leaching of chalcopyrite. Surprisingly, the rate, up to approximately 50% reacted, is essentially independent of initial particle size as shown in Fig. 13. These experiments were done by first completing the exchange reaction and establishing a silver sulfide layer of

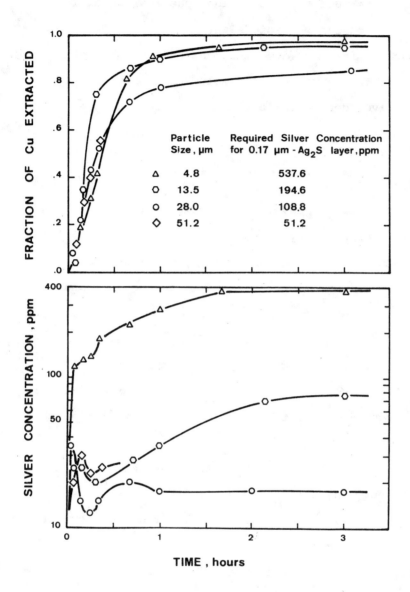

The plot legend (inside the figure) reads:

Particle Size, μm	Required Silver Concentration for 0.17 μm - Ag_2S layer, ppm
△ 4.8	537.6
◦ 13.5	194.6
◦ 28.0	108.8
◇ 51.2	51.2

Y-axis (top): FRACTION OF Cu EXTRACTED
Y-axis (bottom): SILVER CONCENTRATION, ppm
X-axis: TIME, hours

Fig. 13. The effect of particle size on the rate and extent of the catalysed reaction at 0.25 M H_2SO_4, 1.0 M Fe^{3+}, 0.3% solids, 600 rpm and 90°C. Also the corresponding plot of silver concentration in the aqueous phase as a function of reaction time is shown for the respective experiments.

fixed thickness (0.174 μm) assuming spherical particles of the specified median particle size.

It is clear from the data that the Ag_2S film reacts rapidly with the ferric sulfate solution as revealed by the plots of silver concentration in the aqueous phase as a function of time.

$$Ag_2S + 2Fe^{3+} \longrightarrow 2Ag^+ + S^o + 2Fe^{2+} \tag{9}$$

The silver sulfide layer is not completely removed and a rapid rate of chalcopyrite leaching, independent of initial particle size, is observed. Frequently a steady state concentration of 20-25 ppm is established in the aqueous phase until much of the reaction has occurred. After longer times increased dissolution of silver sulfide happens. Under certain circumstances for the 51.2 μm sample the Ag_2S film may dissolve completely during the first few minutes and the reaction becomes passivated due to sulfur formation at the chalcopyrite surface.

Only after extensive reaction ($\nsim$50% reacted), does the sulfur product, which appears to form in the silver sulfide film, become protective. The very distinct difference between the sulfur which forms in the silver catalysed reaction and that which forms during the uncatalysed reaction is revealed by the SEM photographs presented in Fig. 14. Note that the surface sulfur created in the case of the silver catalysed reaction is very porous with well defined sulfur crystallites seen. In the case of the uncatalysed reaction a smooth tenacious layer of elemental sulfur forms.

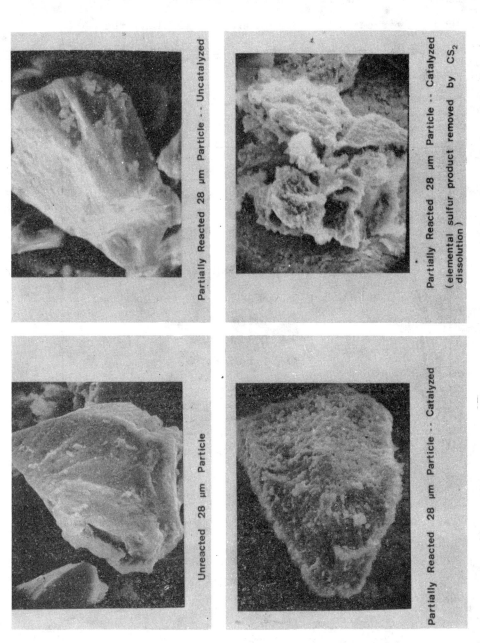

Fig. 14. SEM photographs contrasting the nature of the elemental sulfur reaction product layer which forms during the catalysed reaction with that which forms during the uncatalysed reaction.

<u>Concentration Effects.</u> Unlike the uncatalysed reaction, a definite Fe^{3+} dependence of the rate is observed in the case of the silver catalysed reaction. In addition, the reaction kinetics are also extremely sensitive to the Fe^{2+} concentration as shown in Fig. 15.

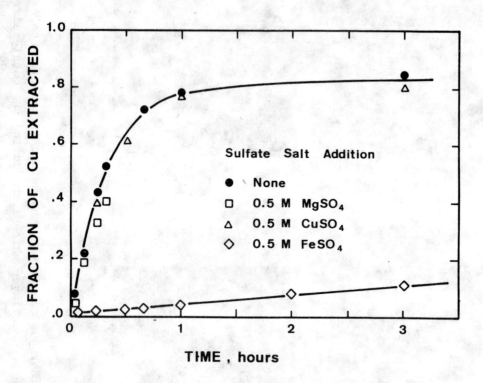

Fig. 15. The effect of ferrous sulfate addition on the rate and extent of reaction for 28 μm particles at 0.25 M H_2SO_4, 1 M Fe^{3+}, 0.3% solids, 600 rpm and 90°C. (0.17 μm Ag_2S layer).

Note that the addition of 0.5 M $FeSO_4$ essentially passivates the system and very little reaction is achieved. On the other hand, the addition of 0.5 M $CuSO_4$ or $MgSO_4$ does not alter the reaction rate. These results are somewhat anomalous in that the rate is dependent on one of the reaction products (Fe^{2+}) but independent of another reaction product (Cu^{2+}).

Discussion. A possible explanation for these observed results is that the rate may be controlled by the electrochemical reaction of Ag_2S with Fe^{3+}.

$$Ag_2S + 2Fe^{3+} \longrightarrow 2Ag^+ + S^o + 2Fe^{2+} \qquad (9)$$

It is hypothesized that this electrochemical reaction occurs at the surface of silver sulfide crystallites throughout the Ag_2S film. The crystallites act as short circuited microelectrodes allowing for the discharge of Fe^{3+} and the release of Ag^+. Under these circumstances, the kinetics would show a dependence on the Ag^+, Fe^{3+}, and Fe^{2+} concentration and would be independent of the initial particle size, i.e., the rate is dependent on the internal area of the crystallites rather than on the external area of the particle. Elemental sulfur replaced the Ag_2S crystallites forming a porous, non-protective layer. The silver ion generated acts as a transfer agent while the silver sulfide film, necessary to prevent extensive sulfur formation at the chalcopyrite surface, is continually restored. A schematic representation of this mechanism is presented in Fig. 16.

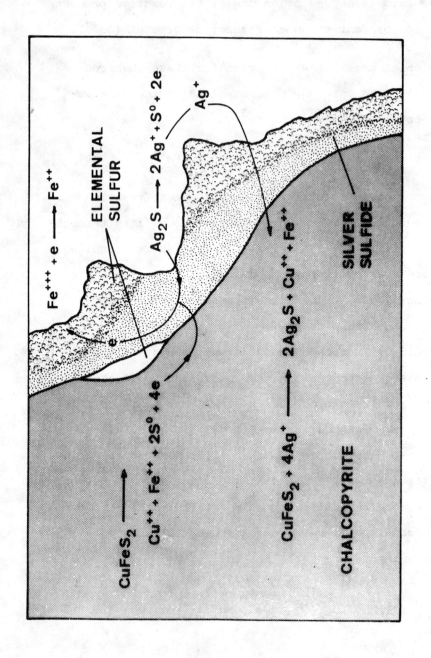

Fig. 16. Schematic representation of the silver catalysed ferric sulfate leaching of chalcopyrite with possible reactions of kinetic importance included.

890

Perhaps of even more interest from an industrial stand-
point is the reaction rate of the Pima concentrate with the
normal distribution of particle sizes (50% minus 20 μm)
and the reaction rate of 3.5 h attritor-ground concentrate
(50% minus 0.5 μm - the same product that has been used in
other studies [4, 8]). Another continuous leaching study [26]
using this material has recently been completed and the
results interpreted in terms of a population balance model [27].
The rates of reaction of these samples in batch reactors are
contrasted in Fig. 17 and the rapid rate of reaction of the
3 h attritor ground material (50% minus 1.5 μm) for the case
of silver catalysis is remarkable.

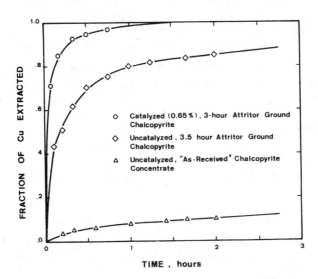

Fig. 17. Fraction of copper extracted as a function of time
for different products at 1 M Fe^{3+} and 90^0C.

ACKNOWLEDGEMENTS

The authors wish to acknowledge the LASPAU fellowship awarded
to Mr. Portillo for his studies at the University of Utah as
well as discussion and helpful laboratory assistance from gra-
duate students in the Department of Metallurgy and Metallurgical
Engineering.

REFERENCES

1. Kuhn M. C. CIM Bull., 67, 62-73 (1974).

2. Atwood G. E. and Curtis C. H. Duval Corp., U.S. Patents
   3,785,944 and 3,879,272 (1974).

3. New Copper Process from Cyprus is Billed as Technological
   Breakthrough, EMJ, 178, No. 10 (1977).

4. Herbst J. A., Miller J. D., Wadsworth M. E., Hayden W.,
   Kolbe J. and Tawari B. An Acid Ferric Sulfate Process for
   the Leaching of Chalcopyrite Concentrates, presented at the
   Annual AIME Meeting, New Orelans (February 1979).

5. Lowe D. F. The Kinetics of the Dissolution Reaction of
   Copper and Copper-Iron Sulfide Minerals Using Ferric Sulphate Solutions, Ph.D. Thesis, University of Arizona, Tucson,
   1970.

6. Linge H. G. Hydrometallurgy 2, 51-64 (1976). See also,
   Linge H. G. Hydrometallurgy 2, 219-233 (1976).

7. Dutrizac J. E. et al. Metallurgical Transactions, 245, 955-
   958 (1969).

8. Beckstead L. W. et al. Acid Ferric Sulfate Leaching of
   Attritor-Ground Chalcopyrite Concentrates, Extractive Metal-
   lurgy of Copper, 2, The Metallurgical Society of A.I.M.E.,
   New York, 1976, 611-632.

9. Munoz P. B., Miller J. D. and Wadsworth M. E. Metallurgical
   Transactions B, June 1979.

10. Sullivan J. D. Trans. AIME, 106, 515-546 (1933).

11. Jones D. L. and Peters E. The Leaching of Chalcopyrite with Ferric Sulfate and Ferric Chloride, Extractive Metallurgy of Copper, The Metallurgical Society of A.I.M.E., New York, 1976, vol. 2, 633-653.

12. Baur J. P., Gibbs H. L. and Wadsworth M. E. Initial-Stage Sulfuric Acid Leaching Kinetics of Chalcopyrite Using Radio-chemical Techniques, U.S.B.M., R.I. 7823 (1974).

13. Peters E. The Physical Chemistry of Hydrometallurgy, Internat. Symp. on Hydromet. A.I.M.E., New York, 1973, 205-228.

14. Pawlek F. E. The influence of Grain Size and Mineralogical Composition on the Leachability of Copper Concentrates, Extractive Metallurgy of Copper (Eds. Yannopoulos and Agarwal), A.I.M.E. 1976.

15. McElroy R. O. and Duncan D. W. British Columbia Research Council, Vancouver, Canada V6F 2L2, The Silver Institute Letter, 5, No. 8, Sept. 1975.

16. Snell G. J. and Sze M. C. New Oxidative Leaching Process Uses Silver to Enhance Copper Recovery, EMJ, 178, No. 10, 100-105, October (1977).

17. Weiss E. L. and Frock H. N. Rapid Analysis of Particle Size Distributions by Laser Light Scaterring, Proceedings of the 7th Annual Fine Particle Society Conference, Philadelphia, 1975.

18. OUTOKUMPU OY, PERMARAN Operating Instructions, Research Laboratory, Tapiola, Finland.

19. Permaran Theory and Operating Instructions, prepared by Metallurgy and Metallurgical Engineering Department, University of Utah, 1978.

20. Pierce W. C. et al. Quantitative Analysis, John Wiley and Sons, New York, 1958, p. 312-315.

21. Cabri L. J. et al. Economic Geology 68, 443-454 (1973).

22. Harriott P. AIChE Journal, 8, No. 1, 93 (1962).

23. Wadsworth M. E. and Miller J. D. Rate Processes of Extractive Metallurgy, Plenum Press, 1978, p. 222.

24. Ranz W. E. and Marshall W. R. Chem. Eng. Progr. 48, 141 (1952).

25. Beckstead L. W. and Miller J. D. Ammonia, Oxidation Leaching of Chalcopyrite - Reaction Kinetics, p. 19-29, and - Surface Deposit Effects, p. 31-38, Metallurgical Transactions B, 8B, March (1977).

26. Fernandez J. R. Continuous Leaching of Attritor Ground Chalcopyrite in Acid Ferric Sulfate Solution, M. S. Thesis, University of Utah, 1978.

27. Sepulveda J. E. and Herbst J. A. A Population Balance Approach to the Modeling of Multistage Continuous Leaching Systems, Fundamental Aspects of Hydrometallurgical Processes, AIChE Symposium Series, 1978.

ABSTRACT

The slow reaction kinetics for the acid ferric sulfate leaching of chalcopyrite can be explained to be due to rate control by electronic transport through the elemental sulfur reaction product.

$$CuFeS_2 + 4Fe^{3+} \longrightarrow Cu^{2+} + 5Fe^{2+} + 2S^{o}$$

However, the addition of a soluble silver salt to the leach causes a significant enhancement in the reaction rate. Initially, this catalytic action involves the surface by the exchange reaction:

$$CuFeS_2 + 4Ag^+ \longrightarrow 2Ag_2S + Cu^{2+} + Fe^{2+}$$

The exchange reaction is rapid and the initial reaction kinetics are controlled by transport through the mass transfer boundary layer as evidenced by: the reaction order (1st order with respect to silver), the magnitude of the reaction velocity constant (equivalent to mass transfer coefficients predicted for monosize particles in stirred tank reactors), and the temperature dependence (activation energy of 3.1-4.2 kcal/mole).

The same reaction stoichiometry for ferric sulfate leaching of chalcopyrite is observed both in the presence and absence of silver catalyst. However, reaction kinetics for silver catalysed ferric sulfate leaching of chalcopyrite are complicated by the formation of mixed reaction products, silver sulfide, silver chloride (when chloride impurites are not removed) and elemental sulfur, as well as being sensitive to the experimental procedure used for reaction initiation. The leaching rate is largely independent of particle size and shows a significant dependence on the Ag^+, Fe^{3+} and Fe^{2+} concentrations. Initial evaluation of the experimental results suggests that the rate may be limited by the electrochemical reaction of Fe^{3+} at the surface of

Ag_2S crystallites present in the film which forms during the exchange reaction.

$$Ag_2S + 2Fe^{3+} \longrightarrow 2Ag^+ + S^O + 2Fe^{2+}$$

Elemental sulfur replaced the Ag_2S crystallites forming a porous, non-protective layer and the Ag^+ generated acts as a transfer agent continually restoring the silver sulfide crystallites via the exchange reaction.

Uncatalysed ferric sulfate leaching of attritor-ground chalcopyrite (median particle size 0.5 μm) to 80% reaction requires a 1 h retention time. On the other hand in the presence of a silver catalyst, 80% reaction for a coarser attritor ground concentrate can be achieved in 7 min.

RÉSUMÉ

Les cinétiques de la réaction lente du lessivage de la chalcopyrite par le sulfate ferrique acide peuvent être expliquées en considérant le contrôle de la vitesse, par le transport électronique à l'aide du soufre élémentaire produit dans la réaction:

$$CuFeS_2 + 4Fe^{3+} \longrightarrow Cu^{2+} + 5Fe^{2+} + 2S^O.$$

Cependant, l'addition d'un sel soluble d'argent à la lessive provoque une accélération significative de la vitesse de reaction. Initialement, cette action catalytique comprend en premier la formation du sulfure d'argent (argentite) á la surface de la chalcopyrite par la réaction d'échange suivante:

$$CuFeS_2 + 4Ag^+ \longrightarrow 2Ag_2S + Cu^{2+} + Fe^{2+}$$

La réaction d'échange est rapide et les cinétiques de la réaction initiale sont contrôlées par le transport de masse à travers la couche de liaison mise en évidence par l'ordre de réaction (1er ordre par rapport à l'argent), par la grandeur de la constante de vitesse de réaction (équivalent aux coefficients de transfert de masse prévus pour des particules à taille unique dans des réacteurs mélangeurs) et par la dépendance avec la température (énergie d'activation de 4.2 kcal/mole).

On observe la même stoechiométrie de réaction pour le lessivage de la chalcopyrite par le sulfate ferrique en présence d'un catalyseur d'argent au sans catalyseur. Cependant, les cinétiques de la réaction du lessivage de la chalcopyrite par le sulfate ferrique, catalysé par l'argent, sont compliquées par la formation de produits de réactions mixtes: le sulfure d'argent, le chlorure d'argent (quand les impuretés en chlorure ne sont pas séparées) le soufre élémentaire et sont sensibles au procédé experimental utilisé pour l'initiation de la réaction. La vitesse de lessivage est en grande partie indépendante de la taille des particules et montre une dépendance importante vis à vis des concentrations en Ag^+, Fe^{3+} et Fe^{2+}. L'évaluation initiale des résultats expérimentaux suggère que la vitesse peut être limitée par la réaction électrochimique à la surface des cristallites d'Ag_2S, de Fe^{3+} présent dans le film qui se forme pendant la réaction d'échange:

$$Ag_2S + 2Fe^{3+} \rightarrow 2Ag^+ + S^0 + 2Fe^{2+}$$

Le soutre élémentaire remplace les cristallites d'Ag_2S en formant une couche poreuse, non-protectrice et l'Ag^+ engendré agit comme un agent de transfert restituant continuellement les cristallites de sulfure d'argent par la réaction d'échange.

Le lessivage non-catalysé par le sulfate ferrique de la chalcopyrite fragmenté profondément par attrition taille moyenne des particules 0.5 μm (nécessite un temps de rétention d'une heure pour que la réaction se fasse à 80%. D'autre part en présence d'un catalyseur d'argent, une réaction á 80% pour un concentré fragmenté profoundement par attrition commun peut être achevée en 7 minutes.

ZUSAMMENFASSUNG

Die Kinetik der bei der Auslaugung von Kupferkies mit Eisen (III)-Sulfat langsam verlaufenden Reaktionen kann als Funktion der Geschwindigkeitskontrolle des Elektronenübergangs durch das Reaktionsprodukt des elementaren Schwefels gedeut werden.

$$CuFeS_2 + 4Fe^{3+} \longrightarrow Cu^{2+} + 5Fe^{2+} + 2S^{o}$$

Der Zusatz eines leicht löslichen Silbersalzes jedoch verleiht
der Lauge eine nachweisbare Freundlichkeit hinsichtlich der
Reaktionsgeschwindigkeits-steigerung. Anfags wirkt sich der
Einfluss des Katalysators in der Bildung von Silbersulfid
(Argentit) an der Oberfläche des Kupferkieses infolge der
katalytischen Umsetzung:

$$CuFeS_2 + 4Ag^{+} \longrightarrow 2Ag_2S + Cu^{2+} + Fe^{2+} \quad \text{aus.}$$

Die katalytische Umsetzung verläuft schnell, und die Kinetik der Anfangsreaktion wird mittels Übertragung durch die
Grenzschicht kontrolliert, worauf folgende Erscheinungen hin-
weisen: Reaktionsordung (Reaktion erster Ordnung in bezug auf
Silber), Grösse der Reaktionsgeschwindigkeitskonstanten) äqui-
valent zu den Massenübertragungskoeffizienten, die für Mono-
grössenteilchen in mit Rührern versehenen Behälterreaktoren
vorgegeben sind) und die Temperaturabhängigkeit (Aktivierungs-
energie - 4.2 kcal/Mol).

Die gleiche Reaktionsstöchiometrie ist beim Auslaugen von
Kupferkies mit Eisen(III)-Sulfat sowohl in Gegenwart als auch
in Abwesenheit eines Silberkatalysators zu beobachten. Die
Reaktionskinetik des Auslaugens von Kupferkeis mit Eisen(III)-
Sulfat ist jedoch recht kompliziert infolge der Bildung kom-
plexer Reaktionsprodukte: Silbersulfid, Silber-Chlorid (im
Fall wenn Chloridverunreinigungen nicht entfernt worden sind)
und elementaren Schwefels, wie auch wegen ihrer Empfindlichkeit
gegen die zur Auslösung der Reaktion angewandten Verfahren.
Die Geschwindigkeit des Auslaugens ist im wesentlichen von der
Grösse der Mineralteilchen unabhängig, weist aber eine markante
Abhängigkeit von Ag^{+}, Fe^{3+} und Fe^{2+}-Konzentrationen auf. Eine
präliminäre Bewertung der Versuchsergebnisse führt zu der
Vermutung, diese Geschwindigkeit lasse sich durch die elektrochemische Reaktion von Fe^{3+} an der Oberfläche von Ag_2S-Kristal-
liten einschränken, welche im Film, der sich während der katalytischen Umsetzung bildet, auftreten.

$$Ag_2S + 2Fe^{3+} \longrightarrow 2Ag^+ + S^O + 2Fe^{2+}$$

Elementarer Schwefel ersetzt die Ag_2S-Kristallite und bildet eine poröse, keineswegs schützende, Schicht, während das hierbei gebildete Ag^+ die Rolle des Übertraugungsmittels übernimmt, indem es kontinuierlich Silbersulfidkristallite innerhalb der katalytischen Umsetzung ersetzt.

Nichtkatalysietes Auslaugen von gemahlenem Chalkopyrit (Kupferkies) (mittlere Korngrösse 0,5 μm) mit Eisen(III)-Sulfat benötigt bei 80%-tiger Ausbeute eine Rückhalte-zeit von 1 Stunde. In Gegenwart eines Silberkatalysators dagegen kann eine 80%-tige Reaktion eines grob gemahlenen Konzentrats in nur 7 Minuten durchgeführt werden.

РЕЗЮМЕ

Замедленную кинетику реакции при выщелачивании халькопирита кислым сульфатом железа можно рассматривать как следствие регулировки скорости за счет переноса электронов в продукте реакции в виде элементарной серы

$$CuFeS_2 + 4Fe^{3+} \longrightarrow Cu^{2+} + 5Fe^{2+} + 2S^o$$

В то же время добавление растворимой соли серебра к исходному раствору вызывает значительное увеличение скорости реакции. Первоначально это каталитическое воздействие влечёт за собой образование прежде всего сульфида серебра (аргантита) на поверхности халькопирита в результате реакции обмена:

$$CuFeS_2 + 4Ag \longrightarrow 2Ag_2S + Cu^{2+} + Fe^{2+}$$

Реакция обмена происходит быстро и кинетика первоначальной реакции регулируется путём переноса через граничный слой проникновения массы, о чём свидетельствуют ряд реакций (первого порядка по отношению к серебру), величина константы скорости реакции (равнозначна коэффициенту проникновения массы для частиц с одинаковыми размерами в реакторах, снабжённых мешалками), а также температурная зависимость (энергия активации, составляющая 4,2 ккал/моль). Стехеометрия реакции для выщелачивания халькопирита сульфатом железа одинакова как в присутствии, так и при отсутствии серебряного катализатора. Тем не менее кинетика реакции при катализированном серебром выщелачивании халькопирита сульфатом железа усложняется вследствии образования смешанных продуктов реакции: сульфида серебра, хлорида серебра (если хлористые примесия не были устранены), а также элементарной серы. Кроме того, кинетика реакции зависит от метода, применяемого для инициирования реакции. Скорость выщелачивания, в основном, не зависит от размеров частиц, а в значительной степени зависит от концентраций

$$Ag^+, Fe^{3+}, Fe^{2+}$$

Предварительная оценка экспериментальных результатов позволяет предполагать, что скорость может быть ограничена путём электрохимической реакци Fe^{3+} на поверхности кристаллических частиц Ag_2S находящихся в слое, образующимся во время реакции обмена

$$Ag_2S + 2Fe^{3+} \longrightarrow 2Ag^+ + S^0 + 2Fe^{2+}$$

Элементарная сера замещает кристаллический Ag_2S создавая пористый слой, а Ag^+ действует как проникающее вещество, непрерывно регенерирующее кристаллический сульфид серебра посредством реакции обмена.

Некатализированное выщелачивание сульфатом железа халькопирита, измельченного путём истирания (средний размер частиц 0,5 мкм), с выходом реакции 80% требует времени порядка I часа. В присутствии серебрянного катализатора выход реакции 80% для более крупного концентрата, измельченного истиранием, может быть достигнут в течение 7 минут.

RECENT ADVANCES IN HYDROMETALLURGY

F. Habashi

Department of Mining and Metallurgy, Laval University, Quebec City, Canada

INTRODUCTION

In the past five years, hydrometallurgy has been making significant advances. In the present review, less emphasis is given to pressure hydrometallurgy since this topic is a subject of a paper to be presented at the International Conference on Chemical Metallurgy to be held in Bombay, India in January 1979.[*]

Monographs on general hydrometallurgy [1-3] as well as on special topics [4-6] have been published. Numerous symposia and conferences on certain areas of hydrometallurgy were held [7-21]. Conferences on extractive metallurgy include many papers of interest to hydrometallurgists. Annual reviews on hydrometallurgy now appear regularly in Journal of Metals (March issue), International Metals Reviews, London (September issue) and other journals. Conferences on solvent extraction are also held

---

[*] Work on this manuscript terminated in August 1978.

regularly and the proceedings are published [22-27]. Numerous
review articles on hydrometallurgy are also available [28-42].
In the present review some hydrometallurgical processes that
has been recently commissioned either on a pilot or a commercial scale, will be discussed together with some research activities in this field.

ALUMINA FROM NON-BAUXITE SOURCES

In recent years, the world production of aluminium has been
nearly twice that of copper. North America produces about 50%
of the world's aluminium, yet must import more than 90% of the
raw material needed, although there is abundant domestic resources of aluminium-bearing minerals such as clay, shale, anorth-
ite, alunite, and dawsonite. That is why there is extensive research underway to recover alumina from these non-bauxitic
sources [43-45].

The Soviet Union has the only viable peacetime aluminium
industry based partly on non-bauxite raw materials. The non-
bauxite ores of aluminium in the USSR are a nepheline syenite
that contains apatite in the Kola peninsula, a related igneous
rock in Central Siberia, and alunite in the Zaglik district in
Azerbaijan. The Kola nepheline operation, active for more than
a decade, was possible because of the large production of apatite for fertilizer, and the production of Portlant cement as
a co-product.

None of the numerous processes that have been proposed has
yet proved economically competitive with the Bayer Process
using imported bauxite. Extensive testing by the US Bureau of

Mines is under way to solve this problem. The French company Pêchiney [46], on the other hand, came up with a new interesting concept for the recovery of Al_2O_3 from clay. In this process 65% H_2SO_4 is used at $140^\circ C$ to attack the clay directly without prior dehydroxylation, which is an added advantage as compared to all other previously suggested processes. After solid-liquid separation, aluminum sulfate is then crystallized. Instead of purifying the sulfate and its subsequent decomposition to oxide which is an energy-consuming process because of the high temperature involved, the sulfate is converted to chloride by HCl. Hydrated aluminum chloride is easier to decompose to oxide than the sulfate.

COPPER

Oxide Ores

Anamax Mining Company is a joint venture owned equally by the Anaconda Company and Amax Incorporation. Its new operation [47] which produced its first copper later in 1975 at Twin Buttes, Arizona represents a milestone in hydrometallurgy for the following reasons:

(1) The size of operation at 10,000 ton/day is enormous, and the recoverable copper content is only 0.9%.

(2) Sulfuric acid is used as a leaching agent although the acid consumption is excessive (about 12 kg/ton ore) due to the presence of limestone and other acid-consuming gangue minerals. Acid for leaching is brought in tank cars from San Manuel, a distance of about 75 km. This decision was based mainly on two grounds:

(a) Sulfuric acid leaching and metal recovery technology from the leach solution is well established.

(b) The sulfur dioxide produced at San Manuel smelter was originally emitted to the atmosphere, thus converting it to sulfuric acid, would abate pollution in that region.

(3) The operation includes a large solvent extraction plant for copper which strengthens the position of this technology for base metal recovery.

Sulfide Concentrates

The treatment of copper sulfide concentrates, in particular those of chalcopyrite, is at present dominating hydrometallurgy [48-52]. Numerous reviews describing the different processes, have been published. The present discussion will outline only those processes that were investigated on a large pilot scale, or recently applied industrially.

1. The Treadwell Process

This process was one of the first processes aimed at solving the pollution problem of the copper industry [48]. It was developed to a large pilot scale plant by the Treadwell Corporation in New York under contract with the Anaconda Company in Tucson, Arizona in the early 1970's. In this process, chalcopyrite concentrate is treated with concentrated H_2SO_4 at about $200^\circ C$:

$$CuFeS_2 + H_2SO_4 \rightarrow CuSO_4 + FeSO_4 + SO_2 + S + H_2O$$

Sulfur dioxide is separated from the water vapour and converted to H_2SO_4 for recycle: The residue containing the anhydrous sulfates, elemental sulfur and the gangue minerals, is leached with water to solubilize the sulfates, precipitate CuCN by HCN, crystallize $FeSO_4 \cdot rH_2O$ which is then decomposed to recover the SO_3 for recycle as H_2SO_4. The process had the advantage of forming elemental sulfur, but had the disadvantage of solubilizing iron and the necessity of regenerating H_2SO_4 by decomposing the ferrous sulfate. There has nothing been published on this process except in the patent literature. The plant was shut down and dismantled after a turmoil that followed the change in the management of the Company.

2. The Arbiter Process

This process named after its inventor, also in the Anaconda Company, displaced the Treadwell Process in 1974 [48]. In essence it is a variation of the Sherritt-Gordon ammonia leaching process. It has the disadvantage of forming ammonium sulfate, which had to be decomposed by CaO to recover the NH_3 for recycle because there was no local market for this type of fertilizer. After testing on a pilot scale, it was operated for a short time on an industrial scale in Anaconda, Montana. However, it proved to be a costly operation, and the plant was shut down for good.

3. The Duval Process

This process is based on the leaching of chalcopyrite concentrate by a ferric salt solution [48]. It has the advantage of forming elemental sulfur but the disadvantage of solubilizing iron as well as the necessity of regenerating the leaching agent. It is believed that this process is conducted on commercial scale in Tucson, Arizona.

4. The Hecla Process

This process operated on a commercial scale at Casa Grande, Arizona in the past few years, and was shut down recently because of general depression in the industry [48]. Chalcopyrite concentrate is oxidized under controlled conditions to form $CuSO_4$ and Fe_2O_3:

$$2CuFeS_2 + \frac{15}{2}O_2 \longrightarrow 2CuSO_4 + Fe_2O_3 + 2SO_2$$

Copper sulfate is then leached with water and electrolyzed, while SO_2 formed is converted to H_2SO_4 to be used locally for leaching an oxide ore. This process appears to be the first industrial application of sulfation roasting of copper concentrates.

5. The Cyprus Process

This process is being tested in a pilot plant by Cyprus Metallurgical Processes Corporation, Tucson, Arizona [53]. Chalcopyrite concentrate is leached by hot ferric chloride-cupric chloride solution:

$$CuFeS_2 + 4FeCl_3 \longrightarrow CuCl_2 + 5FeCl_2 + 2S$$

$$CuFeS_2 + 3CuCl_2 \longrightarrow 4CuCl + FeCl_2 + 2S$$

The leach solution which is high in cuprous chloride is cooled to crystallize CuCl. The crystal are then washed, dried, and reduced to metallic copper. The mother liquor containing $FeCl_2$ and the remaining CuCl is oxidized by oxygen to form $FeCl_3$ and $CuCl_2$. Part of $FeCl_3$ hydrolyzes to $Fe(OH)_3$ and HCl; this is separated and the acid solution containing $FeCl_3$ and $CuCl_2$ is recycled in the leaching step.

6. Sherritt-Cominco Process

This process was developed in Canada by Sherritt-Gordon Mines in Fort Saskatchewan, Alberta, and Cominco in Trail, British-Columbia [54]. It is based on a thermal pretreatment step of chalcopyrite (referred to as activation step) before leaching. In this pretreatment step, the concentrate is heated in a specially designed furnace, such that in the upper part of the furnace (an oxidizing atmosphere) the following reaction takes place:

$$5CuFeS_2 + 2O_2 \longrightarrow Cu_5FeS_4 + 4FeS + 2SO_2$$

while in the lower part (a reducing atmosphere) the following:

$$5CuFeS_2 + 2H_2 \longrightarrow Cu_5FeS_4 + 4FeS + 2H_2S$$

The two gas streams are collected separately and conducted over a catalyst to react forming elemental sulfur. The residue is then subjected to three acid leaching steps. In the first, the bulk of the iron is removed as follows:

$$FeS + H_2SO_4 \longrightarrow FeSO_4 + H_2S$$

In the second, referred to as activation leach, the iron in the bornite is removed by leaching with copper sulfate solution from the next step:

$$Cu_5FeS_4 + CuSO_4 \longrightarrow 2Cu_2S + 2CuS + FeSO_4$$

In the third, referred to as oxidation leach, copper sulfides are solubilized by leaching with H_2SO_4 in presence of oxygen to form copper sulfate, from which copper is recovered by electrowining. Ferrous sulfate solutions have to be subjected to crystallization, and the crystals obtained decomposed for the recovery of Fe_2O_3 and SO_2.

The process involves numerous steps, but this is claimed to be necessary for treating Canadian concentrates which are difficult to leach by the Sherritt-Gordon pressure leaching process.

7. The Lurgi-Mitterberg Process

This process is practically the same as the Sherrit-Gordon Process developed in the 1960's for the direct pressure leaching of chalcopyrite concentrate according to the equation [48]:

$$CuFeS_2 + H_2SO_4 + \frac{5}{4} O_2 \longrightarrow CuSO_4 + FeOOH + \frac{1}{2} H_2O + 2S$$

It was operated on a pilot scale for about two years and proved to be successful. However, the plant was shut down and dismantled because the Mitterberg mine in Austria has been exhausted.

GOLD AND SILVER

New advances in the hydrometallurgy of gold and silver
have been in the leaching as well as in the recovery steps.
The Cortez Gold Mines in Nevada [55] has been leaching successfully low-grade limestone gold ore using heap leaching,
a technology that is already well established in the copper
industry. About 0.7 millions tons of ore containing less than
one ppm gold is treated in this way. The leaching agent is
0.03% NaCN solution at pH 10.5 is sprinkled at the top of the
heaps, and the pregnant solution is collected at the bottom
in rubber-lined canals. It takes about three months to ter-
minate a leaching cycle.

The recovery system is also a novelty. Gold is adsorbed
from solution by pellets of activated carbon packed in columns
2.1 m in diameter and 2.4 m high. The gold-loaded charcoal
is then eluted by a hot (115°C) 1% NaOH solution at 410kPa
pressure. Gold is recovered from the eluate by electrowinning
using a perforated carbon anode, and steel wool packed in
a perforated polypropylene basket which acts as cathode on
which the gold deposits. The depleted carbon is then washed
with water, dewatered, then, activated by heating at 730°C
in absence of air in an oil-fired furnace. The activated
carbon is then quenched and recycled for the adsorption
circuit.

ILMENITE PROCESSING

The problem of beneficiating ilmenite (45-55% TiO_2) into synthetic rutile (~96% TiO_2) has been actively investigated in the past few years. A review of these processes is given in Table 1 [56-58]. Robinson et al. [59] developed the Laporte Process which is claimed to be more efficient than the other processes [59]. The process comprises the following steps:

(1) Oxidation of ilmenite at high temperature (>900°C);

(2) Partial reduction of the iron to the ferrous state;

(3) Leaching at atmospheric pressure with 18% HCl for $3\frac{1}{2}$ h;

(4) Washing and calcination.

The novelty of the process lies in the first step. Heating below 850°C even for few hours produces no major structural changes, but heating at 950°C for less than an hour results in complete transformation to pseudobrookite and rutile:

$$2FeTiO_3 + \tfrac{1}{2}O_2 \longrightarrow Fe_2TiO_5 + TiO_2$$

The reaction is reversed in the second step through partial reduction. These structural changes result in maximum porosity and surface area, thus the third step can be conducted rapidly under mild leaching conditions without losses of titanium in solution or having a Ti-Fe phase in the residue. Ferrous chloride solution obtained by this treatment is oxyhydrolyzed by conventional methods to Fe_2O_3 and HCl.

TABLE 1

Summary of Hydrometallurgical Processes
for Producing Synthetic Rutile from Ilmenite

Thermal Treatment before Leaching	Process	Leaching Agent	Remarks
Reduction of ferric to ferrous	Benilite Wah Chang Dhrangadhra Chemicals	HCl HCl HCl	Minor structural change during reduction. Severe leaching conditions. Loss of titanium in solution
Reduction to ferrous and partial reduction to metallic iron	Ishihara	H_2SO_4	Minor structural change during reduction. Severe leaching conditions
Complete reduction to metallic iron	Consolidated Tin	HCl	Some of the titanium is reduced. Poor manganese and magnesium removal
Oxidation followed by reduction to metallic iron	Murso BTP/Woodall Duckham Laporte	HCl HCl HCl	Improved solubility of ferrous iron
Oxidation followed by reduction to metallic iron	Western Titanium Summit	Air + NH_4Cl soln. NH_4 $FeCl_3$	Some of the titanium is reduced. Poor manganese and magnesium removal

MANGANESE NODULES

Extensive research is being conducted to find a method for
the recovery of metal values from the manganese nodules found
at the bottom of the ocean [60-63]. On the average, the air-
dried nodules contain about 30% Mn, 15% Fe, 1% Ni, 1% Cu,
0.2% Co, 10% combined water and about 30% gangue minerals.

The manganese is mainly in the form of MnO_2, the iron is hydroxide while Ni, Cu and Co do not form minerals [64-69]. The fact that the nodules when collected, contain appreciable amounts of water, suggests that their treatment by pyrometallurgical methods would not be practical because of the cost of drying. The high porosity (~200 m^2/g) suggests that hydrometallurgical methods could be more suitable. These methods fall into two categories: complete dissolution and selective leaching.

Complete Dissolution

In these methods, the interest is to recover manganese as well as the other nonferrous metals, Cu, Ni, and Co. The leaching process is usually fast and complete extraction can be obtained, but the drawback is that the production of nonferrous metals will be dependent on the manganese market. The following methods have been suggested.

(1) Sulfurous Acid: Manganese dioxide dissolves readily in aqueous solutions of SO_2 (70-71):

$$MnO_2 + SO_{2(aq)} \longrightarrow MnSO_{4(aq)}$$

At the same time, nickel and cobalt are also dissolved. Copper, on the other hand is not; a second acid leaching is necessary for extracting copper.

(2) Hydrochloric Acid: While CuO, NiO, CoO, and iron oxide dissolve readily in hydrochloric acid, forming a metal chloride and water, MnO_2 dissolves liberating chlorine [62-62]:

$$MnO_2 + 4HCl \longrightarrow MnCl_2 + Cl_2 + 2H_2O$$

The large proportion of acid used per mole MnO_2, necessitates its regeneration from the chlorine as well as from the aqueous solutions. Although this technology may be well established, yet it becomes costly because of the large number of circuits involved.

(3) Oxalic Acid: Although this method has been developed for analytical purposes, yet it is of metallurgical interest [72]. Manganese nodules are completely soluble at room temperature in a dilute solution of oxalic acid with the evolution of CO_2.

Selective Leaching

In these methods, the interest is only to leach copper, nickel, and cobalt leaving behind manganese and iron. The nodules are treated in practically the same way as copper oxide ores or nickel laterites. The following methods have been studied.

(1) Sulfuric Acid: Dilute H_2SO_4 at atmospheric temperature and pressure is capable of extracting most of the copper and nickel, a major part of cobalt, and minor amounts of iron and manganese [73-74]. However, the process is slow and few days are needed with intensive agitation. To accelerate the leaching process, it was suggested to operate at high temperature and pressure, and use more concentrated acid, in the same way laterites are treated at Moa Bay, in Cuba.

(2) Ammonia: This process resembles the Nicaro Process used in Cuba for leaching laterites, i.e., the ore is first heated under reducing atmosphere followed by ammoniacal leaching [62-63].

914

MERCURY

A conference on the various aspects of mercury science and technology was held in 1974 in Spain, the largest mercury producer in the world. Some new hydrometallurgical processes were presented, e.g., the leaching of cinnabar by hydrochlorid acid [75], aqueous chlorine solutions, and other reagents [76].

NICKEL

The Freeport Sulphur's nickel refinery at Port Nickel near New Orleans, Louisiana which has been idle since 1960 as a result of political conflict with Cuba, started operation in 1974. It is presently owned by Amax Incorporation which imports nickel-copper matte from Africa for this purpose. The process makes use of normal pressure and high pressure leaching circuits [77]. Acid leaching at normal pressure removes the bulk of nickel and cobalt, while in the high pressure, copper sulfide is dissolved together with the remaining nickel and cobalt. Copper is recovered by electrowinning, while nickel and cobalt are separated by a series of precipitations and crystallizations, and finally the metals are recovered by precipitation with hydrogen under pressure.

TIN

A hydrometallurgical process for the recovery of tin from low-grade concentrates is under development at the Warren Spring Laboratory in England [78-79]. Flotation concentrates containing 10-15% Sn are less suitable for direct smelting than are high-grade concentrates. As a result, a hydrometallurgical

915

route is being sought. Cassiterite is readily reduced to stannous oxide or tin metal, both of which are soluble in acids; but stannous oxide is unstable and disproportionates to Sn and SnO_2 below $1100^{\circ}C$. A further difficulty with the leaching of siliceous materials with acids is the production of voluminous residues of hydrated silica which are difficult to filter. It has been found that both these difficulties can be overcome by melting the concentrate under reducing conditions, then quenching. The glassy material formed contain tin in the divalent state as a discrete microphase can then be crushed and leached with H_2SO_4 to extract the metal values leaving the siliceous residue behind. Pure tin is then recovered from solution by electrowinning.

URANIUM

There is intense activity in uranium ore processing to increase the potential sources of energy [80]. The following new operations are worth mentioning.

Solution Mining

This process [81] which has been adapted from the copper industry, consists of pumping the leaching agent into the ground to dissolve uranium deposits in sandstone beds and bringing the uranium-rich solution up to the surface. As a leaching agent, ammonium carbonate is used together with sodium peroxide as oxidizing agent. The ammonium uranyl carbonate solution is then passed through an anion exchange resin that selectively adsorbs uranyl carbonate ions. After a washing step, these are stripped from the resin, then adding more

916

ammonia precipitates ammonium diuranate. The similarity of this process with oil drilling has prompted a number of oil companies to participate in this venture. Arco, for example, is planning to recover 113,400 kg U_3O_8 annually by this method in Texas.

Uranium from Copper Ore Tailings

The awarness of the need to recover all the metal values from an ore deposit has resulted in developing a process for extracting traces of uranium present in copper ores [82]. After leaching these ores with dilute H_2SO_4 and precipitating copper by scrap iron, the solutions were found to contain about 10 ppm U. Although this is a low concentration, recovery was found to be justifiable because of the large volume of the solutions treated. A plant is presently under construction in Bingham Canyon in Utah designed to produce 64,000 kg/year U_3O_8 using a combination of ion exchange and solvent extraction.

Uranium from Phosphate Rock

Phosphate rock contains on the average 150 ppm uranium. When considering the world production of phosphates of 110×10^6 tons, the amount of uranium associated with this material would be 16,500 tons. The great part of the phosphate rock is used for making fertilizers, which will also contain all the uranium originally present in the rock. The fate of uranium in the fertilizer is not known. If it is absorbed by the plant, there is the danger of entering the food chain, and if not, it will accumulate in the field, and may become an environmental hazard over the years. At present, some companies in USA and Canada have installed plants for recovering the uranium from technical phosphoric acid as a by-product of the fertilizer industry [83]. The original process involved reduction of uranyl ion in phosphoric acid to uranous ion using scrap iron, then extraction by the organic solvent octyl pyrophosphoric acid (OPPA). Because of the instability of this solvent, other stable extractants were developed [84]:

(1) Di(2-ethylhexyl)phosphoric acid + trioctylphosphine oxide.

(2) Octylphenyl phosphoric acid + tributyl phosphate.

These new solvents are characterized by being a mixture of organic compounds which exhibits a synergic effect, and can extract uranium in the hexavalent state, thus eliminating the reduction step, but they are more expensive and have lower extraction coefficient than OPPA.

A different approach was persued by the Israel Mining Industries. In this process, phosphate rock is digested with hydrochloric acid in presence of iron powder to maintain reducing conditions, so that the oxidation of uranium is prevented. In this way, it is found that the major part of uranium remains in the residue which is composed mainly of calcium fluoride and amounts to about 10% of the rock acidulated. In the absence of iron, however, uranium will be found in the leach solution.

Another approach was developed by the same company, based on the selective leaching of uranium from calcinated phosphate rock by acetic acid. The acetate solution containing uranium is enriched on ion exchange columns.

Another process of interest recovers uranium during the purification of technical phosphoric acid. When phosphate rock is leached with hydrochloric acid, the phosphoric acid formed can be extracted with butanol or pentanol leaving behind in the aqueous phase the impurities including uranium which can be recovered by known methods. The organic phase is washed with water to recover pure H_3PO_4.

Tube Autoclaves

Lurgi Company in Germany has recently announced the use of tube autoclaves for the leaching of uranium ores [85]. These autoclaves were up to the present used only for the leaching of bauxite by the Vereinigte Aluminium Werke, in Germany. The advantage of this technique is the high reaction rates due to the elevated temperature used.

ZINC

In the past few years, the production of zinc by the hydrometallurgical method has surpassed the pyrometallurgical methods. However, three problems have always been a matter of concern for the hydrometallurgical method. These are:

1. Ferrite Formation

During the roasting step, the formation of ferrite according to the reaction

$$ZnO + Fe_2O_3 \longrightarrow ZnFe_2O_4$$

has been a problem because the ferrite is insoluble in the spent electrolyte (dilute H_2SO_4) used to leach the ZnO. Although ferrite formation may be decreased in many cases by operating at low temperature, yet most plants operate at high temperature to achieve high production rate. As a result, large piles of residues containing about 10% of the zinc originally present in the concentrate, have accumulated over the years. Recovering zinc from these residues can be achieved by leaching with hot H_2SO_4; but under such conditions, a substantial part of the iron also dissolves. As can be seen from the above equation, for each ton of zinc dissolved, nearly two tons of iron will go into solution.

2. Sulfuric Acid Problem

During the roasting step, SO_2 is emitted and must be converted to H_2SO_4 for which a nearby market must be available.

3. Mercury Problem

Most zinc sulfide concentrates contain 100-300 ppm Hg which during the roasting step is volatilized as metallic mercury with the SO_2 gases, and contaminate the acid from which it is made, thus introducing the possibility of entering the food cycle.

Solutions to all three problems have been found, but at the same time new problems, in some cases, have been introduced. Thus, for the ferrite-containing residues, hot acid leaching processes have been developed followed by precipitation of iron in a crystalline form easy to filter and wash, e.g., the jarosite, the goethite, and the hematite processes [86]. The sulfuric acid problem has been solved by attaching a phosphate fertilizer plant to the zinc plant, while for the mercury problem, methods · for its separation from the SO_2 gases and its recovery have been developed and applied by many companies.

But, consider the jarosite process that has gained wide-spread use: the ferrite-containing residue is leached with hot H_2SO_4, and after solid-liquid separation, ammonium hydroxide or

920

sodium carbonate are added under prescribed conditions of concentration, temperature, etc., to precipitate ammonium or sodium
jarosite which have the general formula $M[Fe_3 (SO_4)_2 (OH)_6]$ where
M is NH_4 or Na. Beside, the added cost of the reagent used for
this process, and the additional plant equipment, the zinc industry became faced with a disposal problem because the jarosite
cannot be used in the blast furnace. The disposal problem is the
result of the characteristics of jarosite itself:

(1) It is a bulky precipitate, three to four times the weight
of the original residue,

(2) It has poor piling properties; it takes about three times
the space used for the original residue of the same weight.

Consequently, researchers started to solve this new problem
by converting the jarosite to a material suitable for using in
the blast furnace, e.g., by roasting to expell SO_2, or hydro-
thermal conversion at 220-250°C, etc., none of these, however,
has been used yet. It should be recalled at this point that all
the three problems mentioned above, are due to the roasting step.
A completely different approach that avoids this thermal step
would, therefore, be welcome to the zinc industry. This new
approach has been proposed many years ago, by Bjorling in Sweden,
and Forward and Veltman in Canada. The key solution is direct
pressure leaching of the concentrates according to the equation:

$$ZnS + \tfrac{1}{2}O_2 + H_2SO_4 \longrightarrow ZnSO_4 + S + H_2O$$

According to this equation, (1) No ferrite are formed, (2) No SO_2
and consequently no dependence on fertilizer-making, and (3) Mercury in the concentrate remains in the reactor and can be isolated without polluting the environment. Sherrit-Gordon and

921

and Cominco in Canada have operated a pilot plant successfully to test this process, and it is expected that a commercial operation by Cominco will follow soon [87].*

DESULFURIZATION OF COAL

Sulfur in coal is a problem of special importance because it is a source of pollution when the coal is burned, and a source of contaminating metal during their production. As a result, much research is underway to remove sulfur before utilizing the coal [88]. Coal contains about 4% sulfur. It is present in two forms: inorganic sulfur which comprises about 80% of the total sulfur (mainly pyrite, a small amount of pyrrhotite and calcium sulfate), and organic sulfur compounds which account for the rest.

Unlike manganese nodules, the prospect for coal desulfurization seems to be in gasification and not in the hydrometallurgical approach. The reasons for that are the following:

(1) The necessity of dewatering the treated coal before marketing which may be a costly operation.

(2) Aqueous desulfurization processes result in a certain loss of the calorific value of coal as a result of the oxidation of the carbonaceous matter.

(3) Most aqueous desulfurization processes are not capable of eliminating the organic sulfur.

Some of the hydrometallurgical processes suggested are summarized in Table 2. All of these are conducted in pressure reactors.

---

* Plans for building a commercial unit were announced in May 1979.

922

TABLE 2

Hydrometallurgical Desulfurization of Coal

Process	Reagent	Temp. °C	Pressure kPa	Remarks
Meyers Process	$Fe_2(SO_4)_3$	130	700	Oxygen is used to regenerate the leaching agent. Excess $FeSO_4$ is crystallized or precipitated
Pittsburgh Energy Research Center	Water + Air	150-200	5500	A dilute acid solution of $FeSO_4$ is formed
Kennecott Ledgemont Laboratory	NH_4OH + O_2	130	2000	Carbonate is formed as a result of oxidation of carbon
Iowa State University	2% Na_2CO_3 + O_2	150	800	Na_2CO_3 is added to neutralize the acid formed; converted to Na_2SO_4
Battelle, Columbus	NaOH	250-350	4000-17,000	Na_2S is formed which is converted to Na_2CO_3 by CO_2, then to NaOH by CaO, H_2S generated is converted to S

RECOVERY OF MINERALS FROM SURFACE WATERS

The recovery of minerals from surface waters is not only of interest to the hydrometallurgist but also to the mineral dressing engineer as will be shown below. A review of the Dead Sea operations was recently published [89]. A typical composition of Dead sea brine is in g/l: 41 Mg^{2+}, 17 Ca^{2+}, 40 Na^+, 7.5 K^+, 215 Cl^-, 5 Br^-, and 0.65 SO_4^{2-}; Sp.gr. 1.220. A flowsheet for processing the sea water is shown in Fig. 1. The water of the Sea is pumped into large evaporation basins which cover an area of about 130 Km^2. When the total salt concentration reaches about 350 g/l, NaCl begins to crystallize and continues to do so during further evaporation until the volume of the water has diminished to about half of its original value. At this stage about 90% of the NaCl and more than 95% of the $CaSO_4$ are crystallized. The brine (mother liquor) is then transferred to other basins where evaporation is continued, and carnallite $(KCl \cdot MgCl_2 \cdot 6H_2O)$ together with some NaCl begins to separate. A carnallite slurry conther with some NaCl begins to separate. A carnallite slurry containing 10-20% solids (crystals), is then pumped to thickeners and then vacuum filters. This filter cake froms the basis for recovering pure $MgCl_2$ and pure KCl.

At first, $MgCl_2$ is removed by water leaving behind a solid phase of sylvinite (KCl + NaCl). Two methods are used for separating NaCl from KCl. In one method, the mixture is slurried and long chain fatty amines are added to float KCl. Here, the mineral processing engineer plays an important role. In the other method, the salt mixture is leached by a hot saturated solution of NaCl. After thickening, and centrifugeing, the hot brine, now saturated with respect to both salts, is allowed to cool; only KCl crystallizes out because its solubility in water rises steeply with temperature whereas that of NaCl is almost constant.

When the $MgCl_2$ brine is evaporated, bischofite $(MgCl_2 \cdot 6H_2O)$ is formed. On heating the hexa-hydrate, the solid dissolves in its own water of crystallization. This brine is then thermally hydrolyzed in a spray reactor at $800^\circ C$ to form MgO and HCl.

924

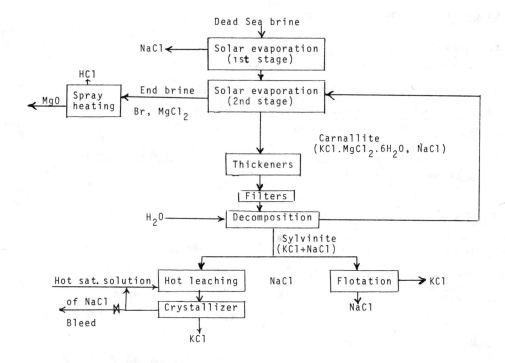

Fig. 1. Simplified flowsheet for the processing
       of Dead Sea brine.

Other chlorides which include NaCl, KCl, and $CaCl_2$ are not de-composed. They are removed from the MgO by washing, which in turn is converted to $Mg(OH)_2$. It is then dried, calcined back to MgO, then sintered.

REFERENCES

Monographs, General

1. Łętowski F. Principles of Hydrometallurgy
   PWNT, Warsaw 1975. Polish text.

2. Zelikman A. N., Vol'dman G. M. and Belyaevskaya L. V.
   Theory of Hydrometallurgical Processes, Metallurgia,
   Moscow, 1975. Russian text.

3. Dobrokhotov G. N. Metallurgical Processes and Apparatus
   Leningrad Mining Institute, Leningrad, 1976. Russian text.

Monographs, Special Topics

4. Nabochenko S. S. and Smirnov V. I. Hydrometallurgy of
   Copper, Metallurgia, Moscow, 1974. Russian text.

5. Yazawa A. and Eguchi M. Hydrometallurgy and Waste Water
   Treatment, Kyoritsu Shuppan Press, Tokyo, 1975. Japanese text.

6. Woodcock J. T., Henley K. J. and Cathro K. J. Metallurgy of
   Gold and Silver with Special Reference to Other Precious
   Metals. Australian Mineral Foundation, Adelaide 1976.

Conferences and Symposia, General

7. Journees d'etudes, Anonymous, Caen, France, Mai 1976. Supplement to Industrie Minerale - Mineralurgique 1977.

8. Arshinski V. M., Klets V. E., Nadol'ski A. P., Skobeev I. K.
   and Mikhnev A. D. (eds.), Physicochemical Studies in the
   Hydrometallurgy of Nonferrous Metals, Polytech-
   nic Institute, Irkutsk, USSR 1975. Russian text.

926

9. Burkin A. (ed). Leaching and Reduction in Hydrometallurgy, Inst. Min. Met., London, 1975.

10. Cadek J. and Paces T. (eds). Proceedings International Symposium on Water-Rock Interaction, 1974, Ustred. Ustav. Geol., Prague, 1976.

11. Davies G. A. and Scuffham J. B. (eds). Symposium on Hydrometallurgy, Inst. Chem. Engineers, London, 1975.

12. Evans D. J. I. and Shoemaker R. S. (eds). International Symposium on Hydrometallurgy, AIME, New York, 1973.

13. Kuhn M. C. et al., Chemistry of Metal Recovery from Natural Sources, Symposium held by the Division of Ind. and Eng. Chem. at the 175 Amer. Chem. Soc. Annual Meeting, Anaheim, Calif., March, 1978.

14. Laskorin B. (ed.) Hydrometallurgy: Autoclave Leaching, Sorption, Extraction, Proc. First All-Union Conf. on Hydrometallurgy, Moscow, 1974, Nauka, Moscow, 1976. Russian text.

15. Pavlova M. I. ed. Hydrometallurgy of Nonferrous and Rare Metals, Transl. from Russian by Freund Publ. House, Tel Aviv, Israel, 1978. Russian original publ. by the Uzbek Academy of Sciences, 1971.

Conferences and Symposia, Special Topics

16. Anonymous, Proceedings of the Third Bauxite Symposium, Kingston, Jamaica, May, 1975.

17. Anonymous, Symposium on Advances in Geology, Geochemistry and Treatment of Bauxite, Dubrovnik, Octobre 1975, publ. Yougoslave Acad. Sci. Arts, Zagreb, 1976.

18. Aplan F. F. et al., eds. , Solutions Mining, Proc. Symp. Dallas, Texas, AIME, New York, 1974.

19. Murr L. E., Torma A. E. and Brierly J. A. (eds). Metallurgical Applications of Bacterial Leaching and Related Microbiological Phenomena, Academic, 1978.

20. Schwartz W. (ed.), Conference on Bacterial Leaching, Verlag Chemie, Weiheim, 1977.

21. Winand R., International Symposium on Chloride Hydrometallurgy, Benelux, Metallurgie, Brussels, September, 1977.

Conferences and Symposia, Solvent Extraction

22. Symposium on Solvent Ion Exchange, Arizona Section, Amer. Inst. Chem. Engineers, Tucson, Arizona, 1973.

23. Proceedings of the International Solvent Extraction Conference, Lyon, 1974, Publ. by Society of Chemical Industry, London, 1974, vol. 3.

24. Interaction Between Solvent Extraction and Electrochemical Technology, London, 1975.

25. The Aqueous/Organic Interface and Its Role in Solvent Extraction, London, 1976.

26. The Theory and Practice of Ion Exchange, Cambridge, England, 1976.

27. International Solvent Extraction Conference, Toronto, 1977.

Review Articles

28. Agarwal J. C. et al., Comparative Analyses of Hydrometallurgical Processes, paper presented at the Can. Inst. Min. Met. 7th. Annual Hydrometallurgy Meeting, Vancouver, B.C., August, 1977.

29. Agarwal J. C., Flood H. W. and Beecher N. J. Metals, 26, No. 1, 26-33 (1974).

30. Agrawall R. D., Metal and Minerals Review, 15, No. 5, 1-9 (1977).

31. Bautista R. G., Advances in Chem. Eng., 9, 1-110 (1974).

32. Brandela M., Ind. Minérale-Minéralurgie (Supplement) 7-33 April (1977).

928

33. Dresher W. H., Dasher J., Brown F. and Davis F. F., Deci-
    sion Factors in Choosing Between Pyro and Hydro-Processes,
    Paper presented at the Soc. Min. Eng. AIME Meeting, Acapulco,
    Mexico, September 22-25, 1974.

34. Gandon L., Ind. Minerale-Mineralurgie, 114-126, May 1977.

35. Habashi F., Hydrometallurgy Its Past, Present and Future.
    Metal Sci. Conf., Varanasi, India, 1977.

36. Jansen M. L. and Milligan D. A., J. Metals, 27, No. 1, 13-23
    (1975).

37. Kirby R. C. and Barclay J. A., Trans. Soc. Min. Eng. AIME,
    42-47, June (1975).

38. Kirby R. C. and Prokopovitsh A. S., Science, 191, 713-719
    (1976).

39. Kumar G., Trans. SAEST, 11, No. 1, 207-236 (1976), and 11,
    No. 2, 295-313 (1976).

40. Natarajan K. A. and Iwasaki I., Minerals Sci. and Eng.,
    6, 35-44 (1974).

41. Rosenbaum J. B., Science, 191, 720-723 (1976).

42. Sastri V. A. and Mackinnon D. J., Some Effects of Ultra-
    sonics and Their Applications in Processing Metallic
    Ores, Report MRP/MSL, 76-71 (1976), Canada Energy, Mines
    and Resources, Ottawa.

Alumina

43. Bliss N. W., Bull. Can. Inst. Min. and Met., 75-85 (1976).

44. Patterson S. H., Amer. Scientist, 65, 345-351 (1977).

45. Winer A. A., Sources of Canadian Non-bauxite Alumina,
    Rept. MRP/MSL 77-130, Canada Energy, Mines and Resources,
    Ottawa, 1977.

46. Cohen J. and Mercier H., Recovery of Alumina from Non-
    Bauxite Aluminum - Bearing Raw Materials, pp. 3-18 in
    Light Metals 1976, 2, (S. R. Leavitt, ed.) AIME, New
    York, 1976.

Copper

47. Hopkins W. R. and Lynch A. J., Eng. and Min. J., 178, No. 2, 56-64 (1977).

48. Habashi F., Chalcopyrite - Its Chemistry and Metallurgy, McGraw Hill, New York-Dusseldorf, 1978.

49. Hurbert J. C., Reimers J. H., Kellogg H. H. and Dasher J. J. Metals, 26, No. 8, 16-24 (1974).

50. Osina A. V. and Press Yu. S., Tsvetn. Met., No. 3, 25-30 (1978); CA 88 195 114 m.

51. Wadsworth M. E. et al., Advanced Chemical Processing of Copper Sulfide Concentrates, pp. 55-63 in Vol. 3, Proc. Symp. Research Applied to National Needs, National Science Foundation, Washington, D.C., 1977.

52. Yannopoulos J. C. and Agarwal J. C. (eds.) Extractive Metallurgy of Copper, Vol. 2, Hydrometallurgy and Electrowinning, AIME, New York, 1976.

53. McNamara J. H. et al. A Hydrometallurgical Process for the Extraction of Copper, Paper presented at AIME meeting, Denver, Colorado Avail. from Cyprus Metallurgical Processes Corp., Tucson, Arizona, February 1978.

54. Swinkels G. M. et al. Bull. Can. Inst. Min. and Met. 71, 105-139 (1978).

Gold and Silver

55. Duncan D. M. and Smolik T. J., Eng. and Min. J. 178, No. 7, 65-69 (1977).

Ilmenite

56. Meyer K. and Pietsch H., Erzmetall, 27, 345-350 (1974).

57. Immartino N. R., Chem. Eng., 100-101, May, (1976).

930

58. Sinha H. N. Murso Process for Producing Rutile Substitute,
    pp. 233-245 in Titanium Science and Technology; 1 (eds.
    R. I. Jaffee and H. M. Burke), Plenum Press, New York-London,
    1973.

59. Robinson M., Clamp F., Mobbs D. B. and Pearse R. V. The
    Laporte High-Efficiency Ilmenite Beneficiation Process,
    In: Advance in Extractive Metallurgy (ed. M. J.
    Jones), Inst. Min. and Met., London, 1977, pp. 89-96.

Manganese Nodules

60. Agarwal J. C. et al. J. Metals, 28, No. 4, 24-31 (1976).

61. Faugeras P., Traitement chimique des nodules sous-marins
    en vue d'une exploitation industrielle, Industrie minerale -
    Minéralurgie, 213-222, June (1977).

62. Granville A. Minerals Sci and Eng., 7, 170-188 (1975).

63. Hubred G. Minerals Sci. and Eng., 7, 71-85 (1975).

64. Halbach P. Erzmetall, 27, 161-168 (1974).

65. Horn D. R. (ed.) Conference on Ferromanganese Deposits on
    the Ocean Floor, New York, Jan. 1972, Office for the Inter-
    national Decade of Ocean Exploration, Washington, D.C.
    1972.

66. Kruppa C. (ed.) Interocean Int. Kongr. Ausstellung Meeres-
    forschung und Meeresnutzung, 2nd, 2 vols., Seehafen-Verlag
    Erik Blunenfeld, Hamburg, 1973.

67. Margolis S. V. and Burns R. G. Ann. Rev. Earth and Plane-
    tary Sci., 4, 229-263 (1976).

68. Mielkel J. E. Ocean Manganese Nodules, Gov. Pub. Office,
    Washington, D.C. (1975).

69. Tooms J. S., Summerhayes C. P. and Cronan D. C. Oceanogr.
    Mar. Biol. Ann. Rev. 7, 49-100 (1969)

70. Hänig G. and Meixner M. J. Erzmetall, 27, 335-340 (1974).

71. Schwarz K. H. and Boin U. Erzmetall, 27, 341-345 (1974).

72. Burzminski M. J., Fernando Q. and Zeitlen H. Anal. Chem., 50, 1177-1180 (1978).

73. Fuerstenau D. W., Herring A. P. and Hoover M. Trans. Soc. Min. Eng. AIME, 254, 205-211 (1973).

74. Han K. N. and Fuerstenau D. Trans. Inst. Min. and Met. Sect. C., 84, C105-C110 (1975).

Mercury

75. Calvo F. A. and Forn Alonso, Recovery of Mercury from its Minerals by Oxidation in Aqueous Media. In: Congreso Internacional del Mercurio, 1, Barcelona, Spain 1974, pp. 327-342.

76. de la Cuadra A. et al. Cinnabar Leaching in a Chloride Medium Using Oxygen as Oxidizer. In: Congreso Internacional del Mercurio, 1, Barcelona, Spain, 1974, pp. 369-376.

Nickel

77. Hoppe R. W. Eng. and Min. J., 178, No. 5, 76-79 (1977).

Tin

78. Holt G. and Pearson D. Trans. Inst. Min. and Met., 86, C77-C81 (1977).

79. Pearson D. et al., Trans. Inst. Min. and Met., 86, C140-C146 (1977), ibid 86, C175-C185 (1977).

Uranium

80. Uranium Ore Processing, Proc. Advisory Group Meeting in Washington, November 24-26, 1975. Intern. At. Energy Agency, Vienna, 1976.

81. O'Sullivan D. A. Chem. and Eng. News, 54, 19-20, October
    (1976).

82. Brooke J. N. Min. Congr. J., 63, No. 8, 38-41 (1977).

83. Ross R. C. Eng. and Min. J., 176, No. 12, 80-85 (1975).

84. Ring R. J. At. Energy Australia, 20, 12-20 (1977).

85. Processus metallurgiques de lixiviation sous pression dans
    le reacteur tubulaire, Lurgi Information Express, C1242/6, 77.

Zinc

86. Gordon A. R. and Pickering R. W. Metall. Trans., 6B, 43-53
    (1975).

87. Doyle B. N. et al. Acid Pressure Leaching of Zinc Concen-
    trates with Elemental Sulfur as a By-Product, XIth Common-
    wealth Mining and Metallurgical Congress, Hong Kong, 1978.

Coal Desulfurization

88. Wheelock T. D. (ed.), Coal Desulfurization, ACS Symp. Ser.
    No. 64., Am. Chem. Soc., Washington, D.C., 1977.

Recovery of Minerals from Surface Waters

89. Epstein J. A. Hydrometallurgy, 2, 1-10 (1976).

ABSTRACT

A review of research activities and industrial development in
hydrometallurgy in the past five years is presented. Special
emphasis is given to the recent hydrometallurgical process for
copper, gold, mercury, nickel, tin, uranium, and zinc ores. The
production of alumina from non-bauxite sources, the production
of synthetic rutile from ilmenite, the treatment of deep-sea
manganese nodules, coal desulfurization, and the recovery of
minerals from surface water are also discussed.

RÉSUMÉ

Une revue des activités de recherche et de développment
industriel en hydrométallurgie est presentée pour les 5 der-
nières années. Un relief spécial est donné aux récents procédés
hydrométallurgiques pour des minerais de cuivre, d'or, de
mercure, de nickel, d'étain, d'uranium et de zinc. Il est aussi
discuté la production d'alumine de sources autres que la
bauxite, la production de rutile synthétique à partier d'ilmé-
nite, le traitement de boules de manganèse des fonds marins,
la désulfurisation du charbon, et la récupération des minerais
de l'eau de surface.

ZUSAMMENFASSUNG

Der Beitrag enthält eine Übersicht über die Forschungstätig-
keit und industrielle Weiterentwicklung im Bereich der Hydrome-
tallurgie im Verlauf der letzten fünf Jahre. Besonders werden
moderne, neuetwickelte hydrometallurgische Prozesse zur Aufbereitung von Kupfer, Gold, Quecksilber, Nickel, Zinn, Uran und
Zinkerzen besprechen. Die Herstellung von Tonerde aus nichtbauxi-
tischen Quellstoffen, die Produktion synthetischen Rutils aus
Ilmenit, die Aufbereitung der im marinen Bereich gewonnenen
Mangankonkretionen, die Entschwefelung von Kohle und die Gewinnung von Mineralen aus flachen Gewassern werden ebenfalls
erörtert.

934

РЕЗЮМЕ

Произведен обзор исследовательских работ и развития гидрометаллургических технологий за последние 5 лет.

Особое внимание сосредоточено на новейших гидрометаллургических процессах для руд меди, золота, ртути, никеля, олова, урана и цинка.

Рассмотрено получение окиси алюминия из небокситного сырья, получение синтетического рутила из ильменита, переработка марганцевых нодулей с морского дна, десульфаризация угля, а также извлечение минералов из поверхностных вод.

NON-OXIDATIVE LEACHING OF BASE METAL SULPHIDE ORES

H. Majima amd Y. Awakura

Department of Metallurgy, Kyoto University, Japan

INTRODUCTION

The non-oxidative leaching of base metal sulphide ores in an acid solution involving the release of hydrogen sulphide has been extensively studied and was applied industrially at one time to extract metals from sulphide ores. Forward and Warren [1] have pointed out that most of the work up to the mid-20th century was done for the purpose of sulphating sulphide minerals with sulphuric acid. There are also many references on the methods for generating hydrogen sulphide from mineral sulphides with brine solution. Typical patents of brine leaching were filed by Christensen and these have been the basis for the commercial Snyder-Christensen Process [2] for the treatment of complex sulphide ores.

In recent years, increasingly strict environmental standards in regard to sulphur dioxide have had a strong impact on the smelting of sulphide concentrates and, consequently the problem of the over-production of sulphuric acid and gypsum has suddenly been noticed. Under such circumstances, an intense effort has been made to develop new metallurgical processes for base metal sulphides to fix sulphide sulphur in an elemental form. Elemental sulphur can be stored indefinitely and there is no necessity to produce sulphuric acid or gypsum. The hydrometallurgical hydrogen sulphide route of sulphide decomposition is attractive at the present time because of its inherent flexibility. The technology for producing elemental sulphur from hydrogen sulphide is well established.

There are two ways to decompose base metal sulphides in acidic solutions with the evolution of hydrogen sulphide, as may be expected from the Eh-pH diagram of the metal-sulphur-water system: (1) Acidification of sulphides in a non-oxidative aqueous solution, (2) Reduction of sulphides in an acidic solution. Some of the sulphides are unsuitable for decomposition through the hydrogen sulphide route for thermodynamic and/or kinetic reasons. Activation of these difficult-to-leach sulphides often allows their decomposition, partially by acidification.

In this paper, we have reviewed the literature dealing with the chemistry and technology of sulphide decomposition in aqueous acidic solutions generating hydrogen sulphide. Included in this review are a thermodynamic and kinetic consideration of the reaction involved in the generation of hydrogen sulphide from base metal sulphide, activation treatments of difficult-to-decompose sulphide and some of the important processes which have been proposed so far. The paper also discusses the experimental results which pertain to the generation of hydrogen sulphide, and which were obtained by the present authors.

Acidic Decomposition of Base Metal Sulphides in Non-Oxidative Aqueous Solution

The basic reaction for the acid decomposition of sulphides of divalent metals and its equilibrium are given by Eqs. (1), (2) and (2')

$$MS + 2H^+ = M^{2+} + H_2S(g) \qquad (1)$$

$$K = \frac{a_{M^{2+}} \, p_{H_2S}}{(a_{H^+})^2} \qquad (2)$$

$$pH = \frac{1}{2}(\log K - \log a_{M^{2+}} - \log p_{H_2S}) \qquad (2')$$

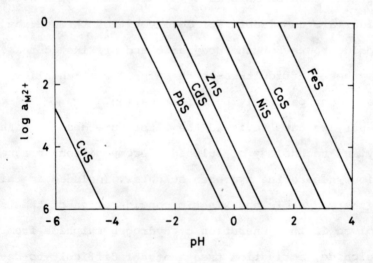

Fig. 1. Effect of pH on the acid decomposition of base metal sulphides.

The ease of decomposition of various sulphides is summarized in the form $-\log a_{M^{2+}}$ vs. pH, and depicted in Fig. 1. Ferrous sulphide is certainly easiest to decompose, as is obvious from this Fig. Increasing difficulty of decomposition can be expected with the sequence FeS < CoS < NiS < ZnS < CdS < PbS < CuS.

The values of standard free energy change of the reaction (1) were calculated for all the sulphides shown in Fig. 1 at temperatures of $25^\circ C$ and $100^\circ C$. By elevating the temperature from $25^\circ C$ to $100^\circ C$, the free energy changes of the acidification reaction of sulphides are generally small, and this fact indicates that one may expect that temperature has only a slight effect on the leaching of these sulphides from the thermodynamic point of view. The only exception is lead sulphide, though its free energy change at $100^\circ C$ is still positive. In these calculations, the role of anions constituting acids was neglected. Acid-constituting anions, however, may also play an important role in the acidification decomposition of sulphides. This anion effect is attributable to the complexing ability of anions, or to the formation of insoluble salts. The selection of acid is important in this respect. Further discussion is impossible at this stage because of lack of thermodynamic data. The addition of various salts to an acid solution may also change the complexing character and at the same time it may greatly affect the activity of the acid-constituting ions. Thus, an accelerating or a retarding effect on the decomposition rate of sulphides may be expected.

Tarabaev and his collaborators [3] studied the solubility of various sulphides in acidic chloride solutions. They found that the solubility of metals in acidic chloride solution is proportional to the ratio $[HCl]^2/[H_2S]$. All sulphides, particularly galena, become more soluble in the presence of sodium chloride. From these findings, they proposed a selective leaching method for complex sulphide ores or concentrates in a weak acid solution containing sodium chloride.

It is a well known fact that plumbous ions react with most anions, forming insoluble precipitates. Taking this into consideration, the leaching reaction expressed by Eq. (1) should be rewritten in another form, where the formation of insoluble salts is involved. For example, if galena is leached with sulphuric acid, we obtain Eq. (3):

$$PbS(s) + H_2SO_4(aq) = PbSO_4(s) + H_2S(g) \tag{3}$$

The corresponding standard free energy change was found to be $\Delta G^o = -2.29$ kcal/mol at 25^oC, and this suggests a far easier decomposition of galena in sulphuric acid than might be expected from Fig. 1.

Reductive Decomposition of Sulphide in Acidic Solutions

Metal sulphides are also decomposed in a reducing acidic solution with the generation of hydrogen sulphide. Metals are reduced to either elemental form or metal sulphides of lower oxidation state, according to Eq. (4) or (4')

$$M_mS_n + 2nH^+ + 2ne^- = mM + nH_2S(g) \tag{4}$$

$$M_mS_n + 2n\left(1 - \frac{p}{m}\right)H^+ + 2n\left(1 - \frac{p}{m}\right)e^-$$

$$= \frac{m}{p}M_pS_{np^2/m^2} + n\left(1 - \frac{p}{m}\right)H_2S(g) \tag{4'}$$

Electron requirements for these reactions may be satisfied either by coupling them with an appropriate redox system or by using electrochemical techniques.

Equilibrium conditions for the reductive decomposition of various sulphides were calculated at $25^{\circ}C$ and 1 atm partial pressure of hydrogen sulphide, and then tabulated in Table 1 in terms of redox potential. If the reductive reaction actually

TABLE 1

Equilibrium Conditions for the Reductive Decomposition of Various Sulphides at $25^{\circ}C$ and $p_{H_2S} = 1$ atm. $(M_mS_n + 2nH^+ + 2ne^- = mM + nH_2S)$

M_mS_n	E (V vs. SHE)	M_mS_n	E (V vs. SHE)
Ag_2S	-0.037	Cu_2S	-0.275
HgS	-0.068	PbS	-0.309
CuS	-0.083	FeS	-0.335
Bi_2S_3	-0.114	MoS_2	-0.414
NiS	-0.213	CdS	-0.557
CoS	-0.258	ZnS	-0.857
FeS_2	-0.261	MnS	-0.911

obeys Eq. (4), Ag_2S and HgS must be the easiest sulphides to decompose. Also CuS, which is hardly leached at all in an acid solution, should be readily decomposed in the presence of suitable reductants. In contrast, CdS, ZnS, and MnS, which are known soluble sulphides in acidic solutions, respond poorly to reductive decomposition. The redox system whose potential is rather low is applicable as a coupling reductant. The redox system Cr^{3+}/Cr^{2+} is a typical example of the reductants with its potential of -0.41 V vs. S.H.E. Thus, Ag_2S or CuS may be decomposed generating hydrogen sulphide in the acid solution containing chromous salt.

Free energy change for the decomposition reaction of copper sulphides in acidic chromous solution were calculated at a temperature of $25^\circ C$ and $100^\circ C$. The results are summarized in Table 2. The ΔG° values for the reductive decomposition of copper sulphide minerals other than bornite appear to be negative as

TABLE 2

Free Energy Changes for the Decomposition Reactions of Copper Sulphides in Acidic Chromous Solution at Temperatures of $25^\circ C$ and $100^\circ C$

Reaction	ΔG_R° (kcal/mol)	
	$25^\circ C$	$100^\circ C$
$CuS+2H^++2Cr^{2+} = Cu+H_2S+2Cr^{3+}$	-12.69	-2.55
$Cu_2S+2H^++2Cr^{2+} = 2Cu+H_2S+2Cr^{3+}$	-4.60	5.55
$Cu_5FeS_4+8H^++6Cr^{3+} = 5Cu+Fe^{2+}+4H_2S+6Cr^{3+}$	1.04	20.45
$CuFeS_2+4H^++2Cr^{2+} = Cu+Fe^{2+}+2H_2S+2Cr^{3+}$	-6.61	-0.97

shown in Table 2, suggesting that these reductive reactions are favored. A rise in temperature, however, may have a deleterious effect on the reactions, as anticipated from the ΔG° values at $100^\circ C$. In any case, the reductive decomposition of copper sulphide ores or concentrates in an acidic chromous solution is thermodynamically favorable. A moderate temperature seems to be more desirable from thermodynamic point of view than elevated temperatures.

Papers published by previous researchers on the kinetics of non-oxidative leaching of base metal sulphides in acidic solution are rather scarce.

In most leaching processes, including the non-oxidative leaching of metal sulphides, a number of reactions are possible. These are usually of two types: (1) the most common type, where the reactant in solution reacts with the solid at the surface, and (2) more rarely, where two substances in solution migrate to react with one another at the surface of the solid.

The slowest stage determines the overall rate of the process. The effect of the stirring rate, an increase of which increases the rate of reaction, and the value of low activation energy of the order of 2 ~ 7 kcal/mol [4] are two of the criteria for mass transfer control.

Stages of, adsorption, reaction, and desorption are often grouped together, and referred to as chemically controlled. The criteria for desorption control were listed by Salzberg, one of these criteria being a much higher activation energy of approximately 25 kcal/mol. Heterogeneous reactions are sometimes controlled under joint chemical and mass transfer rates, which are referred as mixed control processes [5]. However, activation energy and the influence of stirring speed are of limited utility as criteria for distinguishing the rate-determining stage.

Although some kinetic investigations on the non-oxidative leaching of metal sulphides were reported by Tseft et al. [6] and Tarabaev and his coworkers [7a], kinetic studies which permit

meaningful speculation on the mechanism of hydrogen sulphide
release from metal sulphides during acid leaching are of more
recent origin.

Pohl [8] has shown that the rate of leaching of very finely
ground FeS, CdS, and ZnS immersed in acid solutions is directly
proportional to the concentration of hydrogen ions. The rate-
controlling stage in FeS leaching involves a single hydrogen ion
which is consistent with reaction (5):

$$FeS + H^+ \xrightarrow{\quad\quad} Fe^{2+} + HS^- \tag{5}$$

$$HS^- + H^+ \longrightarrow H_2S \tag{6}$$

Yazawa et al. [9] studied the acidic dissolution of approximately stoichiometric pyrrhotite in sulphuric acid under vigorous
agitation. They found that the initial rate of leaching was directly proportional to both the surface area of the pyrrhotite
and the concentration of H_2SO_4. The agitation effect on the
leaching rate was actually insignificant, and the activation
energy of the reaction was 13.2 kcal/mol. From these results,
they speculated that the chemical reaction on the surface of the
pyrrhotite is the rate-determining stage.

Tarabaev [3b, 7b] has shown that the rate of zinc dissolution from sphalerite is diffusion-controlled when the acidity and
chloride ion content are held reasonably constant. The presence
of an excess of chloride ions also increases the leaching rate.
They concluded that the chemical reaction at the mineral surface
shown in Eq. (5) is normally rapid and that the diffusion of H^+
or HS^- ions in the boundary layer will be rate-determining for
the overall reaction. When the interfacial area is very large

944

and the diffusion layer thin, the chemical reaction on the sulphide surface becomes the rate-controlling stage. Ichikuni et al.
[10] have observed that the dissolution rate of sulphides in an
acid solution is decreased by increasing the hydrogen sulphide
pressure. Their observation does not conflict with the diffusion
model of HS^- in the boundary layer.

Ingraham and his coworkers [11] measured the leaching rate of
non-stoichiometric pyrrhotite under non-oxidizing conditions in
aqueous solutions containing hydrochloric acid, and observed that
the amount of elemental sulphur formed is directly proportional
to the non-stoichiometry of the pyrrhotites. The accumulation of
elemental sulphur on the mineral surface retards the later stage
of the leaching processes. They concluded that the first half of
the dissolution process is probably controlled by the diffusion
of some species through a boundary layer that is adjacent to the
mineral surface.

Recently, a few studies have been published dealing with the
non-oxidative leaching of galena and sphalerite in a solution
with high acid and chloride concentrations. Scott and Nicol [12]
have studied the dissolution rate of natural galena in mixed
solutions of LiCl-HCl or LiCl-HClO$_4$, respectively using a rotating disk technique. Galena has been shown to dissolve at a rate
which is diffusion-controlled and which is a strong, non-linearly
increasing function of the chloride concentration. It increases
with increasing acidity, but levels off at a high hydrogen ion
concentration, and exhibits an activation energy of 12.3 kcal/mol.
In addition, the dissolution rate was proportional to the square
root of the disk rotation speed. They concluded that the rate-

determining stage in the dissolution process is the mass transfer away from the solid-liquid interface of the lead chloro complexes and soluble hydrogen sulphide.

One of the present authors and his coworkers [13] measured the dissolution rate of galena in $HClO_4$ and $HClO_4$-NaCl solution, where the effect of agitation on the dissolution rate was eliminated. The speculated mechanism of galena dissolution differs according to whether the leaching solution contains sodium chloride or not. In the absence of sodium chloride, the initial rate of the leaching reaction has a 2nd order relation with respect to the hydrogen ion concentration, exhibiting an activation energy of 15.8 kcal/mol. In the presence of sodium chloride, the initial rate is proportional to the concentration of both hydrogen ions and chloride ions, and the activation energy is 11.7 kcal/mol. Masuko et al. [14] investigated the non-oxidative leaching of sphalerite in a HCl-NaCl solution. They found that the formation of a $ZnCl_4^{2-}$ complex results in the increase in the leaching rate when NaCl is present in the solution.

In the leaching studies, a finely ground sample or a disk specimen is generally employed to determine the leaching rate. With a finely ground sample, the reaction rate is often estimated by the McKewan [15] or Jander Equation [16], whereas the reaction rate for the rotating disk specimen is usually estimated by the Levich Equation [17]. Without doubt, these Equations are useful in speculation on the nature of the leaching mechanism if they are properly applied. However, the careless application of these Equations may be misleading, and to avoid such errors careful thought is required.

Of course, chalcopyrite is the most important mineral source of copper. Pyrite was at one time regarded as an important source of elemental sulphur. However, it has long been known that these sulphide minerals respond very slowly to treatment by acid. The primary breakdown of sulphide minerals such as chalcopyrite or pyrite so that they may be affected by leachants, has been termed "activation" by Subramanian and Jennings [18]. They have discussed the possibility of the activation of chalcopyrite using Schlegel's data [19]. As shown in Fig. 2, very much ternary compounds exist in the Cu-Fe-S system. However, the absence of com-

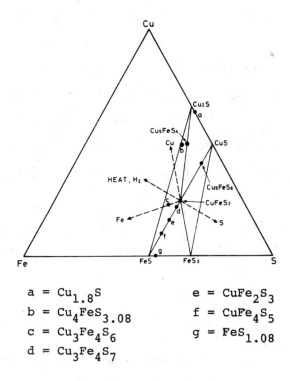

$a = Cu_{1.8}S$

$b = Cu_4FeS_{3.08}$

$c = Cu_3Fe_4S_6$

$d = Cu_3Fe_4S_7$

$e = CuFe_2S_3$

$f = CuFe_4S_5$

$g = FeS_{1.08}$

Fig. 2. Known compounds in the Cu-Fe-S system and the activation of chalcopyrite [19].

pounds on the side of the Cu_2S-FeS section poor in sulphur and on the sulphur rich side of the CuS-FeS$_2$ section imposes limitations on the quantities of these elements that can be absorbed. The treatment for altering the mineralogical composition of chalcopyrite is to change the ratios of copper, iron and sulphur; this can be done by adding an excess of one of the components or by removing part of sulphur. The dotted lines drawn in Fig. 2 indicate the directions of the activation of chalcopyrite. Table 3, which has been summarized by Subramanian et al., gives the results of activation treatments and includes thermodynamic data derived from a standard source. As can be seen in the Table, FeS is formed in most cases of chalcopyrite activation, and thus the resulting mixture of sulphides is generally more amenable to acid leaching than the original chalcopyrite.

The activation treatment of chalcopyrite may also be achieved by a hydrometallurgical method. As already mentioned, chalcopyrite may be decomposed in an acidic chromous solution to form metallic copper as a final product. The intermediate products of this reaction may be bornite and/or chalcocite. This means that there is a space for the activation of chalcopyrite.

Chalcopyrite can be decomposed to chalcocite in the presence of metallic copper, zinc or iron particulates in an acidic solution according to Eq. (7) [20].

$$CuFeS_2 + Cu + 2H^+ = Cu_2S + Fe^{2+} + H_2S \qquad (7)$$

Pyrite is also difficult to decompose in an acidic solution. When treating pyrite, the expulsion of labile sulphur from the pyrite is necessary prior to leaching. Many of the processes

948

TABLE 3

Heat Requirements in Activation Processes of Chalcopyrite [18]

Method of Activation (Reference)	Reaction	Reaction Temp. (T·C)	Heat of Reaction at 298°K	Sensible Heat in Products at T°C	Total Heat Input Required
			kcal/mole of $CuFeS_2$		
Heating in vacuo	$CuFeS_2 = \frac{1}{2}Cu_2S + FeS + \frac{1}{4}S_2$	850	+16.09	22.1	38.19
Hydrogen	$CuFeS_2 + \frac{1}{2}H_2 =$ $\frac{1}{2}Cu_2S + FeS + \frac{1}{2}H_2S$	800	+5.94	22.9	28.84
Copper	$CuFeS_2 + Cu = Cu_2S + FeS$	450	-1.46	14.9	13.44
Iron	$CuFeS_2 + \frac{1}{2}Fe =$ $\frac{1}{2}Cu_2S + 1\frac{1}{2}FeS$	500	-3.06	8.3	5.24
		600		10.1	7.04
		700		11.8	8.74
Sulphur	$CuFeS_2 + \frac{1}{2}S_2 = CuS^* + FeS_2^*$	475	-13.56	13.5	0.06

* Reaction products identified by X-ray diffraction.

proposed describe the generation of hydrogen sulphide at some
stage in the procedure [21].

THE HYDROGEN SULPHIDE ROUTE FOR THE LEACHING
OF SULPHIDE CONCENTRATES

Direct Acid Leaching

The direct acid leaching process may be applied to the leaching of the sulphide ores or concentrates of Zn, Pb-Zn, Cu-Zn,
and Cu-Pb-Zn and of pyrrhotite ores. However, the leaching of
base metal sulphides in a sulphuric acid solution is often very
slow and thus only a limited space is remained in the industrial
application. On the other hand, the leaching of sulphides in a
brine solution acidified by hydrochloric acid is attractive
because of its high leaching rate. To give an example, the
complex Cu-Pb-Zn-Ag sulphide ore was treated with a brine leachant in a pilot plant. Brine leaching was the basis of the commercial Snyder-Christensen Process [22], as previously mentioned.
However, the pilot stage of this method was not successful because of operational difficulties such as the disposal of the
large quantities of hydrogen sulphide generated and the corrosion of equipment by warm brine solutions. In relatively recent
years, Ermilov [23] used a mixture of HCl and $CaCl_2$ brine solution in a pilot plant process for treating a complex Cu-Zn-Pb
sulphide concentrate.

The shortage of rich mineral reserves forces one to utilize
ores which are difficult-to-treat. This is occasionally the case
with Pb-Zn ores. We often experience great difficulty in separating sphalerite, galena and iron sulphide differentially by

the flotation technique because of their complexity and closeness to each other. It might be advisable to recover a bulk concentrate in which PbS, ZnS and Fe sulphides are collected and follow this by metallurgical separation. Leaching with sulphuric acid may be a useful way to decompose the bulk concentrate, but the leaching rate is usually too slow under atmospheric conditions. As reported by previous researchers, some sulphide minerals, particularly galena, respond with modified non-oxidative dissolution when a HCl brine solution is employed as leachant. Recent developments in material science and the establishment of the technology of hydrogen sulphide conversion to elemental sulphur provide the answer to difficulties such as corrosion or air pollution which have been experienced in the past. Under these circumstances, the authors intend to reaffirm the usefulness of the brine leaching technique in the treatment of Pb-Zn sulphide bulk concentrates. In the leaching experiments with a HCl-NaCl solution and bulk concentrate, the authors observed that the dissolution rate of PbS is markedly greater than that of ZnS. However, the solubility of PbS in the brine solution controlled its dissolution rate, and this suggests that an appropriate process for the removal of dissolved lead from the solution is necessary.

The studies by Masuko and his coworkers, and the one of the present authors and his collaborators are also related to the brine leaching of base metal sulphides for the recovery of elemental sulphur by the Claus method from the hydrogen sulphide generated.

951

Industrially important processes in this category are the treatment of Cu-Ni matte and the production of elemental sulphur from pyrite ore. In the well-known Falconbridge process, nickel sulphides in the Cu-Ni matte which is obtained from a converter is selectively dissolved in a strong hydrochloric acid to liberate H_2S while the copper sulphide and other noble metals remain in residue [24, 25]. Since the early part of this century, numerous articles have been published on the hydrometallurgical decomposition of nickel matte with the evolution of hydrogen sulphide.

The recovery of sulphur and iron from pyrite-type ores has been the subject of much research, and many of the patents and proposed processes deal with the generation of hydrogen sulphide at some stage in the procedure. However, pyrite responds very slowly to treatment by acid, and this indicates that another step is necessary to remove some of its sulphur content. Habashi outlined a general flowsheet for the recovery of elemental sulphur from sulphide ores in his review [21]. Acids such as hydrochloric and sulphuric acids are commonly used as a leachant. The Estelk [26] and Bacon method [27] are rather old and McGauley method [28] has been proposed in relatively recent years. However, the treatment of pyritic ore to recover iron and sulphur has suddenly declined more recently.

Masuko [29] has recently proposed a novel process for the treatment of chalcopyrite concentrate and termed it the "5C process" in which hydrometallurgical and pyrometallurgical methods are combined. His process consists of five stages:

(1) Calcination

$$2CuFeS_2 = Cu_2S + 2FeS + \frac{1}{2}S_2 \qquad (8)$$

(2) Conversion leaching

$$2FeS + 4HCl = 2H_2S + 2FeCl_2 \qquad (9)$$

(3) Convertion

$$Cu_2S + O_2 = 2Cu + SO_2 \qquad (10)$$

(4) Claus Process

$$SO_2 + 2H_2S = 2H_2O + 3S \qquad (11)$$

(5) Chloride Oxidation

$$2FeCl_2 + 2H_2O + \frac{1}{2}O_2 = Fe_2O_3 + 4HCl \qquad (12)$$

In this process, chalcopyrite, which is known as a extremely stable mineral for acid leaching, is activated in the pretreatment step and then leached with a hydrochloric acid solution to generate hydrogen sulphide. The final products of this process are metallic copper, ferric oxide and elemental sulphur. His proposal may involve some difficulties, but it is very interesting that the hydrogen sulphide route is intended to be used for the treatment of chalcopyrite concentrates.

Reductive Decomposition of Sulphides in an Aqueous Acidic Solution

No commercial process in this category has been proposed for the decomposition of base metal sulphides. One of the present authors and his coworkers [30] observed about 10 years ago that the decomposition rate of certain sulphides is greatly increased in an acidic chromous solution. Recently, the authors studied the reductive decomposition of copper sulphides in acidic chromous solution again. A minus 200 mesh fraction of covellite, chalcocite, bornite or chalcopyrite, each weighing 0.5 g, were subjected to the leaching test at ambient room temperature in 200 ml of an aqueous chromous sulphate solution. The approximate concentration of chromous sulphate was 0.6 M, and the pH was adjusted to be zero with sulphuric acid. The leaching reaction proceeds rather rapidly, ceasing after 10 to 30 min of retention. Figure 3 shows the results of X-ray diffraction analysis for the leaching products. It is noteworthy that metallic copper may be directly produced from any of these copper sulphides by this re-

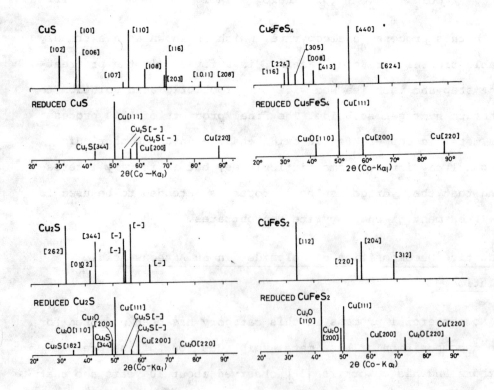

Fig. 3. X-ray diffraction patterns of copper sulphide minerals and their reductive leach products.

954

ductive decomposition method, although the formation of calco-
cite was detected as an intermediate product when covellite was
leached. The direct formation of metallic copper from copper
sulphide minerals, especially from chalcopyrite, by reductive
decomposition in acidic solution is considered attractive. However, further study is necessary before a new hydrometallurgical
process may be applied.

REFERENCES

1. Forward F. A. and Warren I. H. Met. Rev., 5, 137 (1960).

2. Liddell D. M. Handbook of Non-Ferrous Metallurgy-Recovery of
   Metals, 2nd. ed., McGraw Hill, New York, 1947, 531.

3. Tarabaev S. I. et al. Akad. Nauk. Kazakh S.S.R.(A).Ser.Gorg-
   nogo. Dela. Met. Stroitel. i Stroimaterial, 4, 59 (1957).

4. Salzberg H. W., Knoetgen H. and Molless A. M. Trans. Electro-
   chem. Soc., 98, 31 (1951).

5. Zimmerman J. J. Phys. Colloid Chem., 53, 562 (1949).

6. Tseft A. L., Yalivinskii D. and Vygoda R. M. Vestnik Akad.
   Nauk. Kazakh S.S.R., 15, No, 2, 38 (1959); No. 5, 65 (1959).

7. Tarabaev S. I. et al. Trudy. Inst. Met. i Obogashcheniya,
   Akad. Nauk. Kazakh S.S.R., (A) 3, 134 (1960); (B) 14, 3 (1965)

8. Pohl H. A. J. Am. Chem. Soc., 76, 2182 (1954); J. Chem. Eng.
   Data, 7, 295 (1962).

9. Yazawa A. and Eguchi M. Bull. Res. Inst. Min. Dress. Met.,
   Tohoku Univ., 23, 143 (1967).

10. Ichikuni M. and Kamiya H. Bull. Chem. Soc. Japan, 34, 1780
    (1961).

11. Ingraham T. R. et al. Can. Met. Quarterly, 11, 407 (1972).

12. Scott P. D. et al. Trans. Inst. Min. Met., 85, C40 (1976).

13. Majima H., Tamura H. and Ohno T. J. Min. and Met. Inst.
    Japan, 93, 895 (1977).

14. Masuko N., Suzuki T. and Musiake K. Seisan Kenkyu, 28, 436 (1976).

15. McKewan W. M. Trans Met. Soc. AIME, 212, 791 (1958).

16. Jander W. Z. anorg. allgem. Chem., 163, 1 (1927).

17. Levich V. G. Physicochemical Hydrodynamics, Prentice Hall, Inc. New York, 1962, p. 69.

18. Subramanian K. N. and Jennings P. H. Can. Met. Quarterly, 11, 387 (1973).

19. Schlegel H. and Schuller A. Die Bergakademie Frigerg. Forch. Beihafte Reihe. Huttenw. No. 2 (1952).

20. For Example, M. Wadsworth and J. B. Hiskey. In: Solution Mining Symposium, 1974 (Eds. F. F. Aplan, W. A. McKimey and A. D. Pernichele), AIME, New York, 1974, 422.

21. Habashi F. Montana Bur. Mines, Geol. Bull., 57, March, 1966.

22. Christensen N. C. U. S. Pat. 1,549,062 (Aug. 11, 1925).

23. Ermilov V. V., Taraskin D. A., Chemezov N. S., Burov G. D. and Tseft A. L. Vestn. Akad. Nauk Kazakh S.S.R., 24, 43 (1968).

24. Thornhill P. G. et al. J. Metals, 20, 13 (1971).

25. Falconbridge Nickel Mines Ltd., Brit. Pat. 902,413 (1962).

26. Estelle A. U. S. Pat. 1,162,150 (1915).

27. Numerous patents were filed by R. F. Bacon during 1930-1935.

28. McGauley P. J. Ger. Pat. 1,127,596 (Cl. 40a) (1962); U.S. Pat. 2,808,938 (1957).

29. Masuko N. Seisan Kenkyu, 29, 59 (1977).

30. Majima H. and Peters E. The Physical Chemistry of Hydro-metallurgical Processes for the Decomposition of Sulphide Minerals. University of British Columbia, Dep. of Metallurgy. Quarterly Report, No. 3 (1966).

ABSTRACT

Over-production of sulphuric acid as well as the gypsum
derived from the pyrometallurgical treatment of base metal sulphide ores focusses attention on new processes for sulphur fixation. The hydrogen sulphide route to sulphur recovery by hydrometallurgical treatment is attractive at present because of its
inherent flexibility.

The literature dealing with the chemistry and technology of
sulphide decomposition evolving hydrogen sulphide in an aqueous
system has been reviewed. Included in this review are thermodynamic and kinetic considerations of generating hydrogen sulphide
from base metal sulphides, the activation treatment of difficult-
to-decompose sulphides, and some of the more important processes
proposed so far.

The paper also discusses the experimental results obtained
by the present authors on the chloride system for decomposing
lead-zinc sulphide bulk concentrate evolving hydrogen sulphide
and the acid decomposition of some copper sulphide minerals
under reducing conditions, yielding metallic copper and hydrogen
sulphide.

RÉSUMÉ

La surproduction d'acide sulfurique ainsi que de gypse lors
du traitement pyrométallurgique des minerais sulfurés de métaux
communs attire l'attention sur le développment de nouveaux procédés de fixation du soufre. Actuellement la méthode utilisant
du sulfure d'hydrogène pour la récupération du soufre par traitement hydrometallurgique est l'object d'un considérable
intérêt du fait de sa flexibilité inhérente.

La bibliographie concernant la chimie et la technologie de
la décomposition du sulfure par l'évolution du sulfure d'hydrogène dans le système aqueux, a été révisée. Les aspects inclus
dans cette révision comprennent des considérations thermody-
namiques et cinétiques de la génération du sulfure d'hydrogène
à partir de sulfures de métaux communs, le traitment d'activa-

957

tion des sulfures difficiles à décomposer, et quelques procédés importants proposés jusqu' á l'heure actuelle.

Cet article parle aussi de résultats expérimentaux obtenus par les présents auteurs sur le système chlorure dans le but de décomposer la pulpe du concentré contenant du sulfure de plomb - zinc, en formant du sulfure d'hydrogène et en décomposant dans un milieu acide quelques minéraux de sulfure de cuivre sous les conditions de réduction, ce qui donne du cuivre métallique et du sulfure d'hydrogène.

ZUSAMMENFASSUNG

Der bei der pyrometallurgischen Benhandlung schwefelhaltiger Erze unedler Metalle anfallende überschuss an Schwefelsäure und Gips fordert die Entwicklung neuer Verfahren zur Bindung des Schwefels. Das Wasserstoffsulphid-Verfahren zur Rückgewinnung von Schwefel mittels hydrometallurgischer Behandlung ist dank der ihr eigenen Anpassungsfähigkeit vielersprechend.

Die auf dem Gebiet der Chemie und der Technologie der Zersetzung von Sulfiden, in deren Folge in einem wässerigen System Wasserstoffsulfid ensteht, vorhandene Literatur ist eingehend analysiert worden. Der vorliegende Bericht enthält thermodynamische und kinetische Betrachtungen über die Bilding von Wasserstoffsulfid aus Sulfiden unedler Metalle, wie auch über die Aktivierung schwer zerlegbarer Sulfide und über einige wichtige, bisher vorgeschlagene Prozesse.

Der Bericht erörtert darüberhinaus die durch die Verfasser erhaltenen Ergebnisse experimenteller Untersuchungen eines Chloridsystems zur Zerlegung von Blei-Zink-Konzentraten unter Herausbildung von Wasserstoffsulfid, sowie über die Zersetzung einiger kupfersulfidhaltiger Minerale durch Säuren in Reduktionsbedingungen, wobei sowohl metallisches Kupfer als auch Wasserstoffsulfid gebildet werden.

958

РЕЗЮМЕ

Перепроизводство серной кислоты, а также и гипса, побочных продуктов пирометаллургической переработки сульфидных руд, основных металлов, обращает внимание на необходимость разработки новых процессов связания серы.
Способ получения серы в виде сероводорода в результате гидрометаллургических процессов в настоящее время представляет интерес ввиду своей эластичности.

Проведён обзор литературы, касающейся химии в технологии разложения сульфидов в водных растворах с выделением сероводорода. Вопросами, рассматриваемыми в настоящем обзоре, являются термодинамика и кинетика выделения сероводорода из сульфидов основных металлов, активированная обработка трудноразложимых сульфидов, а также некоторые важные процессы предлагаемые до настоящего времени.

В докладе обсуждаются также опытные результаты, полученные авторами по разложению сульфидного свинцово-цинкового концентрата в хлоридной системе с выделением сероводорода, а также кислотного разложения некоторых сульфидных минералов меди в восстановительных условиях с образованием металлической меди и сероводорода.

LYOMETALLURGICAL TREATMENT OF POROUS OXIDIZED ORES

S. Raghavan, I. Harris and D. W. Fuerstenau

Department of Materials Science and Mineral Engineering University of California, Berkeley, USA

INTRODUCTION

The recovery of metals from clarified ore leach solutions
by solvent extraction or ion exchange has been practiced in
the hydrometallurgical industries for many years. Many
attempts have been made to investigate the possibility of
eliminating the expensive clarification step in a hydrometallurgical circuit in order to substantially reduce process
costs. These approaches can be categorized into three groups:

(1) Resin-in-pulp (RIP) methods

(2) Solvent-in-pulp (SIP) methods

(3) Lyometallurgical methods

The resin-in-pulp method consists of contacting either the
usual ion exchange resins[1] or the solvent-impregnated
resins[2] with the unclarified leach liquor and extracting
the desired metal values. A fluidized counter-current resin

960

ion exchange system has been found to work well for the recovery of uranium[3].

In the solvent-in-pulp process the aqueous leach pulp is contacted with the solvent (a diluent containing an extractant) in a countercurrent fashion. Despite higher solvent losses by entrainment and adsorption in the pulp, the SIP process for uranium is estimated to be cheaper than the extraction from clarified solutions[4].

A lyometallurgical technique, as defined by Gaudin and co-workers in as early as 1950, is leaching process in which an organic solvent, initially free of a separate water phase, is used to leach a dry or slightly damp solid material[5]. The solid may or may not have received prior treatment by acid digestion or roasting, and the organic solvent may or may not contain a dissolved acid. Gaudin and his co-workers used such polar solvents as ethylacetate, ethylether, acetone and isopropyl ketone in conjuction with HCl (liquid or gas) and HNO_3 to extract metal values. Magner and Bailes[6] were able to successfully extract uranium from a carnotite ore with iso-octyl phosphoric acid dissolved in polar organic solvents such as isopropyl ether and methyl ethyl ketone in the presence of small amounts of sulfuric acid. In neither of the aforementioned works was any attempt made to recycle the polar organic liquid.

The results reported in this paper are the outcome of a novel experiment to combine the leaching and solvent extraction steps together into a new process which differs from the SIP process in that only trace amounts of aqueous lixiviants are used, and from a lyometallurgical technique in that only nonpolar inert diluents containing an extractant very selective to the valuable metal are employed. In essence, the attempted new process consists in extracting copper from chrysocolla, a highly porous hydrated copper silicate mineral, and copper, nickel and cobalt from manganese nodules, a potentially promising non-land based source for Ni and Co, with a solution of LIX in kerosene in the presence of very small amounts of strong aqueous ammonia. The feasibility of the process under various operating conditions is reported in this paper.

Physical and Chemical Characteristics of Chrysocolla and Manganese Nodules

Numerous studies have been reported on the structure of chrysocolla. A good review of the various conflicting postulates put forth by researches can be found in an article by Newberg[7]. Until the late 1960's chrysocolla was considered to be a mixture of a crystalline copper silicate phase dispersed in an amorphous silica hydrogel with a composition that can be expressed in terms of CuO, SiO_2 and H_2O. Recent articles by van Oosterwyck-Gastuche[8, 9] reveal that chrysocolla is a definite mineral with a characteristic fibrous structure and has an orthorhombic unit cell. Van Oosterwyck-Gastuche has proposed a combination sheet and chain silicate structure of nominal composition $Cu_8 (Si_4 O_{10})_2 (OH)_{12} n H_2O$, where n = 9, 4 or 8. Magnetic susceptibility measurements indicate that copper is present in chrysocolla in the form of Cu^{++} rather than as CuO [10]. Investigations [10, 11, 12] on the

structural nature of chrysocolla have revealed that it is a
very porous solid and that a cosiderable fraction of the
pores are in the macropore/micropore transition region (i.e.,
of radius 1.5 nm and less). The porous nature of chrysocolla
can be considerably reduced by heat treatment above $500^{\circ}C$ [11].

Ocean floor manganese nodules are comprised mainly of
extremely fine-grained manganese and iron oxides [13]. The
valuable metals copper, nickel and cobalt are distributed in
the manganese dioxide phase which actually consists of a
mixture of todorokite, birnessite and $\delta-MnO_2$. Early claims
were made that the cobalt was present in the iron oxide phase
comprised of ferric hydroxide gels and goethite, but the
results of a recent study indicate that this might not
be so [14].

Nodules are highly porous in nature. The porosity of nodules varies between 40-50% by volume, and nodules in which
60% of pores are smaller than 100 nm in size are quite common.
Consequently, manganese nodules are characterized by very
high surface areas, generally, in the order of 200 m^2/g. The
porous nature of nodules results in considerable entrapment
of water in the pores (approximately 20-25% by weight). The
microporous nature of nodules is considerably reduced on
heating in the temperature range $400-600^{\circ}C$ but the total
porosity value seems to remain approximately constant,
although more recent results indicate an increase in measured
porosity up to about $600^{\circ}C$ [15].

EXPERIMENTAL MATERIALS AND METHODS

Materials. The chrysocolla sample used in this investigation is a high-grade chrysocolla from Miami, Arizona,
containing small amounts of malachite. The DH-2 nodule
samples [13, 15] used in the investigations are samples dred-
ged at a location of $21^{\circ}50'N$ and $115^{\circ}112'W$ in the Pacific
Ocean at a depth of 3430 m. Both these materials were crushed, ground and sieved into different size fractions. Synthetic
cupric oxide marketed by Matheson, Coleman and Bell was used
in the leaching experiments. LIX 63 and LIX 64N samples were
obtained from General Mills Chemicals, Inc. Reagentgrade
odorless kerosene marketed by Baker Chemical Company was used
as the diluent for the LIX sample. The ammonium hydroxide
and ammonium chloride used were also of reagentgrade.

Methods. The leaching experiments were conducted by adding
the solid to a predetermined volume of a kerosene solution
containing LIX, followed by the addition of NH_4OH and stirring of the contents of the vessel. Suitable aliquots were
withdrawn at various intervals of time, diluted appropriately and analyzed for the metal values. In the case of the
experiments with chrysocolla the loaded solution was analyzed
for copper spectrophotometrically at 425 nm, a different analytical technique was used to analyze for the metal values
in the organic solution in contact with manganese nodules.
In this case, the samples taken at different times were diluted with methyl iso-butyl ketone and analyzed for copper,

964

nickel and cobalt with a Perkin Elmer 603 atomic absorption spectrophotometer..

The leaching experiments involving grinding were conducted in an attritor manufactured by Union Process Company, Ohio. Stainless steel balls of 3/16 inch diameter were used as the attriting medium.

Experiments involving a reductive treatment of the nodules were carried out in a mixture of 60/40 vol. percent CO/CO_2 flowing through a tube furnace at a rate of 500 cc/min.

Results. The feasibility of the lyometallurgical technique was first tested on chrysocolla. As a first step towards testing the feasibility of the process the effect of ammonia concentration on the extractability of copper was investigated. The amount of copper extracted from two different size fractions of chrysocolla* (35 x 48 mesh and 270 x 400 mesh) for ammonia concentrations of 1 cc to 5 cc is presented in Fig. 1 as a function of conditioning time.

---

*The copper content in the various size fractions of chrysocolla is given in Table 1.

TABLE 1

Chemical Analysis of Chrysocolla

Mesh Size	Copper Content, %
8 x 12	23.0
35 x 48	24.5
65 x 100	25.5
150 x 200	26.1
270 x 400	27.0

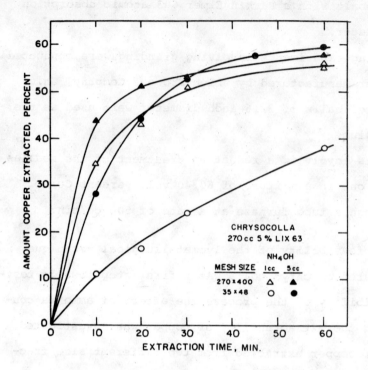

Fig. 1. Rate of extraction of copper from samples of
35 x 48 mesh and 270 x 400 mesh chrysocolla at two
different ammonium hydroxide concentrations,
viz. 1 cc and 5 cc, at a stirring speed of 860 rpm.

Increasing the ammonia concentration five-fold from 1 cc to

5 cc increases the amount of copper extracted from the

35 x 48 mesh size fraction by more than a factor of two during

the first 30 min of leaching. The extraction from the finer

size fraction is much less sensitive to the ammonia concentra-

tion, even during the early stages of leaching.

High concentrations of ammonium hydroxide, in spite of

yielding better extractions, results in the formation of a

second phase, a phenomenon that defeats the purpose of this new technique being investigated. Hence, it was decided to test the effect of other variables which might increase the amount and rate of copper extracted without requiring so much ammonia that a second phase formed. Temperature was the first variable studied and the results of the effect of temperature on the extraction from 35 x 48 size fraction with 1 cc NH_4OH and 270 cc of 5% LIX 63 in kerosene is given in Fig. 2.

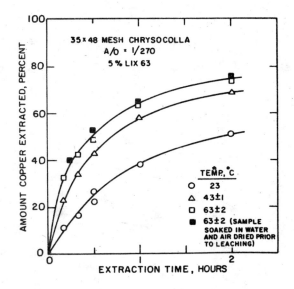

Fig. 2. Percentage of copper extracted from a sample of 35 x 48 mesh chrysocolla as a function of time at different temperatures in the presence of 1 cc NH_4OH.

As can be noted from the results in this figure, an increase in temperature increases not only the rate but also the amount of copper extracted.

As the investigation of particle size effect on the rate of extraction revealed that fine particles leach much more rapidly, it was decided to carry out a novel experiment in which size reduction and leaching take place simultaneously, that is, the experiments were conducted in the attritor mill. The extraction kinetics from 35 x 48 mesh particles with an aqueous to organic (A/O) ratio of 1/270 was investigated at two different impeller speeds, viz. 220 and 460 rpm. The results of this investigation are compared with those obtained just by ordinary stirring in Fig. 3, and they show that the rate of extraction can be boosted many fold by this new technique. Very high recoveries are obtained in a time period of 15 to 20 min.

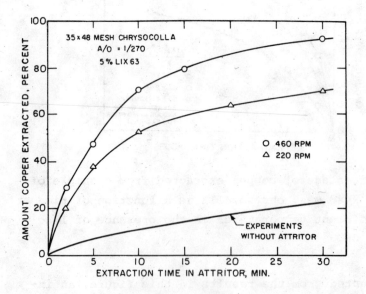

Fig. 3. Effect of impeller speed on the rate of extraction of copper from a sample of 35 x 48 mesh chrysocolla in an attritor.

As the leaching behaviour in the attritor was interestingly different, it was decided to further explore the process by investigating the effect of other experimental variables. The first variable chosen was the aqueous/organic ratio. The results of the leaching of Cu from 3 g of 35 x 48 mesh chrysocolla (which contains 0.735 g of copper) with 270 cc of 5% LIX 63 in kerosene with varying amounts of NH$_4$OH are presented in Fig. 4.

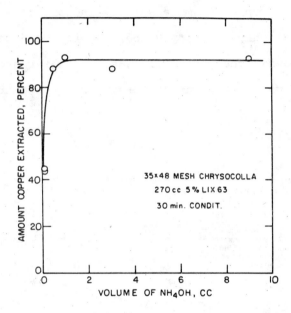

Fig. 4. Percentage of copper extracted in one half hour from a sample of 35 x 48 mesh chrysocolla as a function of the volume of NH$_4$OH in an attritor.

One interesting observation is that ammonia contents above 0.5 cc are superfluous to the extraction process. In spite of the fact that the ammonia content in 0.5 cc of 58% NH$_4$OH is approximately one eigth of the stoichiometric quantity of ammonia needed to complex the copper content in the ore as the stable Cu(NH$_3$)$_4^{++}$, the observed high extraction with this low ammonia content reflects the potential of this process. Even with 0.1 cc of NH_4OH, a recovery of 40% was achieved in a conditioning period of one-half hour.

Heating the chrysocolla prior to treatment has been reported to assist in its processing. For example, Dugdale and Habashi [16] found that the recovery of copper with ammoniacal solutions increased significantly on preheating the ore to 500-600°C and concluded that "copper is more soluble in partially dehydroxylated (activated) chrysocolla". Hence, it was decided to study whether removing the physically adsorbed water and chemically bound water would have any effect on this new extraction process.

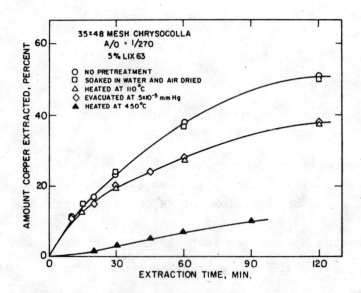

Fig. 5. Effect of various kinds of pretreatment on the kinetics of extraction of copper from a sample of 35 x 48 mesh chrysocolla in the presence of 1 cc NH_4OH.

In Fig. 5 the results of copper extraction from 35 x 48 mesh chrysocolla particles are summarized for the following pretreatment conditions: (1) preheated for 24 h at $110^{\circ}C$; (2) evacuated at 5 x 10^{-5} mm Hg for 24 h; (3) preheated for 24 h at $450^{\circ}C$; (4) soaked in water and air dried, and (5) untreated. Some observations that can be made from the information given in this Fig. are:

(1) Soaking the ore in water followed by air drying prior to leaching affects neither the recovery nor the rate of extraction of copper significantly at both $23^{\circ}C$ and $63^{\circ}C$ (Fig. 3). This probably indicates that the pores of untreated chrysocolla are already filled with water.

(2) Preheating the ore at $110^{\circ}C$ or evacuation to remove the physically adsorbed water is not beneficial to the extraction process in the sense that it lowers the amount of copper extracted.

(3) Preheating the ore to $450^{\circ}C$ decreases the initial rate of extraction tremendously. However, the extraction reaches 56% after 48 h (not shown in the Fig.).

A very important conclusions that can be reached from the results plotted in Fig. 5 is that drying the ore to remove either the physically adsorbed or chemically bound water is deleterious to the leaching process.

Since copper is considered to be present in chrysocolla as Cu^{++} rather than as CuO or $Cu(OH)_2$ the leaching characteristics of chrysocolla and copper oxide may be expected to be different. Hence, it was decided to investigate the amenability of CuO to leaching with LIX 63 diluted with kerosene in the presence of small quantities of NH_4OH. The synthetic CuO used in this investigation was nonporous. The results given in Fig. 6 shows that the leaching of CuO takes place very slowly even in the presence of 5 cc NH_4OH and only about 15% of the copper is extracted after 3 days.

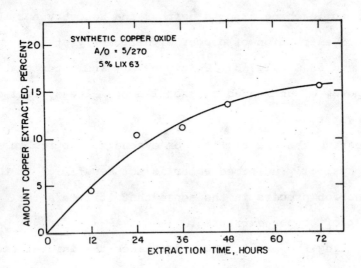

Fig. 6. Leaching of synthetic copper oxide with 5% LIX 63 in kerosene and 5 cc of NH_4OH.

If the leaching experiments were conducted in an attritor, the leaching takes place comparatively faster, even for lower amounts of NH_4OH as evident from the results given in Fig. 7. However, in the way of comparison, to obtain about 90% recovery of copper from chrysocolla, only one-half hour of attritor leaching is required.

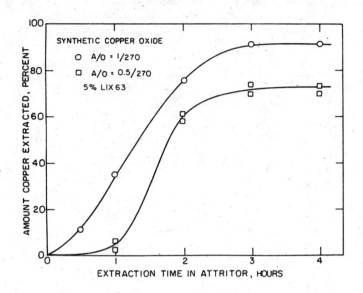

Fig. 7. Leaching of synthetic copper oxide in an attritor with 5% LIX 63 in kerosene and 1 cc or 0.5 cc of NH_4OH.

As previous work on the ammoniacal leaching of chrysocolla by Dugdale and Habashi [16] indicated that the copper recovery depends on the NH_3/NH_4^+ ratio (and hence on pH), it was decided to investigate the effect of NH_3/NH_4^+ ratio in this leaching/solvent extraction process. Two types of experiments were performed:

(1) At fixed total ammonia concentration (0.25 g total ammonia in 1.00 cc of 58% NH_4OH), the NH_3/NH_4^+ ratio was varied thereby changing the pH of the solution.

(2) The pH was varied by adding NH_4Cl without keeping the total ammonia concentration fixed.

The results of these two types of experiments are given in Fig. 8 and 9.

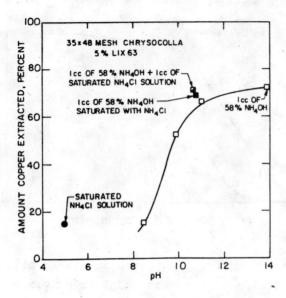

Fig. 8. Percentage of copper extracted after 24 h from a sample of 35 x 48 mesh chrysocolla as a function of the pH of the aqueous (NH_3/NH_4^+) solution.

Figure 8 presents the extraction behavior of copper as a function of pH after a conditioning time of 24 h. As can be observed from this Figure, for a given total ammonia content, the higher the pH (i.e., the higher the free ammonia content) the higher is the extraction. Addition of ammonia in the form of NH_4^+ to 1 cc of 58% NH_4OH solution does not seem to improve the extraction in any manner. Figure 9 shows how the extraction rate is affected by the two types of experiments. Two important observations can be made from these results:

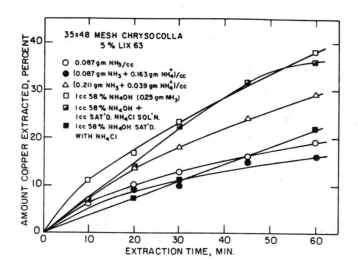

Fig. 9. Rate of extraction of copper from a sample of
35 x 48 mesh chrysocolla in presence of aqueous
ammoniacal solutions of varying NH_3/NH_4^+ concentrations.

(1) The higher the free ammonia concentration, the higher
is the rate of extraction. This is evident from the
results obtained with 1 cc NH_4OH (0.251 g NH_3), 1 cc NH_3
(0.212 g)/NH_4^+ (0.04 g) solution and 1 cc NH_3 (0.083 g)/
NH_4^+ (0.164 g) solution.

(2) Addition of NH_4^+ tends to decrease the initial rate of
reaction at high ammonia concentrations and has a
negligible effect both on the rate and extent of extraction at low ammonia concentrations (c.f., 1 cc NH_3
(0.087 g) solution and 1 cc NH_3 (0.087 g)/NH_4^+ (0.163 g)
solution).

EXTRACTION OF COPPER, NICKEL AND COBALT
FROM MANGANESE NODULES

In investigating the possibility of using this new process
to extract metals from deep sea manganese nodules, two parameters were considered: namely, the effect of pretreatment and
the effect of particle size. It is a well-established fact [13]
that prereduction of nodules prior to ammoniacal leaching aids
the dissolution of metals and that the prereduction temperature
is also an important variable. Hence, the effect of preheating
in an inert atmosphere and preheating in a reducing atmosphere

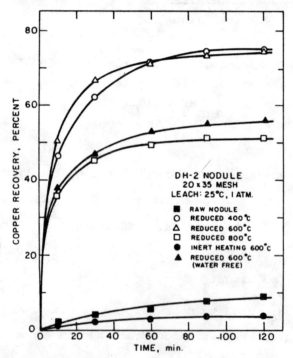

Fig. 10. Effect of pretreatment on copper extraction
from DH-2 nodule.

on the recovery of copper, nickel and cobalt were investigated. Figure 10 shows how the extraction of copper from a 20 x 35 mesh nodule sample is affected by pretreatment. Unlike the case of chrysocolla, preheating in inert atmosphere is not very detrimental to the extraction process while, by the same token, it does not seem to improve the very low recoveries obtainable from the raw nodule. However, treatment in a CO/CO_2 atmosphere is beneficial and a prereduction temperature of $400^\circ C$ yields about 75% copper extraction. This temperature seems to be the optimum temperature for copper recovery, similar to previous findings on normal ammonia leaching of nodules [17].

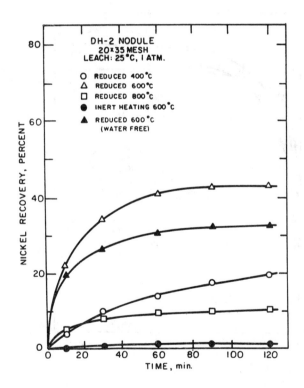

Fig. 11. Effect of pretreatment on nickel extraction from DH-2 nodule.

The kinetics of nickel extraction, as shown in Fig. 11, is also considerably accelerated by a reductive roast prior to leaching. In the case of nickel, the highest recoveries obtainable are only of the order of 40%. In contrast to the copper recovery, a higher reduction temperature up to 600°C facilitates the nickel removal from the solid, again similar to normal ammonia leaching procedures [17]. Cobalt recovery from 20 x 35 mesh samples was found to be negligible, irrespective of the mode of pretreatment.

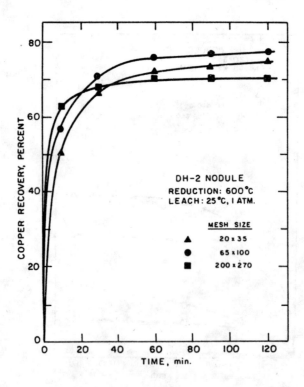

Fig. 12. Effect of particle size on copper extraction from DH-2 nodule after reduction at 600°C.

The effect of particle size on the extraction of copper, nickel and cobalt are given in Figs 12, 13 and 14. These results indicate that particle size has a negligible effect on copper recovery whereas for nickel and cobalt it is significant; that the smaller the particle size, the better is the kinetics of extraction for all metals; and that no cobalt recovery is detected for a 20 x 35 mesh sample, but first appears at 65 x 100 mesh.

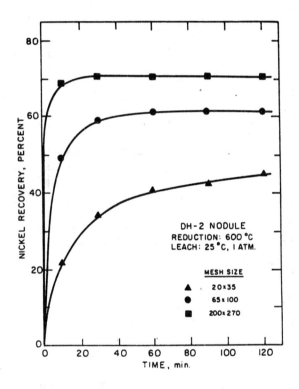

Fig. 13. Effect of particle size on nickel extraction from DH-2 nodule after reduction at 600°C.

The presence of capillary-condensed water seems to assist the extraction process though not essential for the feasibility of the process, as can be discerned from the results given in Figs 10 and 11. A comparison of the extraction values for pre-heated and prereduced samples indicate that reduction and not a change in physical structure is necessary for the successful leaching and extraction of nickel and copper.

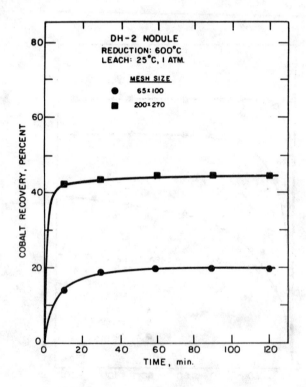

Fig. 14. Effect of particle size on cobalt extraction from DH-2 nodule after reduction at 600°C.

DISCUSSION

The underlying mechanism of the lyometallurgical process will be explained in the next few pages with reference to chrysocolla. The same type of reasoning should apply for the processing of manganese nodules.

To explain the success and the mechanism of the lyometal-lurgical process reported in this paper the following two points have been taken into consideration:

(1) Chrysocolla is a porous solid and the pores are filled with capillary condensed water. Removal of this water in the pores by heating decreases the rate and extent of extraction. Hence, the water in the pores of the solid seems to play a very important role in this novel extraction process. Synthetic copper oxide, which is non-porous, is not very amenable to treatment by this technique.

(2) The amount of ammonia required to give good extrac-tions is far less than the amount needed to complex all the copper as $Cu(NH_3)_4^{++}$

Bearing these two points in mind, and based on the experimental results we propose the following mechanism which is schematically illustrated in Fig. 15.

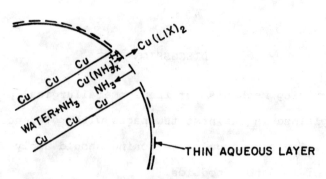

Fig. 15. Schematic diagram depicting the extraction
process.

(1) Since the solubility of ammonia in kerosene is low and
its distribution coefficient into water is very high,
it should be reasonable to expect that most of the
ammonia added enters the water in the pores while the
rest remains in a thin liquid layer around the
particles.

(2) The ammonia inside the pores reacts with copper and
produces a cuproammonium complex $Cu(NH_3)_x^{++}$ which
diffuses out towards the exterior of the particle.

(3) The cuproammonium complex diffusing out towards the
mouth of the pores at the surface of the particle
reacts with LIX 63 in kerosene as follows:

$$Cu(NH_3)_x^{++} \Big|_{aq} + 2\ RH \Big|_{org} + 2OH^- = CuR_2 \Big|_{org} + 2\ H_2O + xNH_3$$

The ammonia is regenerated during this reaction and returns to the aqueous phase within the pores.

The marked increase in the rate of extraction when the conventional stirring is substituted by grinding could be due to a number of reasons. Two very probable reasons are the reduction in diffusion path lengths due to size reduction and the increased reactivity of the freshly produced surface during grinding. Further systematic investigation is required to elucidate these phenomena more fully.

The main differences in the leaching behavior of CuO and chrysocolla may stem from a number of factors. Chrysocolla is very porous and the water filling the pores acts as a carrier for ammonia molecules to penetrate the interior of the solid particles. On the other hand, CuO (used in this investigation) is almost non-porous and the added ammonia has to remain as a fluid film around the particles and then diffuse into the particles. Agglomeration of water coated particles in an organic medium is quite possible. This tendency to agglomerate will be reduced when the experiments are conducted in an attritor. Finally, the inherent solubility or "leachability" of copper in the two minerals may simply be the cause for the differences in leaching behavior. Recall, for example, that Prosser et al. found copper to be present in chrysocolla as Cu^{++} rather than as CuO.

Drying the ore to remove either the physically adsorbed or chemically bound water seems to be deleterious to the extraction process, and the reasons for this behavior can only be speculated on. Removing the physically adsorbed water from

the pores may cause the organic phase to enter and fill the
pores. Upon the addition of aqueous ammonia, the added ammonia
should spread et the organic/solid interface and react with
the copper in the solid lattice. The ammonia regenerated on
the transfer of the cuproammonium complex to the organic phase
will now be localized, unlike the conditions where the pores
are filled with water. More ammonia must diffuse through the
organic fluid to keep the extraction process going. Once
a certain quantity of aqueous ammonia accumulates the pores,
it may form a continuous phase by displacing kerosene which
does not wet the polar copper silicate. This latter process
may take time and this perhaps explains why even though the
initial rate of copper extraction from the solid preheated to
$450^{\circ}C$ is low, a recovery of 56% can be achieved after 48 h.
It should be recalled that heating the chrysocolla to $450^{\circ}C$
dehydroxylated the surface partially and this partial dehydroxylation may cause the rate of extraction from the ore heated
at $450^{\circ}C$ to be much slower than after heating only at $110^{\circ}C$.
Removal of surface hydroxyls may result in the formation of
CuO and, as pointed out in the previous section CuO leaches
much slower than the chrysocolla.

The role of the NH_4^+/NH_3 ratio in this process is really
intriguing. An NH_4^+/NH_3 ratio of approximately one is known
to be optimal for the recovery of copper in normal ammoniacal
leaching processes. In total contrast to this, the recoveries
obtained in this lyometallurgical method seem to depend only
on the free ammonia concentration. An explanation for this
may be that the copper in ammoniacal-leach solutions is

usually present in the form of $Cu(NH_3)_4^{++}$ whereas due to the starvation conditions existing in the lyometallurgical method, the copper is present in the pore water only as $Cu(NH_3)_n^{++}$ where n is likely to be less than 4. Another possible reason is that copper is present in chrysocolla in the form of Cu^{++} and hence the removal of Cu^{++} from the lattice and its transfer to the organic phase is easily effected only by free ammonia in the pores.

Unlike chrysocolla, manganese nodules respond poorly to the lyometallurgical treatment unless they are given a pre-reduction treatment. Such a prereduction has been found to be necessary even for the conventional ammoniacal leaching of manganese nodules [13]. In the case of manganese nodules a higher aqueous/organic ratio was used since the nodules are characterized by a pore volume per unit weight which is almost three that of chrysocolla (0.25-0.3 cc/gram of nodule vs. 0.08-0.1 cc/gram of chrysocolla) [13, 15].

The results of lyometallurgical extraction of metals from a 65 x 100 mesh size fraction of nodules are given in Table 2 along with a summary of typical results of a conventional ammoniacal leach of nodules. A comparison of the results indicate that the lyometallurgical technique is quite com-parable   to an ammoniacal leach in terms of recoveries.

The different behavior of nodules reduced at $400^\circ C$ and $600^\circ C$ can be explained in terms of the oxidation state of nickel and copper in the nodules as these temperatures.

TABLE 2

Lyometallurgical Treatment of 65 x 100 Mesh DH-2 Manganese
Nodules Produced at 600°C

Aqueous phase/Oil phase = 1/100

Metal	Recovery, %
Cu	77
Ni	61.6
Co	19.6

Summary of the Results of Ammonia-ammonium Carbonate
Leaching of a 48 x 100 Mesh Sample of DH-2 Nodules
After Pre-reduction

Leach system	Reduction temp.	% Recovery Ni	Cu	Co	Mn	Fe
Carbonate	400°C	43	85	22	4	1
Carbonate	600°C	65	44	50	4	2
Sulphate	400°C	68	95	50	10	0
Sulphate	600°C	74	60	50	42	0

Reduction conditions: 2 h roast with a $CO:CO_2$ gas mixture
(60%:40%) at 400°C and 600°C

Leach conditions: 1 h at 25°C with 1.6M NH_3 and 1.6M
$(NH_4)_2CO_3$ or 1.6M NH_3 and 1.6M $(NH_4)_2SO_4$

A temperature of 400°C may have been sufficient only to effect
a partial reduction of nickel oxide to the nickel metal and
copper oxide to copper metal. However, in the case of copper,
cuprous oxide formed along with the copper metal is likely to
leach faster with the ammoniacal solution than the copper
metal, as has been observed by other researches [17]. Hence
a higher copper recovery is obtained with a nodule reduced

at 400°C. A higher reduction temperature should favor the formation of metallic nickel and nickel extraction from nodule samples prereduced at 600°C are indeed better.

The poor recoveries after reduction at 800°C might be attributed to two possibilities. Firstly, between reduction at 600°C and 800°C the pore diameters might have become too large to effectively contain the ammoniacal lixiviant within the pores (Table 3).

TABLE 3

Average Pore Diameter of Nodule After Reduction

Reduction Temperature (°C)	Diameter Size Range* (nm)	Average Pore Diameter** (nm)
400	6-110	27
600	44-260	107
800	54-680	192

*Majority of pores were estimated to occur between 20 and 99% cumulative pore volume.

**Pore size distribution is a logarithmic plot, therefore geometric mean was used $x = (x_1 \ x_2)^{1/2}$

This would result in poorer leaching and extraction. Secondly, nodules may contain sodium chloride from their original sea environment. At high reduction temperatures significant formation of gaseous metal chlorides may have occurred with the consequent loss of metal chlorides from the sample. This was indicated by the deposition of a green colored film at the exit of the quartz tube used for pretreatment. This would account for the apparent poorer recoveries upon reduction at 800°C.

There are reported results on the effect of particle size on the extraction of metals from nodules by ammoniacal leaching. Experimental data gathered by Fuerstenau et al. [13] on the extractability of metals with a sulfuric acid leaching technique show that copper and also cobalt extraction are much more particle-size dependent than nickel extraction. However, the sensitivity to particle size was found to be a function of nodule type. This observed difference in the leachability of copper, nickel and cobalt from nodule particles was considered to be due to the different modes of occurrence of these metals and to differences in pore size distributions in the nodules, as mentioned in the background section. The observed dependence of the lyometallurgical extraction of metals on the particle size is in direct contrast to the results of the acid leaching of nodules. In the lyometallurgical technique nickel and especially cobalt extraction is markedly dependent on particle size whereas copper extraction is almost independent of particle size.

SUMMARY AND CONCLUSIONS

The proposed lyometallurgical process involving simultaneous leaching and extraction appears to work well for the extraction of metal values from chrysocolla and deep-sea manganese nodules. Roughly 70 to 75% of the copper can be extracted from chrysocolla even with an ammonia content which is about one-fourth the stoichiometric quantity required to

988

leach copper in normal aqueous-phase leaching systems. The large quantities of physically adsorbed water in the pores of chrysocolla is actually a blessing in disguise for this extraction process in that this water provides a transport vehicle for transfer of the copper from inside the solid to the organic phase. The recovery of copper and the extraction rate can be greatly improved if the experiments are conducted in an attritor mill.

Unlike chrysocolla, manganese nodules respond poorly to the lyometallurgical technique unless they are given a prereductive treatment. Such prereduction has been found to be necessary even for the conventional ammoniacal leaching of manganese nodules. The best kinetics and highest recovery of metal values have been achieved for nodules subjected to a reductive treatment at $600^{o}C$. Recoveries of 71% of the nickel, 69% of the copper and 44% of the cobalt have been obtained from such pre-reduced samples. This low recovery of cobalt is of the same magnitude as normally experienced in nodule leaching with aqueous ammonia.

REFERENCES

1. Anon S. A. Mining and Engineering Journal, p. 27, March (1977).

2. Hughes M. A. and Purdey C. Trans. IMM, 85, p. C 124 (1976).

3. Haines A. K. et al. XI IMPC., paper 32, Cagliari 1975.

4. Ritcey G. M. Chem. and Ind., 51, p. 1294 (1971).

5. Report dated Aug. 15, 1950 submitted by F. W. Bloecher Jr., to Professor A. M. Gaudin Department of Metallurgy, MIT.

6. Magner J. E. and Bailes R. H. Proc. Second International Conference on Peaceful Uses of Atomic Energy, Geneva, 1958, pp. 446-448.

7. Newberg D. W. Econ. Geol., 62, 932 (1967).

8. Van Oosterwyck-Gastuche M. C., C. R. Acad. Sci., Paris, Ser. D., 271, p. 1837 (1969).

9. Van Oosterwyck-Gastuche and Gregoire C. Inst. Mineral Assc., Pap. Proc. Gen Meeting, 7th, 1, 196 (1970).

10. Prosser A. P., Wright A. J. and Stephens J. D. Trans. IMM, 14, 23? (1965).

11. Raghavan S. and Fuerstenau D. W. Int. J. Mineral Processing, 4, 381 (1977).

12. Pohlman S. L. and Olson F. A. Solution Mining Symposium, (F. F. Aplan et al., ed.), AIME, New York, 1974, p. 466.

13. Fuerstenau D. W. and Han K. N. Extractive Metallurgy in Marine Manganese Desposits, (ed. G. P. Glasby), Elsevier Oceanography Series, 15, pp. 357-390 (1977).

14. Agarwal J. C. et al. Journal of Metals, 28, 24 (1976).

15. Harris I., M. S. Thesis, College of Engin., University of California, Berkeley, Calif. 1977.

16. Dugdale R. and Habashi F. Trans. AIME, 256, 28 (1973).

17. Han K. N., Hoover M. and Fuerstenau D. W. Int. J. Mineral Processing, 1, 215 (1974).

ABSTRACT

An interesting and unconventional process for the recovery
of metal values from oxidized ores has been investigated. This
process consists in contacting the ore particles with a kerosene solution containing a LIX extractant in the presence of
small amounts of strong aqueous ammonia. The extraction of
copper from chrysocolla and copper, nickel and cobalt from
ocean floor manganese nodules have been investigated using
this technique. The effect of such variables as particle size,
concentration of ammonia and the nature of pretreatment on the
feasibility of this technique are reported in this paper.

RÉSUMÉ

On a essayé un procédé intéressant et non-conventionnel de
récupération des métaux de valeur issus de minerais oxydés
Cette méthode consiste à mettre en contact les grains de
minerai avec la solution de kérosène comprenant le solvant
d'extraction LIX en présence d'une petite quantité de solution
aqueuse avec une grande concentration d'ammoniaque. On a
essayé l'extraction de cuivre des chrysocolles ainsi que de
cuivre, nickel et cobalt du minerai de manganèse poreux
provenant du fond des océans. On a présenté l'influence de la
dimension de grains, de la concentration de solution aqueuse
d'ammoniaque et du caractère de prétraitement.

ZUSAMMENFASSUNG

Es wurde ein interessanter und unkonventioneller Prozess
der Gewinnung wertvoller Metalle aus oxydierten Erzen untersucht.
Die Methode besteht in einem Kontakt der Erzkörner mit
einer Kerosinlösung mit geringenz Gehalt an LIX - Extrakt,
bei gleichzeitiger Anwendung einer geringen Menge einer
wässerigen Ammoniaklösung.

In dem Beitrag sind die Ergebnisse der Axtraktion von Kupfer, aus Chrysokollen und von Kupfer, Nickel und Kobalt aus den Tiefseelagerstätten der Mangan-Eisen-Konkretionen besprochen.

Es sind: der Einfluss der Korngrösse, der Ammoniaklösungkonzentration und das Wesen, der Voraufbereitung untersucht worden.

РЕЗЮМЕ

Исследован интересный и нестереотипный процесс извлечения ценных металлов из окисленных руд.

Метод основан на контакте рудных частиц с керосиновым раствором, содержащим экстрагент LIX в присутствии небольшого количества сильного аммичного водного раствора.

Исследовано использование этой технологии для извлечения меди из хризоколлы, а также меди, никеля и кобальта из океанических морганцевых нодулей.

Изучено влияние на исследуемый процесс размеров частиц, концентрации аммичного раствора и предварительной обработки руды.

PRESSURE LEACHING PROCESS FOR COMPLEX ZINC-LEAD CONCENTRATES

G. L. Bolton, N. Zubryckyj and H. Veltman

Sherritt Research Centre, Sherritt Gordon Mines Ltd., Fort Saskatchewan, Alberta, Canada

//

INTRODUCTION

The process discussed here, and its application to low grade zinc-lead concentrates such as those produced from ores found in the Province of New Brunswick in Canada, represents Sherritt's most recent work on the recovery of zinc by pressure leaching. It is a successful combination of the acid pressure leach process with conventional purification and electrowinning technology which permits the economical recovery of zinc from concentrates not suitable for treatment by the roast-leach process.

There are no gaseous pollutants such as SO_2 associated with the pressure leach process. Instead, sulphide sulphur is oxidized only to its stable elemental form and is stored in a tailings pond; future recovery for sale or use is possible. An important advantage of the process is that there is no necessity to produce sulphuric acid.

The suitability of the process was studied for the treatment of both a zinc-lead bulk concentrate, and a previously processed tailings which had been upgraded to an acceptable zinc concentrate. To produce 100,000 short tons per year of cathode zinc from bulk concentrate, the capital and operating costs in mid-1979 Canadian dollars are estimated to be approximately $130,300,000 and $0.30/kg of zinc, respectively.

In view of the low copper content of the concentrates used, and the assumed availability of relatively inexpensive sulphuric acid, the single stage leach process option was selected as a result of this study. However, since some New Brunswick bulk concentrates may contain up to 3% copper, additional work was performed employing a two-stage leach system. This enhances copper extractions and makes the recovery of that metal economically feasible. Adoption of the two-stage leach system would increase capital and annual operating cost by approximately $1,400,000 and $0.009/kg of zinc, respectively.

History of the Sherritt Zinc Process

Development of the Sherritt Zinc Process was begun in 1959 by Forward and Veltman [1] who investigated the direct pressure-oxidation-sulphuric acid leaching of a low grade zinc concentrate. That work was conducted at about $110^{\circ}C$, which is below the melting point of sulphur. If the sulphur was allowed to melt, it coated the unreacted metal sulphides and prevented leaching beyond about 50% of the zinc. Extractions of between 95% and 99% of the zinc in a concentrate ground to 100% minus 44 μm were achieved with single-stage batch retention times of 2 h to 4 h, and oxygen partial pressures between 70 kPa and 410 kPa (100 kPa = 14.5 psi = 1.0 kg/cm^2).

A pilot plant study using the 110°C leach was conducted in 1962-1963. It indicated that for the low temperature leach, 96% zinc extraction could be reached with a 6 h retention time in a continuous operation. About 90% of the sulphide sulphur in the high grade concentrate was converted to elemental sulphur. Parallel laboratory tests found that the leach solutions were suitable for treatment by a conventional purification-electrowinning scheme.

During subsequent years, further work by Sherritt resulted in improvements to the process [2-6]. It was found that when providing up to a 50% excess of concentrate to the leach, and then recycling unleached sulphides, the leach could be conducted at 150°C, which is above the melting point of sulphur [4]. This greatly accelerated the reaction and zinc extractions of 96% to 98% were possible in a 2 h bath retention time. However, flexibility of residue disposal was limited since the elemental sulphur had to be removed to permit recycle of the unleached zinc sulphides.

Laboratory studies conducted at various times from 1965-71 produced one of the most important improvements to the process. It was discovered that certain surface active agents inhibit the wetting of metal sulphides by molten elemental sulphur [5]. The addition of synthetic or naturally occurring organic compounds permitted the leach to be conducted at 150°C, giving zinc extractions of at least 96% from both high and low grade concentrates without the need for any residue recycle, in batch retention times of the order of 1 h.

A further improvement to the process was the development of the two-stage countercurrent leach option [6]. This method of operation was seen as a way to achieve maximum utilization of return electrolyte acid. Pregnant leach solution coming from the first stage would now have only about 2 g/l free sulphuric acid and less than 1 g/l iron. Zinc extraction was as high as 99% in this leaching mode.

Recently, Sherritt has investigated the pressure leach response of a wide variety of zinc concentrates, including its own concentrates from the Province of Manitoba [7]. A considerable amount has been learned, not only about the leach, but also about impurities deportments, liquid-solids separations, solution purification and residues treatments. An independent evaluation of the Sherritt Zinc Process, as compared with the well known roast-leach process, has shown a significant capital cost advantage in favor of the Sherritt process. Operating costs are similar, unless a penalty is assessed against the roast-leach operation for losses on sales of sulphuric acid, or its neutralization, in which case the Sherritt process again shows a decided economic advantage.

In 1977, Sherritt and Cominco cooperated in a pilot plant campaign which successfully demonstrated the large scale continuous leaching of zinc sulphide concentrates. Methods for the separation of elemental sulphur from the leach

996

residues were also tested and proven to be viable. This
piloting venture has proven the technical integrity of the
process to the point that commercial application of direct
zinc pressure leaching will now become a reality in the near
future. When this occurs Sherritt intends to license the
process to interested companies.

Now it has been shown on a bench scale that the low grade
bulk zinc-lead concentrates produced from complex New
Brunswick ores also respond very well to the Sherritt process.
Zinc extractions of 95% to 99% are obtained for single or
two-stage leaches in retention times of 1.0 h to 2.0 h.
Lead is recovered as a 19% to 35% lead residue which can be
upgraded to a 33% to 63% lead concentrate.

Process Description

The Sherritt Zinc Process comprises pressure acid leaching
of zinc concentrates in return electrolyte solution to dissolve the zinc, followed by more conventional solution purification and electrowinning of metallic zinc. The leach
residue consists of lead and iron as basic sulphates, elemental sulphur, and gangue; it can be further processed to
recover by-products of lead sulphate and elemental sulphur.
Most of the silver in the concentrate is carried with the
lead and iron sulphates, and may also be recovered.

The process is illustrated in Fig. 1 and may be detailed
as follows.

Finely ground zinc-lead sulphide concentrate is slurried
with return electrolyte acid and directly leached under an

997

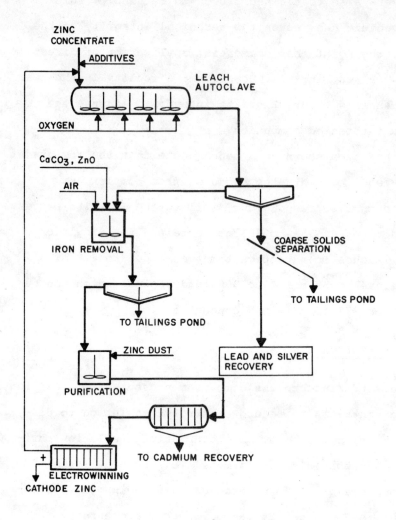

Fig. 1. Single Stage Leach Zinc Process.

overpressure of oxygen at about 150°C for 1 h to 2 h. In the

autoclave, zinc is dissolved by the sulphuric acid, and

sulphide sulphur is oxidized to its elemental form according

to the following overall reaction.

$$ZnS + H_2SO_4 + 0.5O_2 \rightarrow ZnSO_4 + S^0 + H_2O \qquad (1)$$

This reaction is very rapid and gives nearly complete zinc extraction from all of the many concentrates tested by Sherritt.

While reaction (1) describes the result, it does not reveal the leaching mechanism. The presence of dissolved iron has been found to be beneficial, or even necessary, which suggests the following as a major leaching reaction.

$$Fe_2(SO_4)_3 + ZnS \rightarrow 2FeSO_4 + ZnSO_4 + S^0 \qquad (2)$$

The ferrous sulphate is rapidly re-oxidized to ferric sulphate as shown in reaction (3).

$$2FeSO_4 + H_2SO_4 + 0.5O_2 \rightarrow Fe_2(SO_4)_3 + H_2O \qquad (3)$$

Other redox couples, for example the cuprous-cupric couple, may perform a similar function in the leaching of sphalerite. The major reactions undergone by other metal sulphides are shown below. Note that lead sulphate, formed by the reaction of galena with sulphuric acid, may react further to yield lead jarosite, as shown in reaction (6).

$$2FeS + 3H_2SO_4 + 1.5O_2 \rightarrow Fe_2(SO_4)_3 + 2S^0 + 3H_2O \qquad (4)$$

$$PbS + H_2SO_4 + 0.5O_2 \rightarrow PbSO_4 + S^0 + H_2O \qquad (5)$$

$$PbSO_4 + 3Fe_2(SO_4)_3 + 12H_2O \rightarrow Pb\left[Fe_3(SO_4)_2(OH)_6\right]_2 + 6H_2SO_4 \qquad (6)$$

$$CuFeS_2 + 2H_2SO_4 + O_2 \rightarrow CuSO_4 + FeSO_4 + 2S^0 + 2H_2O \qquad (7)$$

Pyrite does not react to any significant extent at the conditions normally chosen for the leaching of zinc.

Some of the dissolved iron is removed from solution in the lead jarosite. Additional iron may be removed as a basic sulphate compound such as hydronium jarosite.

$$1.5Fe_2(SO_4)_3 + 7H_2O \rightarrow (H_3O)Fe_3(SO_4)_2(OH)_6 + 2.5H_2SO_4 \quad (8)$$

Still further iron removal occurs as the sulphuric acid is depleted; this iron may appear as a complex hydrated ferric oxide, as shown in reaction (9).

$$Fe_2(SO_4)_3 + (x + 3)H_2O \rightarrow Fe_2O_3 \cdot xH_2O + 3H_2SO_4 \quad (9)$$

Slurry discharged from the autoclave is separated into solution and residue solids fractions by countercurrent decantation and/or filtration. The zinc sulphate solution is purified by conventional methods, and zinc is recovered by electrowinning. The spent electrolyte is recycled to leaching.

The residue solids are separated into an elemental sulphur-pyrite fraction and a basic lead-iron sulphate (+ silver) fraction by sieving or flotation. There is a tendency for the elemental sulphur formed during the leach to agglomerate with pyrite and other unleached metal sulphides. When the leach slurry cools below the melting point of sulphur, the agglomerates solidify to form pellets. Typically, in laboratory leach tests, these pellets are uniform spheres which are easily retained on a 100 mesh Tyler screen. The elemental sulphur-pyrite fraction can be stored indefinitely in a tailings pond or processed to recover an elemental sulphur

which would be suitable, possibly with some additional cleaning operations, for marketing to sulphuric acid manufacturers.
The lead-iron basic sulphates are upgraded by additional
leaching to give a lead sulphate suitable for feed to a lead
smelter. Most of the silver in the concentrate would be recovered with the lead sulphate.

Application to Low Grade Bulk Concentrates

Low grade bulk concentrates of the type obtained by the
bulk flotation of ores of the New Brunswick type are a fine
grained mixture of sphalerite, galena, pyrite and chalcopyrite which may analyze about 30% Zn, 3-13% Pb, 35% pyrite
and 1% Cu. They cannot be upgraded commercially to high grade
concentrates of the separate metals without significant sacri-
fices in overall recovery of metal values.

Treatment of such low grade bulk concentrates by the
conventional roasting process would create two major difficulties. First, a very large tonnage of sulphuric acid would
have to be disposed of ($\sim$3.4 t of acid per ton of zinc), and
second, much of the zinc in the calcine would be converted to
ferrite ($ZnO \cdot Fe_2O_3$) during the roast. The latter would necessitate the use of a second stage hot acid ferrite leach,
with the attendant jarosite or goethite precipitation stages,
for recovery of much of the zinc.

Laboratory Investigations

Concentrate Analyses. Two different concentrates from
New Brunswick were used for this study; one was a tailings
material which had been upgraded by flotation and the other
was a typical bulk flotation concentrate. Average chemical
analyses of the major elements in the concentrates are given
in Table 1. The as-received upgraded tailings was approximately 90% minus 40 μm and the bulk concentrates were essentially 100% minus 40 μm, so no further grinding was required.

TABLE 1

Average Analyses of New Brunswick Concentrates

Concentrate	Chemical Analysis, (%, ppm Ag)					
	Zn	Fe	Pb	Cu	S_T	Ag
Upgraded Tailings	31.0	21.6	3.6	0.76	35.8	154
Bulk	29.9	17.9	12.4	0.67	33.3	398

Zinc Leaching. Two alternatives were investigated, these
being single-stage leaching and two-stage countercurrent
leaching. The single-stage and two-stage leach schemes are
shown in Fig. 1 and 2, respectively. Other conditions common
to these leaches, and a summary of extractions, are given
in Table 2. Note that zinc extraction is always greater than
95%.

Typical residue and pregnant liquor analyses are compiled in Table 3. In the single-stage leaches, the iron and sulphuric acid levels in the pregnant liquor are high enough that a two-stage iron removal is needed. The two-stage leach gives a more efficient utilization of acid, and the pregnant liquor is therefore low in both sulphuric acid and iron. A single-stage of iron removal is sufficient for treating two-stage leach electrolytes.

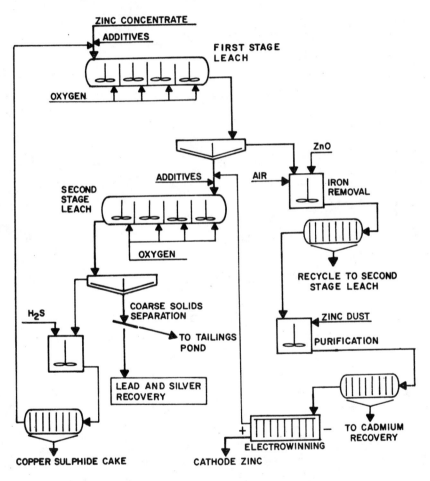

Fig. 2. Two Stage Leach Zinc Process.

TABLE 2

Typical Laboratory Leach Results for New Brunswick Zinc/Lead Concentrates

Common Conditions: $H_2SO_4/(Zn+Pb+Cu)$ mol ratio $\simeq$ 1.05/1.0, 345 kPa O_2 partial pressure, 1.0 h, 0.3 g/l Additives, 150°C

Concentrate	Leach Stages	Pregnant Liquor g/l		Distribution (%)					
				Solution			Solids		
							+100 mesh	−100 mesh	
		Fe_T	H_2SO_4	Zn	Cu	Fe	S^{o}*	Pb	Ag
Upgraded Tailings	One	2.0	23.4	96.9	57.0	3.2	36.7	96.7	75
	Two	0.2	pH 5.3	99.2	93.1	−	38.2	>95	−
Bulk	One	0.78	20.8	96.9	48.7	1.3	45.0	95.2	75
	Two	0.17	0.1	99.1	93.8	−	48.8	98.6	−

*The amount of sulphur in feed solids reporting as elemental sulphur in residues.

TABLE 3

Typical Leach Residue and Pregnant Liquor Analyses

Concentrate	Chemical Analysis (% or g/l)						ppm
	Zn	Cu	Fe	Pb	S^o	H_2SO_4	Ag
Upgraded Tailings							
1. 150°C, Single Stage Leach							
Pregnant Liquor	130 – 140	0.8 – 1	2			15 – 25	
+100 mesh residue	1	0.5	32	0.2	25.0		44
-100 mesh residue	2	0.2	25	19	8		830
2. 150°C, Two-Stage Leach							
Pregnant Liquor	130 – 140	<0.1	0.5			<1.0	
2nd stage residue							
+100 mesh	0.4	<0.1	30	<1	30		89
-100 mesh	0.4	<0.1	10	33	4		1165
Bulk							
1. 150°C, Single Stage Leach							
Pregnant Liquor	130 – 140	1	1			20	
+100 mesh residue	0.3	0.7	30	1	29		199
-100 mesh residue	2	0.2	17	33	3		600
2. 150°C, Two-Stage Leach							
Pregnant Liquor	130 – 140	<0.1	0.3			<1.0	
2nd stage residue							
+100 mesh	0.2	<0.1	26	0.4	41		
-100 mesh	0.5	<0.1	18	33	1		

Only about half the copper is extracted in a single-stage leach conducted at 150°C. This copper can be recovered by cementation on zinc dust during solution purification. In the two-stage leach alternative, much higher copper recovery is possible for concentrates containing only about 1% of copper. Greater than 90% of the copper is put into solution in the second stage (high acid concentration stage) of the leach. Since this copper would be largely precipitated as basic copper sulphate in the low acid first stage leach, an inter-stage copper removal is necessary to prevent build-up of a recycling load. The copper removal may be achieved by a sulphide precipitation or by cementation on zinc dust, followed by filtration. Laboratory tests have also confirmed a high second-stage leach copper extraction from New Brunswick bulk concentrates which were "spiked" to 2.5% Cu with a typical Canadian Shield chalcopyrite concentrate.

The leach residues are readily separated into two fractions by sieving; the coarser fraction contains nearly all of the elemental sulphur and pyrite; while the finer fraction contains the lead and about 75% of the silver. The former residue may be stored in a tailings pond, while the latter is processed for the recovery of metal values.

Although the two-stage leach gives slightly better metallurgical results and much better acid utilization, it requires additional capital investment over a single-stage leach circuit processing the same amount of zinc. The choice of leaching mode, therefore, becomes an economic decision.

Presence of significant copper values in the concentrate, e.g., 1-3%, would favour the two-stage leach option, since it would then be possible to recover about 90% of the copper. As the copper grade increases above 3%, the copper recovery decreases, eventually dropping to about 60% because of preferential pelletization of chalcopyrite with pyrite and elemental sulphur during the leach.

Residue Treatment. Although the elemental sulphur-pyrite fraction of the residues could be treated, for example, by solvent extraction to recover a high grade elemental sulphur and pyrite tailings or by roasting to produce SO_2 for acid production, a premium marked would have to be available to make its processing economic. In New Brunswick this material is best regarded as a product of no current economic interest, and should be stored for possible future use.

The lead/silver bearing residues on the other hand can be upgraded easily and sold to a lead smelter for the contained values. Flotation removes sulphur and unleached sulphides, leaving a lead/silver material which typically grades 19% lead and 500 to 700 ppm silver from upgraded tailings concentrate. From bulk concentrate, this material would analyze 25% to 35% lead and 700 ppm silver. Further upgrading takes either of these materials to as much as 60% Pb. The silver content will be similarly upgraded.

Iron Removal. As was shown in Table 3, single stage leach
liquours typically contain 15 g/l to 25 g/l of sulphuric
acid and less than 2.0 g/l of iron. The acid must be neutralized to a pH of 3.0 to 3.5 in order to remove part of the
iron. Limestone from New Brunswick was shown to be a good
base for use in this neutralization step. The resulting hydrated iron oxide-calcium sulphate slurry is filtered to separate the liquid and solids, and the solids cake is discarded
after first washing to recover entrained zinc.

The liquor is then neutralized in a second stage to a pH
of 4.0 to 4.5 using zinc oxide (or zinc dross which has been
treated to remove chloride), and the iron content is lowered
to below 10 mg/l. Since some zinc and copper also precipitate at this pH, the small solids cake from this stage is
repulped with pregnant leach liquor going to the first
stage of iron removal.

Solutions derived from two-stage leaching are already low
in both acid and iron, so require only one stage of iron
removal using zinc oxide or dross as the neutralizing agent.
To minimize losses of zinc and copper, the solids cake from
iron removal would be recycled to the second stage of pressure leaching.

Zinc Dust Purification. Iron free zinc sulphate electrolyte may be subjected to any one of several zinc dust purification techniques known in the industry.

Two methods were tested on liquor derived from leaching
New Brunswick upgraded tailings concentrates. The first

method involved use of antimony trioxide (Sb_2O_3) as a zinc
dust activator. The hot copper sulphate-arsenic trioxide
($CuSO_4$ + As_2O_3) method was also used with good success.

Electrowinning. Electrowinning of metallic zinc from
purified zinc sulphate solutions would also be performed
using technology well known to the zinc industry. The results
of typical laboratory electrowinning tests are summarized in
Table 4. The tests were done on solutions being recycled
through complete process loops. That is, pregnant leach solution was purified, zinc was electrowon, and the resulting
acid solution was returned to the leaching stage of the next
cycle. This was done to demonstrate that detrimental impurities build-ups do not occur.

Commercial Application

Based on the results of the laboratory test work a commercial scale plant was evaluated for the production of 100,000
short tons per year of zinc metal using zinc-lead bulk concentrate as feed material.

Plant Design. A summary of the processing steps required
to treat a low grade zinc-lead concentrate is presented
in Fig. 3. The overall design basis is given in Table 5.
Fifteen days of concentrate storage capacity is proposed.
Reclaimed concentrate is slurried and is injected into one
of three, four-compartment acid brick and lead lined horizontal autoclaves along with spent electrolyte returned from
electrowinning. Acid leaching is accomplished at a total

TABLE 4

Electrowinning; Closed Circuit Recycle of Solution

<u>Conditions:</u> Cell voltage ≈ 3.2V, temperature ≈ 32°C,
amps variable, cathode area = 95 cm²/side

Cycle	Purif. Method	Ave. Amps	Ave. H_2SO_4 (g/l)	Plate Time (h)	Current Density (A/m²)	Current Efficiency (%)	Cathode Zn Assay (ppm)				
							Fe	Pb	Cd	Cu
1	RSb*	14.4	~162	24	575	92.3	–	37	5	–
6	As**	24.8	142	12.3	990	88.4	1.1	19	1.5	5

* Reverse - antimony method.

** Hot Copper - arsenic method.

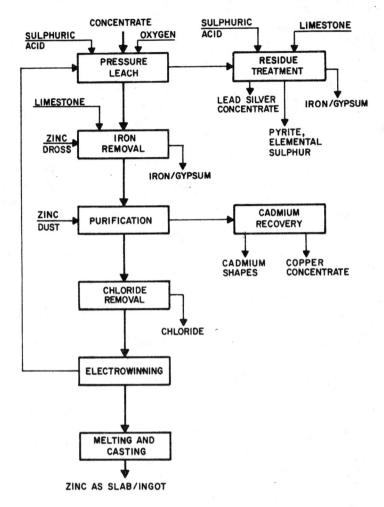

Fig. 3. New Brunswick Zinc Simplified Process Flow Diagram.

pressure of 690 kPa and 150°C, using commercially pure
oxygen as an oxidant. The final leach slurry is cooled and
brought to atmospheric conditions by flashing. After liquid/
solid separation in a thickener, the leach residue is washed
in six countercurrent thickeners and is pumped to the leach
residue treatment circuit.

TABLE 5

Overall Design Basis

Production

Zinc as Slab/Ingot (t/year)	90,720
Cadmium as Cadmium Shapes (t/year)	127
Copper Precipitate (t/year)	
- Copper (t/year)	1,025
- Zinc (t/year)	172
Lead/Silver Upgraded Leach Residue	
-Lead (t/year)	28,100
-Silver (kg/year)	67,200

Feed Rate

Concentrate (t/year)	298,500

Feed Analysis (%, Dry Basis)

Zinc	32.0
Lead	10.0
Copper	0.7
Cadmium	0.052
Iron	18.0
Sulphur	36.0
Silver (ppm)	300
Water	5.0

Recoveries (%)

Zinc	95
Cadmium	82
Copper	49
Lead	95
Silver	75

Operation   24 h per day, 340 days per year

Pyrite and elemental sulphur are removed from the leach residue by hydrocycloning and finally by flotation for transfer to a lined pond. The hydrocyclone separates the larger sulphur and pyrite pellets from the lead and silver portion of the residue. Flotation is then used to remove the remaining pyrite and sulphur to further upgrade the lead/silver residue. The residue is then further upgraded by sulphuric acid leaching, and becomes a lead/silver sulphate concentrate. This is a valuable by-product which can be sold as such or treated in a separate refinery on site.

The pregnant solution containing the zinc from the pressure leach is treated in two stages to remove iron. This is done by first neutralizing the bulk of the acid in the solution with limestone while sparging oxygen rich vent gases from the leach autoclaves into the tanks. The resulting iron-gypsum slurry is filtered and the solids are rejected to the gypsum pond. A final stage of neutralization with chloride free dross ensures an essentially iron free solution.

The solution then undergoes two stages of conventional batch purification in agitated atmospheric tanks. The precipitates formed are retained on pressure filters and transferred to cadmium recovery.

Cadmium recovery is a four stage batch operation in which cadmium and zinc are first leached from the purification circuit filter cakes. This leaves a copper cake which is filtered and sold as a by-product. Next, cadmium is precipitated from the solution with zinc dust and is then washed, briquetted, melted and cast into conventional shapes.

The purified pregnant zinc solution is transferred to a jumbo cathode zinc electrowinning plant. Here, in electrolytic cells, zinc plates onto 2.6 m square aluminum cathode sheets. After two days these cathodes are pulled and mechanically stripped. Jumbo cathode electrowinning has been included because it employs the most recent technological advances and reduces the physical labour associated with manual cathode stripping.

Cathode zinc is melted and cast into conventional slabs and ingots to provide the final product.

In concluding the plant description, a few final points should be added. Main plant slurry and solution flows are in the 100-135 m^3/h range. Except for the acid leach autoclaves, which are operating at 150°C and 690 kPa, all operations occur at atmospheric pressure with temperatures ranging from 20°C to 99°C. Materials of construction are mainly rubber lined carbon steel or stainless steels, with some brick lining for more severely corrosive applications. In addition to the main process facilities described, the battery limits plant would also contain steam and power generation and distribution, oxygen plant, water treatment, limestone handling, sulphuric acid storage and a full complement of administrative, maintenance, warehouse and product storage buildings.

Capital Costs. A summary of the capital costs for the battery limits plants is presented in Table 6. These costs are accurate to within ±30% in mid-1979 dollars. The capital costs do not include escalation or interest charges during construction. Cost data for a U.S. Gulf Coast location are also included for comparison purposes when evaluating other locations in the world.

Operating Costs. Table 7 outlines the annual operating costs for the process plants in mid-1979 dollars. Unit costs for the major operating requirements in New Brunswick were established in Canadian dollars as: $25/mt[*] for sulphuric acid, $13/mt for low grade limestone, $19/mt for high grade limestone, $0.11/1 for Bunker 'C' fuel oil and $21/MWh for electric power. Similar data for a U.S. Gulf Coast location are given, in U.S. dollars, as: $33/mt for sulphuric acid, $22/mt for low grade limestone, $0.11/1 for fuel oil and $39/MWh for electric power.

Process Alternatives. Depending on the feed composition or unit costs of major operating requirements, modifications can readily be made to make the process more suitable.

A two-stage countercurrent pressure leach process can replace the single stage process evaluated here. This would conservatively increase copper recoveries from 50% to at

---

[*] mt = metric ton

TABLE 6

Capital Cost Summary

	New Brunswick in C $ x 10^6	Gulf Coast in U.S. $ x 10^6
Leach and Purification	36.7	31.5
Electrowinning	35.0	30.0
Melting and Casting	3.2	2.7
Auxiliary and Utilities	18.4	15.7
Sitework and Non-Process Building	10.1	9.0
Indirect Costs	26.9	22.1
Total Capital Cost	130.3	111.0

TABLE 7

Operating Cost Summary

	New Brunswick in C $ x 10^6	Gulf Coast in U.S. $ x 10^6
Labour	6.8	7.5
Oprating Supplies	6.2	7.7
Maintenance Materials	1.4	1.1
Utilities	12.0	19.9
Taxes and Insurance	1.1	1.0
Total Annual Operating Cost	27.5	37.2
Operating Cost, S/kg	0.30	0.41

least 75% for a feed concentrate containing 2% copper. The
increased copper by-product net revenues would offset additional capital requirements of $1,400,000 and increased
annual operating costs of $0.009/kg of zinc for New Brunswick
conditions.

If the limestone cost is prohibitive, or the quality
inadequate, zinc calcine can be utilized for solution neutralization in the iron removal step of the process.

If sulphuric acid is not readily available, the required
sulphuric acid could be produced from the elemental sulphur
in the storage pond.

Conclusion. It was shown in laboratory tests that direct
pressure leaching of New Brunswick zinc-lead concentrates
results in zinc extractions of 95% to > 99%. Furthermore,
it was demonstrated that the resulting leach solutions could
be purified by conventional means, and that Special High
Grade zinc could be electrowon at high current efficiency.

Lead and silver values report to the leach residues,
and are recoverable as a saleable concentrate. Alternatively,
preliminary tests indicated that other residue treatment
schemes may give high recovery of contained values in the
form of metals or high grade concentrates. These routes
require further laboratory development before they can be
integrated with the zinc leach process.

Capital and operating cost data for a plant producing
90,720 mt of slab zinc per year were generated and indicate

a capital cost for a New Brunswick location of $1436/mt of zinc and an operating cost of $0.30/kg of zinc.

ACKNOWLEDGEMENTS

Financial support provided by the Government of the Province of New Brunswick and the Federal Government of Canada if gratefully acknowledged. The contributions to this work by Dr. Eva Haffenden are particularly appreciated. The chapter on the commercial application of the process including the plant cost estimates was summarized from work performed by the staff of Sherritt's Development Department, in particular Mr. Karl Best and Mr. Oleh Hnatiuk. The authors express their gratitude to these and numerous other contributors. The authors also thank the Management of Sherritt Gordon Mines Limited and the Government sponsors for permission to publish this paper.

REFERENCES

1. Forward F.A. and Veltman H. J. Met., 12, 836-840 (1959).

2. Kunda W., Veltman H., Evans D.J.I. and Mackiw V.N. Recovery of Zinc and Elemental Sulphur from Sulphide Concentrates by Aqueous Oxidation Under Pressure. Presented to the fourth CIMM Conference of Metallurgists, Ottawa, 1965.

3. Mackiw V.N. and Veltman H. Can. Min. Met. Bull., 70, 16-21 (1967).

4. Veltman H. and O'Kane P.T. Accelerated Pressure Leaching of Zinc Sulphide Concentrates. Presented at the 97th Annual Meeting of the AIME, New York, 1968.

5. Kawaluka P., Haffenden W.J. and Mackiw V.N. Recovery
   of Zinc from Zinc Sulphides by Direct Pressure Leaching.
   U.S. Patent 3,867,268, Feb. 18, 1975.

6. Veltman H., Mould G.J.J. and Kawaluka P. Two-Stage
   Pressure Leaching Process for Zinc and Iron Bearing
   Mineral Sulphides. U.S. Patent 4,004,991, Jan. 25, 1977.

7. Doyle B.N., Masters I.M., Webster I.C. and Veltman H.
   Acid Pressure Leaching Zinc Concentrates Produces
   By-Product Elemental Sulphur. Presented to The Eleventh
   Commonwealth Mining and Metallurgical Congress, Hong
   Kong, 6-12 May, 1978.

ABSTRACT

Recent advances made by Sherritt Gordon Mines Limited in
Canada on the development of its direct pressure leaching
process for typical zinc sulphide concentrates have led to
a study of the application of this technique to complex pyritic zinc-lead bulk concentrates.

Results of this work have shown that the optimum process
conditions developed for high grade zinc concentrates can
also be applied to bulk concentrates with very good success.
At a leaching temperature of 150°C the rate of zinc dissolution is rapid and final one stage leach zinc extraction is
in the 95% to 98% range. Sulphide sulphur is converted to
elemental sulphur, forming the main portion of the leach
residue together with the pyrite which is not attacked in
the pressure leach. Lead is converted to lead sulphate or
lead jarosite and is separated, together with the silver,
from the elemental sulphur-pyrite fraction of the leach
residue, by flotation as a tailing which can be upgraded
for lead and silver recovery. The sulphur/pyrite concentrate
can be stockpiled if there is no market for sulphuric acid.
The operation is thus liberated from the necessity to produce
sulphuric acid. Since this process does not include a
roasting step, zinc ferrite formation is avoided. The zinc
sulphate leach solution produced by pressure leaching can
be processed by conventional purification techniques followed
by standard electrowinning to recover high purity cathode
zinc.

RÉSUMÉ

Les récents progrès réalisés par les mines de Sheritt Gordon
au Canada pour le développement de son procédé de lessivage
direct par pression pour des concentrés   typiques de sulfure
de zinc ont reposé sur l'étude de l'application de cette technique à des concentrés   ayant une grande quantité de complexe
zinc-plomb.

Les résultats de ce travail ont montré que les conditions
optimales du procédé développé pour des concentrés de zinc de
haute qualité peuvent être aussi appliquées à de gros concentrés avec un très bon résultat. A une température de lessivage de 150°C, la vitesse de dissolution du zinc est grande et
l'extraction finale du zinc de la lessive d'une phase est de
l'ordre de 95% à 98%. Le soufre du sulfure est converti en
soufre élémentaire formant la partie principale du résidue de
la lessive simultanément avec la pyrite qui n'est pas attaquée
par la lessive de pression. Le plomb est converti en sulfate
de plomb ou jarosite de plomb et est séparé de même que l'
argent, de la fraction élémentaire soufre-pyrite du résidue de
la lessive par flottation ainsi qu'un déchet qui peut être
séparé pour la récupération du plomb et de l'argent. Le concentré soufre-pyrite peut être stocké en piles s'il n'y a pas
de marché de l'acide sulfurique. L'opération est de suite
libérée par la nécessité de produire de l'acide sulfurique.
Depuis que le procédé ne comprend plus d'étape de calcination,
la formation de ferrite de zinc est évitée. La solution de
lessive du sulfate de zinc produite par lessivage par pression
peut être traitée par des techniques conventionnelles de purification suivies par une extraction standard par la voie
électrolytique du métal pour retrouver le zinc de haute pureté
de la cathode.

ZUSAMMENFASSUNG

Die neuesten Erfahrungen der Firma Sherritt Gordon Mines
Ltd. in Kanada, im Bereich der direkten Auslaugung typischer
Zinksulfate unter Druck haben Anlass gegeben Untersuchungen
über die Anwendung eines solchen Verfahrens im Falle komplexer
pyritischer Zink-Blei-Konzentrate einzuleiten.
Die Ergebnisse dieser Untersuchungen haben erwiesen, dass
die für hochprozentige Zinkkonzentrate ermittelten optimalen
Prozessbedingungen mit gutem Erfolg auch im Falle grosser Kon-
zentratmengen Verwendung finden können. Bei einer Auslauge-
temperatur von 150°C verläuft die Auflösung des Zinks sehr
schnell, so dass am Ende des Auslaugungsprozesses etwa 95 bis

98% Zink extrahiert worden ist. Sulfidischer Schwefel wird in elementaren Schwefel umgewandelt und bildet zusammen mit dem, im Verlauf der Druckauslaugung nicht angegriffenen Pyrit den Hauptbestandteil der Auslaugerückstände. Blei verwandelt sich in Bleisulfat bzw. Bleijarosit und wird zusammen mit dem Silber der elementaren Schwefel-Pyrit-Fraktion mittels Flotation als Rückstand ausgeschieden, der dann bei der Blei- und Silberaufbereitung angereichert werden kann. Gibt es keinen Absatz für Schwefelsäure, so kann das Schwefel/Pyrit-Konzentrat gelagert werden. Auf diese Weise ist es bei einer solchen Operation nicht notwendig, Schwefelsäure herzustellen. Da dieser Prozess keine Röstphase einschliesst, wird die Bildung von Zinkferrit vermieden. Die beim Druckauslaugen gebildete Sulfatlösung lässt sich mittels konventioneller Reinigungsverfahren mit darauf folgender standardisierter Elektrogewinnung aufbereiten, um Kathodenzink von hoher Reinheit zu erhalten.

РЕЗЮМЕ

Последние успехи, достигнутые на заводе Sherrit Gordon в Канаде, в области разработки прямого автоклавного выщелачивания типичных концентратов сульфида цинка, привели к исследованиям, касающимся применения этого метода к комплексным пиритовым свинцово-цинковым концентратам.

Результаты исследований показали, что оптимальные условия процесса, разработанные для высокопроцентных концентратов цинка, можно также применить с хорошими результатами к полиметаллическим концентратам. При температуре выщелачивания 150^0 С растворение цинка происходит быстро, и окончательное одноступенчатое извлечение выщелачиваемого цинка составляет от 95 до 98%. Сульфидная сера переводится в элементарную серу и составляет основную часть остатка после выщелачивания вместе с пиритом, который остаётся ненарушенным при автоклавном выщелачивании. Свинец переходит в сульфат или ярозит свинца и выделяется вместе с серебром из фракции, содержащей элементарную серу и пирит, методом флотации в виде отходов, которые можно обогатить с целью извлечения из них свинца и серебра. Серно-пиритный концентрат можно складировать в том случае, если нет сбыта на серную кислоту. Благодаря этому нет необходимости производства серной кислоты. Поскольку этот процесс не включает обжига, можно избежать образования феррита цинка. Раствор сульфата цинка, полученный в результате автоклавного выщелачивания, можно перерабатывать традиционными методами очистки, после которой происходит обычный электролиз цинка высокой чистоты.

DISCUSSION

PAPER 27

V. A. CHANTURYA

(1) What is the mechanism involved in the electrooxidation of chalcopyrite particles; does it take place on the surface or in the bulk of the particles?

(2) What is the construction of the device - its material, type of anode, diaphragm etc. What is the energy consumption per 1 t of concentrate?

(3) Does the release of gaseous chlorine take place under optimal electrooxidation conditions?

A. RIESENKAMPF (Institute of Metallurgy, Academy of Sciences, Kraków, Poland)

I would like you to give the mineralogical specifications of the ores used in the investigations.

PAPER 28

V. A. CHANTURYA

Have you investigated the influence of sulphides on the kinetics of oxidation? If so, what is the quantitative relationship between the rate of oxidation and the total surface area of sulphides?

PAPER 30

W. MULAK (Wrocław Technical University, Wrocław, Poland)

(1) Have you checked whether the final oxidation product of the sulphide ion was elementar sulphur only?

(2) I would like to know what your opinion is as to the mechanism of the catalytic effect that metal ions such as Cu^{2+} and Fe^{3+} have on the rate of dissolution of metal sulphide when hydrogen sulphide is evolved. I would also like to draw your attention to our investigations into the Ni_3S_2 - nitric acid system. We have found that the slowest dissolution step is a chemical reaction taking place on the surface during which hydrogen sulphide is oxidized. The rate of dissolution can be raised by an increase in nitric acid concentration, by bubbling air or oxygen through the solution, or by the addition of small amounts of Cu^{2+} or Fe^{3+} ions. The highest rate of dissolution is obtained in the presence of small amounts of Cu^{2+} or Fe^{3+} and the final sulphide ion oxidation product is sulphate. These results would seem to indicate that the catalytic effect of Cu^{2+} or Fe^{3+} involves the oxidation of sulphide ion to sulphate.

F. HABASHI (Laval University, Quebec City, Canada)

In light of the present paper, I think that it would be worthwhile to study the effect of adding silver sulphide to chalcopyrite during leaching because it seems possible that a galvanic cell would be formed by the two sulphides which probably would in turn result in an enhanced dissolution of chalcopyrite. Similar phenomena were observed by E. Peters in Canada when he studied the effect of adding PbS, FeS_2, and other sulphides to chalcopyrite. Would the authors care to comment?

Z. M. DOGAN (Middle-East Technical University, Ankara, Turkey)

I should like to congratulate Dr. Miller and Mr. Portillo on their excellent paper.

I should like, however, to ask the authors about the bacterial leaching (thiobacillus ferrooxidans) of ground chalcopyrite in the presence and absence of silver nitrate. Our work and the research carried out in Japan has showed that silver ions are toxic to thiobacillus ferrooxidans. On the other hand, it is stated that silver ions help the bacterial leaching process. Will you clarify this point, please?

P. M. SOLOZHENKIN (Institute of Chemistry, Academy of Sciences of Tadzhikskaya SRR, Dushanbe, USSR)

We followed with great pleasure the fundamental paper by our colleagues from the U.S.A. where the adsorption mechanism of silver on chalcopyrite was analysed in detail, as was the effective catalytic role of silver in the leaching of copper concentrates.

I would like to ask the authors of this paper the following questions:

(1) Have you established the existence of a sulphur vacancy in the chalcopyrite?

According to the principle of valence compensation in the $CuFeS_2$ + Ag^+ system, the substitution of $Cu^{2+} \rightarrow Ag^+$ is only possible where there is a deficiency of sulphur in chalcopyrite. Is the formation of metallic silver possible in this system?

(2) It follows from Fig. 2 that copper in chalcopyrite is found in the oxidized state which is equal to two. This is contrary to the latest results obtained by some authors who consider both Cu(I) and Fe(III) in $CuFeS_2$.

I would also like to add to the very interesting paper presented information about the reactions of silver exchange on other sulphide minerals apart from chalcopyrite. In these experiments, samples of sulphides of iron, zinc and antimony (2 g) were initially treated with a solution of nitric acid, washed carefully with water, brought into contact with sodium-diethyldithionic carbonate (100 mg/1), and then treated with 5 ml of benzol for 15 min. The copper and silver concentrations in the organic extract were defined by the EPR method [1]. Copper in its complex form with dithionic carbonate was analysed in an aqueous solution.

Silver sorbed on the surfaces of arsenopyrite, pyrrhothite and pyrite takes part in the surface reactions with the formation of dithionic silver.

Surface saturation is achieved at a certain concentration of silver which is characteristic for each mineral. The intensity of the EPR spectrum of dithionic divalent silver remains stable. In this case, the behaviour of copper in the surface layer of minerals is unusual.

The amount of copper taking part in the formation of copper dithionic carbonate initially increases, then passes through its maximum and then decreases steadily.

In the supernatant aqueous solutions the concentration of copper increases steadily.

Such copper concentration changes result from the depth of displacement of copper cations by silver.

Sorption on the minerals increases with an increase in silver concentration; a considerable part of silver keeps penetrating the surface layer to the considerable depth. In this case, copper cations of a mineral lattice are displaced first of all into the surface layer, and then into the pulp volume.

During the activation of the sphalerite and antimonite surface by silver under analogous conditions, only the EPR spectra of copper dithionic carbonate were found in the products of the desorption of surface compounds.

The lack of silver dithionic carbonates in the products of desorption is connected with the considerable rate of silver migration into the bulk of sphalerite and antimonite.

A. M. Goden has established that a silver ion actively displaces zinc in sphalerite, at least after the formation of a monolayer. In this case, redisplacement occurs in the subsequent formation of a new surface of zinc sulphide [2].

The results of pyrite flotation initially treated by silver nitrate showed that an increase in flotability of pyrite was observed with an increase of the amount of silver dithionic carbonate formed and a reduction of the copper dithionic carbonate concentration, i.e., silver sorption takes place with the displacement of copper.

On the basis of these data it may be assumed that the activation mechanism of sulphide minerals by silver is connected both with adsorption of silver and the formation of silver sulphide on their surfaces, and with the displacement of cations or impurity atoms into the surface layer (or into the pulp).

REFERENCES

1. Solozhenkin P. M., Kopicya N. I. and Tregubenko N. I. Izv. A.N. Tadzh. S.S.R. Otd. fiz.-mat. i geol. nauk, 2, 49 (1970).

2. Gaudin A. M. Flotation, Gosgortehizdat, 1959, 239.

PAPER 31

M. CARTA (Universita di Cagliari, Cagliari, Italy)

I wish to refer to the problem of coal desulphurisation. Contamination of coal with pyritic or organic sulphur was discussed for 10 days at the VIII International Coal Preparation Congress in Donietsk (Soviet Union) and in the papers presented in the course of a specialist seminar which I had honour to chair.

From the point of view of hydrometallurgy, the investigations carried out at the laboratories of the Dept. of Energy (Pittsburg, USA), seem very interesting. In the investigations the solubilization of the organic sulphur by means of hydrochlorides, which is a real problem in the preliminary desulphurization of coals (mainly steam coals), was taken into account. I must agree with Dr. Habashi that hydrometallurgical processes are still very far from the solution of engineering and economic problems. Well liberated pyrites and marcasites can be treated by flotation as well as by fluidized gravity separation and high intensity magnetic and electrostatic separations.

As for organic sulphur and finely dispersed sulphides (-50 μm), they might rather be separated at the proper stage of the process of coal gasification. Coal gasification methods, however, no matter how promising they appear, require high conversion factor values and are all of a low energetical efficiency.

The method left over for steam coals is the desulphurisation of the combustion gases.

Z. M. DOGAN (Middle-East Technical University, Ankara, Turkey).

I was expecting to hear mention of bacterial leaching in Prof. Habashi's excellent review on "Recent advances in hydrometallurgy". It seems to me that bacterial leaching appears to be losing favour in the I.M.P.C.

Bacterial leaching could at least find application in the chemical mining of copper and uranium as well as in the desulphurization of coal with about 80% of the total sulphur being inorganic mainly pyrite. Would the author comment on these points?

K. A. FERN (Avenue Technical Services, United Kingdom)

Although the paper refers to recent advances, reference should be made, as a matter of history, to the pioneer work of American Cyanamid Co and Chemical Construction Corporation over 25 years ago. A pressure leaching/reduction process was developed which produced nearly pure copper and nickel in powder form. A pilot plant was built at the Calera smelter in Utah, USA, but unfortunately corrosion problems prevented the commercial adoption of the process. Details of this process and the research work behind it were the subject of a paper by F. A. Schaufelberger, published in the Transactions of the Institution of Mining and Metallurgy in 1956.

I. M. CASES (E.N.S.G., Nancy, France)

You have pointed out in your paper that at present numerous studies are being carried out on the beneficiation of deep-sea polymetallic nodules. I would like to know what the prospects of economical realability of such studies are? Do not you feel that these research projects might be compared to studies aiming at digging potatoes by means of a controllable balloon?

S. U. LASKORIN (Academy of Sciences, USSR)

(1) What is the possibility of using the process of sorption from the pulp for oxidized copper, molybdenum, or gold ores which are difficult-to-treat by flotation?

(2) Do you know of any hydrometallurgical methods that have been developed for the treatment of low grade concentrates containing lead minerals?

S. B. LEONOV (Irkutsk Polytechnik Institute, U.S.S.R.)

(1) What factor, in your opinion, retards the application of hydrometallurgical processes in practice? Are these economical factors, or are there difficulties in finding the proper equipment? Do you have other reasons?

(2) Except for closed water circulation systems, what is the trend in the utilization of industrial hydrometallurgical waste solutions? Is the solution evaporated under vacuum or purified?

PAPER 32

Z. M. DOGAN (Middle-East Technical University, Ankara, Turkey)

I was extremely interested to hear the paper by Prof. Majima and his associate on the non-oxidative leaching of base metal sulphide ores in an acid solution releasing hydrogen sulphide.

In Turkey, we have a difficult-to-treat complex ore similar to your Kuroko type, comprising intimately mixed chalcopyrite, sphalerite and iron sulphides. A certain amount of success was achieved in differential flotation through the use of SO_2 to depress sphalerite. On the other hand, it is easy to obtain a bulk concentrate in which $CuFeS_2$, ZnS and Fe sulphide are collected.

Do the authors think the brine leaching technique useful in the treatment of Cu-Zn sulphide bulk concentrate?

J. HERBST (University of Utah, Salt Lake City, USA)

This is a very interesting and unique piece of work in non-aqueous leaching. We at the University of Utah have examined the advantages of ultra-fine grinding in an attritor prior to leaching for several aqueous systems and find, as you do, that very large increases in leaching rate are possible without excessive grinding cost.

With regard to the use of simultaneous grinding and leaching, our experience has been that this processing method will not be particularly advantageous in many instances because grinding requires high % solids to be efficient, while lixiviant solubilits constraints require lower % solids during leaching. Also corrosion of media and mill in the leaching environment may be very large. Finally, unless the grinding rate is faster than the leaching rate a significant reduction in retention time can not be achieved.

Have you compared individual grinding and leaching with simultaneous grinding and leaching for this system?

C. ABBRUZZESE (Laboratorio per il Trattamento dei Minerali,

C.N.R., Roma, Italy)

The proposed lyometallurgical process is an interesting novel technique involving simultaneous leaching and solvent extraction. This process eliminates the expensive clarification step necessary before the extraction of metals from ore leach solutions.

In relation to the experimental work performed on chrysocolla, I would like to know whether the less expensive H_2SO_4
is as effective as NH_3 as regards the amount and the rate of
copper extracted.

I am sure that lyometallurgical treatment can be also extended to non porous ores when a pretreatment occurs which
favours the reduction in diffusion path lengths and/or the
production of fresh surfaces.

F. HABASHI (Laval University, Quebec City, Canada)

I would like to comment on the heating of chrysocolla which
is a typical hydrated silicate mineral. When such minerals are
heated, the following opposing processes take place simultaneously:

(1) Removal of water as a result of dehydration and dehydroxylation

(2) Sintering of the product.

The first reaction results in increased porosity because
the product formed is amorphous, while the second process
results in decreased porosity. Both processes, however, are
favored by increased temperature and time. Therefore a compromise should be made if all the water has to be removed while
minimizing the sintering. This can be achieved by heating, for
example at 150°C for 1 h. Should the time of heating be increased to 24 h as indicated in Fig. 5 of the paper, strong
sintering of the product will be observed. In our work on
chrysocolla we heated for 1 h only and observed significant
activation because the product was highly porous and amorphous.

D. S. FLETT (Warren Spring Laboratory, United Kingdom)

A similar study to that described by Professor D. W. Fuerstenau was made in the mid-sixties by Chittenden and Prosser at Imperial College, London, wherein they attempted to directly solvent extract copper from oxidised copper ores with naphthenic acid. Success was only achieved by providing a thin film of H_2SO_4 between the organic phase and the mineral surface. The technique which worked well using ore columns was abandoned as inpracticable. It is difficult to believe that the current approach is more practical. I would be interested to know what pulp densities are envisaged for practical operations. Nothing is said about separation of the leached solids from the organic phase, the recovery of entrained and probably adsorbed organic from the leach residue nor the recovery of ammonia. On both environmental and economic grounds recovery of both solvent and ammonia from the leached pulp will be mandatory. Would the authors provide information on how they propose to comply with these economic and environmental constraints?

PAPER 34

A. RIESENKAMPF (Institute of Metallurgy, Academy of Sciences, Kraków, Poland)

(1) What are the possibilities of application of pressure leaching instead of the roast-leach process of zinc sulphide concentrates in the future?

(2) Can you tell us about the possibilities for the removal of magnesium salts from zinc sulphate electrolyte? This

problem is very important for zinc plants treating raw materials
from dolomitic deposits.

Z. M. DOGAN (Middle-East Technical University, Ankara, Turkey)

We noted from the results of laboratory tests that zinc extractions of > 99% were obtained by direct pressure leaching
of New Brunswick zinc-lead concentrate.

I should like, however, to ask the authors to compare overall
this process with both blast furnace smelting of lead followed
by slag forming of zinc, and with imperial smelting regarding
a zinc-lead bulk concentrate.

D. W. FUERSTENAU (University of California, Berkeley, USA)

I would think that one of the problems in the Sherritt
(Cominco) process is the wetting of the unreacted ZnS by S. In
your 2-stage process, are the additives put into the system to
help de-wet the ZnS by S. If so, what is the additive?

I. A. E. WILKOMIRSKY, R. S. BOORMAN, R. S. SALTER* (Research
    and Productivity Council, Fredericton, New Brunswick, Canada)

THE RPC SULPHATION ROAST PROCESS FOR RECOVERY
OF METALS FROM COMPLEX BASEMETAL ORES

The New Brunswick Research and Productivity Council has
developed a sulphation roast-leach-electrowinning process to

----

* Contributed Remarks

enhance metal recoveries from complex basemetal ores. The process is ideally suited to the treatment of high iron zinc concentrates, or bulk metal concentrates which cannot be treated economically in conventional electrolytic zinc plants or smelters.

The RPC Process has been successfully demonstrated in mini-pilot trials. The pilot plant consisted of a 14-inch diameter fluidized bed reactor integrated with a zinc-copper leaching, solution purification and electrowinning circuit with a capacity pf 200 kg of concentrate per day. Lead and silver were recovered from residues via flotation and sodium chloride brine leaching.

Sulphide feeds tested included a bulk concentrate containing 32% zinc, 10% lead, 0.7% copper and 8.8 oz/T silver, and a tailing refloat product containing 30% zinc, 3.6% lead, 0.6% copper and 4.4 oz/T silver. Overall metal recoveries are 96% zinc, 97.5% copper, 95.2% lead and 88% silver. Zinc and copper are recovered as metals and lead and silver as a high grade lead oxide-silver product. Residues consist of hematite and gypsum.

The RPC Process has particular application in the treatment of bulk concentrates and middling products from fine grained massive sulphide ores such as are exemplified by the Bruncwick-type ores in New Brunswick, Canada, the McArthur River deposit in Australia, and other such similar ores found throughout the world. Many of these ores are presently unexploited or suffer from inefficient metal recoveries to separate concentrates as a result of poor response to conventional flotation practice.

In addition, certain impurities present in the ores, namely halogens, silica and silicates, make the treatment of concentrates by dead roasting or purely hydrometallurgical processes most difficult, even when high grade concentrates can be produced. The sulphation roast-leach technology significantly reduces the problems associated with these impurities.

Figure 1 is a conceptual flowsheet of the R.P.C. Sulphation Roast-Leach-Electrowinning Process. There are two innovative concepts in this process.

(1) Excess heat produced in the roasting of sulphides is sufficient to thermally decompose the hot acid leach liquor produced from the leaching of minor zinc ferrite and remnant sphalerite in the neutral leach residue. Accordingly, all the iron in the concentrate reports eventually as hematite in the residue, eliminating zinc losses in handling hydroxide or sulphate precipitates and producing a plant residue suitable for disposal or possible sale after upgrading.

(2) The oxidation and precipitation of ferrous iron (less than 1.5 g/l) after copper solvent extraction by addition of excess manganese dioxide followed by neutralization with limestone results in efficient stripping of organic carryover from the pregnant zinc liquor. Recycling the iron oxidation sludge to neutral leach results in eventual elimination of this iron from the circuit as hematite, combustion of the organics, and no associated zinc losses.

Figure 2 is a generalized flowsheet of the lead/silver recovery plant. Flotation of the hot acid leach residue results in a high grade silver concentrate containing more than 80% of

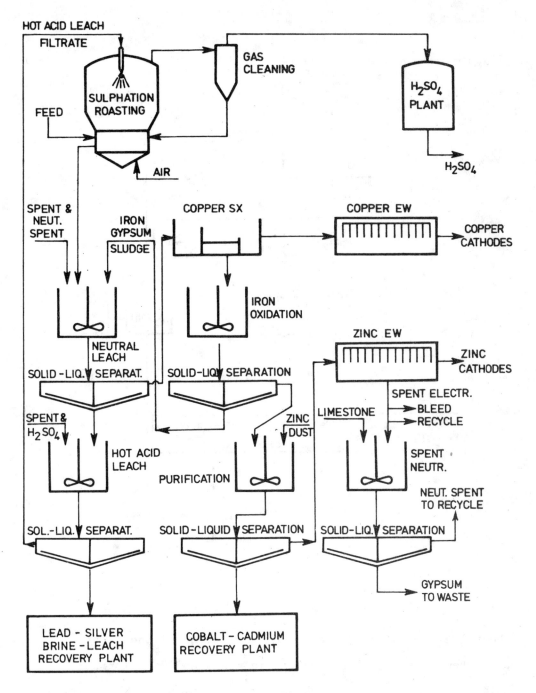

Fig. 1. The R.P.C. sulphation roast leach electrowinning
process - conceptual flowsheet.

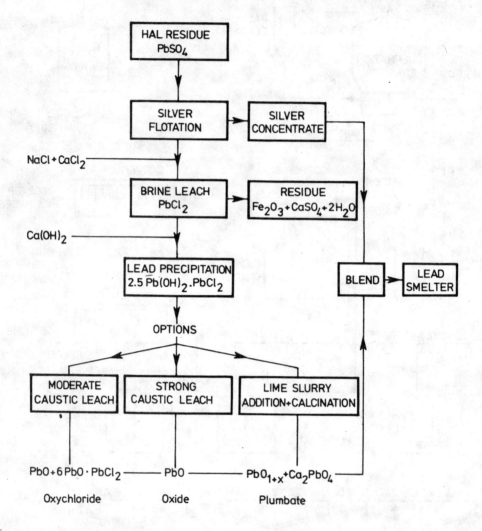

Fig. 2. SR-L-E. Lead/Silver Recovery Plant (Generalized
flow sheet).

the silver in the plant feed. The flotation tailings are
subjected to an ambient temperature mixed sodium chloride-
calcium chloride brine leach. After separation of the hematite-
gypsum residue, the lead chloride solution is treated with lime
to precipitate a lead oxychloride. This product can then be

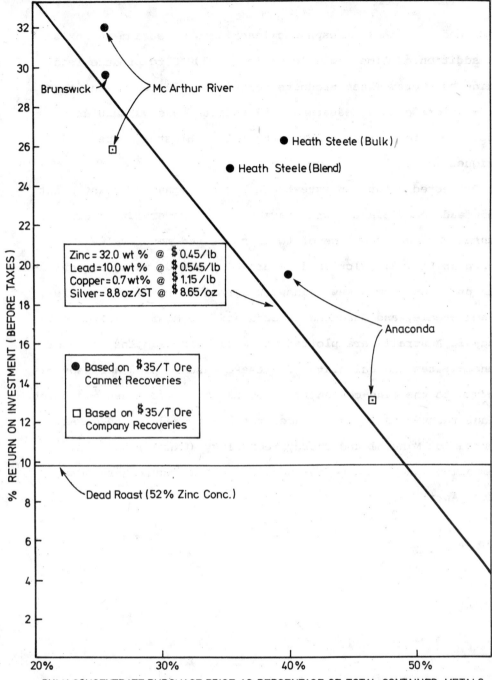

Fig. 3. Bulk concentrate. Return on investment vs. value
of bulk concentrate.

upgraded by either atmospheric leaching with sodium hydroxide or addition of lime and calcination at 300°C to produce lead oxide products. These products contain 50-71% lead, less than 0.5% chloride, and less than 1.5% sulphur, and as such are ideal feed for direct addition to a lead blast furnace after briquetting.

Projected return on investment for a sulphation roast plant and dead roast plant vs. payment for a generalized bulk concentrate as a percentage of total contained metal value is shown in Fig. 3. Calculated returns for plants using concentrates produced from 3 New Brunswick orebodies, namely Brunswick, Heath Steele, and Anaconda Caribou and the McArthur River orebody in Australia are plotted as particular examples. Cost of concentrates was calculated for these cases, using a reasonable return to the mine-concentrator of $35/t of ore mined and pilot plant recoveries to bulk concentrates obtained by the Canada Centre for Mineral and Energy Technology (Canmet) and the companies concerned in the operations. All figures are $Canadian, April 1979.

AUTHORS' REPLIES

M. AMMOU-CHOKROUM

With regard to Professor Chanturya's remarks we would comment as follows:

(1) Chalcopyrite pulp electrooxidation involves only the superficial zone of the grains; according to the proposed .reactional scheme, electrochemical oxidation is essentially carried out on the acidic reaction products, CuS and H_2S, which are localized in the superficial sulphur layer.

The cation solubilization anomaly, particularly obvious during the initial phase, is explained by the participation of copper in a secondary precipitation reaction: thus it does not seem necessary to invoke, as we have previously done, a different solid-state diffusion for cations and so admit the development of a concentration gradient in the interior of the chalcopyrite.

(2) The equipment utilized for carrying out the potentio-static electrodissolution of the chalcopyrite pulps was the laboratory set-up precisely represented in Fig. 16. While this apparatus allows the quantity of electricity consumed by the sulphide electrodissolution reaction to be established because of its scale and its constitution, it does not allow the overall energy consumption of an industrial electrodissolution operation to be calculated.

(3) In our opinion, electrooxidation should be effected in conditions such that the formation of chlorine, a powerful oxidising agent, is avoided. The production of chlorine in pulp presents the following disadvantages:

- a drop in energy efficiency,

- higher oxidation of the sulphide material, which on the one hand produces sulphate ions and not elementary sulphur, and on the other prevents any selectivity during the attack of composite material.

In reply to Dr. Riesenkampf, schematically, complex sulphide ores containing copper, lead and zinc, which are difficult to process using ordinary beneficiation techniques (selective flotation - pyro or hydrometallurgical processing of concentrates) mainly contain a pyritic gangue in which valuable minerals (chalcopyrite, galena, sphalerite) are finely disseminated. In a given ore, the types of association between these minerals are extremely variable, from simple filling of millimmetric cracks to internal precipitates (100 Å) and micronic inclusions. Thus, grinding which aims at the liberation and then selective flotation of useful minerals is extremely difficult to carry out; this is why it seems that, at best, prior beneficiation by flotation can yield an overall concentrate relatively rich in pyrite.

R. BERTRAM et al.

I think, Professor Chanturya, that you are interested in the quantitative influence of the concentration and particle size of chalcopyrite on the electrochemical reaction. In fluidized

1044

bed cells, Galitis reported a dependence on particle size. Quantitative results were not given.

For a suspension the current density is directly proportional to the concentration of solid $CuFeS_2$:

$$i(A/m^2) = k \; c_{CuFeS_2} \; (g/l)$$

For example, k depends on the potential of the feeder-electrode, the reaction time and particle size. At a potential of E = 1250 mV vs. SCE., the value of k in our cell and according to our conditions is $4 \cdot 10^{-3} (A/m^2 \; 1/g) \cdot k$ is independent of the rotation speed of the stirrer (U > 1300 rpm).

REFERENCES

Bertram et al., Erzmetall 30, 708 (1977).
Bertram et al., Erzmetall, to be published 1980.

J. D. MILLER

In response to Dr. Mulak's first question, I would like to point out that sulphur was detected not only by XRD but also by the wet chemical technique described on p. 866. The material balance for the elemental sulphur was not completely satisfactory but in view of the analysis for copper and iron (II) presented on p. 879 it seems that over 99% of the sulphur was oxidized to the elemental state.

Dr. Mulak's second question is with respect to metal sulphide systems in which H_2S is evolved, or in which H_2S may participate as an intermediate species in the reaction sequence. For

the case of silver catalysed ferric sulphate leaching of chalcopyrite, it is known that the exchange reaction is largely independent of acidity (p.871). This information together with
other data (Ref. 9) that demonstrates the rate independence of
acid addition for the uncatalysed case suggests that an H_2S
intermediate is improbable.

The catalytic influence of Cu^{2+} in other sulphide systems
that are known to evolve H_2S may involve a displacement reaction resulting in the formation of the more stable Cu_2S and
allow the reaction to proceed through a different reaction
sequence. Our experience in these systems is limited. It would
be interesting to know how the Cu^{2+} concentration changes
during reaction progress for the catalytic leaching of Ni_3S_2
by nitric acid.

The matter of bacterial activity raised by Professor Dogan
and the bacteria's toxicity to silver was of little concern
during this study because of the high acidity of the silver
catalysed ferric sulphate leach. The conflicting results to
which he refers, i.e., the work of McElroy and Duncan [15] who
report enhanced bacterial leaching in the presence of silver,
suggest that in their experiments the bacteria may have been
destroyed and that they simply observed enhanced leaching due
to a silver catalysed reaction similar to the phenomenon
reported in our contribution.

Professor Habashi's comment is an interesting possibility
which we have not tried. My intuitive feeling on this matter,
in view of the results presented in Figs. 11 and 12, is that
complete coverage of the chalcopyrite surface by the Ag_2S film

is required to prevent the growth of the tenacious sulphur film
on the chalcopyrite which passivates the system. The key to
understanding the behaviour of this catalytic reaction appears
to be the structural transformation of the elemental sulphur
reaction product rather than intrinsic electrochemical rate
enhancement via a galvanic couple.

F. HABASHI

I thank Professor Carta for his comments. I am not sure,
however, that hydrometallurgical techniques could be of any
value in the desulphurization of coal, for the following
reasons: (1) most processes are only capable of eliminating a
part of the inorganic sulphur but not the organic sulphur,
(2) in most processes there is a loss in the calorific value
of the coal due to oxidation, (3) the leaching agent has to be
thoroughly washed away from the coal, otherwise corrosion
problems may be introduced into the boilers, and (4) after
filtration, the coal must be dried before use. In my opinion
desulphurization of coal should be done via gasification. The
South African plants are excellent examples. Sulphur compounds
are removed from the gases before their transformation into
liquid fuels.

Bacterial leaching is still an active field of research as
can be judged from the two references I gave in the review.
These references are proceedings volumes for two conferences
held on this subject in 1978. I agree with Prof. Dogan that in
the recovery of copper and uranium from low-grade ores,
bacteria are playing an important role. However, I do not think

that this technology can be applied in the treatment of sulphide concentrates because it would not be possible to recover elemental sulphur. Thus, sulphate disposal problems will arise. Further, I do not feel that hydrometallurgy is the correct route for the desulphurization of coal. I dealt with this problem in my answer to Prof. Carta's question.

In reply to Mr. Fern, the Calera plant was producing cobalt powder from a cobalt arsenide concentrate. The failure of this operation was a setback to pressure hydrometallurgy. A description of this plant and the reasons for its failure were given by W.M. Fassell, jr. in Pure and Appl. Chem. $\underline{5}$, 683-699 (1962). It was the extensiv efforts of Sherritt-Gordon Mines in Canada that erased this gloomy picture and put pressure hydrometallurgy in its proper prospective.

In reply to Professor Cases I would like to point out that the extensive research presently conducted on the extraction of metals from manganese nodules does not mean that there is a rush to get metals from this source. It is the tradition of large companies equipped with the necessary facilities and the qualified staff to plan for the technology of the future. They acquire the know-how through research and get the patents to be available for licensing. This is the difference between the leader and a follower. I believe that in this case hydrometallurgy can be of great service because the nodules contain appreciable amounts of water, and to drive away all the water before charging to a furnace would be costly. I hope I have answered your question.

With regard to Professor Laskorin's remarks, to my knowledge, sorption from the pulp is practised in industry only in uranium recovery by the Resin-in-Pulp Process (RIP). The solvent extraction of copper is done from clear solution. However, research is underway to take advantage of the RIP system by impregnating the commercial organic solvents on preformed poly-styrene beads, or by incorporation of commercial organic solvents during polymerization of ion exchange resins. Also, the development of specific resins which contain complexing groups as integral parts of one of the copolymers is under investiga-tion. When these methods are fully developed, it is expected that a new dimension will be added to sorption processes.

Regarding the second question, I am sorry but I am not familiar with this problem.

Professor Leonov's first question already implies that hydro-metallurgy is not making progress. This is not true. I have in my paper numerous examples showing the great expansion in hydro-metallurgical applications. In fact this field is advancing so rapidly that my paper in which I reviewed the literature to August 1978 needs a revision. For example, the following new monographs appeared: a symposium volume by the American Insti-tute of Chemical Engineers entitled, "Fundamental Aspects of Hydrometallurgical Processes" [1], a symposium volume by the German and the British metallurgical societies entitled, "Complex Metallurgy 78" [2], the proceedings of the Common-wealth Mining and Metallurgical Congress held in Hong Kong in 1978 [3], and the Proceedings of the joint meeting of the AIME and the Mining and Metallurgical Institute of Japan [4].

The last three volumes include numerous hydrometallurgy papers. The Proceedings of the International Conference on Chemical Metallurgy held in Bombay in January 1979 included my paper "Recent Advances in Pressure Hydrometallurgy", and as well as many others is now available [5]. The American Institute of Mining, Metallurgical, and Petroleum Engineers (AIME) held its Annual Meeting in New Orleans, Louisiana, in February 1979 and included many important contributions on hydrometallurgy [6].

A study by Prof. Dobrokhotov [7] at the Leningrad Mining Institute entitled "Processes and Equipment for the Hydrometallurgical Industry", and a two-volume book by Ritcey and Ashbrook entitled, "Solvent Extraction. Principles and Application to Process Metallurgy", have also been published [8]. Łętowski's book, "Podstawy Hydrometallurgii", has been translated into English and is in the process of being published [9]. Scott reviewed hydrometallurgy and its implications for the developing countries at a symposium arranged by the United Nations [10].

In the Province of Quebec, great interest has been expressed recently in the production of magnesium and its compounds from asbestos tailings by hydrometallurgical methods.

In the leaching of sulphides, Reilly and Scott in Canada [11] presented an evidence in favor of the electrochemical mechanism of dissolution. They studied the aqueous oxidation of copper sulphide in an ammoniacal medium in the presence of tetrachloroethylene, which is an organic solvent for sulphur immiscible in the aqueous phase. In this way they were able to recover about 60% of the sulphur in elemental form because it was dissolved in the organic phase as soon as it was formed. Previous in-

vestigators who were unable to recover elemental sulphur concluded that the metal sulphide is oxidized directly to thiosulphate and other compounds. In the light of Reilly and
Scott's work, the initial step in the aqueous oxidation of
sulphides, whether in acid, basic, or neutral medium is the
anodic reaction:

$$MS \longrightarrow M^{2+} + S + 2e^-$$

where M is a divalent metal. While elemental sulphur is stable
in an acid medium, it undergoes further oxidation in a basic
or neutral medium.

Leaching of lead sulphide has received great attention by
researchers at the US Bureau of Mines in an attempt to simplify
the present technology of lead [12] . Galena concentrate is
leached with a hot acidified solution of ferric chloride.

In the treatment of manganese nodules, a study entitled,
"Technological and Economic Assessment of Manganese Nodule
Mining and Processing", was published by the Arthur D. Little
Incorporation [13] . Also, researchers at Kennecott Copper Corporation came up with a new concept [14] . They were able to
solubilize copper, nickel, cobalt, and molybdenum from the
nodules leaving behind a slurry of manganous carbonate which
can be stock-piled as a potential source of manganese. The
reactions take place at room temperature but because of the
exothermic nature of the process, the temperature rises to 50°C.
The nodules are leached with ammoniacal cuprous carbonate
solution:

$$MnO_2 + 2\left[Cu(NH_3)_2\right]^+ + 2\ NH_3 + (NH_4)_2CO_3 \rightarrow MnCO_3 + 2\left[Cu(NH_3)_4\right]^{2+} + 2\ OH^-$$

The mangenese dioxide matrix is decomposed to form an insoluble manganese carbonate, the metal values of Cu, Ni, Co, and
Mo go into solution, and the iron remains unattacked. This is an
oxidation-reduction process in which tetravalent mangenese is
transformed to the divalent state while the cuprous is transformed to the cupric. When leaching is conducted in the presence
of CO, the cupric is reduced back to cuprous:

$$2\left[Cu(NH_3)_4\right]^{2+} + CO + 2\ OH^- \rightarrow 2\left[Cu(NH_3)_2\right]^+ + 2\ NH_3 + (NH_4)_2CO_3$$

Thus, the overall reaction is:

$$MnO_2 + CO_{(aq)} \rightarrow MnCO_3$$

and the cuprous ammine complex is acting as a catalyst. The
efficiency of utilization of CO was found to be greater than
90%, the recovery of Cu and Ni, 90%, and the extent of transformation of MnO_2 to $MnCO_3$, 98%. The process was tested successfully in a pilot plant treating 350 kg ore/day.

There are, of course, many other important papers that were
published recently, but because of limited space, it is not
possible to review all of them.

To come back to Prof. Leonov's question, I would say it is
not possible at this stage to make a generalization because
under certain sets of conditions hydrometallurgical processes
can be uneconomical. However, I do not feel that finding the
proper equipment could be a problem.

1052

Regarding the second question, there are many things that could be said assuming I have understood the question properly. For example, the hydrometallurgical waste solutions from the chemical beneficiation of ilmenite to produce synthetic rutile are usually treated by oxyhydrolysis at high temperature. Another example is the effluent from dump leaching solutions after the recovery of copper by cementation with iron, which is treated by ion exchange methods to recover traces of uranium.

REFERENCES

1. Chapman T. W. et al., editors. Fundamental Aspects of Hydro-metallurgical Processes, Am. Inst. Chem. Eng. Symposium No. 173, vol. 74, AICHE, New York, 1978.

2. Jones M. J., editor. Complex Metallurgy 78, Inst. Min. and Met., London, 1978.

3. Anonymous, Proceedings of the Eleventh Commonwealth Mining and Metallurgical Congress, Hong Kong, 1978, Inst. Min. and Met., London, 1979.

4. Weiss A., editor. World Mining and Metal Technology, vol. 2, AIME, New York, 1976.

5. Anonymous, Proceedings of the International Conference on Chemical Metallurgy, Bombay, 1979.

6. Journal of Metals, January 1979.

7. Dobrokhotov G. N. Processes and Equipment for Hydrometallur-gical Industry (in Russian), Leningrad Mining Institute, 1978.

8. Ritcey G. and Ashbrook A. W. Solvent Extraction. Principles and Applications to Process Metallurgy, vol.2, Elsevier, Amsterdam, 1979.

9. Łętowski F. Principles of Hydrometallurgy (transl. from the Polish) — in press.

10. Scott T. R.   Recent Advances in Hydrometallurgy with Implications for the Developing Countries in Economics of Mineral Engineering,   Mining Journal Books, Kent, England, 1978. Inter-regional seminar arranged by the United Nations in Ankara 1976.

11. Reilly I. G. and Scott D. S. Recovery of Elemental Sulphur During the Ammoniacal Leaching of Copper Sulphide, Metal. Trans., 9B, 681-686 (1978).

12. Haver F. P. and Wong M. M. Ferric Chloride-Brine Leaching of Galena Concentrates, U.S. Bur. Mines. Rept. Invest., 8105 (1976).

13. Arthur D. Little, Inc., Technological and Economic Assessment of Manganese Nodule Mining and Processing, Government Printing Office, Washington, D.C., 1978, CA 90, 587275.

14. Agarwal J. C. et al. The Cuprion Process for Ocean Nodules, Chem. Eng. Prog., 75 (1), 59-60 (1979).

H. MAJIMA

In reply to Professor Dogan, we suppose that the brine leaching technique is not so useful for the treatment of Cu-Zn sulphide bulk concentrate. Generally, the dissolution rate of sphalerite is not large enough in brine solutions for the treatment of Cu-Zn bulk concentrates. Moreover, metal sulphides in complex sulphide ores associate intimately each other. To overcome such problems, it is necessary to grind the concentrates until perfect liberation is attained.

Although a number of studies have been published on the brine leaching of Cu-Zn sulphide bulk concentrate, no commercial plant has been successfully operated. This is a good indication of the limitations of this method.

D. W. FUERSTENAU

We thank Professor Herbst for his recognition of the potential of our work. From our results on the effect of particle size on the leaching kinetics of chrysocolla we are tempted to conclude that the simultaneous grinding and leaching technique is superior to the individual grinding and leaching technique. But we have not conducted leaching tests on particles of size less than 37 μm. Since it is very likely that particles of this size will be produced during attrition grinding we are presently not in a position to categorically claim the superiority of the simultaneous grinding and leaching technique.

In reply to Professor Habashi, our investigations on the porous nature of chrysocolla using nitrogen gas adsorption have indicated that prolonged heating at $150^{\circ}C$ has no significant effect on the porous nature of chrysocolla. No evidence for sintering was found even after heating for 48 h at $150^{\circ}C$. Sintering was found to take place only if the heating temp. was raised above $400^{\circ}C$.

We have conducted a few preliminary investigations with sulphuric acid. These investigations have revealed, and this is our reply to Dr. Abbruzzese, that sulphuric acid is as effective as ammonia.

In reply to Dr. Flett, first of all we would like to mention that with the limited results we have at our disposal we are in no way claiming that our approach is more practical, at least for copper. Our investigation is different from those reported in the literature on lyometallurgy primarily because it uses a non-polar diluent.

No quantitative investigations were conducted to ascertain
the efficiency of separation of solids from the organic phase.
However, we observed during our experiments that the solids
settled pretty fast. This can be expected since hydrophilic
particles in an organic medium cannot be stabilized by electrical double layer phenomena.

We are considering carrying out experiments to estimate the
organic loss by adsorption. In short, the process has been
found feasible on a laboratory scale and is far from being
proved to be a success on a commercial scale.

G. BOLTON et al.

In reply to Professor D. W. Fuerstenau, coating of zinc
sulphide particles by molten elemental sulphur was a problem
which for many years limited the practical application of the
direct pressure leach to a temperature below the melting point
of sulphur. Now, with the use of low cost additives, it is possible to prevent the coating, and high zinc extractions are
obtained at 150 $^\circ$C in a leach from a wide variety of zinc sulphide concentrates with a batch retention time of the order of
one hour. Additives found to be suitable are generally wood
derivatives such as lignin sulphonate salts and tannins.

With regard to Professor Dogan's remarks, no cost comparison has been made by Sherritt between the pressure leach process and these pyro-smelting processes for the treatment of
zinc-lead bulk concentrates. The pressure leach process differs
significantly from smelting processes, particularly in the way
that sulphur is handled. The elimination of SO_2 production and

1056

the rejection of pyrite with the leach residues are characteristics of the pressure leach process that may have special
significance in some locations. Furthermore, low grade bulk
concentrates which are not suitable for pyro-smelting could
still be treated by a pressure leach process. Comparison of
the various process options would be made on a case by case
basis.

In response to Dr. Riesenkampf's question, the first commercial application of the zinc pressure leach process was
recently announced by Cominco Ltd. for intergration into their
existing roast-leach plant at Trail, Canada. Start-up of this
facility is expected to occur in 1981. At present, there is
keen interest from a number of other zinc producers, and as
a result, additional pressure leach autoclaves will probably
be installed at existing zinc plants. Interest is also high
in the use of the pressure leach process for "grass roots"
zinc plants. However, the current state of the zinc market
does not encourage new plant construction at this time, so
a "grass root" refinery may be several years away.

Dr. Riesenkampf's second question is with respect to
magnesium control. The problem of magnesium control in electrolytic zinc plants would be similar in the pressure leach
and roast-leach processes. Currently, industrial practice is
to either pre-leach the zinc concentrate to remove magnesium
or to bleed the solution in some fashion to reject magnesium
while attempting to minimize zinc losses. We agree that magnesium can be a serious operating difficulty, particularly
when treating concentrates derived from dolomitic ores, but
we have not looked for alternate control methods.